McKNIGHT **&** McKNIGHT
PUBLISHING COMPANY
BLOOMINGTON, ILLINOIS

AUTOmotive
DIAGNOSIS AND TUNE-UP

GUY F. WETZEL

Member, Society of Automotive Engineers
and Society of Automotive Testers
Technical Editor, Automotive Digest
Author, Automotive Body and Frame Service

Introduction

For the past fifteen years in the columns of *Automotive Digest* and later in *Motor Service*, the author has been answering questions asked by automotive service men throughout the world. In addition he has published over 1,000 magazine articles on automotive subjects. From this and years of practical experience he has analyzed the information needs and problems of mechanics, tune-up men, and service managers. A member of the Society of Automotive Engineers, his long and broad experience in the automotive service industry has made his writings accepted and preferred as most authentic and dependable.

This book clearly presents the basic theory necessary for an understanding of the automotive power plant which will help the mechanic to pinpoint troubles and aid him in their proper correction. It analyzes the various systems composing the power plant, presenting the "anatomy" and correct functioning of each. It also describes various other systems in which difficulty may arise. Specific usage and operation of the various test instruments utilized in modern trouble finding and repair (diagnosis and correction) and tune-up is provided.

A great deal of information is given that is not readily available to the average service man, such as analyzing engine noises, a comparison of firing orders, and the causes of bearing failures.

While intended for men in the automotive service business, this book has been found to be a valuable text for automotive classes in private and public technical and trade schools. It is particularly helpful to those who plan to specialize in automotive diagnosis and tune-up work, as well as those in general automotive service work. Service managers will find it very informative.

This book is presented to the automotive service industry as an adult study of "Diagnosis and Tune-Up." It is primarily intended to promote more efficient maintenance through the practical use of scientific trouble-finding and testing methods.

Acknowledgments

The author wishes to acknowledge with sincere appreciation the co-operation of the following companies in the compilation of material and illustrations used in this book.

Special mention is made of the outstanding cooperation of Carter Carburetor Company, Prestolite Division of Eltra Corporation, Delco-Remy Division of General Motors Corporation, Rochester Division of General Motors Corporation, and Sun Electric Corporation.

Sources of illustrations other than his own photographs or drawings are acknowledged in the body of the book by the letter or letters (in parenthesis) after each of the following names:

Prestolite Division, Eltra Corporation (PR)
Delco-Remy Division (DR)
Sun Electric Corporation (Sun)
Allen Electric and Equipment Company (A)
Electro Products Company (E)
King Electric Equipment Company (K)
Oldsmobile Division, General Motors Corporation (Olds)
Chrysler Motor Company (Chrysler)
Ford Motor Company (Ford)
Rochester Carburetor Division, General Motors Corporation (RC)
Carter Carburetor (CC)
Bendix Products Division, Bendix Aviation Corporation, (Stromberg) (S)
Holley Carburetor Company (H)
Stewart Warner Company (SW)
Autopulse Corporation (AP)
Society of Automotive Engineers (SAE)
Association of American Battery Manufacturers (AABM)
Sealed Power Corporation (SP)
Ramsey Corporation (R)
Federal Mogul Corporation (FM)
AC Division, General Motors Corporation (AC)
King-Seeley Corporation (KS)

Table of Contents

Section III   Mechanics of the Internal Combustion Engine

Section IV Working Tools of Diagnosis and Tune-Up

Section V Generation and Storage of Electricity

Section VI   The Ignition System

Section IX   Tune-Up and Diagnosis Procedure

SECTION I   **Purpose
and
Aims
of
this
Book**

CHAPTER ONE

Tune-Up—
Its Meaning
and Opportunities

The term "tune-up" as applied to automobile service holds various meanings for various people. To the average car owner it means doing something more-or-less-important to his car which makes it run better. To some mechanics it means cleaning and gapping spark plugs, adjusting the carburetor for idle mixture and idling speeds, and perhaps performing a few other minor operations. To the highly trained "tune-up" man, "tune-up" means checking all phases of engine operation and making any adjustments, repairs, and replacements required for the engine auxiliaries and accessories to conform to the car builder's specifications. This, assuming that the engine is in good mechanical condition, will make its performance approximate (within reason) that which it delivered when new.

The term "tune-up" is frequently used by the layman in a much broader sense than was originally intended. For him it often indicates the periodic checkup of a number of automotive parts other than the engine, its accessories, and auxiliaries. For example one often hears of appearance tune-up, performance tune-up, tuning-up the front end, tuning-up the cooling system. Tune-up in these cases refers to corrective measures designed to bring the unit or system as near to its original condition as possible.

Scope of Tune-Up Work

The scope of this book will be confined to the engine and the units and systems necessary to its performance. The clutch, transmission, and drive line will not be considered since these are generally not within the province of the tune-up man.

Tuning an engine does not mean rebuilding or performing repair operations on the engine itself even though these may be required. However, checkup operations which are a part of every tune-up job may reveal serious engine defects which require corrective measures.

It is as essential to check engine operation *after adjustments are made* as it is to test before doing corrective work. The only assurance of a correct adjustment is a double check after work has been completed. Trying to tune an engine that has poor bearings, rings, pistons, or valves, is difficult if not impossible. Tune-up as it will be used here means reestablishing original factory specifications as nearly as possible. This can be done satisfactorily only on engines that are in reasonably good condition so that proper tuning will cause a noticeable improvement.

The term "power plant" as used in this book includes not only the engine but the electrical systems, the exhaust system, and the fuel system as well. The term "engine" describes the cylinder block, crankcase, oil pan, flywheel, water jacket, water pump, cylinder head, crankshaft, connecting rods, camshaft, valves, oil pump and all other internal parts. Auxiliary units or systems include the fuel system, generating system, ignition system, starting system, cooling system and exhaust system. The fuel system is composed of the fuel pump, carburetor, connecting tubing, tank and fuel gauge. The generating system includes the generator, battery, ammeter, voltage and current regulator, cut-out relay, switches, lights and low-tension wiring. The ignition system covers the distributor, coil, condenser, low-tension wiring, spark plugs and high-tension wiring. The starting system includes the starting motor, starting motor control, cables and wiring necessary to complete the starting circuit.

Tune-up is not a panacea for motor ills. In fact, a substantial portion of the cars that come into the shop are not immediate candidates for a tune-up job. Preliminary checking operations frequently show that an engine must have mechanical work done before a satisfactory tune-up job is possible.

Sequence of Tune-Up Operations

Tune-up, like many supposedly complicated operations, is in reality merely a series of simple operations, with each a step toward the desired result. The most complicated job can be broken down into simple details. The thoroughly trained tune-up man understands this fact. Furthermore, he is aware of the necessary steps in each operation and why these steps are taken.

There are two general types of tune-up men: (1) those who simply follow the instructions and put the red wire on terminal *1* and the black wire on terminal *2* then push button *3* and read meter needle *4*; merely going through a routine without any particular understanding of the underlying theory — and (2) those who know their theory, and not only follow the routine, but *know* the reasons for following them; these men know the significance of the

operations and the indications of test instruments.

The good tune-up man will keep up with current developments in automotive servicing procedure, by trying to learn more about the most effective methods and equipment available. In addition, he will add to his knowledge about engine operation, and know the functioning and underlying principles of operation of the electrical and fuel systems.

Divisions of Tune-Up Work

Engine operation can be separated into three major divisions: (1) compression (2) ignition and (3) carburetion. When any one of these does not function properly, the entire engine is affected; if the degree of efficiency loss is great enough, the engine won't function at all. The

Fig. 1.1. Tune-up means testing the electrical and fuel systems and restoring them to original specifications as nearly as possible.

Fig. 1.2. Checking cylinder compression is one of many tests that are made.

three fundamental divisions of tune-up procedure can also be considered as: (1) the engine (2) electrical systems and (3) the fuel system. These three designations cover the same items as the terms compression, ignition and carburetion.

Satisfactory performance of the modern, high-speed, high-compression engine requires maintenance of all the conditions which existed in the power plant when it was new. All automobile manufacturers specify the various adjustments and operation standards. Since it is impossible to judge many of the actual operating conditions, adjustments, and standards by our human faculties, it is necessary to use highly sensitive scientific testing equipment. This equipment provides the tune-up man with information concerning the condition and oper-

Fig. 1.3. The voltmeter and ammeter are commonly used in tune-up work.

Fig. 1.4. The vacuum gauge responds to reduced pressure in the intake manifold, indicating engine condition. It may also be used to check the fuel pump.

ation of the distributor, speed data, fuel efficiency, and gas and liquid pressures. Checking with the test equipment will give information as to the condition of the engine at the time it is brought to the shop. After adjustment and replacements, further testing will tell how close to the original specifications the part, unit or system has been brought. The manufacturer's specifications should be adhered to as closely as possible, with all needed adjustments made in order to obtain smooth performance of the engine with economical results.

Cars Wear Out

As soon as a car leaves the dealer's delivery floor and is put into service, it begins to wear out. As a rule, properly maintained modern automobiles are serviceable for approximately 150,000 miles; however, predictable depreciation does occur. For example, there is friction wear on bearings, cylinder walls, pistons and rings within the engine. In the ignition system, breaker points in the distributor deteriorate with use and condensers may cease to function properly (although infrequently). Mechanical parts, such as distributor shaft, bearings, driving gears, breaker plate bearings and internal electrical connections, may wear and become defective. Both high-tension and low-tension wiring is subject to deterioration due to oxidation, heat, oil deposits or age. Terminals can become loose or corroded. Generator armatures, commutators and brushes frequently cause difficulty. Generator controls, commonly known as "voltage regulators," are subject to defective contact points and broken resistors, springs and electrical connections. Batteries have a normal life of one to three years and wear out more rapidly than other electrical car parts.

The tune-up man must first detect the faulty parts and units whose deterioration is affecting the proper functioning of the power plant. He must then report engine faults and correct defects of auxiliary units by adjustment, repair or replacement, restoring the units as near to their original condition as possible. The large number of electrical units in the automobile requires that the tune-up man be accomplished in testing, installing and adjusting electrical units.

The recent trend toward commission-based pay for mechanics has resulted in apathy on the part of many tune-up men. They frequently sacrifice quality to gain quantity in their work, since the greater their output, the larger their pay check. As a result, they omit much necessary testing, returning an automobile with defects that would have been detected through proper testing. This book will consider that "tune-up" and "diagnosis" refer to proper, adequate applications of testing and corrective procedures.

Testing Equipment

The motoring public simply takes for granted the great amount of progress that has been made from the days of Model *T* Fords to our contemporary, powerful, mechanically efficient automobiles. However, automobile service men know that it takes a high degree of automotive knowledge as well as the assistance of modern instruments to keep the machines running satisfactorily. Necessity has made service procedures keep pace with automobile improvement. Parallel to this progress has been the development of automotive analyzing and testing equipment. The haphazard methods employed during the

early days of automobile servicing have necessarily given way to scientific methods. It is impossible to service, test, analyze, and adjust properly the intricate automobile of today without using sensitive instruments to make measurements beyond human perception.

Fig. 1.6. The carburetor requires adjustment periodically for best engine performance. The combustion analyzer being used here aids in getting the best setting.

Fig. 1.7. A distributor tester or distributorscope shows the firing pattern and checks the automatic and vacuum advance.

Fig. 1.5. The testing and tune-up of trucks is an important and profitable field.

Scientific testing and analyzing equipment is to the tune-up man as hand tools are to the man in the mechanical division of service work. There is one great difference, however: the equipment used by the tune-up man requires a basic understanding and knowledge of electricity, combustion, carburetion, valve action, engine operation, and the manipulation and application of the instruments themselves.

A detailed study and analysis of the tune-up instruments and equipment is covered in the section "Working Tools of Diagnosis."

Tune-Up Opportunities

The field of tune-up has just begun to expand, for though it is now considered an essential part of engine maintenance and performance, only within the past decade have any noticeable advances been made in tune-up methods and instruments.

Along with the increased popularity and technological advances in this field has come a growing need for manpower. This need can only be met by men who have a comprehensive knowledge of the basic principles of electricity, automotive ignition, fuel and air mixtures, and the mechanical actions of engine parts, as well as the functioning devices included in the engine's auxiliary and accessory systems.

Special schools and classes, such as those operated by the Sun Electric Corporation and the distributors of testing equipment made by Allen Electric and Manufacturing Company, train many men for tune-up work. Otherwise, the necessary knowledge may be acquired through self-organized study and experience. For example a substantial knowledge of testing equipment may be acquired while obtaining practical experience by studying each instrument's instruction booklet and by talking with manufacturer's representatives.

There is such a definite need for tune-up work in preventive maintenance and general engine service that every car dealer and independent service shop should have some tune-up equipment and do at least a minimum of diagnosis and tune-up work.

Shops featuring tune-up work will attract additional valuable business. Futhermore, more tune-up work means more tune-up jobs for competent men.

Diagnosis of the engine and its auxiliary systems is an important element of tune-up, since without knowing what is needed, it is difficult to know what should be done. A good tune-up job, therefore, consists of two parts: (1) diagnosis, analysis, or trouble shooting, and (2)

Fig. 1.8. The ignition timing is advanced or retarded by loosening the screw indicated and slightly rotating the distributor (on Chrysler-built cars).

Fig. 1.9. There are many classes available for instruction in testing and tune-up. This book provides a foundation in the basic principles and their applications.

correction, which may be adjustment, replacement, or repair.

The following pages contain the important facts and basic principles used in diagnostic and corrective work on the automotive power plant as well as the answers to questions that arise in the study of this work.

Summary

Tune-up means checking all phases of engine operation, making needed light repairs, replacements and adjustments. Checking before and after adjustments are made is a basic part of tune-up. Engines in poor condition cannot be tuned satisfactorily.

The *automotive power plant* consists of a number of systems, units and parts. The three main divisions are: (1) compression, (2) ignition, and (3) carburetion. These divisions can also be classified as (1) engine, (2) electrical systems, and (3) fuel system.

When first put into service, cars begin to *wear out* slowly. There is mechanical wear on moving parts and deterioration in the electrical systems and the fuel system. However, 50,000 to 150,000 miles of reasonably satisfactory service may be expected.

The tune-up man must detect improperly adjusted and defective parts and correct the condition. Scientific *testing instruments* are important "working tools" and must be used with accuracy and speed. Parts changing and omitting important tests is a poor way to tune an engine.

There are great *opportunities* for trained, conscientious men in this field and a definite need for tune-up and diagnostic work.

Questions

1. What does tune-up mean to you?
2. What is the difference between "tune-up" and rebuilding an engine?
3. Can an engine in need of work on valves or rings be tuned satisfactorily? Explain.
4. Name six parts of the engine.
5. Name four parts of the fuel system.
6. Name five parts of the ignition system.
7. Tune-up is a "cure-all" for motor ills. True or False? Explain.
8. What does the term "automotive power plant" really cover?
9. Name the three divisions of the power plant.
10. Why should testing instruments be used in tune-up and diagnostic work?
11. How many miles of reasonably satisfactory service can be expected from the average motor car, fairly well maintained?
12. What is the difference between mechanical wear and deterioration?
13. Which is the generally preferred procedure (1) testing and correction, or (2) replacement? Why?
14. How important are automotive testing instruments? Why?
15. How important is a knowledge of the principles of electricity, carburetion and mechanical actions?
16. Name three ways in which you can improve your knowledge of the principles and operations involved in tune-up.
17. What type of men can find opportunities in diagnostic and tune-up work?
18. What is the difference between tune-up and diagnosis?
19. Mention several of the types of trouble to which a power plant may be subject.
20. What is the general procedure in analyzing the condition of an automotive power plant?

SECTION II

Elements
of
Automotive
Electricity

CHAPTER TWO

Electrical Fundamentals

Electricity as a general subject covers such topics as: alternating current (AC) and direct current (DC) power generation; power transmission; wiring; lighting; electric motors and their controls; electric devices; telephone, radio and television; radar and electronics; electrical measuring instruments; magnetism and extensive combinations and applications of these elements.

Fortunately, only a very small segment of the electrical field applies to automotive diagnosis, tune-up and service work, and the applications involved are among the easiest to understand. One important application is shown in Fig. 2.1. On current automobiles, alternating current generators are used in place of the direct current generators used previously. In these generators, the AC is rectified into DC to power the automotive electrical devices. Direct current circuits and devices are relatively easy to understand, trouble-shoot and repair.

A few basic principles completely mastered by the tune-up man will be of invaluable assistance to him. These principles are: (1) composition of matter, (2) nature of electricity, (3) electrical measurement, (4) energy and work, (5) magnetism, (6) induction, and (7) electrical circuits.

Composition of Matter

Matter is anything that is considered to have weight. This includes air and other gases, water and other liquids, metals, minerals and all other solids. Matter may be roughly divided into two general classes: (1) *elements,* which contain only one kind of matter and (2) chemical *combinations* of elements. All matter (gases, liquids and solids) is made up of inconceivably small particles called *molecules.*

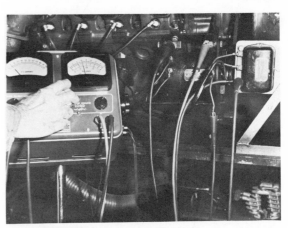

Fig. 2.1. A very important application of fundamental electrical theory is made when using testing equipment. The various phases of high- and low-tension electrical pressure, magnetism, induction, resistance, capacity and current flow are all applied.

A *molecule* is the smallest particle into which a substance can be divided without changing its identity. Molecules are made up of *atoms*. Although each element contains only one kind of atom, molecules may contain atoms of different elements. Molecules of elements are made up of two or more atoms of the same kind.

A familiar illustration of a mixture of elements is air, which is principally composed of oxygen and nitrogen, although other rare gases are included. Water is also a combination of two chemical elements, each molecule being composed of two atoms of hydrogen and one atom of oxygen.

Composition of Atoms

Just twenty-five years ago the atom was considered to be the smallest division of matter. More recent scientific investigation, however, indicates that the atom itself is made up of still smaller particles. Theoretically, each atom is composed of three groups of particles: *protons, neutrons* and *electrons*. All protons, regardless of the element in which they appear, are the same. This is also true of neutrons and electrons. Therefore these are considered to be the absolute basis of all matter.

Protrons and neutrons form a *nucleus* surrounded by electrons. The nucleus is assumed to be relatively stationary while the electrons revolve around it in circular or elliptical paths.

The protons and neutrons are approximately equal in weight. The *proton* carries a *positive* charge of electricity while the neutron has no electrical charge. The electrons are very tiny in proportion to the protons and neutrons, being approximately 1/2000 of their individual weights. The *electron* is assumed to carry a *negative* electrical charge. Each electrically neutral atom contains the same number of protons and electrons, the number of which determines the quality of the element. Through complicated physical experiments and mathematical calculations it is possible for scientists to determine the number of protons in the different elements. These range from 1 to 102, and are called the *atomic numbers* of the elements. A second characteristic quality of an atom is its atomic weight: gold, lead, and platinum, which are very heavy, have high atomic weights; hydrogen, which is one of the lightest elements known, has a very small atomic weight.

An important part of the electron theory is that the number of electrons is equal to the number of protons in any electrically neutral atom. The protons form part of the nucleus of the atom, but the electrons rotate around this nucleus. In the copper atom, for example, there are 29 protons and 29 electrons. Their actual arrangement in space has been found. In a copper atom there is one group of two electrons nearest to the nucleus, then a group of eight electrons; further out is a group of eighteen electrons, and beyond these, one electron.

Diagrams of atoms which represent the arrangement and number of protons, neutrons and electrons are valuable. However, they are

ATOMS & ELECTRONS

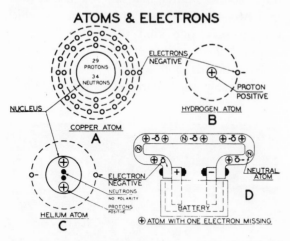

Fig. 2.2. (A) A copper atom nucleus containing 29 protons and 34 neutrons. Since the number of electrons equals that of the protons in an electrically neutral atom, this copper atom has 29 electrons orbiting its nucleus. (B) A hydrogen atom, the simplest of all, with 1 proton, 1 electron, and no neutron. (C) A helium atom with 2 neutrons, 2 protons, and 2 electrons. (D) A heavy conductor, connected to the terminals of a battery, has free electrons which are attracted toward the positive terminal and repelled from the negative. They will move, causing current flow, when the circuit is completed.

not true pictures since the actual arrangement of these particles is not known. For simplicity they are assumed to be spherical. As some basis for visualization, it would require 160 billions of electrons aligned side by side to equal an inch.

There are as many different kinds of atoms as there are elements, 102 at this time. The number of external electrons in the atom varies in proportion with the charge of each nucleus. Heavy atoms contain more electrons, protons and neutrons than atoms of light atomic weight.

Hydrogen has the simplest atomic structure of any of the elements, consisting of only one proton and one electron. Hydrogen does not have a neutron. Next in simplicity is the helium atom which has two protons, two neutrons, and two electrons. In the helium atom, as in all other atoms, the negative and positive charges are equal. Refer to Fig. 2.2, Parts A, B, and C. Uranium, with 92 electrons, has a very complex structure.

Electrons and Electricity

If some of the external electrons of an atom are removed, the positive and negative charges are no longer equal. The excess of protons in the nucleus gives the atom a positive charge. If the electrons are allowed to return, a neutral atom again results. Therefore the *positively charged body* is one which *lacks* electrons.

Fig. 2.3. One end of this test light wire is grounded, and the other end has a test prod which puts the lamp in series with the wire. Electrical pressure between the grounded clip and the test prod will cause current to flow and light the lamp.

Conversely a *negatively charged body* is one which has an *excess* of electrons since electrons are assumed to have a negative electrical charge.

A glass rod rubbed with a piece of silk will become positively charged because some of its electrons will be deposited upon the silk. On the other hand, a rod of sealing wax will become negatively charged when rubbed with a piece of wool because some of the wool's electrons will be deposited on it. If the wool should be tested it would be found to be positively charged by its shortage of electrons.

Free Electrons

In such nonmetallic materials as rubber and glass, the electrons are held rather rigidly to their nuclei, but in metals such as copper or iron some of the electrons are only loosely held to their nuclei and can be made to flow. These are called *free electrons*.

In addition to the electrons contained in atoms, a tremendous number exist that are not part of any atom. Probably at some time these free electrons were part of atomic structures which have since been broken down. This "breaking down" process is continuously taking place at the sun causing a constant flow of free electrons from the sun to the earth.

Radioactive elements have seven layers or rings of electrons; the outer ring is so far from the atom's nucleus that the electrons in it can easily be separated from the atom. All radioactive elements will inherently change to some less complicated element, freeing all of the electrons originally in their outer ring.

Electrons may be freed as they move and collide in their orbits. Shaken off and separated

Fig. 2.4. Checking battery cell voltage (electrical pressure) with one type of open-circuit voltage tester.

from the atom, they remain free electrons, unless they recombine with their nucleus.

Electrons can also be released as a result of chemical reaction. Materials such as lead, when put into solution with acid, will release electrons from their outer ring. These electrons remain free until the process is reversed and they are once more forced back into the lead atom.

Effect of Heat

Heat application will separate electrons from their atoms. Heat is molecular motion; the higher the temperature the more rapid the motion. As the molecules move they collide, not only with each other, but also with the free electrons in the substance. These collisions knock or shake off free electrons of the conductor at great speeds. If the heated substance is exposed to atmospheric air, most of the electrons will collide with molecules of the surrounding air and bounce back into the conductor. In a vacuum however, they will be emitted. Since their velocity is not great, they will remain in a cloud near the emitting surface. As electrons are shaken off, other free electrons rush in to take their place. This is

the basic principle used in the electronic tube, tungar, and charging tube.

The Nature of Electricity

Electricity is evidenced in two forms: (1) static electricity, and (2) current electricity. *Static electricity* is a form generated from such instances as rubbing a glass rod with a piece of silk or a rod of sealing wax with wool. It is the form which accumulates in clouds and discharges as lightning. It has no practical application in automotive work and therefore can be disregarded. Electrons are responsible for all manifestations of static electricity, as for current electricity. The electron theory seems to satisfactorily account for the action of both types of electricity.

Flow of Electricity

Current electricity is assumed to be the flow of free electrons through conductors. The flow may be induced by chemical means as in a battery, or by putting mechanical energy into an electromagnetic machine (a generator). Fig. 2.5 shows a typical automotive electrical system. It may also be induced to flow in limited amounts by the application of heat to dissimilar metals in contact (a thermocouple). When a heavy copper wire (or a wire of any material that has free electrons) is connected to the terminals of a battery, making one end of the wire positive and the other negative, the free electrons (being negatively charged) will be attracted to the positive terminal. Electrons repel each other, because it has been found that particles with like charges repel each other while those with unlike charges attract each other. In other words, positive particles will attract negative, and repel positive, as well as negative repelling negative. Refer back to Fig. 2.2, Part D.

In the closed battery circuit mentioned, electrons after passing through the copper conductor, will pass through the battery, then through the wire again and so on. This flow of electrons constitutes an electric current. In

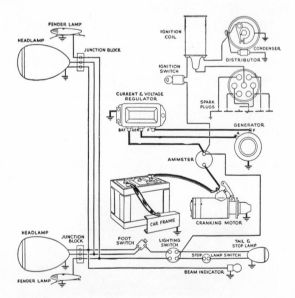

Fig. 2.5. Typical car electrical system, illustrating the various electrical units and their connections.

a conductor, the electrons move from the negative to the positive. Early students of electrical science, not knowing the actual direction of current flow, arbitrarily assumed that it was from positive to negative. Electrons actually flow from negative to positive, instead of in the reverse direction.

Electrical Conductors

An electrical conductor is a material which possesses a quantity of free electrons. On the other hand, an insulator possesses few free electrons. Such materials as rubber, asphalt, glass, and certain oils have good insulating properties.

Resistance to Electron Flow

When a current flows in a conductor, the movement of the free electrons is hindered by collision with the atoms of the substance. This hindrance constitutes the *electrical resistance* of the conductor. Naturally the amount of resistance varies with different materials. It also varies with the temperature of the material. Higher temperatures cause agitation of the molecules and atoms and consequently there are more frequent collisions, resulting in a greater resistance.

As the number of electrons flowing in a given conductor increases, there will be a greater number of collisions between the atoms and electrons. This explains why a conductor carrying a current is always heated, and why the extent of heat is determined by the amount of current. It also accounts for the fact that conductors with high resistance become heated more with a given current flow than those with less resistance.

Movement by Electron Repulsion

Remember current electricity is the movement of free electrons and that electrons repel each other. When an electron is moved, the nearest free electron, being repelled, also moves. This electron in turn causes the next one to move, and so the motion continues.

If a conducting material has its two ends connected to a means for inducing the flow of electric current, the electrons merely travel around the wire and back to their starting point. The electrons traveling through a wire must be set in motion by a force which is able to overcome the repulsion the electrons have for each other. If electrons could move through a conductor without any electrical resistance, it would be impossible to build up more than a slight pressure since as one electron is moved, another would immediately fill its space.

Summary

The subject of *electricity* is very broad but fortunately electricity as applied to automotive diagnosis and tune-up is direct current and is simple and easy to understand. The alternator is somewhat different from the DC generator, but its final output is direct current.

Matter (gases, liquids, solids) is divided into (1) elements, and (2) chemical mixtures. All matter is composed of molecules which are made up of atoms.

Atoms in turn are composed of protons, neutrons and electrons, the number and arrangement of which determine the nature and characteristics of the element. The electrons are the smallest and carry a negative electrical charge. In most of the elements there is an equal number of protons and electrons. Hydrogen is the simplest atom, with one proton, one electron, and no neutrons.

The *electron* determines the electrical charge. A material with an excess of electrons has a negative charge, while one with a lack of electrons has a positive charge. There are enormous numbers of free electrons. Radioactive elements have seven layers or rings of electrons and can easily lose electrons.

Electrons can be released by chemical action and also by heat. The nature of electricity is not known but its action and results are known. It is evidenced in two forms, (1) static electricity, and (2) current electricity.

Current electricity is assumed to be the flow of free electrons along conductors. An electrical conductor is a material which possesses free electrons in large quantities. An insulating material possesses very few free electrons. The hindrance to the free progress of electrons through a substance is its electrical resistance.

In a *conducting material* with two ends connected to a means for inducing current flow, electrons will travel along the wire and back to the starting place. The current inducing force must overcome the electron repulsion.

Questions

1. Name the two kinds of electricity with which you may come in contact in automotive work.
2. Name three ways in which an electric current may be induced to flow.
3. What is matter? Give examples.
4. What are the two general classes of matter?
5. Of what are molecules composed?
6. Name the three basic parts of an atom.
7. Which component has negative polarity?
8. What element has the very simplest atomic structure?
9. What is the effect of a shortage of electrons? Of an excess of electrons?
10. State a characteristic of radioactive elements.
11. What is one effect of heat on electrons?
12. What is one effect of a chemical reaction?
13. What is the action of electrons in a vacuum?
14. Mention two forms of electricity, one of which you will deal with in tune-up work.
15. Name two ways of inducing current flow in a closed circuit.
16. Do electrons flow from negative to positive or from positive to negative?
17. What causes resistance in a circuit?
18. How much current will flow in an open circuit?
19. What is an important result of resistance in a circuit?
20. Where do the electrons go in a closed circuit in which current is flowing?

CHAPTER THREE

Electrical Measurements

There are two qualities of electric current that are of interest to those working with automotive electricity: (1) the *electrical pressure* that causes current flow and (2) the *quantity* or intensity of current flow.

The electrical pressure is frequently called the *electrical potential*. The pressure difference between two terminals of a battery or generator is the difference of potential or the *voltage*, also referred to as *electromotive force* (EMF). The difference in pressure or potential between any two points in an electric circuit is the *voltage drop*. This is very important as it is used frequently in analyzing circuits and in locating points of trouble.

The electrical units by which current electricity is measured are: (1) the *volt*, the unit of electrical pressure, potential, or electromotive force, (2) the *ampere*, the unit of amount of current flow, and (3) the *ohm*, the unit of amount of resistance to current flow.

There is an important relationship between electromotive force (volts), rate of current flow (amperes) and resistance (ohms) in any given circuit or part of a circuit.

Electric Current Flow Compared with Water Flow

Electric currents are often compared with water currents. Both require pressure to induce

flow. In both, the amount of flow will vary with the pressure, the size of the conductor, the resistance of the conductor and the capacity of the source of the current flow.

The *volt* in electric currents may be compared to pounds per square inch in water flow, while the *ampere* corresponds to gallons of

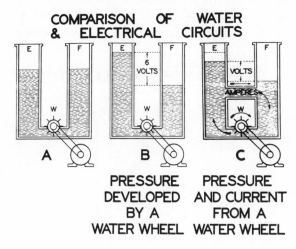

Fig. 3.1. (A) Since there is no pressure difference between *E* and *F*, there is no flow of water. This corresponds to zero voltage difference in an electrical circuit. (B) The powered water wheel forces water from *F* to *E*, corresponding to an electrical circuit with voltage difference, but no current flow. (C) A path allows for liquid flow in proportion to the pressure difference between *E* and *F*. Similarly, electric current will flow when a current circuit is provided and there is a voltage difference.

water per minute. There is no measure similar to the *ohm*, but the surface of a water pipe reduces (resists) the flow of water.

Suppose two containers filled with water are connected near the bottom by a pipe in which there is a motor-driven water wheel. With the water wheel stationary, the water will be at the same level in both containers since a liquid seeks its own level. This would correspond to an electrical circuit without any voltage. Refer to Fig. 3.1.

When the water wheel is put into motion, it will move the water from one container to the other until the back pressure on the wheel due to the higher water level in one of the containers balances the pressure generated by the water wheel. These pressures will be measured in pounds per square inch. Pressure gauges connected to the bottom of each container would show the pressures in each, and the *difference* could be calculated. For electrical circuits a voltmeter is connected across the circuit and the difference in pressure of electromotive force or potential is measured directly in volts on the instrument. Therefore *voltage* is the pressure difference between two sides or parts of a circuit. This is the condition of an electrical circuit with voltage (or pressure) but with no current flowing in the circuit. This condition may also be compared to a closed water faucet. There is water pressure present, even though the closed valve is preventing water flow.

If a second pipe were added between the two containers, with a difference in water level maintained by the water wheel, a circular flow of water would result. This flow would be caused by the pressure difference between the two containers. As long as this difference in level is maintained, water would continue to flow around the circuit, and could be measured in gallons per minute. In an electric circuit the corresponding flow of electricity would be measured in amperes, as shown in Figs. 3.2 and 3.3.

Even though water were forced with a very high pressure, only a very small volume could be discharged through a tiny pipe. On the other hand, a large pipe could discharge a great quantity of water with a minimum of pressure.

In a similar way it is possible to have a small amperage under a very high voltage or a large

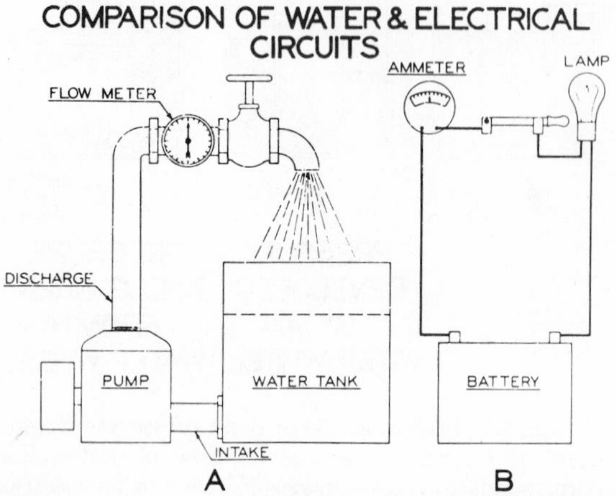

COMPARISON OF WATER & ELECTRICAL CIRCUITS

FLOW METER · DISCHARGE · PUMP · WATER TANK · INTAKE · AMMETER · LAMP · BATTERY

A   B

Fig. 3.2. (A) To measure the flow of water through a pipe a flow meter must be inserted into the pipe so that all moving water flows through the pipe. (B) Similarly, to measure the flow of electricity through a wire, a current meter or ammeter must be inserted in the circuit so that all current will go through it.

COMPARISON OF WATER & ELECTRICAL CIRCUITS

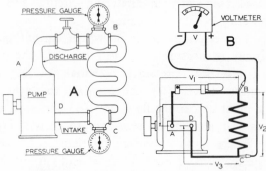

Fig. 3.3. (A) The amount of water flowing through the pipe depends upon the pressure difference between *B* and *C*, as shown on the two pressure gauges. (B) In an electric circuit, the amount of current flowing through conductor *BC* depends upon the electrical pressure difference (voltage) between the two ends. The voltmeter, connected as shown, indicates the voltage difference or voltage drop between the points contacted by the voltmeter leads.

conductor carrying a high amperage under a low potential or voltage.

Size of Electrical Units

At this point it will be logical to ask "just how big is a volt, an ampere, or an ohm?" To give an idea of the size of a volt, it can be illustrated with familiar objects. The storage battery used on passenger cars has a pressure of 6 volts or 12 volts. The electric lights which illuminate our homes are supplied with current at 115 to 120 volts. The voltage which causes a spark to jump across the terminals of a spark plug to ignite the explosive mixtures in a cylinder ranges from 7,000 to 20,000 volts.

The *ampere* is the amount or quantity of current that flows in a circuit having a resistance of one ohm with a pressure or electromotive force of one volt. Refer to Figure 3.4.

The *ohm* is the amount of resistance in a conductor through which the current of one ampere will flow with an electromotive force of one volt.

When water flows in a pipe or tube, the amount of flow is affected by the amount of fluid friction which tends to retard the flow. For example, in a pipe that is rough due to scale, rust or other accumulation, the flow will not be as free as it would be in a pipe having a polished surface. In a similar way there are variations in the ease with which current can flow in electrical conductors, depending upon the physical condition of the conductors and upon the material of which they are made. Copper, aluminum and silver, which are good conductors, have fewer ohms per foot resistance for any given size of wire than iron wire, nichrome or other materials which have a higher resistance.

Any electrical conductor may have any amount of current (amperes) flowing in it, from zero to its maximum carrying capacity. The number of amperes flowing will be exactly proportional to the voltage or electromotive force pushing the current through the conductor. When the maximum carrying capacity

of a conductor is reached, further voltage causes the conductor to be so saturated with free electrons that they interfere with each other. This results in heat being generated in the conductor. If sufficient current is forced through the conductor, the heat will melt the metal and cause the circuit to open. There is, therefore, a definite relationship between the size of a conductor and the amount of current (amperes) that it will safely carry under any given voltage. In automotive electricity it is important that all conductors be of sufficient carrying capacity to pass the required number of amperes without excessive heating or voltage drop.

Factors Affecting Current Flow

Three factors affect the carrying capacity of an electrical conductor: cross-section area, length, and material. A fourth factor which should be considered under some circumstances is temperature. The wires used in automotive electricity seldom get hot enough under normal conditions to be affected by temperature. However some materials, particularly those used in thermo resistors to control the flow of current, may be affected. The resistance of these units decreases as the temperature falls and increases as the temperature rises.

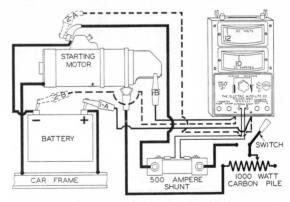

Fig. 3.4. A starting motor circuit with instruments connected to measure voltage drop (or resistance) in cable connections (2-A and 2-B) and corresponding drop in ground connections (1-A and 1-B). Note the external 500-ampere shunt used in the ammeter circuit.

An iron wire 10 feet long has six times the resistance of an identical copper wire. A wire of any diameter 20 feet long has twice the resistance of a wire of the same material 10 feet long. A wire .015″ in diameter has four times the resistance of a wire .030″ in diameter because the cross-section area is proportional to the square of the diameter.

For simplicity, the cross-section area of wire is expressed in *circular mils*. A circular mil is the area of a circle having a diameter of .001″. Thus if a wire had a diameter of .020″ it would have a diameter of 20 mils and a cross-section area of 400 (20 x 20) circular mils. Tables giving the carrying capacity of wires usually state the cross-section area of the wire in circular mils.

Although any electricity flowing through wire generates heat, this heat does not become objectionable until it reaches a point where damage occurs.

The increased molecular motion due to generated heat further increases the conductor's resistance, generating more heat. For this reason tables of electrical conductors usually specify the temperature at which the greatest resistance is effective.

In any given circuit, there must always be a balance between the electrical pressure in volts, the current flowing in amperes and the resistance of the circuit in ohms. Whenever circuits for any reason get out of balance (higher voltage and amperes than the circuit resistance can control), trouble is sure to follow. The automotive electrician, the diagnostician or the tune-up man must locate and remedy this trouble.

Ohm's Law

Ohm's Law is a statement of the relationship between the two fundamental characteristics of an electric current — voltage and amperes — and the basic characteristic of a circuit — its resistance in ohms.

Ohm's Law is most commonly given in equation form and may be written in three different ways. These are merely variations in stating the same relationship.

$$\text{Amperes} = \frac{\text{Volts}}{\text{Ohms}} \qquad \text{Ohms} = \frac{\text{Volts}}{\text{Amperes}}$$

$$\text{Volts} = \text{Amperes x Ohms}$$

The equation may also be written with the terms *intensity* substituted for amperes, *electromotive force* for volts, and *resistance* for ohms.

$$\text{Intensity} = \frac{\text{Electromotive Force}}{\text{Resistance}}$$

$$\text{Resistance} = \frac{\text{Electromotive Force}}{\text{Intensity}}$$

$$\text{Electromotive Force} = \text{Intensity x Resistance}$$

For convenience in using the law it is most often put in algebraic form using the letters *I, E* and *R*.

$$I = \frac{E}{R}$$

$$R = \frac{E}{I}$$

$$E = R \text{ x } I$$

An understanding of Ohm's Law is a basic requirement for the automotive diagnostician and tune-up man since it will give him the knowledge of the relationship of current flow and circuit resistance that will greatly simplify electrical testing and trouble shooting.

For satisfactory and safe operation, there must be a balance between voltage, amperes and ohms in any circuit. If any one of these factors changes, at least one of the others must change, and in some cases the other two must change to maintain balance in the circuit.

Automotive Electrical Circuits

A circuit as used in automotive electricity is a current path which includes: low resistance metal conductors; one or more appliances. The appliance, such as a lamp, a coil, a motor, a battery or resistance unit, must have a voltage drop or ohms of resistance corresponding to the potential of voltage impressed on the circuit.

For an example of how Ohm's law may be applied to an automotive circuit, a tail light bulb may only require .5 ampere to light it with a pressure of 6 volts. Therefore using the equation $R = \dfrac{E}{I}$, $R = 6 \div .5 = 12$ ohms. This means that the lamp bulb filament must have a resistance of 12 ohms for use in a 6-volt system. What would occur if this lamp bulb were inserted in a 12-volt system? The answer is easily ascertained. R is 12 ohms. E in this case is 12 volts. $I = \dfrac{E}{R} = \dfrac{12}{12} = 1$ ampere. Therefore with a pressure of 12 volts, 1 ampere will flow through the filament. The lamp filament has a carrying capacity of only .5 ampere. Forcing twice this amount of current through the filament will heat it so excessively it will burn out and interrupt the current flow.

On the other hand, what would occur if two 6-volt, .5-ampere bulbs were arranged so that the current flowed first into one, then into the other, and finally to the opposite side of the circuit? The resistances of the two bulbs would be added together giving a total resistance of 24 ohms.

Referring once more to the equation $I = \dfrac{E}{R}$ we would have $I = \dfrac{12}{24}$. This equals .5 ampere, which is the capacity of the bulb. Therefore, this arrangement would work satisfactorily. Refer to Fig. 3.5.

Now suppose a .5-ampere, 12-volt bulb were inserted in a 6-volt circuit. The resistance of the bulb would be 24 ohms $\left(R = \dfrac{12}{.5} = 24\right)$. Under a potential of 6 volts, only .25 ampere would flow in the circuit which is only enough current to produce a dull glow.

Application of Ohm's Law

Looking again at the equation $I = \dfrac{E}{R}$, suppose R the resistance increased due to a corroded contact of loose terminals. This will make I (amperes) smaller and there will be less than normal current flow to the appliances in the circuit. To illustrate, sealed-beam lights may require a current of as much as 12 amperes at 12 volts. Their resistance will be $R = \dfrac{12}{12} = 1.00$ ohm. If the circuit resistance were increased .10 ohms because of faulty terminals, the new resistance would be 1.1 ohms. Therefore the current would be reduced from 12 amperes to $I = \dfrac{12}{1.1} = 10.9$ amperes, making the lights dim.

The generator voltage controlled by a modern voltage regulator will be from 14.0 to 14.6 volts on most cars when operating above the minimum generating speed, but battery voltage is only 12 volts. Therefore in a circuit with .4-ohm resistance, current would be $I = \dfrac{12}{.4} = 30$ amperes when operating on battery current and $I = \dfrac{14.6}{.4} = 36.5$ amperes when operating on generator current.

Lamps and other automotive electrical appliances are built to withstand the higher voltage of the generator. However, this variation in current flow due to voltage change explains why lamps are less bright when operating on battery voltage than on generator voltage.

There are no exceptions to the operation of Ohm's Law. Current flow is always proportional to circuit resistance as long as voltage remains unchanged. Also, it is proportional to voltage as long as resistance is unchanged.

There is a variation in the voltage impressed on the car electrical system, depending upon

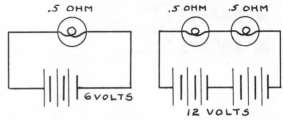

Fig. 3.5. According to Ohm's Law, the current flowing in the left hand circuit will be $1 = \dfrac{6}{.5}$ or 12 amperes since the lamp has a resistance of 0.5 ohm. In the 12-volt circuit on the right, since the resistance is doubled by the insertion of another 0.5-ohm unit, the current will still be 12 amperes. Notice that the two resistances are in series.

whether current is being supplied by the generator or the battery. However, for calculations and general consideration of the electrical system, it is assumed that the battery voltage of 12 volts governs current flow.

With Ohm's Law, if any two of the three factors are known, the third one can readily be calculated by using the equation which has the unknown factor to the left of the "equal" sign. Volts and amperes can usually be determined by the use of the voltmeter and ammeter respectively. Frequently the resistance of an auto appliance is specified; if the voltage of the system is also known, the amperes can readily be found.

Up to this point, it has been assumed that the current conductors had zero resistance. Of course this is not the case. Nevertheless, the resistance of properly sized wires is so small, especially in view of their relative short length, that it can be considered inconsequential.

Resistance and Circuit Balance

Resistance in a circuit is necessary to balance the circuit so that the current will be sufficient to operate appliances satisfactorily, and yet will not be so excessive to cause overheating. For example, Fig. 3.5 shows how additional resistance will make it possible to change from

a 6-volt to a 12-volt circuit without changing amperage.

Resistance may be compared to brakes applied on an automobile. Without brakes the car will run wild, out of control. With efficient brakes it can be controlled. A conductor on which the insulation has been worn off is like an automobile without brakes. If it contacts another conductor with a voltage difference, such as the grounded car frame, the current will flow in excessive amounts and either burn up the wire or burn out a fuse.

Resistance in a circuit is very desirable in the right places. It is definitely needed in various electrical appliances to maintain current balance; however, it is not desired in conductors, terminals or contacts. See Fig. 3.6.

Energy, Work and Power

An understanding of energy and its applications will help the automotive tune-up man to diagnose the trouble in a non-functioning system. He can work quickly from his knowledge of the proper operation of the system. Therefore, some time should be devoted to the subjects of *force, work, energy,* and *power*.

Force

Force is the *tendency to produce movement*. The application of force may not produce movement, but the *tendency* is always present. *Static force* causes no movement, while *dynamic force* does produce movement.

We live in a world of force, surrounded by various kinds every moment of our lives. The force of gravity causes us to apply a pressure to the ground. Reservoir water supplies force to the blades of a turbine wheel as it rushes through the turbine passages seeking a lower level. The wind applies force to the vanes of a windmill and to the sails of a boat. Locomotives apply force to the drawbar to pull a train of freight cars. Force is applied at the periphery of an automobile's rear tires where they contact the road, to drive the car forward, Fig. 3.7. Explosive force is applied to the top of a piston

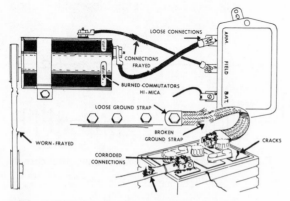

Fig. 3.6. Defects in the generating circuit may cause high resistance or poor performance. These are easily discovered by a visual inspection of the circuit. Note the corroded battery conditions, loose connections, and frayed wiring.

to drive the crankshaft in a gasoline engine as shown in Fig. 3.8. Examples of force application are innumerable.

Work

Work is done when energy is expended to overcome resistance and cause movement through a measurable distance. The amount of work done is the product of the force (in pounds) multiplied by the distance (in feet) through which the movement took place. This product is given in foot-pounds when the English system of measurement is used.

A weight of 10 pounds lifted 5 feet requires 10 x 5 or 50 foot-pounds of work. A traction effort or force of 500 pounds applied to move a car 1000 feet utilizes 500,000 foot-pounds of work.

Time does not enter into the amount of work done since the same energy input is required whether the work is done slowly or quickly. If a 150-pound man walked up stairs to a height of 100 feet, he will expend 150 x 100 or 15,000 foot-pounds of work whether he makes the climb in 5 minutes or 5 hours.

Thus mathematically: Work equals force times distance. $W = F \times D$.

The relationship of work and force can be seen as follows: Work is *force acting through space*. Remember, however, that force may exist without work being done. For example, a man may push against a car without moving it. Work is done when the man's applied force actually moves the car.

Two terminals of a battery have a potential electrical force, but the resistance of air is too great for a current to flow and no work is done. The same is true when a generator is running with an open circuit. When a wire is connected across the terminals of a battery or a generator, the force is able to overcome the resistance of the wire, a current flows and electrical work is done. In this case the work takes the form of heat generation. If a lamp is connected in a circuit the work takes the form of light and heat.

A *joule* is the unit of electrical work; it is the amount of work performed by a current of one ampere flowing for one second with a pressure of one volt.

1 joule=1 volt x 1 ampere x 1 second=.7375 foot-pounds of mechanical work.

Energy

Energy is the *capacity for doing work*; it may appear in a number of different forms. There is *mechanical energy*, such as that transmitted by a moving belt or a rotating shaft; *electrical energy* transmitted by wires; *heat energy* released by combustion: chemical energy, molecular energy, atomic energy, light and sound. The most plentiful form of energy is heat.

One form of energy can be converted into another form. It can go through a number of

Fig. 3.7. The *force* applied to the road by the rear wheels of an automobile driving the car forward is just the same as a *force* which might be applied to pull the car at the same speed (minus the friction power loss in the engine).

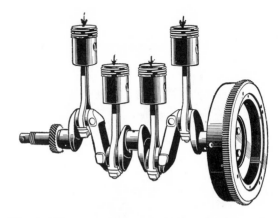

Fig. 3.8. Force applied to the piston heads on the power stroke produces engine power. The compression stroke force opposes that of the power stroke. Therefore the net force which generates engine power is the difference between forces of the power and compression strokes.

energy transformations even ending up again in its original form.

A steam-powered electric generating plant is a good illustration of the conversion of energy. Fuel burned in a furnace releases chemical energy. This in turn causes heat energy which is a form of molecular energy. This heat is transferred through the surfaces of the boiler into the water. The molecular energy of the water is increased to such an extent that it vaporizes and forms steam under high pressure. Allowed to expand, the steam acquires a very high velocity and imparts mechanical energy to the blades of the steam turbine. This mechanical energy is transformed into electrical energy in the generator. The electrical energy is distributed through wires and becomes: mechanical energy when it operates electric motors; light and heat when it operates lamps; heat when it operates electrical heating devices; light, heat and sound when it operates radio sets; chemical energy when it charges batteries as a supply for electrical energy again when the battery is put into an operating circuit.

An important fact is that every transformation of energy is accompanied by the generation of some heat.

In a gasoline engine cylinder at the instant of explosion, chemical and heat energy cause a rapid buildup of pressure. This pressure moves the piston down, imparting rotary motion to the crankshaft (mechanical energy).

Fig. 3.9. The sports car is being *tuned* so that its small, efficient engine will generate its best power output.

Power

Power is the *rate of doing work*. Power is independent of the total amount of work accomplished, but time is an important factor. Since power is the amount of energy supplied per second, per minute or per hour, it cannot be measured without the time element.

Mechanical power per unit of time is usually given in *horsepower*. One horsepower is defined as 33,000 foot-pounds per minute or 550 foot-pounds per second. To find the horsepower required to perform any mechanical operation, divide the work to be done per minute by 33,000.

To compute the horsepower of an engine at any given speed (usually the speed of maximum power) it is necessary to multiply (a) the force applied to each piston by the exploding gases by (b) the number of power strokes per engine revolution, by (c) the piston travel per stroke (in feet), by (d) the revolutions per minute (rpm). Divide this product by 33,000, and the result will be *horsepower*. Refer to Fig. 3.9.

The force applied to each piston by the exploding gases, is found by multiplying the area of the top of the piston in square inches, by the *mean effective pressure* (mep). This mep is really the average pressure in pounds per square inch that is applied to the top of the piston, and it is found by careful engineering tests.

Electrical power is measured in *watts*, with a unit of 1000 watts called a *kilowatt*.

The watt is equivalent to 1 joule of electrical work per second. Therefore watts $= \dfrac{\text{Joules}}{\text{Seconds}}$ $= \dfrac{\text{volts x amperes}}{\text{seconds}}$ x seconds. The *seconds* cancel out and the equation becomes:

$$\text{watts} = \text{volts x amperes.}$$

Therefore, 1 watt $=$ 1 volt x 1 ampere. To get the total number of watts involved (in direct current) simply multiply the total number of volts by the total number of amperes.

Table 1
Electrical Units

Quantity	Prefix	Example
1,000 Watts	Kilo	Kilowatt
1,000,000 Ohms	Mega or Meg	Megohm
.000001 Ohm	Micro	Microhm
.000001 Farad	Micro	Microfarad
.001 Volt	Milli	Millivolt
.001 Ampere	Milli	Milliampere

When referring to watts the time is considered to be 1 hour unless otherwise specified. So, 1 volt x 1 ampere x 1 hour=1 watt hour. A current of 1000 watts supplied for one hour will be 1000 watt hours or one kilowatt hour.

The kilowatt as a power unit is larger than a horsepower. The ratio is: .746 kilowatt= one horsepower. To illustrate, consider a current of 120 volts with 5 amperes flowing for 3 hours. This will be 120 x 5=600 watts; and 600 watts x 3 hours=1800 watt hours. This divided by 1000 watts=1.8 kilowatt hours.

The preceding calculations apply to direct current only. When alternating current is involved other factors must be considered. However, since automotive electricity deals only with direct current as supplied by the alternator, the AC factors are not important.

As previously explained, the flow of electricity through a conductor is similar to the flow of water through a pipe. A flow of water is usually expressed in gallons or pounds per minute. A flow of electricity is expressed in amperes. The power required to keep water flowing against a certain hydraulic head is numerically equal to the flow in pounds per minute x the head, (height, or pressure) in feet. Therefore the power would be equal to pounds per minute x the feet through which the water drops. To determine the horsepower required to force water against a given head, the following equation may be used: hp=lbs. per minute x feet÷33,000.

In a similar way, the power required to keep electricity flowing against a certain resistance is numerically equal to flow in amperes x the

pressure in volts. This product gives the power in watts. Divide this product by 1000 for the kilowatt power.

Summary

Two qualities of *electric current* must be considered: (1) electrical pressure, and (2) quantity of current flow.

Electrical pressure is the "potential" or voltage (electromotive force, emf). The voltage drop is the difference in voltage between any two points in a circuit.

Current flow is measured in amperes. The third electrical unit is the *measure of resistance*, the ohm. The flow of electricity and water flow may be compared.

There is a *relationship* between volts, amperes and ohms in a live circuit. One ampere will flow through a resistance of one ohm with an electrical pressure of one volt.

Current flow through a conductor depends upon resistance and is proportional to the voltage. If the safe current-carrying capacity of a conductor is exceeded, generated heat may cause damage.

Three factors affect the *carrying capacity* of an electrical conductor: (1) its material (2) its cross-section area, and (3) its length. Temperature may also affect its current carrying capacity. The cross-section area of a wire is generally expressed in *circular mils*. A circular mil is a circle with a diameter of 0.001 inch.

Since electricity flowing along wires creates *heat*, the current flow must be kept to a safe amount.

A circuit is kept in *balance* by limiting the voltage and the resulting ampere flow to quantities that the circuit resistance can control.

Ohm's Law is a statement of the relationship between the voltage, amperage and resistance in an electric circuit. It is expressed as

$$amperes = \frac{volts}{ohms}.$$

An *electrical circuit* is a current path which includes low resistance conductors and one or more appliances or accessories having a voltage drop (or resistance) substantially equal to the circuit voltage.

There are *two voltages* in an automotive electric circuit (1) battery voltage, and (2) generator voltage. There is a 2.3 to 3 volts difference between the two.

With *Ohm's Law*, if any two of the three factors (volts, amperes, ohms) are known, the unknown factor can be determined.

Resistance in a circuit keeps the current flow down to a safe value, but the resistance should be in the appliances or accessories, not in the conductors.

Force is the tendency to produce movement. *Work* is done when energy is expended and movement is caused. The *amount of work* is force times distance, given in foot-pounds. *Energy* is the capacity for doing work and may appear in such forms as mechanical, heat, chemical, and electrical energy. *Power* is the rate of doing work.

Watts of energy for direct current is calculated by multiplying together the volts and amperes flowing in a circuit.

Questions

1. Name the two important qualities of electric current.
2. Name the three units of measurement pertaining to current flow in a circuit.
3. Compare the flow of electricity with the flow of water in a pipe.
4. Give the voltage of three common electrical applications.
5. Mention three features of an electrical conductor that influence current flow.
6. What is a circular mil?
7. Express Ohm's Law in two forms.
8. In an electric circuit, which should have the highest resistance: (1) the conductors, or (2) appliances and accessories?
9. How many amperes will flow with a pressure of 12 volts in a circuit with 1 ohm resistance?
10. What is the average generator voltage in an automobile electrical system with a 12-volt battery?
11. Are there any exceptions to Ohm's Law?
12. Why is resistance necessary in an automotive electrical circuit?
13. What is force?
14. What is work?
15. What is energy?
16. What is power?
17. How do you calculate the watts of energy expended in an electric circuit?
18. How does a watt differ from a kilowatt?
19. The flow of water in a pipe is expressed in gallons per minute. In what unit would a flow of electricity in a closed circuit be measured?
20. Pressure in pounds per square inch will cause water to flow in a pipe. What force causes electricity to flow in a closed circuit?

CHAPTER FOUR

Magnetism—
Induced Currents

Magnetism

Magnetism is used in the operation of much automotive electrical equipment, such as ignition coils, starting motors, starting switches, generators and generator controls, electrically controlled valves and switches, and instruments.

There are three classes of magnets: (1) natural magnets, (2) artificial magnets, (3) electromagnets.

Natural magnets have been known for several thousand years. They are pieces of iron ore to which small slivers of iron or steel will adhere due to their natural magnetic force. They have no practical value today and are mentioned merely as a matter of interest.

The *artificial magnets* in commercial, industrial and scientific use are made from refined steel or special alloys. A piece of iron or steel may be magnetized by rubbing it with a magnet, but a more effective way is to use an electric current. An iron bar inserted in a coil of insulated wire will be magnetized when a heavy current is passed through the wire. Hard steel will not magnetize quite as readily as soft steel; however, once hard steel is magnetized, it will retain its magnetism indefinitely. Conversely, as soon as the magnetizing force is removed from soft iron, most of its magnetism disappears and the small amount which remains is called the *residual magnetism.* It is this residual magnetism, as small in strength or amount as it may be, that is the reason generators can build up their normal current output after being inoperative.

Permanent magnets are made of hard steel or magnetic alloy, and temporary magnets are made of soft iron or annealed steel. A relatively new material, the alloy called *Alnico*, is superior to hard steel for permanent magnets. It is used in instruments and other places where the best possible permanent magnet is needed.

Electromagnets

In 1819 a Danish scientist named Oersted first discovered a relationship between magnetism and electricity. He found that an electric current always has certain magnetic effects which are governed by definite laws.

When a straight wire carries electric current, there is a cylindrical magnetic field around.it. When the wire is wound into a coil, it acts like a permanent magnet as long as the current flows. The addition of an iron core greatly increases this magnetic strength.

Magnetic Lines of Force

Magnetism is represented by magnetic lines of force. Each magnet exhibits magnetic force in greatest concentration at its ends, or poles. These poles are designated as *North* and *South*, corresponding to the north and south poles of the earth, which is itself a huge magnet.

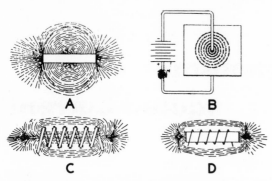

Fig. 4.1. Pattern of magnetic lines of force under different conditions. (A) Lines of force around a straight bar magnet. (B) Circular lines of force around a wire carrying current, as they would be shown with iron filings on a paper at right angles to the wire. (C) Lines of force around a coil carrying current (solenoid). (D) Lines of force around soft steel bar with coil carrying current surrounding it.

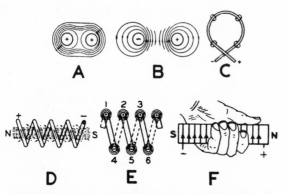

Fig. 4.2. (A) Form of magnetic field around two parallel wires with current flowing in the same direction in each wire. (B) Form of magnetic field around two parallel wires with current flowing in opposite directions. (C) Form of magnetic lines of force around wire bent into loop. (D) Form of magnetic lines flowing through coil. (E) An enlarged section of D, showing how field around the wire neutralizes adjacent field to cause solenoid magnetic effect. (F) Illustrates "Left-Hand Rule", fingers pointing in direction of current flow, thumb pointing to *N* pole.

The magnetic lines of force flow from the north pole, around the outside of the magnet into the south pole, and through the magnet to the north pole. Each magnetic line forms a complete loop called a *magnetic circuit*. The total number of lines in a magnetic circuit makes up the *magnetic flux*. Magnetic lines seem to have a tension along their length, for they tend to shorten as do stretched rubber bands. They also exert a lateral force on each other, producing a crowding effect, and tending to push one another sideways. Various field patterns are illustrated in Figs. 4.1 and 4.2.

The lines of force around an electrical conductor or near the poles of a magnet constitute a magnetic field. The greater the concentration of lines of force, the greater will be the magnetic effect. To see the form of a magnetic field, lay a piece of cardboard on top of a bar magnet and sprinkle iron filings on this. Tap the cardboard lightly to arrange the filings into the field pattern.

The ease with which a magnetic field can pass through a substance is called *permeability*. However, magnetic lines penetrate air with difficulty. Where one line of force will penetrate air, over 1000 lines will penetrate hard steel and 1500 to 2500 lines will penetrate soft steel or wrought iron. These figures will vary with the particular metal specimens.

Magnetic lines pass easily through materials that can be magnetized. When a piece of iron or steel is placed in a magnetic field, the lines pass principally through the metal instead of through the air. Since the metal is a much better magnetic conductor than air, the lines will naturally seek the path of least resistance.

Characteristics of Magnetism

The ability of a magnetic field to pass through any substance such as glass, copper, wood, or paper is not always advantageous. It is sometimes difficult to eliminate the effect which stray magnetic currents have on electric measuring instruments. For example, a conductor carrying a heavy current produces a strong magnetic field, which may easily affect nearby meters. To prevent this, a case of heavy iron around the meter will provide a path for the lines of magnetic force.

If the north pole of one magnet is placed near the south pole of another, there will be mutual attraction between the two poles. The magnetic lines leave the north pole of the first magnet and enter the south pole of the second. As the magnetic lines are under tension, like rubber bands, they tend to shorten and to pull the two poles together.

On the other hand, if the south poles of two magnets are placed near each other, the lines of force coming together, being the same kind, will strongly repel each other. This idea can be stated in a general rule: Unlike magnetic poles mutually attract each other; like poles mutually repel each other. See Fig. 4.3.

Magnetic Compasses

A compass needle is a thin bar magnet, delicately balanced and mounted so it will rotate freely in a horizontal plane. It always will set itself in the direction of the magnetic lines in whatever magnetic field it is placed. The colored end, which is normally the north seeking end, will point in the direction of the magnetic lines. The compass can be used to determine whether or not a material is magnetized. It can also determine the polarity of the poles in a generator, which in turn may indicate whether the field coils have been connected properly.

The compass will also align itself with the magnetic lines of the earth's magnetic field running from south to north. The end of the magnet which points north is called the "North Seeking Pole."

Magnetic Molecules

To explain what happens when iron or steel becomes magnetized assume that the metal is composed of molecules which are very tiny magnets, each with its north and south poles.

When the metal is not magnetized, the molecules are arranged at random in an irregular pattern. When the metal is magnetized, the magnetic molecules arrange themselves with all the north poles pointing in one direction. The cumulative effect makes the piece of metal act like one magnet. Refer to Figure 4.4.

Induction

Induction cannot be understood without knowledge of magnetism, because there can be no induction without magnetism. Without induction there could be no generation of electricity by means of generators, and no action of the induction coil as we use it in connection with automotive ignition.

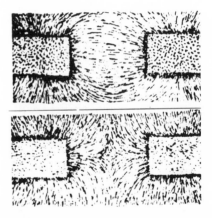

Fig. 4.3. (Above) Shape of field between like magnetic poles, shown by iron filings. (Below) Shape of field between unlike magnetic poles.

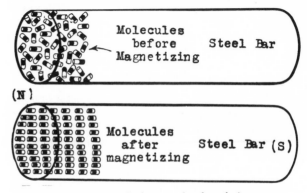

Fig. 4.4. Steel bar before and after being magnetized.

Electromagnetism

Wherever there is an electric current, there is also a magnetic current or magnetic field. The magnetic field around a straight wire or current conductor can be pictured as a number of invisible paper cylinders surrounding the wire. These would have gradually increasing diameters; one would be around another, and all would rotate around the wire like a flywheel.

If this magnetic field could be cut at right angles to the wire, a number of concentric circles (each one representing a line of force) would be seen to surround the cross section of the wire. This can be verified by passing a conductor through a piece of cardboard at right angles to its length, and sprinkling iron filings on the horizontal surface of the cardboard. The filings will arrange themselves in concentric circles around the wire. A compass placed within the magnetic field will assume a position at right angles to the wire and tangent to the circular lines of force.

If the current-carrying wire is bent into a circular loop, the magnetic field will likewise be bent into a "doughnut" of magnetic lines of force. If the wire is bent into two or more turns, the magnetic fields around each turn of wire merge together so that there is still one magnetic sleeve around the turns with the

total magnetic strength equal to the sum of the individual fields. If the wire is bent into a large number of turns, or wound into a coil, the magnetic sleeve will be similar to the magnetic field of force around a permanent magnet.

A magnetic field, whether around a piece of magnetized steel or resulting from a current-carrying wire or coil, follows the same rules of action. There are no different varieties of magnetism. However, magnetism due to currents of electricity only lasts during the time the current is flowing; it immediately disappears when the current flow ceases. If there is a soft iron core inside the coil, the iron will hold a small amount of residual magnetism, but the coil itself loses all magnetic effect, immediately upon current interruption. Refer to Fig. 4.5.

Ampere-Turns

The strength of the magnetic field built up around a coil depends upon (a) the number of amperes flowing in the wire and (b) the number of turns in the coil. Therefore, magnetic effect equals amperes multiplied by the number of turns; the result is given in *ampere-turns*. From this it can be seen that a coil made

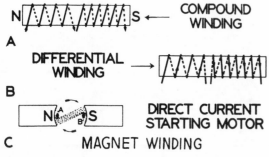

Fig. 4.5. (A) Compound winding, with two coils wound in the same direction, blends its magnetic forces. Used in solenoid starting motor control. (B) Differential winding; two coils wound in opposite directions oppose their magnetic forces. Used in some relays and controls. (C) Principle of the starting motor. A coil carrying current is repelled by magnetic lines of force, and tries to move out of the field, causing tendency to rotate.

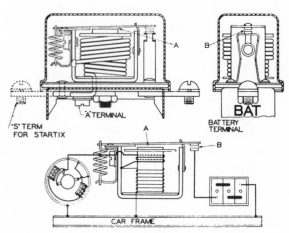

Fig. 4.6. (Upper) Circuit breaker with differential windings. (Lower) Cumulative windings on cut-out relay. Upper coil with heavy wire is the "current coil"; lower coil with fine wire is "voltage coil." Upper coil only transmits current when contact points at *B* are closed; lower (voltage) coil is grounded so current flows at all times the generator is operating. (AL)

up of a large number of turns of very fine wire and carrying a small current may have the same magnetic effect as a coil made up of fewer turns of coarser wire, and carrying a heavier current. Note this application in Fig. 4.6.

Magnetic Interference

A good many electric devices depend for their action upon the results of two or more magnetic fields coming in contact. When two magnetic fields come together, the magnetic lines of force which flow in the same direction will add their magnetic strength, while lines flowing in the opposite direction will neutralize each other. Therefore the field is greatly strengthened on one side of the conductors and weakened on the other side. This results in the application of force as one coil attempts to move out of the field of the other. If one coil is mounted so that it can move, it will do so, impelled by the magnetic repulsion of the interfering magnetic fields. This is the principle on which electric motors operate.

If a conductor carrying current is placed in a magnetic field it will tend to move out of that field. The direction of movement of the conductor will be governed by (a) the direction of current flow in the conductors and (b) the direction of flow of the magnetic lines of force in the magnetic field. If the conductor is in the form of a square or rectangular loop, the current will flow in one direction in relation to the magnetic field on one side and in the opposite direction on the other side. Thus, one side of the loop might tend to move up and the other side down, causing rotation of the loop. If the loop is so mounted that it can readily rotate and if there are other similar loops all mechanically connected, a powerful rotating force will be generated. This force can be used for performing mechanical operations, which is exactly what happens in an electric motor.

An electric motor of an automotive type will have two or four electromagnets to create powerful magnetic fields. Within these electromagnets are armature coils that are free to rotate.

They are so arranged that the conductors cut the lines of force of the surrounding magnetic field at right angles. When current flows, the interference of the two magnetic fields causes rotation of the armature.

This is based on the principle that a wire carrying electric current will endeavor to move out of a magnetic field when the conductor is at right angles to the lines of force of that field.

Solenoid Action

A coil of wire without an iron or steel core is called a *solenoid*. If the coil is long in proportion to its diameter, it will have properties similar to a bar magnet, with an envelope of magnetic lines of force around the outside and a concentration of magnetic lines through the inner core of air.

If a piece of soft steel somewhat shorter than the length of the coil is placed so that (1) its centerline or axis is parallel to the lines of force in the core of the coil, and (2) the center of its length is away from the center of the coil, it will move into the core of the coil with a relatively powerful force when current flows through the coil. In other words, the metal plunger will be "sucked" into the coil. This action is used to move the starting motor pinion into mesh with the flywheel ring gear on some types of starters, and also to operate electrically controlled switches and valves. For example, this idea is the basis of the solenoid switch circuit in Fig. 4.7.

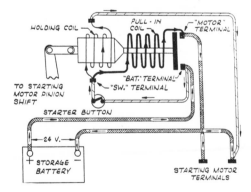

Fig. 4.7. Wiring diagram of solenoid switch circuit, showing the two cumulative coils.

Technically the term "solenoid" refers to a coil with an air core, but in practical use it has come to mean a device consisting of a coil and plunger which will give a powerful linear action. This solenoid has a wider application in automotive electricity than an iron-core coil that attracts a piece of steel or iron at the end of the core, because the amount of movement that can be obtained by a magnet is limited. This is true because the magnetic pull decreases in proportion to the square of the distance from the end of the core to the armature. Thus, a piece of iron (armature) located

.020″ from the end of the core would be attracted with a force four times as strong as if it were .040″ away, and sixteen times as strong as if it were four times as far away or .080″. This restricts the use of electromagnets to applications where a very small movement will accomplish the desired result, such as in cut-out relays and voltage or current regulators. The term *armature* refers not only to the rotating part of a motor or generator, but also to the metal part attracted by a magnet.

Induced Currents

A wire which carries an electric current tends to be forced out of a magnetic field in which it cuts the lines of force at right angles. Conversely, a conductor which is part of a closed circuit will have an electric current generated or *induced* in it if it is forcibly made to cut across the lines of force in a magnetic field. Cutting the lines of magnetic force induces an electromotive force (emf) or voltage in the wire, causing current to flow. Refer to Fig. 4.8.

Voltage induced in a conductor is governed by the strength of the magnetic field measured by the number of magnetic lines, and the speed in lines per second at which the lines are cut. One volt will be induced in a single conductor when the conductor cuts the field flux at a rate of 100,000,000 lines per second.

There are three methods of producing voltage in automotive electric equipment: (1) with moving conductors and stationary magnetic field, used in generators and shuttle type magnetos, (2) stationary conductors and varying magnetic flux, so that in effect the lines of force move, used in ignition coils, and (3) stationary conductors and moving magnetic field used in inductor type magnetos, and the newer automotive alternators.

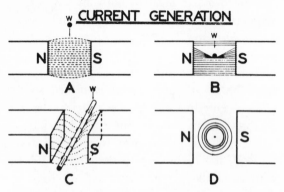

Fig. 4.8. (A) Current carrying wire in an armature about to enter a magnetic field. (B) Wire has entered the magnetic field and is cutting the magnetic lines of force. (C) Bending of the magnetic lines of force and crowding ahead of the lines increases the intensity of the field. (D) Magnetic field around the current carrying wire.

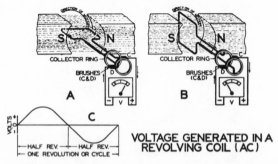

Fig. 4.9. Revolving coil in a magnetic field. (A) Right-hand side of coil is moving up and left-hand side down, generating current. (B) Wires not cutting lines of force so voltage is zero. As the coil revolves and again cuts magnetic lines, the direction of current flow will be reversed in the coil.

Voltage Generated in Moving Coil

Consider a single conductor in the form of a rectangular loop, rotating in a counterclockwise direction at a uniform speed in a magnetic field. When the plane of the loop is parallel to the direction of flow of the lines of force, it will be cutting the greatest number of lines, and a maximum voltage will be induced in the coil. See Fig. 4.9. The side of the loop on the right will be cutting the lines as it moves upward, causing current to flow toward the right-hand terminal. The left side of the loop will be cutting the lines as it moves downward, inducing current flow away from the left-hand terminal.

As the loop rotates, it cuts fewer lines and a constantly reducing voltage is induced until the loop reaches a vertical position at right angles to the field poles, where no lines are being cut and zero voltage is induced. As the coil continues to rotate, it enters the field again, but in a reversed relation to the magnetic lines. The voltage in the loop will be reversed and will again increase to a maximum when the loop reaches a horizontal position where it is once more cutting lines at a maximum rate. The voltage will again decrease to zero as the loop reaches a position at right angles to the magnetic lines. Each revolution of the loop constitutes *one cycle*, with the voltage reaching a maximum in one direction, returning to zero, building to a maximum and returning to zero again.

Since voltage reverses with each revolution, any current supplied to an external circuit would be *alternating current*, as Fig. 4.9. illustrates.

However, if each end of the loop were connected to a semicircular segment, with stationary brushes contacting the two segments, direct current would result. As the loop would rotate, and the direction of current flow reverse, contact would be made with the opposite terminal. The voltage and current delivered to an outside circuit would fluctuate but the flow of electricity would be in one direction only. Segments which act as such a reversing switch make up a *commutator*. See Fig. 4.10.

Two coils and four commutator segments would give a current output which would fluctuate less than the single coil and two segments.

Increasing the number of coils and segments sufficiently will give practically a uniform direct current. Refer to Fig. 4.11.

Many different types of windings and armature circuits are used for automotive and commercial armatures, depending upon the service for which they are designed. The armature is the rotating part which carries the rotating coils; it has a laminated soft steel core. The conductors are placed in grooves running parallel or at a slight angle to the shaft. This metal core has two functions: (1) to serve as a carrier for the conductors of the armature

VOLTAGE GENERATED IN A REVOLVING COIL (PULSATING)

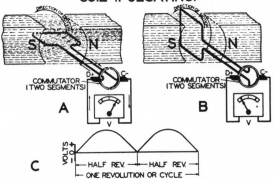

Fig. 4.10. Similar coils connected to commutator segments will have their generated current rectified, giving a pulsating direct current.

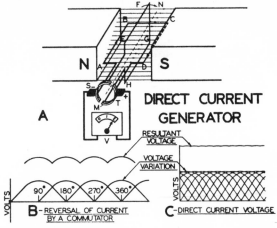

Fig. 4.11. Addition of more coil and commutator segments "levels" out the voltage, giving continuous direct current.

winding, and (2) to provide a highly permeable path for the magnetic field circuit.

Alternating Current Generator

In the alternator, the windings are stationary and the magnetic field rotates. The windings (corresponding to the armature) are carried in slots in a stationary frame supported by end plates of the generator. This is called the *stator*. The field, which is supplied with direct current, rotates, and is called the *rotor*. In this type of generator the magnetic field revolves with its alternate positive and negative poles, and the magnetic lines of force cut the stationary conductors, generating alternating current. The *stator is laminated* to provide a highly permeable path for the magnetic lines of force. Since the rotor metal parts do not cut any lines of force it is not necessary for them to be laminated. (The alternator is discussed in detail in Chapter 18.)

Eddy Currents

As the armature rotates in the DC generator, the core of the armature as well as the armature conductors cuts the magnetic lines of force of the field, causing *eddy currents*. If the armature core were made of solid steel, these eddy currents would become quite powerful. They would absorb a considerable amount of the energy required to drive the generator, and would raise the armature temperature to a level too high for satisfactory operation. Energy lost from this source would greatly reduce the efficiency of the generator.

Similarly in the alternator, wasteful eddy currents would result if the stator frame were made of solid metal.

In order to hold these losses to a minimum, the armature core and the stator frame are made of thin steel laminations approximately 0.022″ in thickness. The surfaces of these laminations are treated to form an oxidized coating which acts as an insulator to cut the strength of the eddy currents to a tolerable level.

Armature cores should not be filed or turned since such treatment will cause electrical connections between the armature laminations, resulting in a higher operating temperature and reduced generator output. Likewise, the laminated frame of the alternator stator should never be filed, either on the outer surface or on the ribs between the slots which hold the windings.

Field Magnets

In automotive and commercial DC generators, electromagnets supply the magnetic field required to induce current flow in the armature conductors. There is enough residual magnetism to initiate voltage buildup in the armature conductors as they cut the magnetic field lines of force.

There are many combinations of field coil windings and numbers of poles, depending upon the service for which the generator is designed. The armature designs will also vary. Most DC automotive generators have two field poles.

An Auto-lite generator, which different car manufacturers have used, has the following specifications:

28 commutator bars	2 field coils
28 armature coils	200 turns per field coil
3 or 4 conductors per coil	440 feet of wire per coil
196 total conductors in armature	226,000 magnetic lines of force
Rating — 35 amperes — 8 volts — 280 watts	

Varying Magnetic Flux Generates Voltage

Current can be induced as long as there is relative movement between the conductor and the magnetic field. It is not important which one of the two moves, since an induced current results.

A magnetic field is created in millionths of a second. Nevertheless, when current is first applied to a coil, there are only a few lines of magnetic force around each conductor. These expand, like rubber bands being stretched, until the full volume of the field is established. When the current supply ceases, the magnetic lines shrink back to zero, as the field collapses.

Consider one coil wound around another, with no electrical connection between them. If current passes through the inner coil, its expanding magnetic lines of force will cut the outer coil. This relative movement between conductor and field results in an induced current flow in the outer coil. The coil to which current is supplied from an outside source, such as a battery or generator, is called the *primary coil* or primary winding; the coil in which the current is induced is called the *secondary coil*, secondary winding, or high-tension winding.

Induced current flow is maintained only during the time when conductors are being cut by lines of force. Since the buildup or collapse of a field is very rapid, the duration of induced current flow is quite short. The lines of force are stationary between the buildup and collapse of the field so that no movement occurs to cause induced current during this period. This is the principle used for the battery ignition system on gasoline engines and spark ignition oil engines. Refer to Fig. 4.12.

If the primary coil were supplied with alternating current it would have a continuously varying magnetic field. (As previously explained, AC builds up from zero to maximum in one direction, returns to zero, builds up to a maximum in the opposite direction, and again returns to zero.) With such a constantly varying magnetic field, a corresponding alternating current would be induced in the secondary coil. This is the principle on which the AC transformer operates. A 60-cycle alternating current which has 60 cycles of current buildup and reversal per second will induce the corresponding kind of AC in the secondary coil.

The voltage of the induced current in the secondary winding will be proportional to the numbers of turns in the two windings. In the automobile, from 8,000 to 20,000 volts are needed to supply the current to jump the spark plug gap, so there will be many thousands of turns of fine wire on the secondary winding, while the primary winding will have only a few hundred turns of coarser wire.

The buildup speed of the magnetic field of the primary winding is not great enough to induce a sparking voltage in the secondary. Therefore it is not used with automotive engine ignition. However with the aid of a condenser, an effective sparking current is induced upon the more rapid collapse of the field. The condenser and its action will be discussed in more detail in Chapter 20. In the literature of electricity-electronics, the type of device called a *condenser* in automotive terminology is referred to as a *capacitor*.

Self-Induction

When the current supply to the primary winding is suddenly interrupted by the opening of the distributor breaker points, a series of actions takes place which combine to produce the sparking current. The collapsing magnetic field of the primary cuts across the conductors of the secondary winding and induces a brief current flow in the same direction as the flow in the primary winding. The lines of force, as they collapse, cut not only the secondary conductors, but also the primary wires, inducing a current in the primary which flows in the opposite direction as that which came from the outside current supply. This is the *self-induced* voltage. It may reach an instantaneous value of several hundred volts.

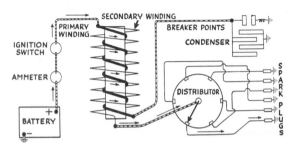

Fig. 4.12. Ignition system, showing arrangement of ignition coil windings. In this case the conductors remain stationary, and the lines of force move as the magnetic field builds and collapses. (Electro)

In any coil in which there are voltage variations, there will be a certain amount of self-induction, due to lines of force cutting conductors. With alternating currents this is an important factor in the design and action of coils with a large number of turns. The term *inductance* is used to describe this effect, and units of inductance are used to measure it. However, this is not important in automotive electricity and can be neglected here for all practical purposes.

Vibrating Coil

Up to 1926 when the last Model T Ford was built, a vibrating coil was used. Basically the coil was much like those used today except that a magnetic vibrator was used to make and break the circuit many times per second, with each cycle producing a hot spark. The rapid series of sparks gave the effect of continuous sparking, though actually each spark was generated in the same way as present ignition sparks. A separate coil was used for each cylinder, four being mounted in a case to supply the ignition current for a four-cylinder engine.

Summary

Permanent magnets retain their magnetism. They have a magnetic field consisting of lines of magnetic force which flow from the north pole to the south pole through the air around the magnet and from the south pole to the north pole through the metal magnet.

Electromagnets are soft iron cores magnetized by electric currents flowing around them in coils of wire. The magnetism lasts only as long as the current flows, except for a small remaining *residual magnetism*.

A coil of wire, with or without a soft iron core, through which electric current is flowing will act like a magnet, having a north and south pole and a magnetic field.

Since magnetic lines of force pass through or *permeate*, soft iron or soft steel very readily, many more lines will pass through these metals than through the same cross-section area of air.

This ratio between the number of lines passing through identical cross sections of a magnetic material and air is called the *relative permeability* of the material. It will be from 1500 to 2500 for soft iron.

Magnetism easily passes through such substances as glass, copper, wood, paper, etc., but *does not attract them*.

Unlike magnetic poles attract each other, and like poles repel each other.

A *compass* will indicate the polarity of a magnet or current-carrying coil. The colored end of the needle points to the north magnetic pole.

There is a *magnetic field* around every wire which carries an electric current whether the wire is a single conductor or in a coil. The magnetic field around a coil has a strength equal to the sum of the magnetic fields that would be around each wire if it were a single conductor.

The number of *ampere-turns*, which is the product of the number of turns in a coil and the number of amperes flowing in the coil, governs the strength of the magnetic field.

Magnetic interference is set up when two or more magnetic fields come in contact, with the magnetic lines running at right angles to each other. There is mutual repulsion, and conductors carrying current will tend to be forced out of the magnetic field.

A *solenoid* is a coil of wire without a soft iron core. When current is passed through it, it will "suck" a bar of iron or steel lengthwise into its center. It is used to operate some designs of starter gear-engaging mechanisms and electrically operated valves and switches.

Induced currents are generated when a conductor which is part of a closed circuit cuts magnetic lines of force or when the magnetic lines cut across a conductor.

A *rotating coil* in a magnetic field, with its ends connected to segments contacted by stationary brushes will generate a pulsating direct electric current. With a sufficient number of coils and segments making up a *commutator*, a reasonably uniform direct current will be generated.

A *rotating DC field* cutting stationary conductors (as in an *alternator*) will generate alternating current in the conductors because the conductors are cut first by lines of force from the north magnetic poles and then by those from the south magnetic poles. (See Chapter 18.)

Eddy currents are currents induced in the metal of the *armature* which carries the armature coils or windings. These always incur some loss, but this loss is minimized by using thin laminations rather than solid metal in the armature.

The ignition coil depends for its action upon the very rapid collapse of the magnetic field built up by the current flow in the *primary winding*. The shrinking lines of magnetic force cut across the large number of turns of fine wire in the secondary winding to induce the high voltage surge of current which supplies the ignition spark.

Self-induction refers to the current induced in any coil by the collapse of its magnetic field when the current flow stops. The term is used in automotive work to apply to the current self-induced in the primary winding of the ignition coil.

Questions

1. What is magnetism?
2. Name three classes of magnets.
3. A. Is hard steel more or less difficult to magnetize than soft steel?
   B. Will hard steel hold its magnetism for a longer or shorter time?
4. Mention one way to magnetize a steel bar.
5. What effect always accompanies an electric current?
6. What do magnetic lines of force constitute?
7. To what can magnetic lines of force be likened?
8. What does permeability mean?
9. Name three kinds of material magnetism can pass through.
10. State the rule of magnetic attraction and repulsion.
11. What is presumed to happen when a piece of steel is magnetized?
12. How can a wire carrying electric current be made more effective magnetically?
13. What is meant by ampere-turns?
14. What is the effect of magnetic interference?
15. What is a solenoid?
16. What action will cause an induced electric current?
17. Mention three methods of producing voltage in automotive electrical equipment.
18. How would voltage be generated in a moving coil?
19. What is the function of the field magnet in a generator?
20. State the principle on which the ignition coil works.
21. When is the high-tension ignition current produced in an ignition coil?
22. What is meant by self-induction?
23. What was the vibrating coil used for and how did it work?
24. Why doesn't the spark occur when the ignition circuit is closed?
25. Why does the alternator generate alternating current when the rotating field is supplied with direct current?

CHAPTER FIVE

Automotive Electrical Circuits

An *electric circuit*, generally speaking, is a closed path through which an electric current may flow. In many of the diagrams used to illustrate circuits, the impression is given that the current path has a uniform resistance throughout its length and that the voltage difference between the positive and negative sides of the circuit drops at a regular rate as the current flows through it.

However, most electric circuits consist of low-resistance conductors which conduct the current, with very little voltage drop, to one or more electric appliances such as a lamp, motor, ignition coil, radio, or horn. The appliance supplies the resistance to keep the circuit in balance in accordance with Ohm's Law —

$$\text{Amperes} = \frac{\text{Volts}}{\text{Ohms}}.$$

Voltage Drop in Appliances

With a 6- or 12-volt system such as is used on passenger cars, each appliance or combination of appliances should have sufficient resistance to make the electromotive force drop 6 or 12 volts respectively when the required amperage is passed through the circuit. That is, each appliance should have enough resistance to limit current flow so that it will work efficiently without excessive heating.

Regardless of the voltage, the circuit must be kept in balance so that the desired current will flow, controlled by the total resistance.

Wire conductors in automotive electrical systems are used for only part of each circuit;

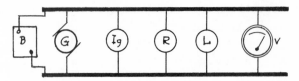

Fig. 5.2. Same electrical conductors, with battery and generator supplying current to the connected load consisting of ignition system *(Ig)*, the radio *(R)*, and lamps *(L)*. Current is flowing in each of the three parallel circuits in exact inverse proportion to the resistance of the appliances and their connecting wires. The voltmeter indicates the voltage difference between the main conductors.

Fig. 5.1. Two conductors connected to battery *(B)* and generator *(G)* with no load. The voltmeter indicates the voltage difference (or electrical pressure) between the electrical conductors.

the frame of the car is used to complete the circuits.

A very necessary part of each circuit is the source of current, which in the motor car is either the battery or the generator, depending upon the engine's operating speed at any given time.

Circuit Compared to Two Rails

We might think of the electrical system on a car as similar to two parallel lengths of railroad rails. One side of the battery and the corresponding side of the generator would be connected to one rail and the other sides of these current sources would be connected to the other rail. When the engine is not operating, but the battery is charged and connected, a voltage difference between the two rails can be read on a voltmeter, but no current would be flowing. Refer to Fig. 5.1.

Now, suppose wires are connected to each rail, and each wire is connected to one side of a lamp of the proper voltage drop. The lamp will light and current will flow in the circuit; another lamp connected up the same way would also light, and more current would make a further increase in the current flow. Additions of other appliances connected in the same way would add to the flow of electricity. This could be continued until the carrying capacity of the "rails" was reached or until the current supply became inadequate. Note Fig. 5.2.

Body, Frame or Engine Block One Side of Circuit

One of our imagined rails represents the main wire conductors from the battery and generator, from which wires lead to the electrical appliances; the other represents the car frame. The frame of the car is the *ground* or grounded side of the circuit. See Fig. 5.3. All conductors connected to the other side of the battery are said to be alive or "hot." Any current path from the live side of the battery circuit to the grounded side will have current flowing in it. If a piece of wire were connected to the live side and touched to any part of the frame or ground, it would carry an excessive amount of current because its resistance would not be sufficient to keep its portion of the circuit in balance. Consequently, there would be "fire-works," resulting in burning the wire or other damage. If the insulation should be worn off of a hot conductor and it should touch the frame, the same thing would happen — a *short circuit* as Fig. 5.4 illustrates. This would mean in effect that the electrical path was too short to supply sufficient resistance for circuit balance.

One-Wire System

The wiring system used on automobiles is called the *one-wire system* because only one wire is used to conduct current to each appliance. Mounting the appliances on the body or frame satisfactorily completes the circuit by providing a ground. The body usually has electrical contact with the frame, so that appliances

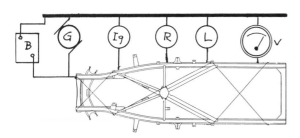

Fig. 5.3. Same circuit as shown in Fig. 5.2, with one of the main conductors replaced by the car frame, illustrating how the frame acts as part of the circuit.

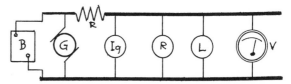

Fig. 5.4. The same circuit with resistance introduced into the circuit such as might be caused by corroded or loose contacts. The voltage and therefore the amperage are reduced. Such resistance may cause poor ignition. It can be detected by checking the various circuits with a voltmeter to indicate excessive voltage drops.

mounted on either of these will have a ground connection through the engine block, equivalent to a direct connection with the other side of the circuit. The battery is usually grounded to the engine block by a heavy cable. It is important to recognize that the absence of good grounds is a frequent cause of electrical troubles.

A wiring diagram of a modern automobile, such as that in Fig. 5.5, may appear as a puzzling jumble of lines. Actually, every lamp and other appliance on the car is on a circuit which is as simple as the illustration previously used of the wires connecting a lamp to two rails. The wiring diagram is really just a combination of a number of individual circuits. In some cases a common conductor is used for two or more circuits; that is, current to a number of appliances will flow over the same main conductor, with branch conductors to carry the current to the individual appliance. Fig. 5.6, for example, clearly represents the cranking or

starting system, the generating system and the ignition system with their effective connections to ground. The lights, horn circuit, radio and accessory circuits are not shown.

Relays

In some cases, it may be necessary for individual circuits to have auxiliary circuits and relays. For example, it is undesirable to have the heavy current required by sealed-beam lamps go through the switch on the dash. Therefore the current will be carried directly to an electrically operated switch located close to the head lamps. The dash switch simply closes the circuit to an electromagnet, which in turn closes the switch in the lamp circuit and turns on the lights. Since it takes only a weak current to operate the magnetic switch, just a limited amperage is required to go up to the dash, through the dash switch and down to the magnetic switch, to control the heavier current needed for the lights.

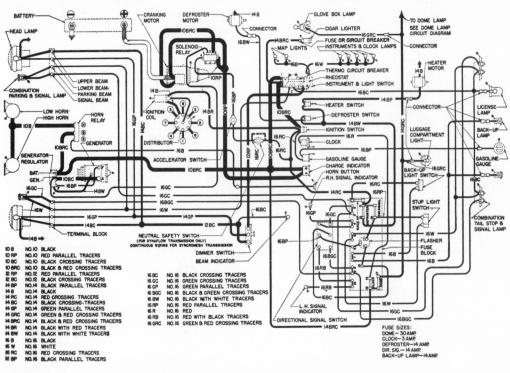

Fig. 5.5. Typical wiring diagram with color code used for the wire connections; also the wire sizes are given.

The auxiliary circuit used to control another circuit by means of auxiliary switches is called a *relay circuit*. The electrically operated switch is a *relay switch*. Sometimes the switch itself is referred to as a relay. Fig. 5.7 illustrates one use of a relay.

Internal and External Circuits

Each appliance used in automotive work can be illustrated by a circuit diagram; each appliance also has its own circuit or series of circuits. The internal circuits of electric motors and generators are relatively simple, and may be shown in diagram form to clearly indicate the current paths through them.

The *generator control*, popularly called the voltage regulator, has more complicated internal circuits, while the car radio has a still greater number of internal circuits, which are interlocking or interdependent.

The internal circuits of motors, generators, generator controls, relays and starting motor controls will be considered in detail in later chapters.

Series and Parallel Circuits

There are two ways to connect appliances and electrical instruments. In each individual case only one is correct; the other way leads to trouble.

The two ways are (1) in series, and (2) in parallel.

An easy way to understand series connections is to think of the appliances, units or parts as the links of a chain. They are connected so that the current flows from one to the other, and their resistances are added to get the voltage drop through them. For example, two lamps with a voltage drop of 6 volts each and with the same resistance could be placed in series in a 12-volt circuit, so that the current would flow through the first lamp, into the second one, from that to the other side of the circuit, and back to the current source.

Notice that it was stated that the two lamps had the same resistance. What would happen

if they did *not* have the same resistance? Suppose one had 6 ohms and the other 12 ohms resistance. The lamps, if by themselves in a 6-volt circuit would carry, respectively, $I=\dfrac{E}{R}$ or $I=\dfrac{6}{6}=1$ amp., and $\dfrac{6}{12}=.5$ amp. When in

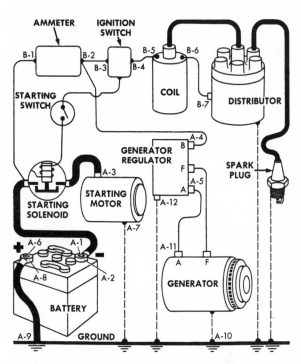

Fig. 5.6. Pictorial presentation of starting, generating and ignition systems, showing the effective ground connections.

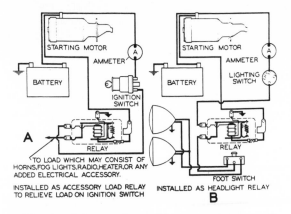

Fig. 5.7. Relays such as this are used to permit a small current to operate a switch which closes a circuit carrying a much heavier current; this avoids having the heavy current go through the ignition switch or light switch. (AL)

series, the combined resistance would be 6 plus 12 or 18 ohms. According to Ohm's Law just used to find the current-carrying capacity of each lamp, the current that would pass through them when in series would be $I = \frac{12}{18}$ or 2/3 ampere. We have just seen that the normal current-carrying capacity of the smaller lamp is .5 ampere. If 2/3 ampere were forced through it, the filament would be overheated and would burn out.

Therefore, an important point to remember is that if two or more lamps are connected in series, they must have the same resistance in each, or one will burn out.

With units connected in series, the current passes from one unit to the next. If any one of the units has an open circuit, the current path will be interrupted and no current will flow to any of the units in the series. A well-known illustration of this is the old style string of Christmas tree lights with eight in series. If one lamp burned out, the whole string went out, because the current path was interrupted and none of the lamps received electrical energy.

Parallel circuits, or units connected in parallel are connected from one side of the circuit to the other. In the railroad illustration the lamps were connected from rail to rail and were in parallel. Parallel circuits may be thought of as the rungs in a ladder.

Series-Parallel Circuit

In some cases there will be combinations of both parallel and series circuits. In generators and starting motors, there are field windings in which the current flows from one coil to the next, being in series. The generator and starting motor are connected in parallel with each other, and with the various lamps, the radio, and other appliances that are included in the car equipment.

The internal circuits of the various appliances are frequently in series, so that with the appliance itself connected in parallel, there will be series-parallel circuits in the combination of the external and internal circuits.

Effective Resistance in a Number of Parallel Circuits

When there are several parallel closed circuits, the total current flow will be proportional to the current flow in each circuit added to that in each of the other circuits. The resistance overall may be found from this equation:

$$\frac{1}{R_T} = \frac{1}{R_1} + \frac{1}{R_2} + \frac{1}{R_3}$$

where R_T is effective circuit resistance, and R_1 is the resistance of the first circuit in parallel, R_2 is the second circuit resistance, R_3 is the third circuit resistance, and so on for any number of parallel circuits.

As an example, let us assume that of four parallel circuits, the first has 1 ohm resistance, the second has 2 ohms, the third 3 ohms, and the fourth 4 ohms. In accordance with the above equation:

$$\frac{1}{R_T} = \frac{1}{1} + \frac{1}{2} + \frac{1}{3} + \frac{1}{4}$$

$$\frac{1}{R_T} = \frac{12}{12} + \frac{6}{12} + \frac{4}{12} + \frac{3}{12} = \frac{25}{12}$$

$$R_T = \frac{12}{25} = .48 \text{ ohm.}$$

In accordance with Ohm's Law, the current in the conductors supplying the four parallel circuits would be (assuming 6 volts emf) $I = \frac{6}{.48}$ or 12.5 amps.

To check this another way, if the resistance of each circuit and the voltage are known, the current that will flow in each circuit can be found. The individual currents added together will give the total current that will flow in the main conductors feeding the individual circuits.

$$I_1 = \frac{6}{1} \text{ or 6 amps.} \quad I_2 = \frac{6}{2} \text{ or 3 amps.}$$

$$I_3 = \frac{6}{3} \text{ or 2 amps.} \quad I_4 = \frac{6}{4} \text{ or 1.5 amps.}$$

The total of $6+3+2+1.5$ is 12.5 amperes. For the total circuit resistance:

$$R = \frac{6}{12.5} = .48 \text{ ohm.}$$

Fuses and Circuit Breakers

Most of the circuits in an automobile wiring system are protected against electrical overloads caused by an unwanted ground, a short circuit, or excessive voltage. Either a fuse will burn out and open the circuit or a circuit breaker will open the circuit, usually buzzing first.

In either case, merely replacing the fuse or resetting the circuit breaker is not enough. It is important to find the cause and correct it.

Symbols Used in Wiring Diagrams

It is often necessary to follow illustrations of both internal and external circuits and to read diagrams of circuits, appliances, instruments and wiring. Symbols are used in these diagrams to represent the various parts and devices entering into circuits such as coils, switches, resistors, condensers, lamps, connectors, commutators, electromagnets, contact points and batteries. Lines of various widths are used to represent the conductors, with heavy lines representing large conductors.

In general the symbols have sufficient picture character to make them easy to remember. A little familiarity with circuit diagrams and knowledge of the meaning of the symbols will enable the worker in automotive electricity to follow wiring diagrams readily. The symbols shown in Fig. 5.8 should be memorized. While there may be some variation in the exact presentation of the symbols in various books, catalogs and diagrams, the symbols are sufficiently alike to be readily recognized.

Summary

An *electric circuit* is a closed path through which electric current may flow. When electrical pressure is impressed on a circuit, its flow may be started or stopped by closing or opening a switch.

Most *electric circuits* consist of low-resistance conductors carrying current to electric appliances. These appliances must have the right amount of resistance to allow the desired amount of current flow for efficient operation without overheating.

The *electrical system* of the car consists essentially of two main conductors connected to each side of the battery and generator, one conductor being the car frame, body, and engine block, and the other conductor connected to the appliances.

Each appliance must have *sufficient resistance* to keep the current flowing through it down to the desired amount.

Automobiles use the *one-wire system*, in which the current return is through the frame, or engine block, which acts exactly the same as if it were another wire. One wire leads to each appliance, and the return connection is made by mechanical attachment of the appliance to the frame or body.

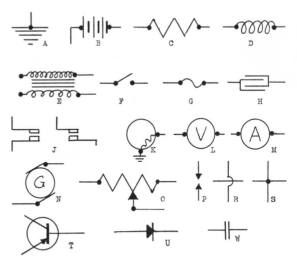

Fig. 5.8. Symbols commonly used in electrical diagrams and drawings in automotive instruction and information sheets. They are: A, Ground; B, Battery; C, Non-inductive Resistance; D, Inductive resistance; E, Induction Coil (Ignition Coil); F, Switch; G, Fuse; H, Condenser; J, Contact Points (Breaker Points); K, Lamp Bulb; L, Voltmeter; M, Ammeter; N, Generator (G), or Motor (M); O, Rheostat; P, Spark Gap; R, Crossed Wires, not connected; S, Crossed Wires, connected; T, Transistor; U, Diode; W, Capacitor.

Each appliance is supplied with current by means of a *simple circuit*. The combination of many simple circuits may appear complicated, but each one can be followed individually with little difficulty.

Relay circuits are sometimes used to operate other circuits. A weak current causes an electrically operated switch to close in a circuit carrying a heavy current.

Series circuits may be compared to a chain, with each link dependent upon the other links. With electric appliances connected in series, the current flows from one unit to the next, and their resistances are added together to find the total circuit resistance. The same amperage flows through each one.

Parallel circuits are like the rungs on a ladder, connecting two conductors. The more circuits there are in parallel, the greater the amount of current that will flow in the main conductors, up to the carrying capacity of the conductors or the output capacity of the battery or generator.

Questions

1. Define an electric circuit.
2. Of what two parts does each circuit consist?
3. State one form of Ohm's Law.
4. Where should the greatest voltage drop take place in a circuit?
5. Is it possible to have voltage in a circuit without current flowing? Explain.
6. If a copper wire conductor makes up part of the automotive electrical circuit, what is the rest of the circuit made up of, excluding appliances and accessories.
7. How does a one-wire electrical system work?
8. How important is a good ground? Why?
9. What is a relay?
10. Name two places where you would find internal circuits.
11. Describe a series circuit.
12. Describe a parallel circuit.
13. How is series circuit resistance figured?
14. What happens in a series circuit if one element or component is open?
15. What happens in a parallel circuit if one element or component is open?
16. Are lamps in most automotive circuits connected in series or parallel?
17. If you know the amount of resistance in each of four different parallel circuits, how would you find the effective resistance of the entire circuit?
18. Why are symbols used to represent various portions of a circuit?
19. Give an example of a series-parallel circuit.
20. How would you find the amount of current needed for the circuit in No. 17?

SECTION III

Mechanics
of
the
Internal
Combustion
Engine

CHAPTER SIX

The Automobile Engine— Its Valves and Firing Orders

The automotive diagnostician and the tune-up man must know the theory and operation of engines. It is important not only to find out what is wrong with an engine, but also the reason for the trouble so that the same thing will not occur again.

It is presumed that the prospective automotive diagnostician knows the four strokes of the four-cycle engine.

The gasoline engine is a device for internally burning an explosive mixture of gasoline and air in order to build up a high pressure in its cylinders. This pressure forces its pistons down, and linkage to the crankshaft changes the reciprocating motion of the pistons to a powerful rotary motion.

The engine is an assembly of coordinating, closely fitted parts, moving on films of lubricant. Accurately timed valves control the flow of fuel and air into the cylinders and permit the burned gases to escape after each power stroke.

This definition of the gasoline engine applies to the engines of thirty years ago as well as to the present engines. However the powerful engines which power the high-performance automobiles of today are far different in detail than the early engines. They have been constantly refined to work more efficiently and flexibly and to give greater power per pound and per cubic inch of piston displacement. The servicing of modern engines can be done efficiently and effectively only by those who well understand the operating requirements of these highly precise engines.

The gasoline engine is a good gas pump, drawing in gaseous charges and compressing them. It is alternately a *power consumer* (on the intake and compression strokes) and a *power producer* (on the power stroke). The exhaust stroke might be called the "coasting" stroke as the engine performs no work on this stroke; it merely rotates the crankshaft and moves the piston in the cylinder, preparing for the intake stroke. Since the power output during the power stroke is much greater than the power required for the intake and compression strokes, the engine can be used as a prime mover. Fig. 6.1 is a typical V-8 engine, while Figs. 6.2 and 6.3 show the Corvair six-cylinder opposed engine.

The efficient operation of the engine depends on its valves, pistons, piston rings, cylinder walls and bearings. Each of these will be discussed in turn calling attention to the factors which affect good operation and those which indicate the need for corrective measures. Fig. 6.4 shows some Ford engine details.

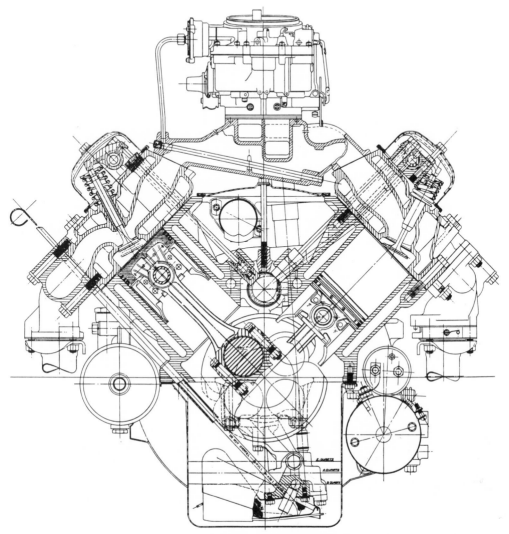

Fig. 6.1. Cross section of a typical V-8 engine, showing the arrangement of the pistons, valves, valve lifters, rocker arms, and gas passages.

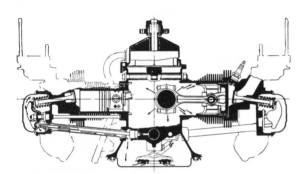

Fig. 6.2. Section through the six-cylinder air-cooled Corvair engine showing the arrangement of cylinders (horizontally opposed), push rods and rocker arms.

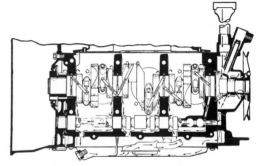

Fig. 6.3. Horizontal view of crankshaft of a Corvair engine, with one cylinder bank removed. The arrows indicate oil flow; plug at left is oil drain.

Firing Order

It is important to understand firing orders and the relation between piston movement, crank movement and valve events when setting tappets and checking valve timing. It is also necessary to know the firing order to wire the high-tension leads from the distributor cap to the spark plugs correctly.

The *firing order* is the order in which the explosions on the power stroke take place in the various cylinders. To minimize engine vibrations, the cylinder which fires should be spaced as far as possible from the previous firing cylinder. The firing order usually starts with a front cylinder which is No. 1. On V-8 engines it may start with the front cylinder in either bank.

There are three general types of automotive power units used in American passenger cars, (1) in-line engines; (2) V-type engines with two banks of cylinders, usually at 90° to each other; and (3) opposed, with two banks of cylinders 180° apart. The relation of the pistons to each other and to crank positions is different in the three engine types.

Fig. 6.4. Engine details of a typical **Ford**.

Fig. 6.5. Six-cylinder crankshaft, with cranks 120° apart. Cranks 1 and 6, 2 and 5, 3 and 4, are in the same planes, respectively. This is a four-bearing shaft.

In-Line Engines

In *in-line engines* the pistons work in pairs with each two pistons attached to crank pins which have a common center line. Thus in an in-line, 6-cylinder engine, piston No. 1 and piston No. 6 go up and down together; also Nos. 2 and 5, Nos. 3 and 4. However, one piston in each of the three pairs is two strokes behind its partner. For example, if No. 1 piston is on the compression stroke No. 6 will be on the exhaust stroke, and the generally adopted firing order will be 1-5-3-6-2-4.

In six-cylinder engines the pairs of crank pins are arranged at angles of 120° apart. From the front end of the crankshaft if Nos. 1 and 6 crank throws are up, Nos. 5 and 2 throws will be pointing down to the left with Nos. 3 and 4 pointing down to the right. A crankshaft arranged in this way is called a right-hand crankshaft. Refer to Fig. 6.5.

On the six-cylinder engine the crank throws are arranged in pairs with 1 and 6, 2 and 5, and 3 and 4 in line. A camshaft for this type engine is shown in Fig. 6.7.

On this engine *one* of the first pair will fire first, followed by *one* of the second pair, then *one* of the third pair. Thus in the first revolution in one cycle, cylinders No. 1, 5, and 3 will fire in that order. Next the second cylinder in the first pair will fire which is No. 6, followed by No. 2 and then No. 4.

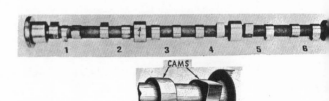

Fig. 6.7. Six-cylinder camshaft. Note the fuel-pump cam between the two cams for No. 1 cylinder. The large cylindrical portions are the four camshaft journals.

Table 2
Comparison of GM, etc. and Ford Cylinder Numbering, Piston Pairs and Firing Orders

	Cylinder Numbers				
GM, etc.	2	4	6	8	
Front	0	0	0	0	(Cyl. R bank)
	0	0	0	0	(Cyl. L bank)
	1	3	5	7	
Ford	1	2	3	4	
Front	0	0	0	0	(Cyl. R bank)
	0	0	0	0	(Cyl. L bank)
	5	6	7	8	

Piston Pairs:
GM, etc.   1-6, 5-8, 4-7, 2-3
Ford   1-6, 3-5, 4-7, 2-8

Firing Orders:
GM, etc.   1-8-4-3-6-5-7-2
Ford   1-5-4-2-6-3-7-8

On the eight-cylinder in-line engine, the same order is maintained with *one* cylinder of each four pairs firing, then the second in each pair firing.

V-8 Engines

The cylinder numbering scheme on V-8 engines varies. On some V-8's the cylinders are numbered 1-3-5-7 on the right bank of cylinders (beginning with the front cylinder in that bank), and 2-4-6-8 for the cylinders on the left bank. Another numbering plan has the right bank numbered 1-2-3-4, and the left bank numbered 5-6-7-8.

On General Motors Corporation cars, Chrysler cars, American Motors cars, and Studebaker V-8's, the cylinders are numbered 1-3-5-7 on the left bank and 2-4-6-8 on the right bank. The firing order on most of these engines is 1-8-4-3-6-5-7-2. Late model Cadillac engines use 1-8-7-2-6-5-4-3.

The crankshaft on all the American V-8's has the front and rear crank pins in the same plane, 180° apart. The second and third crank throws are in the same plane at 90° to the first and fourth and 180° to each other. Thus, the crank positions would be No. 1 at 12 o'clock, No. 2 at 3 o'clock, No. 3 at 9 o'clock, and No. 4 at 6 o'clock.

The Ford (including Mercury and Lincoln) V-8 crankshaft is arranged the same way as the GM and others, but the Ford cylinders are numbered 1-2-3-4 on the right bank and 5-6-7-8 on the left bank. This would make the firing order read differently, being 1-5-4-2-6-3-7-8.

The pairs of cylinders in the GM and other engines are 1-6, 5-8, 4-7, 3-2. On the Ford V-8 engines the pairs are actually the same, even though the different numbering system makes them appear dissimilar, being 1-6, 3-5, 4-7, 2-8.

In a few cases, there are deviations from the firing orders given here, so if there is occasion to refer to a specific firing order, check with the engine specifications.

All of the following V-8 engines have their cylinders numbered 1-3-5-7 on the left bank and 2-4-6-8 on the right bank:

Buick	Imperial
Cadillac	Nash
Chevrolet	Plymouth
Chrysler	Pontiac
Dodge	Rambler
Dart	Studebaker

NOTE: On the Buick 401 and 425 engines, the cylinders are numbered 1-3-5-7 on the right bank and 2-4-6-8 on the left bank, with the firing order given as 1-2-7-8-4-5-6-3.

Valve Function and Timing

Valves are mechanically operated stoppers which open and close the gas intake passages and the exhaust discharge passages at precisely timed positions of the pistons and crankpins. Since it takes four strokes or two complete revolutions of the crankpins to complete one power cycle, the cycle requires 720° of crankpin movement per cycle. While the crankpin is making two revolutions the camshaft makes one revolution causing each valve to open and close once during a complete power cycle of 720°. This cycle involves four strokes of each piston, two down and two up. Re-examine Fig. 6.7 as it illustrates a six-cylinder camshaft.

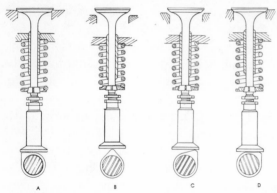

Fig. 6.9. Arrangement of the valves in the "Side Valve" or "L-Head" engine. (A) Intake valve just ready to open. (B) Intake valve wide open. (C) Exhaust valve almost closed. (D) Exhaust valve just closed. The intake and exhaust cams are in their relative positions on the average engine. The exhaust cams lead the intake cams by 90° to 100°. Compare cam position of *A* with *C*, or *B* with *D*. The angle through which the crankshaft turns while both exhaust and intake valves are open in a cylinder is called the "valve lap."

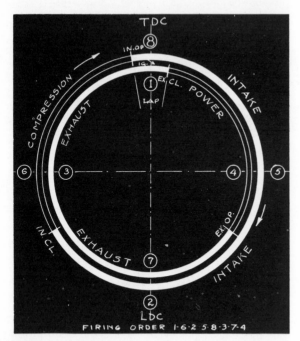

Fig. 6.10. Valve timing for an eight-cylinder engine. The figures in the circles represent the angular positions of each crankpin when 1 and 8 are in TDC position. The solid arcs represent the angle through which a crank rotates while valves are open. Remember that the intake valve is open on the first revolution of the four-stroke cycle while the exhaust valve is open on the second.

Valve timing involves four *valve events* — (1) inlet valve opens, (2) inlet valve closes, (3) exhaust valve opens, and (4) exhaust valve closes.

The inlet valve generally opens a little before top dead center (TDC) and closes 30° to 45° past bottom dead center (BDC). At first thought it seems that the inlet valve should close at lower dead center, but it has been found that the inertia of the moving column of fuel-air mixture causes less gas to be carried into the cylinder at this position than is the case when the valve closes later than BDC. The intake valve closes when the maximum ramming effect of the moving column of gas is reached. From this point the piston picks up the compression duty, and the compression stroke is completed when the piston reaches the top of this stroke. Then the spark occurs to start the power stroke. Valve timing will be discussed in more detail in Chapter 22.

On the power stroke the exhaust valve opens from 30° to 45° *before* bottom dead center to provide effective engine operation. Little power could be gained by delaying the exhaust valve opening until the crankpin reaches the bottom dead center position since the inertia of the exhaust gases prevents immediate flow from the cylinder. Furthermore, it takes a considerable arc of crankshaft travel for the valve to move from its closed position to its open position. It should be remembered that the term *valve opening* or *valve closing* refers to the instant at which the valve *starts to open*, or is *entirely closed*.

The exhaust valve closes at from top dead center to 15 or more degrees after TDC. The valve timing diagram in Fig. 6.9 shows the valve events, as well as the ignition point which starts the power stroke. The valve events are most frequently and conveniently specified in degrees of crankpin travel.

Valve timing is controlled by the camshaft which has two cams for each cylinder to open intake and exhaust valves at the desired position of the crankpin and piston. Fig. 6.10

shows a valve timing diagram for an eight-cylinder engine, and Fig. 6.11 shows relative piston and valve positions.

Valve Lap (or Overlap)

The angle through which the crankpin moves from the initial opening of the intake valve to the final closing of the exhaust valve is called *valve lap* or *overlap*. This brief period is far more important in engine operation than most engine experts realize. At this time there is a direct connection between the intake and the exhaust manifold. Due to the vacuum in the intake manifold which exists most of the time in engine operation, the exhaust gases are drawn into the cylinder and mingle with the explosive mixture there. As much as 70% of the gas in a cylinder during idle and deceleration consists of exhaust gases and up to 40% on acceleration with wide-open throttle. This naturally decreases possible engine power output, and partly accounts for the large power increases made possible by *supercharging*. Supercharging forces an undiluted explosive mixture of gasoline and air into the cylinder. More importantly, it maintains a pressure in the intake manifold above atmospheric pressure which eliminates exhaust gases being drawn into the cylinder during the valve lap period. Supercharging is not generally used on passenger car engines, but a number of "hot rod" engines are equipped with superchargers and it is also used in large aviation piston engines.

Valve Troubles

The valves, particularly the exhaust valve, must withstand severe operating conditions. Although they give remarkably good service on the whole, they can become burned and warped.

Fully half of the valves that fail in service are the result of faulty adjustment of tappet or valve stem end-clearance. Excessive clearance results in delayed valve opening, early closing and noisy operation, but does no serious damage. Too little clearance, on the other hand, frequently means that valves do not close fully,

especially when they are hot. Burning gases are forced by the pressure of the explosion through this crack between the valve and the valve seat. Temperatures may exceed 4,000° F., thus burning valve faces so that it is impossible for the valves to make gas-tight joints with the valve seats. Hydraulic valve lifters (or tappets) automatically maintain correct and safe seating of valves.

The only remedy for burned valves is to replace them. However, the cause must also be diagnosed and corrected to avoid repetitive trouble. Fig. 6.12 shows seat grinding equipment; Fig. 6.13 shows the valve grinding operation.

Other causes of burned valves are eccentrically ground valves due to inaccuracies in the

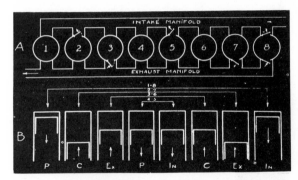

Fig. 6.11. Relative positions of the pistons, with the valves shown as doors opening into the cylinders. The positions of the various doors indicate the valves that are opening or closing.

Fig. 6.12. High-speed valve seat grinder. The motor runs about 20,000 rpm. The stones are dressed to the exact angle desired for the valve seats.

valve grinding machines, warped valves, valves which have stuck in their guides and weak or broken springs.

Valve springs break occasionally due to fatigue or a defect in the material. Moisture in the valve compartment may also account for broken valve springs by starting spots of rust in the springs, which in turn leads to

Fig. 6.13. Valve seat being ground. The abrasive stone with cutting face at the correct angle lightly contacts the valve seat momentarily to grind it concentric with pilot in valve stem guide.

Fig. 6.14. Valve springs should be tested every time the valves are removed. Springs with the wrong tension will not give proper valve action; if below the specified tension, they often have hidden cracks which lead to breakage.

cracks in the spring material. Valve spring inspection procedure is shown in Fig. 6.14.

Whenever tappets become noisy due to increased tappet clearance, the cause of the trouble should be determined before the clearance is readjusted. In some cases, deposits built up on valve faces or seats may hold the valves open partly. If the deposit is uniformly distributed around the valve face or seat, it will raise the valve slightly on the seat, increasing the normal valve end-clearance. If these valves should be readjusted to the specified clearance without the cause being determined, serious consequences could result. The deposits might be oxidized or worn off dropping the valves to their original position in contact with the valve seat. The valve end-clearance would then be reduced, possibly leading to burned valves. Good contact between valve faces and seats is necessary to cool valves, and thus maintain a safe valve temperature.

The clearance may increase due to wear on the tappet end or the valve stem end; or it may be caused if the tappet adjusting screw becomes loose. The clearance may also be increased due to rocker arm wear at its bearing or at the end where it contacts the valve stem. In these instances, clearance can be safely readjusted to the correct amount.

Valve Concentricity

It is helpful in considering the engine valves to think of them as true conical sections whose center lines exactly coincide with the center lines of the stems. If this is not true of any individual valve it will be *eccentric* and will not seat as it should, possibly leading to a burned valve. Valves ground on precision valve-facing machines will be true and concentric if the valve stems are straight and not worn. The ball-type chuck to hold the valve stem is more likely to be accurate than the collet chuck. Both the stem and the chuck should be scrupulously clean before inserting the stem, as a speck of carbon or any foreign matter .001″ or .002″ in diameter can cause eccentricity.

Valve seats are ground by an abrasive stone guided by an arbor inserted in each valve stem guide. The concentricity of the valve seat about the true center line of the valve stem guide will depend upon the accuracy of the arbor. Expanding type arbors are not too dependable. The most accurate arbors have a taper of approximately .001″ on the portion of the arbor which is inserted in the valve stem guide. Seats should be checked for concentricity with a dial indicator and should be within .0015″ to .002″ as shown in Fig. 6.15. The amount and location of any eccentricity should be the same even though the arbor is placed in a different position. At least one seat in each block should be checked to see that the equipment is operating with reasonable accuracy. Fig. 6.16 illustrates valve geometry.

In some engines it is recommended that there be a difference of approximately one degree in the angle of the valve face and valve seat. Thus the face of the valve will contact the interior cylinder edge of the seat. This small difference will insure a very narrow but tight ring of contact between valve face and valve seat. Valve seat and valve face angles of both 30° and 45° are used. Frequently the intake valve has the 30° angle and the exhaust valve the 45°

angle, but in many cases both valves are 45°. Fig. 6.17 shows how seat grinding stones are dressed to maintain sharpness and accuracy.

Adjusting Valve Tappets

Some engines are equipped with hydraulic valve lifters or tappets, but on other engines

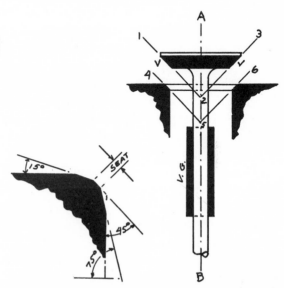

Fig. 6.16. The geometry of valves, their seats, valve stems, and valve stem guides. The cone of the valve face, *1-2-3*, and the cone of the valve seat *4-5-6*, have a common center line *A-B* which is also the center line of the valve guide *VG*. The accuracy of the fit between face and seat depends upon how closely the center lines of the three parts (valve face, valve seat, and valve guide) coincide.

Fig. 6.15. The dial indicator is used to check the accuracy with which the valve seats are ground. The seats should be true within .0015″ to .001″.

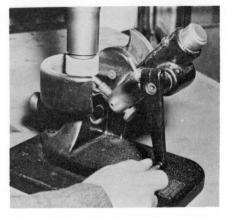

Fig. 6.17. Diamond dresser for cutting seat-grinding stone to a straight and true conical surface of the correct angle.

these parts must be adjusted. This adjustment is very important to the efficient and quiet operation of the engine.

When adjusting valve tappets to give the correct valve stem end-clearance, remember that the cam follower should be on the heel of the cam when the adjustment is made. This will occur between the time the intake valve fully closes and the exhaust valve starts to open, approximately 240° later. The heel of the cam is designed to be perfectly cylindrical so that the valve end-clearance should be constant as the cam rotates from the point at which the valve is fully closed to the point at which the valve just begins to open. Except where cams are badly worn they will be concentric to within a few ten thousandths of an inch.

The safest and most definite point for making these valve end-clearance adjustments is when the piston is in firing position. At that time both valves will be closed and the cam follower will be on the heel of the cam.

As previously seen, in each engine the pistons are paired off, each piston of each pair being in the same relative position in the cylinder. However, each one of the pair is two strokes from the other in the four-stroke cycle. Thus, in a six-cylinder engine pistons 1 and 6 will be in the same position in the cylinders. If one is

Fig. 6.18. Adjusting valve tappets is often included in a tune-up job, especially if the tappets are noisy. Having the correct clearance is important to valve life and fuel efficiency.

on the power stroke the other one will be on the intake stroke. Pistons 2 and 5, and 3 and 4, also work together, being two strokes apart.

If the valves are observed as the crankshaft is turned in the normal operating direction, it will be seen that the exhaust valve opens and closes, immediately followed by the opening of the intake valve. Just at the time the exhaust valve closes and the intake valve starts to open, the piston will be in approximately top dead center position (TDC). The other piston of the pair in this position will then be approximately in firing position with both valves closed and the cam followers located on the heel of both cams. Valve observation gives an easy and definite way to tell when the piston is in its firing position, and this information can be used to good advantage in adjusting tappets.

When the piston of cylinder No. 6 gets into top dead center (TDC) position, it will also put No. 1 in TDC position on the power stroke. This is the correct position for adjusting the tappets on cylinder No. 1. If the engine is a six-cylinder engine, it will have the firing order 1-5-3-6-2-4. Therefore the next cylinder to fire will be No. 5, and it will be in firing position one-third of a turn of the crankshaft after the No. 1 valves are adjusted. Piston No. 2 works with piston No. 5, and therefore when the exhaust valve on cylinder No. 2 has just closed, No. 5 will be in firing position ready to have its tappets adjusted. Another one-third of a turn will put No. 3 in firing position which can be checked by watching the exhaust valve on cylinder No. 4 as it just closes.

Continuing the sequence of valve adjustment in accordance with the firing order will enable adjustment of all twelve tappets on a six-cylinder engine with only two revolutions of the crankshaft.

It is easy to turn the engine over if all of the spark plugs are removed so that there is no compression. Turn the engine by means of the fan blades. Another way is to use a hand-operated switch to control the starting motor, at the same time watching the valves on one cylinder of the pair to be adjusted to tell when the pistons are on TDC.

On V-8 engines, the 1st and 5th, 2nd and 6th, 3rd and 7th and 4th and 8th cylinders in the firing order work in pairs. The crankshaft will be turned one fourth of a turn after each valve is adjusted, requiring two revolutions of the engine for all 16 valves. Fig. 6.18 shows tappets on a six-cylinder engine being adjusted.

Hydraulic Valve Lifters

An increasing number of engines are being fitted with hydraulic valve lifters. They will provide quiet engine operation as long as reasonably clean oil is supplied in a sufficient amount, the lifters are not worn excessively, and there are no varnish accumulations on the plunger or cylinder. The check valve must also be functioning properly.

The hydraulic lifter consists of an outer body or shell which guides the lifter as it goes up and down with its cam lobe. The inner bore of the lifter body is a precision cylinder in which the plunger fits with a clearance of not over 0.0002″. The plunger is held tightly against the lower end of the valve stem by a light spring under it. There is also a check valve at the lower end of the plunger. Fig. 6.19 shows the construction of a hydraulic valve lifter.

The compartment under the plunger is filled with engine oil at engine lubrication system pressure. When the cam raises the lifter to operate the valve and compress the strong valve spring, the plunger maintains its approximate position in the lifter cylinder. This is due to the check valve closing and trapping the oil. Thus the push on the valve push rod is actually provided by the trapped oil. There is always a small leakdown each time a valve is opened, but the lost oil is replaced through the check valve, so that effective, quiet valve operation is provided. The action of a hydraulic lifter is shown in Fig. 6.20, while a leakdown tester is pictured in Fig. 6.21.

Compression Ratio

The compression ratio of an engine has an important effect on engine operation. *Compression ratio* is defined as the ratio of the space above the piston in the engine cylinder when

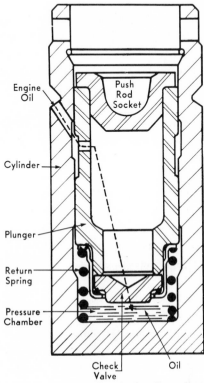

Fig. 6.19. Section of a hydraulic valve lifter or tappet. Oil, under engine lubrication system pressure, flows through a hole in the lifter cylinder, a hole in the plunger, through the hollow plunger, and past the check valve into the pressure chamber where it is trapped. It keeps the plunger from hitting bottom as the lifter pushes on the push rod to open the valve. Some hydraulic lifters use a spring-loaded ball or disc check valve.

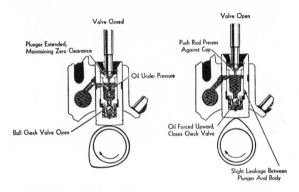

Fig. 6.20. Action of hydraulic lifter.

the piston is at bottom dead center to that above the piston when it is at top dead center. This ratio, therefore, indicates the proportionate amount the air-fuel mixture is compressed in each cylinder on the compression stroke. Refer to Fig. 6.22.

In 1947 compression ratios averaged around 6.5:1, with Cadillac having a high ratio of 7.25:1. At that time, higher ratios could not have been used because the octane numbers of the available fuels were so low that there would have been destructive detonation. Gradually the compression ratios were increased as higher octane fuels were turned out by the oil refiners.

At this time there are two ranges of compression ratios on current engines, one for premium fuel and one for regular-grade gasoline. For premium fuel, the ratios range from about 9.5:1 to as high as 10.5:1 on Cadillac. On engines designed to operate on regular-grade gasoline, the ratios range from around 8.4:1 to 8.8:1. This is quite an increase over the 6.5:1 figure and means that both combustion chamber design and ignition timing must be suitable for handling fuel under high compression. The current engine designs provide for this.

The advantage of higher compression ratios is that the thermal efficiency is higher and more power is derived from a given amount of fuel. However, fuel under high compression burns quickly and may cause destructive detonation if uncontrolled. It can easily burn good-sized holes in aluminum alloy pistons and damage piston rings. Combustion effects are controlled in two ways, (1) by supplying higher octane fuel which burns somewhat slower, and (2) by setting the ignition timing to avoid detonation. However, for the purpose of obtaining best power and performance it is desirable to have the ignition occur as early as possible without producing undesirable effects such as knocking due to pre-ignition or detonation. The compression pressure on most of the late model engines will be from 130 to 170 pounds per square inch.

Recent Valve Developments

Because of the gradually increasing severity of the service which exhaust valves, in particular, must withstand, continual efforts have been made to improve them. Better alloys which will withstand the higher temperatures and corrosive action of the combustion and exhaust gases have helped, as also has the use of stellite welded to the face of the valve to give it a harder surface. Valve seat inserts are in common use, and these have materially increased valve seat life.

Fig. 6.21. Hydraulic valve lifter leakdown tester. The lifter is filled with engine oil and the weighted lever applies pressure on the lifter plunger. The time it takes for the plunger to leakdown is measured with a stop watch or a watch with a sweep second hand. The time is compared with the specified time, and if too rapid, the lifter is replaced.

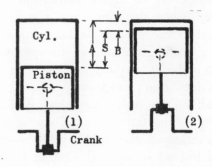

Fig. 6.22. (1) Piston in BDC position. (2) Piston in TDC position. *A* and *B* are respectively the spaces above the piston in the two piston positions. *A* divided by *B* is the compression ratio. *S* is the stroke.

For heavy-duty truck work a valuable development is the sodium-cooled valve. Originally used in high-output airplane engines, its value was demonstrated. The present aircraft type of valve for heavy-duty automotive engines has a hollow head as well as a hollow stem for more efficient cooling.

The hollow stem of this valve is partially filled with metallic sodium. Heat from the valve causes the metallic sodium to melt. As the valve moves, the liquid metal splashes against its interior and conducts heat away from the head through the stem to the valve stem guide. This lowers valve head temperature and results in longer valve life. Sodium-cooled valves have been adopted for heavy-duty engines by Chrysler, Dodge, White Truck, Autocar and other engine builders.

Valve Rotators

The slow rotation of the valves has been found to be a valuable means of increasing valve life. It prevents sticking, thus giving longer life to valve seats with a consequent reduction in valve burning. A device known as the Rotocap is a self-contained assembly that insures positive, controlled rotation of the valve. Ford allows "free rotation" on some engines. Refer to Fig. 6.23.

When the engine is in operation the valve seat and valve face are "wiped" clean by the slow rotating action between the face and the seat. Burning of the valves at any one point is reduced since the rotation allows a constantly changing, cooler portion of the valve head to be exposed to the hottest gases in the combustion chamber. This results in uniform heating of the head and less warping and distortion. The lowered temperature holds stem deposits to a minimum, and lubrication of the valve stem guide is also improved thereby reducing sticking.

A few of the passenger cars at this time have adopted Rotocap. It is interchangeable with and replaces the conventional valve spring retainer. Because of the greater thickness of the Rotocap a special valve spring is supplied

for installations using it. The change from conventional valve retainers to the Rotocap is very simply made and any mechanic can do the work. This should be kept in mind by the automotive diagnostician as certain engines seem to have consistent valve trouble that can be helped by the installation of Rotocaps.

Valve Stem Seals

All late model engines make use of valve stem seals to minimize leakage of air past the valve stems in the valve stem guides. Whenever valves are ground and removed from the cylinder head, it is quite important that new seals be used when the valves are reinstalled. One type of seal is shown in Fig. 6.24.

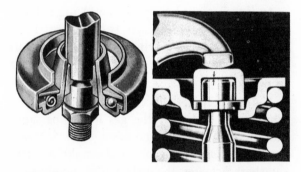

Fig. 6.23. Rotocap (left) provides positive valve rotation, turning the valve stem a few degrees each time the valve is lifted. The free valve (right) allows the valve to slowly revolve due to its own mechanical motion. Each time the valve is opened it is free from tension while the rocker arm moves the distance between the two arrows. Valve rotation is a thoroughly proven means for longer valve life.

Fig. 6.24. One type of valve stem seal. It is quite important that seals be used to prevent air from leaking past the valve stems and upsetting the air-fuel mixture.

Summary

The *gasoline engine* is a good gas pump, alternately a power consumer and a power producer. The power generated during the power stroke is enough to operate the engine and still produce useful output. The operation depends on such engine parts as valves, pistons, rings, cylinder walls and bearings.

Firing order is the order in which the engine cylinders fire. Six-cylinder engines all have the same firing order.

There are three general *engine types* used in automotive equipment, (1) in-line, (2) V-type, with two banks of cylinders at an angle, usually 90°, and (3) opposed, with two banks of cylinders 180° apart.

In-line engines have pistons working in pairs (1-6, 2-5, 3-4) with each two pistons 120° apart. On V-8's the cylinder numbering plan must be known before the cylinder pairs can be designated.

Valves are mechanically operated stoppers which open and close the gas intake passages and the exhaust discharge passages at *precisely timed positions* of pistons and crankpins. The camshaft actuates the valves and revolves at one-half the crankshaft speed. The firing cycle involves four strokes of each piston, two up and two down. Valve events are (1) intake opens, (2) intake closes, (3) exhaust opens, (4) exhaust closes. The intake valve opens a little before top dead center (TDC) and closes after bottom dead center (BDC). The exhaust valves open before bottom dead center and close after top dead center.

Valve timing is controlled by the form and setting of the cams on the camshaft. Valve timing can be affected by an incorrect setting of the valve end-clearance.

Valve lap (or valve overlap) is the angle through which the crankshaft moves from the initial opening of the intake valve to the final closing of the exhaust valve. At this time there is a direct connection from the intake manifold to the exhaust manifold.

Half of the *valve failures* are due to faulty tappet adjustment. The only remedy for *burned valves* is to replace them. Valve *seat deposits* may hold valves open slightly. Good contact between valve faces and seats is necessary for cooling the valves down to a safe operating temperature. Other causes of valve trouble are eccentrically ground valves, warped valve heads, stuck valves, and weak or broken springs.

Valves should be **ground** to true conical sections whose center lines coincide exactly with the center lines of their stems. The valve seats should be concentric with the center lines of the valve stem guides. Some engines have a difference of 1° between the angle of the faces and seats. Seats should be checked for concentricity with a dial indicator and should be accurate within .002 inch.

When *adjusting valve stem end-clearance*, remember that the cam follower or tappet should be firmly on the heel of the cam when the adjustment is made. The piston should be in firing position so that both valves will be fully closed.

Hydraulic valve lifters are used in many of the newer engines. The compartment under the plunger is filled with oil under engine lubrication system pressure. The push on the valve push rod is actually provided by oil trapped in the lifter by its check valve.

Compression ratio is defined as the ratio of the space above a piston when at BDC compared with the space above the piston when at TDC. Average compression ratio on late model cars for regular fuel are 8.4:1 to 8.8:1, and for premium fuel 9.5:1 to 10.5:1.

In *valve production*, improved alloys and manufacturing techniques are producing better valves. Sodium-cooled valves are used frequently for heavy-duty service.

Valve rotators help to prevent valves from sticking, giving them longer life. Rotocap is one rotating device.

Valve stem seals are used on recent engines to prevent leakage of air past the valve stems.

Questions

1. The modern gasoline engine is an assembly of what?
2. What does the gasoline engine do to justify calling it a "good gas pump"?
3. Name the four strokes of the four-stroke cycle.
4. What does efficient operation of the engine depend upon?
5. What is meant by firing order?
6. In six-cylinder engines the cranks are separated by what angle?
7. What is meant by "pairs of pistons"?
8. Give three numbering plans for V-8 engines.
9. If you know the firing order of an engine, how can you tell which pairs of pistons work together?
10. On V-8 engines, do the pairs of pistons fire (1) simultaneously, (2) one stroke apart, (3) two strokes apart, or (4) three strokes apart?
11. How many cams will there be on a six-cylinder camshaft?
12. How may valves be described?
13. Name the four valve events.
14. Should the valve events occur directly at TDC or BDC? Why?
15. What is meant by valve timing and what controls it?
16. How are valve seats checked for accuracy?
17. What is meant by "valve lap"?
18. What is an important cause of valve failure?
19. How are valves kept down to a safe operating temperature?
20. What are two ways to turn an engine over so valves may be adjusted?
21. What is meant by "compression ratio"?
22. What kind of valves are used for heavy-duty service?
23. Why are valve rotators used?
24. Why are valve stem seals used?
25. Why are hydraulic valve lifters used?

CHAPTER SEVEN

Pistons, Cylinder Walls and Rings

Pistons

The piston performs three functions in the internal combustion engine:

1. To act as a gas-tight plug to close the lower end of the cylinder. This permits the variable volume in the cylinder to act as a pump to draw in a charge of explosive mixture, fuel and air, which is then compressed by the piston.

2. To receive the thrust of pressure built up by the rapid burning of the explosive mixture. The powerful thrust of the piston is linear motion which is converted to rotary motion by means of the connecting rod and the crank.

3. To act as a crosshead to guide the upper end of the connecting rod during the compression and power strokes. The piston fills this function in all positions except at top dead center (TDC) and bottom dead center (BDC) crank positions.

Side Thrust

The side thrust on the power stroke is a considerable force and is exerted on the cylinder wall as the explosion forces the piston down. As the piston comes up on the compression stroke, the side thrust is applied to the opposite side of the cylinder wall. However, this side thrust is limited to approximately 20% of the side thrust produced on the power stroke.

When reference is made to the "thrust side of the piston" this means the side which is forced against the cylinder wall on the power stroke, and it is located on the driver's right-hand side.

Piston Pins

Any endwise motion of piston pins will score cylinder walls; therefore the pins must be locked in place. Three ways to do this are:

1. Pin full floating, free to rotate in both piston and connecting rod, with locking rings in a piston groove at each end to keep the pins in place.

2. Pin locked in piston by means of a set screw.

3. Pin locked in connecting rod by a split end and clamping screw or by being tightly pressed into position in the upper end of the connecting rod.

These types are shown in Figs. 7.1 and 7.2.

Piston Troubles

Over long periods of service, pistons are subjected to three kinds of wear: (1) wear on the surface of the piston where it comes in contact with the cylinder, (2) wear at the piston pin bearing, and (3) wear in the ring grooves. In addition to normal wear, pistons occasionally are cracked, spots are burned, the lands between the rings may be cracked and piston skirts may be collapsed.

When an engine is being overhauled it must be determined whether the pistons can be re-used or should be replaced. This decision can logically be made by the automotive diagnostician.

If the cylinder has become tapered too much there is nothing that can be done to the pistons that will make them fit in all points in the cylinder. However if the taper is such that rings can be made to function properly, the piston can be expanded in one of several ways so that it will fit the cylinder close enough to avoid piston slap. Reboring will correct the cylinder, but will require new pistons.

The first step in deciding what to do with the pistons is to check the extent of wear on the sides of the ring grooves. New pistons and rings should have at least .0015″ side clearance as a minimum; however .002″ is generally recommended. As the piston moves in the cylinder, there is wear on the sides of the ring grooves. When this wear has increased the side clearance to .004″, the maximum allowed for good operation has been reached. If the groove side clearance exceeds .006″ the piston is not considered reusable. With this much clearance, the movement of the rings in the grooves will be so much greater than with normal clearance that wear will take place much more rapidly on the sides of the grooves. Even with new rings it would not be long before the grooves would be too wide for the rings to control oil or maintain good compression.

Piston Expanders

If the grooves are in usable condition and the cylinder does not have over .012″ taper, the piston may be expanded to compensate for wear on its surface and on the cylinder walls. A split-skirt piston frequently collapses, making the skirt slap badly.

An important point to remember is that the difference in dimensions between those pistons that are a good fit and those that are not usable without some treatment, is a very small amount — only .002″ to .004″.

The method of expanding pistons includes the use of spring expanders of various kinds, peening the piston on the inside, expanding by heat, shot blasting and knurling.

Spring expanders, made either of flat spring steel or spring steel wire, are used to replace the resiliency that has been lost from the metal of split-skirt pistons. This method will also expand solid-skirt pistons the small amount necessary to give a reasonably good fit in the cylinder. Most of the pistons used in late-model engines are of the solid-skirt type.

Fig. 7.1. Full-floating piston pin, held in place by spring rings recessed in piston-pin bore. Pin can turn in both rod and piston.

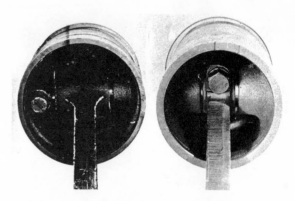

Fig. 7.2. (Left) Locked-in piston pin. The pin is held by the locking screw in the pin base. All movement is in upper rod bearing. (Right) Locked-in rod pin. The pin is clamped in upper rod end. All movement is in bearings in piston. Most current engines have this type.

Peening the piston is done by a small air hammer with the blows applied to the inner surface of the piston on the thrust and counter thrust sides. This "works" the piston metal and re-establishes the spring in the metal, also causing some degree of expansion. This can be done right in the shop and only requires a relatively inexpensive air hammer.

Shot blasting has assumed an important place in bringing pistons back to usable size and form, due primarily to its accurate control of size. Shot blasting also re-establishes the normal spring in the piston skirt and usually prevents further collapsing.

Another method of expanding pistons is to knurl their surfaces which raises the metal,

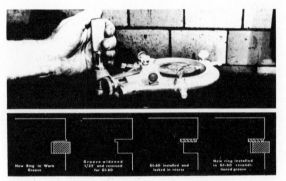

Fig. 7.3. (Above) Tool for recutting worn ring grooves, with added narrow groove for filler ring to replace metal cut away. (Below) Steps in preparing worn ring grooves for new rings. (SP)

Fig. 7.4. Piston burned due to detonation. This can be very destructive to pistons if allowed to continue. Notice how pieces of the rings are held in place by baked carbon.

giving an expanded surface on the thrust side. It is claimed that the grooves made in the surface act as oil retainers and give longer life to the pistons after this treatment.

When the piston is measured with the micrometer, measure the skirt at right angles to the piston pin. Wear is greatest on the surfaces of the piston at right angles to the piston pin, between the ends of the piston pin holes. Remember that cam-ground pistons are approximately .002″ greater on this diameter than on the diameter parallel to the piston pin.

Inspection of Pistons

Many engine overhaul jobs are turned out without adequate attention having been given to the pistons, and these jobs will almost invariably prove to be unsatisfactory. The objective of putting in new rings and doing the other necessary overhaul operations on the engine is to bring it back to approximately the quietness and performance it had when it was new. If the pistons are in bad condition due to wear on piston surfaces and ring grooves, it will be difficult, if not impossible, to reproduce the original compression of the engine which gives it its power.

Remedying Piston Defects

Pistons with worn ring grooves can be reconditioned by cutting the groove square and true with a special rotary tool and inserting steel filler rings to replace the removed material. An effective tool for this purpose is shown in Fig. 7.3.

When new pistons are installed it is highly advisable that they be bought in sets with little variation in their different weights; a variation of more than $\frac{1}{2}$ ounce from the heaviest to the lightest piston may cause vibration and a very rough engine. Some of the new pistons are tin plated; this plating acts somewhat as a lubricant while the pistons are being run in, and seems to give them longer life. A badly burned piston is shown in Fig. 7.4.

If piston-pin bearing holes are over .001″ oversize, noisy engine operation may result, and oversize pins should be used. After honing the holes to the correct size, the oversize pins may be fitted with extreme accuracy by either precision honing or diamond boring the pin hole in the pistons. They are properly fitted with a clearance of 0.0002″ to 0.0003″ in perfectly round, straight holes. Such precision cannot be obtained by reaming. Piston and rod assemblies should always be checked for alignment. Refer to Fig. 7.5.

Cylinder Walls

The condition of cylinders should be carefully analyzed so that necessary steps may be

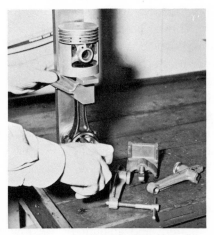

Fig. 7.5. Every piston and rod assembly should be checked for alignment and straightened where necessary before being installed.

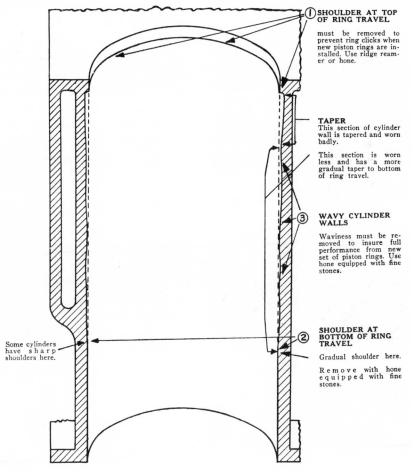

① **SHOULDER AT TOP OF RING TRAVEL**

must be removed to prevent ring clicks when new piston rings are installed. Use ridge reamer or hone.

TAPER
This section of cylinder wall is tapered and worn badly.

This section is worn less and has a more gradual taper to bottom of ring travel.

③ **WAVY CYLINDER WALLS**

Waviness must be removed to insure full performance from new set of piston rings. Use hone equipped with fine stones.

② **SHOULDER AT BOTTOM OF RING TRAVEL**

Gradual shoulder here.

Remove with hone equipped with fine stones.

Some cylinders have sharp shoulders here.

Fig. 7.6. Common wear pattern on cylinder walls. If not excessive, proper installation of new rings will give a long period of satisfactory service.

taken to produce satisfactory engine operation. The owner must be consulted to determine how much expense he is willing to assume.

Somewhere between 20,000 and 60,000 miles most passenger car engines will begin to use oil due to piston wear, ring wear and deterioration, cylinder wear and bearing wear. Although cylinder wear varies, generally the greatest amount of wear will take place near the top of the cylinder.

Cylinder Wear

The pattern and amount of wear will indicate what should be done to cylinder walls for best results. The most severe wear on cylinder walls occurs at the upper end of the stroke covered by the top compression ring. This ring leaves a ridge called the *ring ridge*, the lower edge of which marks the limit of travel of the upper edge of the ring. When an engine is being torn down, this ring ridge should be removed *before* pistons are taken from the cylinders. A good ridge reamer will level the metal of the ridge to the depth of the worn cylinder wall.

The greatest wear results from the explosive force on the inner face of the ring which causes

CYLINDER GAGE

Fig. 7.7. Using the dial indicator to measure out-of-round and taper in a cylinder.

it to exert a very high pressure on its outer surface against the cylinder wall.

At the lower limit of the stroke, the bottom edge of the lower piston ring also forms a ridge; however it is less marked than the upper ridge.

There is usually a decided taper below the upper ridge for ¾″ to 1″, then a fairly uniform diameter down to the lower ridge. Below the lower ridge the diameter is almost the original size since the piston skirt rubbing against the cylinder wall there does not wear as much as the rings do above. Fig. 7.6 shows a common wear pattern on cylinder walls.

Restoring Cylinders

When engines are overhauled there are three procedures that may be followed:

1. Cylinder walls may be left as they are with full dependence on the rings to follow the cylinder wall contour.
2. Cylinder walls may be partially reconditioned by honing, removing .001″ to .002″ of material which will increase the cylinder diameter .002″ to .004″. In many cases honing alone will remove 75% or more of the worn cylinder surface.
3. Cylinder walls may be rebored .020″ to .040″ oversize and finished by honing.

Where walls are honed only, increasing the diameter up to possibly .004″, the old pistons can be used. However, it is advisable to expand the pistons, increasing the diameter an amount corresponding to the metal removed from the cylinder walls.

The cylinder wall surface is an important factor in connection with the seating of rings. After rings have been in use for some time and are seated, the cylinder walls will assume a high polish. The cylinder may be measured with a dial indicator as shown in Fig. 7.7.

Engine Break-In

Until the last few years it was generally considered necessary to remove the high gloss or glaze on cylinder walls when new rings were installed. However, this is no longer the recommended practice. The following steps should be followed when breaking in an engine:

1. Set the tappets, carburetor and ignition timing as accurately as possible before starting the engine.
2. Fill the radiator with water to permit normal warm-up. Do not run cold water through the cooling system.
3. Start the engine and accelerate at once to a speed equivalent to 25 to 35 mph. Maintain this speed until normal operating temperature is reached. Never allow the engine to run at low idle speed during first warm-up because of inadequate low-speed lubrication.
4. When the engine is warmed up, drive the car onto the street, using the proper gears to keep the engine speed. Run at 25 mph; floor the accelerator, bringing the car's speed to 35 mph, and coast back to 25 mph. Repeat this ten to fifteen times. This type of break-in will seat the rings properly. The car should be driven carefully (not over 50 mph) for the first 200 miles.

Piston Rings

Piston rings have a triple duty to perform: (1) sealing against the escape of pressure from the combustion chamber, (2) preventing the escape of oil from the crankcase and (3) controlling the lubrication of pistons and rings as they travel up and down the cylinder. Ring side-clearance is measured with a thickness gauge as shown in Fig. 7.8, and end clearance as shown in Fig. 7.9.

Rings (and ring expanders, where used) have steadily improved, both in material composition and in precise form. An effective oil control ring is shown in Fig. 7.10.

The shape of the cylinder must be considered when selecting piston rings. Cylinders may be (1) new or rebored, straight, and round cylinders, or (2) tapered, possibly out-of-round cylinders. Since these different shapes require correction, various combinations of compression,

oil scraper, and oil control rings are used as shown in Fig. 7.11. The many combinations of rings make it possible to satisfy almost any ring needs for any engine. Ring manufacturers, after studying various engine requirements, have produced a variety of rings, from which a type of ring or combination of rings may be selected that will give excellent results.

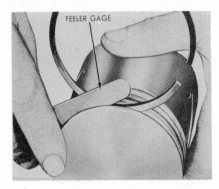

Fig. 7.8. Measuring ring side-clearance in ring groove.

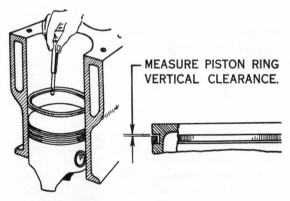

Fig. 7.9. Checking gap between ends of ring with thickness gauge. Ring is pushed into cylinder with piston to get it square.

Fig. 7.10. Combination cast iron and steel oil ring, with expander. (Ramsey)

The combination oil-control ring, with two thin steel rings and a cast-iron center spacer with drain grooves, is receiving general acceptance where flexibility and ability to follow tapered or wavy walls are needed. The usual set of rings in three-ring pistons consists of (1) compression ring, (2) oil scraper, and (3) oil-control ring.

There are over fifty designs of piston rings. The differences in some of the designs are so small that it takes extremely precise measurements to determine them. For example, a one-degree taper on the face of a compression ring has an important effect in controlling oil on a cylinder wall and promoting quick seating.

Other rings have upper or lower faces slightly bevelled to twist the ring, giving an effect of a taper to the outer ring surface. Other rings have square or acute angle grooves cut in their outer faces. For top compression rings, a perfectly rectangular cross section is most often used. The tendency in recent models has been to use narrower rings so that the desired unit pressure against the cylinder walls can be more readily obtained.

The use of tapered-section cylinder rings in aircraft engines has given good results, leading to the adoption of this type of ring in some automotive engines.

Ring Expanders

Ring expanders, which go behind the rings to increase the pressure against the cylinder wall, are important in many engines, and are a necessity where cylinders taper. They are used in some engines with the original installation of rings, and are commonly used in re-ringing jobs where cylinders are not bored. Where cylinders are reconditioned, ring expanders may or may not be used, depending upon the recommendations of the ring makers for the specific engine, or the desires of the rebuilder or customer.

There are numerous varieties of expanders. They are usually made of spring steel approximately .010″ thick. Slots of various widths and lengths, or notches in the edge, are provided to permit a free flow of oil through or past the expanders to the drain holes in the pistons. This is an important feature in the ring expanders because considerable quantities of oil are scraped from the cylinder walls by the oil-control ring. If this oil is not provided with an open path through the piston wall to the oil pan, there will be excessive use of oil by the engine. In some cases severe carbon formation around the rings will result, making the ring inoperative for oil control.

Chrome-Plated Rings

A development introduced in the past few years is the use of chrome-plated rings. These rings, if properly used, remarkably increase ring life and decrease cylinder wear. The rings are plated on the working surface with solid chrome. It has been demonstrated that chrome plating on piston rings is far superior to any other type of plating because it has the highest resistance to wear and scuffing, yet does not scratch the cylinder walls.

Solid chrome-plated compression rings reduce cylinder wear by as much as 5:1 and generally double the life of the entire set of rings.

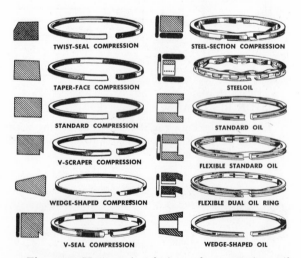

Fig. 7.11. Various ring designs of compression, oil scraper, and oil control piston rings. Note that some are of solid cast iron; some have spring expanders and some, steel side rings.

In fact, because solid chrome wears so slowly, all solid-plated top compression rings are lapped in at cylinder size as one of the factory production operations. Thus they are pre-seated and will require little or no run-in in the engine.

Some piston ring sets include a chome-plated oil stopper in addition to the chrome-plated top compression ring. More chrome than this does not seem to work out satisfactorily.

One excellent type of oil-control or oil stopper ring is composed of two steel rails with a cast iron spacer and a spring expander in the back. The faces of the steel rails are plated with a thick layer of solid chrome. The semicircular face of each rail results in high wall pressure which makes the chrome oil stopper exceptionally effective in wiping oil from the cylinder walls.

The manufacturer's instructions should be strictly followed when piston rings are installed. Care must be taken that the correct side of the ring is on top as there is a considerable difference between sides. It is essential that each type of ring be put in the correct groove since improper installation will upset desired performance. Fig. 7.12 shows the use of a ring compressor when installing pistons. Proper attention to side and end clearance should be given; care should be used to see that the depth of the ring groove and the thickness of the rings correspond, especially when expanders are used. It cannot be over-emphasized that ring selection and installation should always be guided by the ring manufacturer's instructions.

Tightening Cylinder Head Bolts

When the cylinder head bolts are to be tightened, a definite sequence should be followed to avoid strains and possible deformation of head and/or block. In general the procedure is to start from the middle bolt or middle two bolts. Work may progress either in a gradually increasing circle or by going from left to right on one side of the center and then left to right on the other side, tightening two bolts before moving to the opposite side.

Tighten the bolts to approximately one-third of the specified torque the first time around. Bring to two-thirds or three-fourths the required torque in a second tightening; then the third time over, apply the specified pressure. Torque will be 75 to 100 pounds-feet. Fig. 7.13 shows the sequence for several representative engines.

Summary

Pistons perform three functions: (1) close the lower end of the cylinder, (2) receive the thrust of the burning and expanded fuel-air mixture and transfer it to the connecting rods, (3) act as cross-head and guides for the upper end of the connecting rods. The *thrust side* of the piston takes the side thrust on the power stroke. This is the driver's right side.

The ***pistons receive three kinds of wear***, (1) on the surface in contact with the cylinder wall, (2) at the piston pin bearing, and (3) at the ring grooves. They are also subject to cracks; burned spots; cracked, broken or burned lands; and collapsed skirts.

If a ***cylinder is tapered too much***, pistons cannot be made to fit, but if the wear is not excessive, pistons can be expanded or knurled to avoid piston slap.

New pistons should have ***ring side-clearance*** of 0.0015″ to 0.002″. If the side clearance reaches 0.008″, the piston should be replaced

Fig. 7.12. When pistons are installed in the engine, a ring compressor must be used. Oil it well and tap on top of piston with end of hammer handle.

or the grooves machined and filler rings supplied. With good grooves and cylinder taper under 0.012″, pistons may be expanded or knurled and used further.

Piston expanders of various kinds may be used. Pistons may be expanded by peening, shot blasting or knurling. Piston wear of 0.002″ to 0.004″ is excessive.

Piston evaluation is important on engine overhaul jobs. With pistons in poor condition, original compression cannot be obtained. New pistons should be bought in sets with not over one-half ounce difference in weight from heaviest to lightest. Piston-pin holes with over 0.001″ clearance may give noisy operation. The pin should be fitted either by boring or honing.

Cylinder walls should be carefully analyzed. After 20,000 to 60,000 miles most engines start

to use oil. The ring ridge at the top of the cylinder should always be removed before removing pistons. On an overhaul job, the cylinder walls may (1) be left "as is," (2) be partially reconditioned by honing, or (3) be rebored from 0.020″ to 0.040″ oversize.

It was formerly considered necessary to remove *cylinder wall glaze* before putting in new rings. This is no longer recommended.

For *engine break-in* get the engine to normal operating temperature. Run at 25 mph and quickly accelerate to 35 mph. Repeat ten to fifteen times. Do not go over 50 mph for the first 200 miles.

Piston rings perform triple duty by (1) sealing cylinder pressure, (2) preventing the escape of oil from the crankcase, and (3) controlling the lubrication of pistons and rings. There are

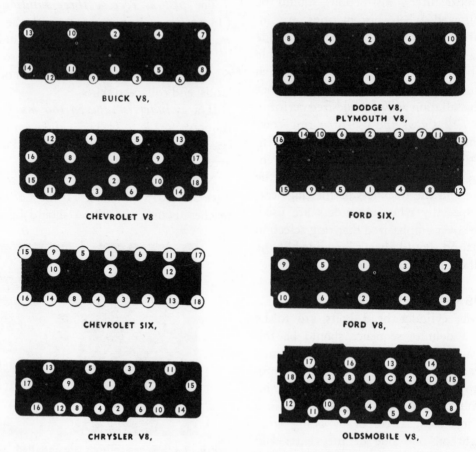

Fig. 7.13. Sequence of tightening cylinder head bolts for several typical engines.

two possible cylinder conditions, (1) with new or rebored walls, or (2) worn tapered or out-of-round walls. Rings are used in sets of compression ring, oil scraper, and oil-control ring.

Piston expanders are used behind rings in some engines to increase ring pressure against the cylinder wall.

Chrome-plated rings increase ring life and decrease cylinder wear. Some ring sets include chrome-plated oil rings in addition to the top compression ring. When installing rings, the manufacturer's instructions should be followed carefully.

The proper *cylinder head tightening sequence* is quite important to achieve the proper tightness without causing undue strains and possible distortion of head and/or block.

Questions

1. What three functions does the piston perform?
2. What kinds of wear does the piston sustain?
3. What is meant by the "thrust side" of a piston?
4. Name three ways of keeping a piston pin properly centered in its piston.
5. In the case of tapered cylinder walls within tolerance, what may be done with the pistons?
6. What is the limit of allowable side clearance in piston ring grooves?
7. What is the allowable cylinder wall taper?
8. What device is sometimes used to improve piston fit in its cylinders?
9. What is the allowable clearance in a honed or bored piston-pin hole?
10. What is the allowable weight variation between pistons in new sets?
11. Where does most of the wear occur in cylinders?
12. What is the visible result of the wear at the top of cylinders?
13. What may appear at the lower portion of the cylinders?
14. There is a choice of three procedures when an engine is overhauled. What are they?
15. What, briefly stated, is the recommended method of engine break-in?
16. How may cylinder wear be measured?
17. What three duties do piston rings perform?
18. Under what two possible cylinder conditions must piston rings perform?
19. What three kinds of rings make up the usual set for three-ring pistons?
20. How is ring side clearance measured?
21. How can worn ring grooves be corrected?
22. Why are ring expanders used?
23. What are the advantages of chrome-plated rings?
24. What, pertaining to piston rings, is just as important as good ring design and manufacturing excellence?
25. What precaution should be taken when tightening a cylinder head into working position?

CHAPTER EIGHT

Engine Bearings

General Types of Bearings

There are three general types of bearings used in modern automotive engines: (1) bored bearings in the cast iron, aluminum, or die-cast metal of engine parts; (2) insert split bearings for main and connecting rod bearings, and (3) solid or one-piece bearings such as camshaft bearings and bronze bushings for the upper ends of connecting rods.

Bored Bearings

Bored bearings are used in some engines for valve stem guides and in most engines for valve lifter or tappet guides. They are also used in the carburetor for throttle shaft and choke valve

shaft bearings, and in a few other places in the power plant.

When valve stem guides become excessively worn they may be bored out oversize and sleeves inserted. Because of the larger diameter of valve lifter guides they seldom need attention. If the bearings in the carburetor become worn, the entire unit is replaced.

Insert Bearings

Insert bearings are of two kinds: (1) interchangeable precision inserts and (2) semi-finished insert bearings.

Interchangeable precision inserts are available in standard and certain undersizes. They are used for both main and connecting rod bearings and are ready for installation. In the majority of cases precision inserts for main bearings will be satisfactory. However, if there has been any warpage or distortion in the crankcase which would be indicated by excessive wear on the one, two or three center main bearings, the semi-finished inserts should be used. The hole can be bored with a line-boring machine. This will compensate for any slight distortion between the bearing holes and will put the final bearing bores in exact alignment. Fig. 8.1 shows how to remove upper crankshaft bearing inserts.

Insert bearings are made of steel blanks formed into semicircular shape and lined with

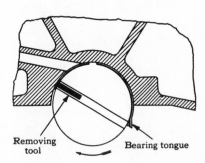

Removing tool   Bearing tongue

Fig. 8.1. It is possible to remove upper crankshaft bearing inserts. Insert a headed pin in the oil hole and rotate the shaft so that the bearing tongue is moved away from its recess. The head on the pin must be large enough to prevent the pin from dropping into the oil hole.

babbitt, cadmium, or a copper-lead bearing alloy. The precision bearing metal lining will only be from .002" to .006" thick as experience has proved that the thin lining stands up better than a greater thickness. When a bearing has worn .002", regardless of whether the bearing metal is a very thin layer or 1/4" or more thick, the bearing is no longer usable. Thus the thin layer of bearing metal is quite sufficient. In addition, the close reinforcement of the bearing by the casting has greater mechanical strength than a thicker bearing.

Solid or One-Piece Bearings

Solid or one-piece bushings are used for piston-pin bearings in connecting rods of the floating pin or locked-in-piston type. They are usually of bronze and are pressed endwise into place at the upper end of the connecting rod. The pressing operation requires that the bearing be honed or reamed to fit the piston pin. With the use of oversize pins, in many cases it is not necessary to replace the piston-pin bushing. It is only necessary to enlarge the bore to fit the oversize pin by honing or boring a few thousandths of an inch.

When bearings are to be replaced a very necessary preliminary is to measure the *journals* which are to have new bearings, checking each one to be certain of roundness within the prescribed tolerance. A journal is the portion of a shaft which rotates within a bearing. The measurements of the journal should be accurate to nearest .0002". In general, connecting rod bearings will require replacement more often than main bearings.

Connecting Rod Bearings

When the crankpin is round within the specified limits; when the journal surface is satisfactory, *i.e.*, straight and free from grooves and ridges; and when the journal size is known, the replacement bearing can be selected.

In some cases the bearing bore for the insert bearing may have become elongated. If this exceeds .002", the rod should be exchanged for a new or reconditioned one to obtain the best performance.

Since connecting rods (through use or abuse) may be bent or twisted, they should be checked for proper alignment. If the center lines of the crankpin hole and the piston-pin hole are not parallel within .001" in 6", they should be aligned. This should be a routine operation in all cases where rod bearings are replaced. Remember that the piston must move in a line at exact right angles to the center line of the crankshaft to assure a free sliding motion without twisting or binding. The piston pin must be accurately parallel with the crank pin to avoid forces which would tend to twist the connecting rods or to tip the bearing at either end of the rod on its journal.

Crankshaft Bearings

There is no use in putting in new crankshaft bearings unless the crankshaft journals are round and free from roughness or grooves. Before new crankshaft bearings will give satisfactory service, the main journals should be round within .003" or less, and the diameter should be within .001" of the original diameter. Crankpin journals should be round within .002" with a diameter within .001" of the original size. Refer to Fig. 8.2. If the crankshaft does not come within these requirements, it should either be replaced or reground with appropriate undersized bearings supplied.

Fig. 8.2. The first step after removing the rods is to check the crankpin journals for roundness and taper with a micrometer. If out-of-round over .002", the crankshaft should be ground.

A properly fitted, pressure-lubricated bearing must have oil clearance. The general rule is: Allow .001″ for each inch of journal diameter, subject to modification depending upon the bearing metal alloy used. The oil clearance is the difference between the inside diameter of the bearing bore and the outside diameter of the journal which it fits.

Installing Bearings

When connecting rod bearing caps have been removed, care must be used in replacing the caps. The general practice is to number the lower end of each connecting rod on the side toward the camshaft. Two points must be observed when putting piston rod assemblies in

Fig. 8.3. After bearing caps are replaced, they should be tightened with a torque wrench to the specified tightness. The lower end of the connecting rod and cap should have the effect of being in one piece, but the bolt should not be stretched.

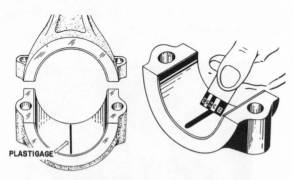

Fig. 8.4. The plastigage comes in an accurately sized strand of plastic material. A short length is placed between journal and surface of bearing insert, and bearing cap is tightened to its correct tension. Bearing cap is then removed. The flattened width of plastic strand, when measured, indicates the amount of bearing clearance.

place, (1) the assembly must be in the correct cylinder bore, according to the number on the rod, and (2) the rod must be facing the correct way.

When replacing the bearing cap, again the numbers must be watched. The bearing cap must go on the rod with the same number, and the number on the cap must be on the same side as the number on the rod.

When checking the fit on new bearing inserts, it is advisable to tighten No. 1 to the correct tightness and check for free turning of the crankshaft. Repeat this operation for each bearing in turn. If one of the bearings is too tight, loosen it and proceed with the next bearing. If there should be one or two tight bearings, investigate to discover the cause, as all should be about the same fit. A speck of dirt or other foreign matter could cause tightness. When all the bearings are tightened correctly, the crankshaft should turn as freely as may be expected considering the drag due to the pistons moving in the cylinders.

The bearing caps should be tightened with a torque wrench to the specified tightness, as Fig. 8.3 illustrates. The bolts should be tight enough to hold the bearing cap in place as if it were one piece with the rod; however, too much force could stretch the bolts. In general, the torque for rod bearings will run from 40 to 50 pound-feet, and for mains from 70 to 100 pound-feet.

Worn Bearings

With quality lubrication, the bearings used in modern cars last a long time. Nevertheless, even if no premature bearing failure is experienced, the bearings eventually reach a point where the oil clearance space becomes excessive due to normal wear. Fig. 8.4 illustrates how bearing clearance is measured. Note the placement of the plastigage.

The bearings will still function in their mechanical duty of supporting the crankshaft or pivoting the connecting rod on the crankpin. However, the excessive clearance permits more oil to be thrown off than the rings can accommodate, so that some oil works up into the cylinder and is burned. Besides this additional consumption of oil, the build-up of cylinder deposits is accelerated and spark plugs foul more rapidly.

When bearing wear reaches a certain point, the operation of the moving parts causes noise; once the bearings begin to pound, failure soon takes place.

Therefore, good engine servicing practice indicates the need for new bearings when oil consumption increases to the point where a quart is needed each 200 to 500 miles. Refer to Fig. 8.5.

Rings in bad condition are also the cause of excessive oil use, but experience has shown that usually ring wear and bearing wear occur simultaneously, both contributing to excessive oil consumption. Whenever new rings are installed, it is highly advisable to install new rod bearings also. Main bearings seem to last longer, and therefore do not need replacement every time rod bearings are replaced. However, they should be checked each time for possible replacement.

Causes of Bearing Failures

An important proportion of bearing failures results from causes which should be corrected before replacements are made. A fairly comprehensive knowledge of these causes is helpful in order to recognize them and thereby avoid repetition of the failure.

The reasons and conditions that bring about bearing failure are grouped under nine headings in the following list. A few of the causes that are under the control of the mechanic are discussed in some detail.

1. Partial load distribution
   a. Dirt under bearing
   b. Bent rod
   c. Misalignment of bearing cap
2. Foreign matter on bearing surface

3. Distortion of bearing seats
   a. Out-of-round main bearing saddles
   b. Crankcase distortion
   c. Out-of-round connecting rod bearing seats
   d. Twisted connecting rods
4. Incorrect fit of inserts in main bearing saddles or connecting rod bearing seats
   a. Loose bearings
      (1) Filed inserts
      (2) Dirt on parting faces
   b. Excessive "crush"
      (1) Filed bearing caps
      (2) Dirt under insert
5. Out-of-round journals
6. Incorrect oil clearance
   a. Insufficient clearance
   b. Excessive clearance
      (1) Wrong fit
      (2) Normal wear

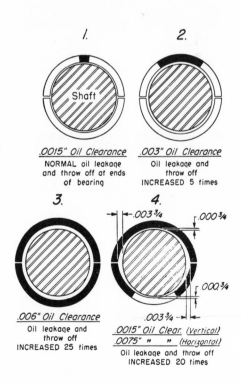

Fig. 8.5. Diagram showing bearing oil leakage and throw-off for various shaft clearances, based on a 2″ shaft. (FM)

7. Lubrication difficulties
   a. Stoppage of oil supply
      (1) Clogged screen
      (2) Mechanical breakage in lubricating system
      (3) No oil
   b. Oil starvation
   c. Incorrect grade of oil
8. Fatigue and overloading
9. Corrosion

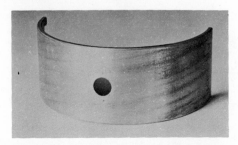

Fig. 8.6. Back of loose bearing. The polished surface indicates the insert was loose in its bearing bore and rubbed against the bore metal.

Fig. 8.7. Loose bearing. Failure caused by overheating due to poor heat transfer through bearing shell to metal of crankcase or rod.

Out-of-Round Main Bearing Saddle

Where the main bearing saddle is out-of-round and precision replacement bearings have been used, the bearing shells take the form of the saddle into which they are placed, resulting in an out-of-round bearing hole. If the deviation from roundness is more than .003″, a dangerous oil clearance condition exists and may cause heavy pressure on parts of the bearing. Insert bearings, align-bored to size and roundness, should be used here.

Out-of-Round Connecting Rods

Connecting rods may be out-of-round at the lower end, due to (1) elongation caused by flexing in service or (2) filing bearing caps. If insert bearings are used in either case, the rods must be reconditioned to give round bores which fit available standard inserts or the rods must be replaced. When new precision bearings are installed in an elongated rod, the oil clearance at the split may be entirely closed causing the bearing to lock on the shaft when the cap is bolted in place.

Twisted or Bent Connecting Rods

A twisted or bent connecting rod puts unusual strain and pressures on both piston-pin bushings and the lower end bearing. In addition, it causes rapid and irregular wear on pistons and cylinder walls. Piston and rod assemblies should always be checked for alignment.

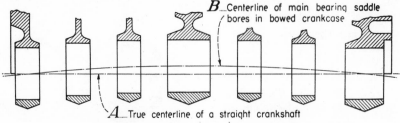

B Centerline of main bearing saddle bores in bowed crankcase

A True centerline of a straight crankshaft

Fig. 8.8. The effect of a bowed crankcase. The seven bearing bores are no longer in alignment, and the bearings will have short service life if precision inserts are installed. Undersize inserts, align-bored, will result in accurately aligned bearing surfaces in the inserts. (FM)

Loose Bearings

A loose bearing can always be identified by shiny areas on the back of the insert, as shown in Fig. 8.6. This cause of failure is due purely to wrong procedure or carelessness on the part of the mechanic — either in filing the bearing insert or in cleaning the parts. Refer also to Fig. 8.7.

Bearing Crush

Bearing inserts are made .001″ to .002″ longer than the exact circumference of their corresponding bearing holes. This excess material is called "crush." If this crush is excessive, when the bearing is tightened down, the extra material will be forced into bulges near the parting faces. This creates areas of undue pressure with a resultant breakdown of the bearing material.

Out-of-Round Journals

Where the deviation from roundness exceeds .003″ for crankpins or crankshaft journals, a somewhat concentrated load is produced because the elliptical journal does not fit into the bearing arc. There is also a certain forging or swaging effect which frequently causes mechanical movement of the bearing metal and promotes fatigue. Out-of-round journals may also affect the oil clearance. Worn or damaged crankshafts may be reground for undersize bearings. Fig. 8.8 illustrates the effect of a bowed crankcase.

Incorrect Oil Clearance

If the oil clearance space is too small, the oil film is not sufficient to keep the rotating journal from making metal-to-metal contact with the bearing. As a result, the mechanical rubbing effect will eventually wipe out the metal in certain spots and deposit it on other parts of the bearing. Note Fig. 8.9. On the other hand, excessive clearance results either from the wrong size bearing being used as a replacement, or from normal wear of the bearing

beyond the point of safe use. This causes an excessive amount of oil to be thrown from the bearings with possible destruction of an adjacent bearing through lack of oil.

Lubrication Difficulties

A lack of lubrication may be due to a clogged oil screen, mechanical breakage in the lubrication system, leakage of the lubricant, or lack of lubrication due to neglect. The cause should be determined to avoid repetition of bearing failure. Figs. 8.10 and 8.11 explain two types of oil pumps.

Babbitt bearing metal is not affected by corrosion; cadmium-silver bearings and copper-lead bearings are affected under some conditions. As long as the temperature of operation is kept below 260° to 270° F. and a good quality of oil is used, it is unlikely that corrosive

Fig. 8.9. Bearing which failed for lack of lubrication. Bearing metal has worn away to steel backing.

Fig. 8.10. Gear-type oil pump. The gears rotate in opposite directions as indicated, carrying oil around in the pockets between the teeth. Note the direction of oil flow through the pump as shown by the arrows.

acids will be formed. However, if the temperature is permitted to get above 300° F., harmful acids may be formed and corrosion of the bearings is liable to follow. An overheated bearing is shown in Fig. 8.12.

Fig. 8.11. Typical rotary vane oil pump. The volume between the rotor and the pump housing varies on each side of the vanes; this forces oil out the discharge side as space decreases in volume when vanes rotate with the rotor. High pressure rotary vane pumps have more vanes.

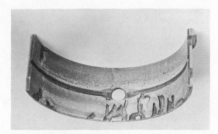

Fig. 8.12. Overheated bearing which started to fail. If it had not been replaced it would have soon failed in service.

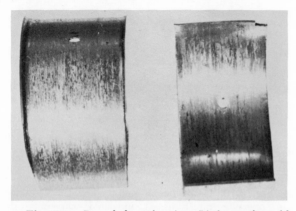

Fig. 8.13. Pounded-out bearing. Little can be told about the cause of failure when a bearing is so badly battered.

Use of any oiliness concentrates or break-in compounds that contain anything other than pure petroleum products should be avoided. Lard oil or inorganic chemicals, supposed to give increased film strength to the lubricating oil, should not be used. Most of the good quality oils now on the market may be safely used in the cadmium or copper-alloy bearings as long as a safe temperature is maintained.

Corrosion

Corrosion or etching on cadmium-silver bearings takes place over the entire surface of the bearing, dissolving the metal in small pockets and reducing the effective bearing surface. The acids which corrode cadmium silver also attack copper-alloy bearings, but the action is different. Copper-alloy is not a true alloy but a mechanical mixture of lead and copper. Because there is no chemical solution of the metals, both are in their original state. When the corrosive acids attack the exposed pure lead, the lead particles form a lead soap which washes away. With decreased lubrication there is a certain amount of metal contact between the remaining copper and the journal, and the journal itself may be scratched or damaged. A pounded out bearing is shown in Fig. 8.13.

Crankcase Ventilation

Even with engines in good mechanical condition, there is a certain amount of blow-by past the pistons and rings into the crankcase, so it is necessary to ventilate the crankcase. Until 1962, the general method of providing ventilation was to have a draft tube leading downward from the crankcase with the lower end cut at an angle. As the car moved forward, a slight suction was created at the lower end of the tube removing gases and vapors from the crankcase. An air filter in the cap of the oil filler tube and in the tube itself admitted fresh air.

While this arrangement worked satisfactorily, it discharged gases from the crankcase into the atmosphere. The Society of Automotive Engineers announced in 1961 that the crankcase discharge gases and vapors contributed more to smog formation than the engine exhaust.

Smog has plagued Los Angeles, California for a number of years, and San Francisco is beginning to be troubled by it. Therefore the California Legislature passed a law requiring all new cars shipped in or assembled in California to be equipped with positive crankcase ventilation (PCV).

PCV Ventilation

Positive crankcase ventilation (PCV) returns the crankcase vapors and gases to the intake manifold, usually through tubing running from the crankcase to a special opening just below the carburetor. Instead of being discharged, the blow-by is returned to the engine cylinders, presumably to be at least partially burned. On Ford Sixes the blow-by is returned to the air filter and drawn into the engine with the air for combustion through the filtering cartridge. With the PCV system, the vacuum in the induction system draws the crankcase gases through the engine. However, the intake manifold vacuum is greatest at idle and low engine speed when the need for crankcase ventilation is the least, and the vacuum is lower at higher engine speeds when the need for ventilation is more acute. To work properly, a modulating valve is used. This is placed in series with the hose or tubing that connects the crankcase and the intake manifold. (When the upper connection is to the air cleaner no modulating valve is needed.) The modulating valve reduces the effective vacuum in the PCV system at idle and low speed and allows it to increase at higher engine speeds, thus changing the vacuum to correspond to the need for ventilation. Refer to Fig. 8.14.

The modulating valve most used has been the AC valve (made by the AC division of General Motors Corporation), which is spring loaded. There has been some trouble with the PCV system because the crankcase discharge contains considerable varnish and sludge-forming elements. The discharge is composed

of unburned leaded fuel and air that pass the rings on the compression stroke and burned and partially burned gases and water vapor that pass on the power stroke. These latter gases contain carbon monoxide, carbon dioxide, some sulphur dioxide and a trace of hydrocarbon acid which comes from the leaded fuel. In addition, oil mist and other complex hydrobromic compounds are produced when the oil throw-off from the bearings is mixed with the other materials by action of the rotating crankshaft.

Servicing PCV Systems

Putting this mixture back through the engine keeps it from being discharged into the atmosphere, but on the other hand, it causes serious engine deterioration. Corrosion occurs on precisely fitted engine parts, and varnish builds up

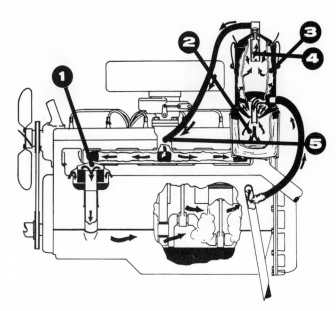

Fig. 8.14. (1) An oil-bath air filter keeps out atmospheric dust. (2) Crankcase vapors are drawn into the residue jar which traps any varnish or sludge. (3) Filter element removes tars, acids, varnish and other impurities not trapped in the jar. (4) Modulating valve governs effective vacuum according to need for ventilation. (5) Filtered fuel vapors going back to engine improve fuel economy.

on valve stems, piston rings and hydraulic valve lifters. Sludge-making material is also distributed throughout the engine.

The AC valves should be checked at least every 4000 miles and preferably every 2000 miles. They are subject to clogging, or may stick in the open position, due to effect of the crankcase discharge materials. The corrosive effect may cause the spring to break, making the valve inoperative. There are two types of AC valves, (1) the throw-away type which is replaced when it ceases to operate, and (2) the separable type which may be taken apart for cleaning or spring replacement. This valve is shown in Fig. 8.15.

A number of devices for purifying the exhaust gases and providing for crankcase ventilation are being tested for approval at this time. They will probably be required on all cars in California (and possibly other states) by 1965-66. The problems of smog and atmosphere contamination are becoming more acute.

There are two excellent positive crankcase ventilation systems on the market which provide a filter to catch the droplets drawn through the system and also a sump to catch condensed varnish-making elements. This combination protects the engine against contamination and deterioration from these elements. The systems are Oildex, made in Tulsa, Oklahoma, (Fig. 8.16) and Salyer's Engine Vent, made in Oklahoma City, Oklahoma (Fig. 8.17). Although somewhat expensive, they are definitely beneficial to engines and give them excellent protection.

Summary

There are three general types of *bearings* used in automotive engines, (1) bearings bored in metal of engine parts, (2) insert bearings, and (3) solid or one-piece bearings.

Insert bearings are available in standard and undersizes, and furnished either semi-finished (for line boring), or as precision inserts.

Replacement of *connecting rod bearings* can only be made for round and straight crankpin journals. The connecting rod bearing bore

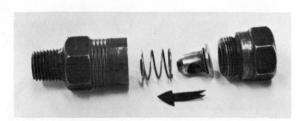

Fig. 8.15. Separate type AC modulating valve for positive crankcase ventilation system.

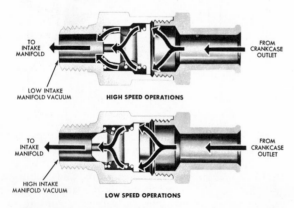

Fig. 8.16. One type positive crankcase ventilation system.

Fig. 8.17. Salyer's engine-vent PCV system.

must not be elongated over .002″. Rods must be straight, with upper and lower bearing center lines parallel.

To replace *crankshaft bearings* crankshaft journals must be round within .003″ and straight. Crankpin journals should be round within .002″.

Properly fitted bearings will allow .001″ for each inch of journal diameter for *oil clearance,* which is the difference between the inside diameter of the bearings and the outside diameter of the journal which it fits.

When *installing bearings* each connecting rod with its bearing cap should be numbered at the lower end, on the side which goes toward the camshaft. Be sure each rod goes into the correct cylinder bore and that the rod faces in the right direction. Check the fit of each new bearing by tightening one bearing at a time to the specified torque.

Worn bearings will still function but the too-large clearance permits excessive oil throw-off and the noise is objectionable. Pounding will soon destroy the bearing.

Cause of bearing failure should be known and understood. Nine main causes of bearing failure are given on page 71.

An *out-of-round main bearing saddle* will cause bearing inserts to take the form of the bearing saddle, resulting in an out-of-round bearing and leading to early bearing failure.

Out-of-round connecting rod ends should be reconditioned or replaced to avoid trouble.

Twisted or bent connecting rods will cause early bearing failure. Piston-connecting rod assemblies should always be checked on an accurate fixture for correct alignment.

Loose bearings will cause early bearing failure. They are a result of wrong procedure or measurement on the part of the mechanic.

Excessive Bearing crush is the length of the bearing insert circumference in excess of .001″ or .002″ over exactly half of the bearing circumference. This condition will cause bulges of metal and breakdown of bearing material.

Out-of-round journals must not have over .003″ maximum deviation from roundness on crankshaft and crankpin journals.

Lubrication difficulties may cause bearing failure, and the cause of the difficulty must be determined to prevent repetition of the trouble.

Corrosion or etching will affect cadmium-silver bearings and attacks the lead in copper-lead bearings.

Questions

1. Name three types of engine bearings.
2. State the requirements pertaining to a crankpin journal before a replacement bearing can be specified.
3. How may worn valve stem guides be corrected?
4. How thick is the layer of bearing metal on precision insert bearings?
5. What is the maximum out-of-round allowed on crankshaft main bearings?
6. What is the maximum out-of-round allowed on crankpin bearings?
7. Where should the cylinder number be placed on a connecting rod?
8. Why should worn bearings be replaced?
9. Mention three causes of bearing failure.
10. What method must be followed to allow a bowed crankcase to be used?
11. What effect do worn bearings have on oil consumption?
12. Mention five causes of bearing failure.
13. What test should be given piston and rod assemblies?
14. How can a loose bearing be identified?
15. What is meant by bearing crush?
16. What is the effect of out-of-round journals?
17. What tool should be used to check the tightness of bearing caps?
18. Name three lubrication difficulties.
19. Name two types of oil pumps.
20. How can worn crankshafts be fixed?

CHAPTER NINE

Diagnosing Engine Troubles

In considering engine troubles, it should be remembered that the *power plant,* which propels the automobile, consists of the *engine* which is the mechanical part of the power plant (cylinder block, head, pistons, crankshaft, camshaft, valves, etc.) and the *auxiliary systems* (fuel, ignition, charging, cooling, starting).

Engine troubles are mechanical. *Power plant* troubles may be either in the engine, in the auxiliary systems, or in both; therefore, they may be (1) mechanical, (2) electrical, or (3) in the fuel system.

Scientific Test Procedure

In the recommended scientific test procedure, which is followed when the cause of poor power plant performance is not known, the different parts are checked in approximately this order:

1. Battery
2. Starting system
3. Spark plugs
4. Compression
5. Distributor
6. Ignition timing
7. Fuel pump
8. Ignition secondary
9. Charging system
10. Air cleaner
11. Manifold vacuum
12. Carburetor
13. Cooling system
14. Visual inspection

The results of these tests will allocate power plant troubles to the systems at fault, and/or the engine. The compression test and engine manifold vacuum test will reveal engine defects that are not obvious but that indicate needed engine service. For further information, the cylinder leakage test is valuable. In many cases engine noises should be analyzed also.

Symptoms of engine trouble that are obvious, such as excessive oil consumption, smoky exhaust, power loss, and certain engine noises, indicate the steps that must be taken to bring the engine back to a satisfactory condition.

The Service Manager and Service Salesman should be sufficiently familiar with the power plant to tell whether a car with troubles should go directly to the shop with definite instructions as to the work to be done, or should go to the diagnostician (or tune-up man) for a scientific test.

The following areas will be discussed in this chapter: the compression test, the cylinder leakage test, the engine vacuum test, and the identification of some engine noises. Therefore, these areas will be mentioned only incidentally in Chapter 30 which covers diagnostic procedures.

Compression Test

The compression tester, described in detail in Chapter 11, gives significant information about the engine condition. The procedure for its use is simple and direct.

The spark plugs should be removed from the engine and the ignition switch turned "off." The carburetor throttle may be either open or closed because a full charge of air will enter the cylinder regardless of throttle position, since the plugs are removed.

The rubber fitting on the compression gauge should be inserted into No. 1 spark plug hole and held tightly. With the starting motor switch closed, crank the engine for at least 4 compression strokes. Note the instrument reading on the first as well as the final stroke, and record the compression reading for No. 1 cylinder. Repeat the same test on each of the other cylinders, keeping a record for each one.

The test should be made with engine at normal operating temperature and the engine should be cranked the same number of turns for each cylinder. The readings should not differ more than 10 pounds between the highest and the lowest cylinders.

The compression tester has a check valve to retain the pressure within the instrument until the reading is made. After the valve is released, it is ready to test the next cylinder.

When the compression test is made the compression gauge will show about 75 pounds on the first turn of the engine if pistons, rings and valves are in good condition. A few more turns of the engine will give the total pressure reading.

If the pressure is built up in jerky steps of ten to twenty pounds at a time, the fuel mixture is leaking past the rings or the valve seats. In most cases this jerky indication is due to sticky valve guides or burned valves.

A low reading on two adjacent cylinders indicates a leaky head gasket between them.

When the compression reading differs ten pounds or more between any of the cylinders, it indicates trouble in the low-reading cylinders which could be due to pistons, rings, or valves. To get an indication as to which of these three is responsible for the low reading, inject a teaspoon of oil on top of the piston in the cylinder which reads low. Crank the engine a few times and then make a second compression test. If the second reading has increased to be approximately the same as the other cylinders, the trouble is due to a scored cylinder or a bad piston or ring condition. If the compression does not increase in this second test to within close range of the rest of the cylinders, it indicates that the valves are not seating properly in the low reading cylinder, or that they are in poor condition.

The compression test is used primarily to show up any differences in compression between the various cylinders. Secondarily it gives the actual amount of compression in pounds per square inch. The readings should be within a few pounds of the specified engine compression at cranking speeds. Fig. 9.1 shows the compression tester and a remote starter switch.

Some engines will show uniform compression in the various cylinders but the readings will be considerably below the compression specified for the engine. This is due to fairly uniform wear throughout the engine after some years of service.

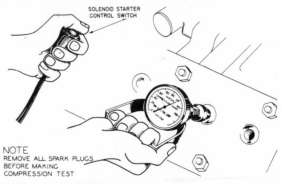

Fig. 9.1. A solenoid starter switch can be used on all engines equipped with solenoid starter control. This makes it easy for one man to operate the engine for the compression test. Be sure to record test results for each cylinder.

Fig. 9.2. Cylinder leakage tester. (Left) Used in a motor analyzer panel. (Right) used as an individual tester. This instrument will give more information than the compression tester.

VACUUM GAUGE INDICATIONS

A SHOWING GOOD CONDITIONS AT IDLING SPEED READING 19 TO 21 INCHES WITH NEEDLE STEADY

B SLOW MOVEMENT ADJUST CARBURETOR TO STEADY NEEDLE

C INTERMITTENT MOTION STICKY VALVE

D CONSTANT DROP BURNT VALVE

E WEAK VALVE SPRINGS MOTION INCREASES WITH ENGINE SPEED

F LOOSE VALVE GUIDES FAST VIBRATION

G LATE VALVE TIMING AT IDLING SPEED

H INTAKE MANIFOLD OR HEAT RISER LEAK

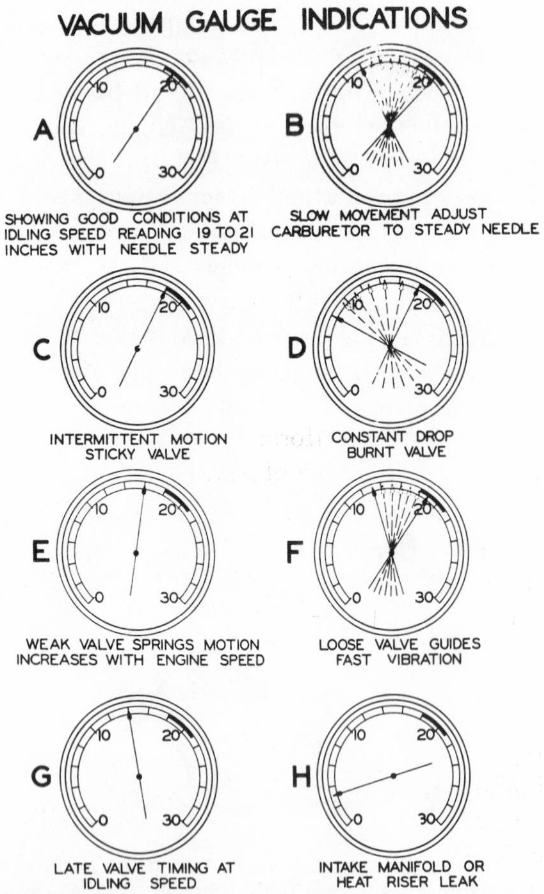

Fig. 9.3. The vacuum gauge is a valuable instrument in checking the performance of the engine, fuel, and ignition systems.

Cylinder Leakage Test

To augment the information that can be obtained about engine condition by using the compression tester, Sun Electric Corporation has developed a cylinder leakage tester. This device maintains air pressure (from an outside source) in the engine cylinder through a calibrated opening. Leakage of air through valves, past rings, or through a leaky head gasket, lowers the pressure in the cylinder. This leakage is indicated on a pressure gauge calibrated in percent of leakage. The cylinder leakage test is superior to the compression test. Fig. 9.2 shows the tester in use.

To make the test, the instrument is connected to No. 1 spark plug hole, with the piston in top dead center position. The reading on the gauge is noted. If leakage is through the intake valve, it can be heard at the carburetor. If through the exhaust valve, it can be heard at the tail pipe. If past the rings, it can be heard at the oil filler pipe. If bubbles appear in the radiator, leakage is past the head gasket. Note that the points of leakage can be determined as well as the relative amount of leakage.

For the next cylinder, the engine is cranked until the piston is in TDC position. This may be spotted by watching the valve (on overhead valve engines), by connecting the dwell meter and watching the indicating hand for a full-scale reading as the breaker points close, by attaching an indicating disc to the fan pulley on the end of the crankshaft, or by using a whistle that stops blowing when the piston reaches TDC on the compression stroke.

Engine Vacuum Test

As stated earlier, the engine is a good gas pump and one of its functions is to produce a vacuum in the intake manifold. With an engine in good condition, this vacuum will be 19 to 21 inches at idle, down to zero at open throttle. At a uniform speed of 50 mph the manifold vacuum will average around 8 to 10 inches.

Various readings of the vacuum gauge will indicate different engine conditions, as shown in Fig. 9.3. The vacuum gauge can be connected on most engines; in cases where it cannot be conveniently connected, it is advisable for a mechanic to drill and tap for 1/8″ pipe thread in the intake manifold and put in a plug or a 1/8″ cock, so the vacuum gauge can be readily connected.

Tracing Engine Troubles by Sound

Loose pistons, excessively worn piston rings, loose piston pins, worn connecting-rod bearings, worn main bearings and worn camshaft bearings, all make characteristic noises. When properly interpreted, these noises will help materially to diagnose engine mechanical difficulties.

The ability to diagnose engine noises with a fair degree of accuracy is vital in the profitable operation of any service department. The diagnostician should be able to recognize and identify the noises that may develop due to normal wear and tear over long periods of use, or may appear because of failure of one or more of the engine parts.

There are so many sources and varieties of engine noises that *wild guesses* in regard to them will result in many mistakes. On the other hand, a careful diagnosis of an engine noise can often avoid expensive labor in tearing down an engine, or prevent an engine needing extensive repair from being ruined by continued use.

Whether the mechanical diagnosis of engine troubles is made by the diagnostician or by a mechanic the analysis should be made before engine tear-down, so that only the needed and correct operations will be involved, with no extra work and charges to the customer.

Automotive Stethoscope

All moving mechanical parts create sound waves of various pitches, frequencies, qualities and intensities. Many of these sound waves can be heard by the unaided ear. On the other hand, there are sounds that cannot be heard at all without help. Even though the sound can be heard, it is frequently difficult to localize it and identify it.

A stethoscope type instrument makes use of a metal prod, about 8″ long and 1/8″ in diameter, which passes through a rubber bushing and terminates against a metal diaphragm held in a plastic housing. The sound from the diaphragm chamber is carried to the ears by two ear tubes. This instrument is very moderate in price, enabling any shop or individual mechanic to acquire one. Although the stethoscope is not generally included in diagnosis or tune-up equipment, it is a distinct aid in locating engine difficulties. One type of soundscope is shown in Fig. 9.4.

Engines in good operating condition make noises with which the mechanic, service manager and diagnostician should be familiar. When excessive wear, damage, or maladjustment occur, abnormal noises result. The value of the sound detecting and amplifying device lies in its ability to help determine the *location* of the noise and identify its *cause*.

Sounds To Be Heard

Among the sounds not ordinarily heard by the human ear are generator bearing noises.

Fig. 9.4. The sound scope (stethoscope type) helps to localize engine noises. A knowledge of normal and abnormal noises is of value in diagnosing mechanical troubles.

There is a difference in the sound of the shaft revolving in the plain bearing and the ball bearing moving in the pulley end. Such sounds as: the spark at the spark plugs, the action of the breaker arm in the distributor, the action of the fuel pump and the vibrating points in the voltage regulator can be picked up. Defective action can be detected when the sound varies from normal.

Noises that can be identified or classified as "knocks" come from loose pistons, worn piston pins, piston-pin bearings in rods or pistons, broken rings, or ring lands and new rings striking the edge of unremoved ring ridges. In addition, knocks may be due to excessive carbon build-up, poor connecting-rod bearings, worn main bearings, crankshaft end play, worn camshaft bearings, a loose flywheel, a loose vibration damper and perhaps other causes.

Piston slap is a very common noise and is more noticeable when the engine is cold. It may be heard at low engine speeds under load, becoming faster and more intensified when the engine is accelerated. It usually can be quieted temporarily by shorting out a spark plug or by feeding oil through the carburetor.

The knock of a loose piston pin is easily traced to the upper or cylinder portion of the engine. It is a sharp, light, metallic rap that may seem to be a rattle if all the pins are loose. Shorting a spark plug at idle speeds will cause a double knock, as the piston strikes once at the bottom and once at the top. In some cases,

customers complain of a knock of this description occurring at certain times and then not being heard again for some time. It has been found that this can result from a pin lock either broken loose or left out by a mechanic. Since this can cause a scored cylinder, such a noise cannot be dismissed as unimportant until some time has been spent in trying to locate and identify it.

A broken ring or a ring land will usually result in a knock of much higher pitch than the piston-pin noise. It might be better described as a click than a knock and is likely to be in one cylinder. It ordinarily cannot be shorted out. Sometimes it will rap once per stroke of the piston, sometimes twice, but it can always be traced to the upper portion of the engine. Sound detecting instruments are very useful for spotting this type of noise as well as localizing it.

The very distinct rap of new rings striking the ring ridge at the top of the cylinder will not be experienced very frequently, but the possibility should never be overlooked. Mechanics generally remove the ring ridge before taking out the pistons, as should be done. However, there is also the possibility that an amateur did the job and either did not know enough or did not take the trouble to remove it. Sometimes loosened piston pins and bearings will allow the upper ring to strike the ring ridge. This high-pitched metallic clicking noise is usually audible at all speeds, but it is particularly so on deceleration. Fig. 9.5 shows the ring ridge being removed before pistons are taken out.

Engine Valve Timing

The engine camshaft is driven by (1) a crankshaft gear and camshaft gear which mesh together or (2) a crankshaft sprocket and camshaft sprocket, connected by a silent chain.

When an engine is originally assembled or is reassembled, the valve timing must be set correctly by getting the marks on both gears or both sprockets in line as specified. It is always

Fig. 9.5. Before removing pistons on an engine that has been in service for some time, it is necessary to remove the ring ridge at the top of the cylinder. A good ridge reamer is needed for this job.

possible, though not likely, that the valve timing may be set wrong.

Valve timing may be changed if the timing chain stretches. It is possible (on engines that have seen very high mileage) for the chain to stretch enough to allow it to jump one or more teeth. When this occurs the engine will have very little power or will not run at all. Fig. 9.6 shows gears off one tooth. Fig. 9.7 illustrates a stretched timing chain.

Carbon Knocks

Knocks due to carbon formation on pistons, cylinder heads or valve heads, must not be overlooked. This knock will occur when the carbon forms a solid surface on one or more of the parts mentioned so that they strike together when the piston is at the top of its travel or when the valves open. This type of knock has been confused with everything from a connecting rod knock to a broken piston. It occurs most prominently on deceleration, either when driving or when testing on the floor. On some cars this knock becomes very noticeable and will usually scare a customer into the shop when he hears it. When the car is slowing down from road speed to a stop, the individual knocks of each piston striking carbon blend into a solid volume of knocks, making the driver think that he is losing the better part of the engine.

To produce the noise at the test bench, bring the engine speed up with the throttle and let it retard suddenly. It sounds something like a lockwasher or small nut striking the head.

Frequently a good solvent treatment followed by some fast highway driving will quiet the noise down temporarily. At other times it is necessary to remove the head and clean the valve heads and piston heads to remove the carbon deposits.

Bearing and Other Knocks

The camshaft bearings will seldom give trouble because of their large size and the slower speed of the camshaft as compared with the crankshaft. However they cannot be overlooked in the case of unusual or hard-to-find knocks. Camshaft knocks can be deadened and

Fig. 9.7. Worn timing chains will retard valve timing and make sluggish engines. When the stretch in the chain due to wear is great enough, it will jump and prevent the engine from running.

Fig. 9.8. For every second set of rod replacements, camshaft bearings usually need replacement; however, they should be checked whenever rod bearings are replaced.

Fig. 9.6. On the engine shown, the gears were out-of-time one tooth. This is always a possibility on new engines and upon installation of new timing gears.

thus identified by loading the shaft at each end and in the middle. This can be done by working feeler gauges between two valves at each of these locations successively. The feelers will hold the shaft steady in its bearing momentarily at the speed at which the knock is audible. Replacement requirements for camshaft bearings are explained in Fig. 9.8.

Connecting rod and main bearing knocks are usually simple to produce and to recognize. However, in engines with high pressure lubrication systems, the rod bearings may be worn enough to cause excessive oil consumption long before they are loose enough to produce an audible knock. It is not safe to assume that rod bearings are not excessively worn simply because they are not knocking. The complaint may be that a knock is heard on a pull or upon coasting at speeds above 35 mph. The mechanic can usually produce the knock by increasing the engine speed above this rpm, and then playing the throttle back and forth sharply. A medium heavy knock or rattle will be heard if the connecting rod bearings are loose. A heavier knock will be heard if the rings have

Fig. 9.9. Every time piston assemblies are removed, they should be checked for alignment before being reinstalled. Misaligned rods soon cause enough wear to make a noisy engine.

too much clearance. If one cylinder is producing the knock, it can usually be quieted by grounding the plug in that cylinder. A loose, but not a burned-out, connecting-rod bearing knock will short out so it can be heard also. The diagnostician must always keep in mind the possibility of a lubrication fault causing bearing knocks. Thus he must check oil pressure and condition of the oil; if these conditions are poor, a knock can appear even with proper bearing clearance. One or more bent connecting rods may cause a knock similar to a bearing knock. Fig. 9.9 illustrates rod alignment.

Crankshaft end-play usually results in a heavy thump at irregular intervals with a varied effect. The sound can be produced and thereby identified by "playing" the throttle while engaging and releasing the clutch.

A loose vibration damper can cause a deceptively heavy rumble or thump in the front of the engine during pick-up from idle speed under load, or at an uneven idle, while it remains silent at higher speeds or smoother operation. A loose flywheel can be detected by turning off the switch at idle speeds and turning it on again just before the engine dies. Working the clutch pedal at the time the noise is heard at running speeds will also vary the noise to identify it. It can either be a heavy thump or a light knock at the back of the engine, depending upon the degree of looseness and the type of engine.

Valve tappet noises are usually easily identified by their light sound and slow timing. Inserting a feeler gauge between the valve and lifter or rocker arm will tend to isolate the noise. If proper clearance adjustment doesn't quiet it, worn or damaged parts may have to be replaced.

"Adjusting out" a valve noise by decreasing the clearance to below the factory recommendations or by making adjustments when the engine temperature is not up to the proper operating point, is inviting trouble, and should never be done.

The "ping" of detonation knock, carbon knock, spark knock or fuel knock, as it is variously called, does not cause as much concern as it formerly did. A slight ping, heard on hard acceleration at low speeds, seems to be fairly normal; if it occurs too prominently when the engine is running at higher speeds, excessive carbon should be removed or the spark advance mechanism checked. Excessive ping can be very harmful to engines and the cause should be corrected.

Systematic Sound Tracing

Engine diagnosticians have learned to conduct their search for various noises in a systematic and scientific manner. Instead of standing back and guessing that this or that is the trouble they carefully eliminate possible causes until they are fairly certain of the source of the trouble. Listening with one of the new instruments will help materially to localize and identify noises. Zoning the engine and making running tests to isolate the noise to the narrowest possible section will also help. Both unfamiliar and familiar sounds can be traced to the portion of the engine where they seem to originate by following the sound to where it is most intense. When this spot is determined, a knowledge of engine operation should be a guide to the most likely cause of the noise.

A quick check of the mechanical condition of the engine auxiliaries and accessories can also be made with sound-detecting devices.

A detailed study, made primarily to help operators of fleets of trucks and coaches with their service problems, has reduced vehicle and engine noises to a group of basic sounds: (1) squeak, (2) rattle, (3) thump, (4) grind, (5) knock, (6) scrape, and (7) hiss. Identifying sounds by these names will help to clarify the kind of noise to look for and will be some hint as to the possible cause.

Tracing engine knocks by sound is not new, since listening rods have been used for years. The new instruments provide ease of application, speed, convenience, increased accuracy and increase the information that may be obtained. This method of diagnosis is still more valuable than ever. A feature that helps to sell service is the fact that the customer can listen to noises that may be picked up by the instrument so that there will be no doubt in his mind as to the need for corrective service.

Frequent Causes of Poor Engine Performance

When an engine, after a long period of normal use (or a shorter period in the case of misuse, abuse or accident), begins to show several or all the following symptoms, a major repair job is indicated:

1. Smoky exhaust
2. High oil consumption
3. Lack of power
4. Poor acceleration
5. Low fuel mileage
6. Engine knocks
7. Spark knock (detonation)
8. Low oil pressure
9. Engine misses
10. Escaping fumes
11. Failure to respond to corrective adjustments

These are indications of conditions which are at least partly due to defective main, connecting-rod or camshaft bearings, and worn rings, pistons, and cylinder walls. The causes which are largely responsible are as follows:

Smoky Exhaust

1. Oil pumping, accelerated by excessive oil throw-off from worn or defective bearings.
2. Worn, weak or broken rings.
3. Oil rings stuck in grooves due to caked carbon, with drain slots clogged.
4. Cylinder wall worn tapered, or scored.
5. Carburetor out of adjustment.
6. Punctured vacuum booster pump diaphragm.

High Oil Consumption

1. Excessively worn bearings or defective bearings which permit abnormal oil throw-off.

2. Carboned oil-control rings with drain slots or holes clogged.
3. External oil leaks at front or rear main bearings.
4. Worn, weak or broken rings.
5. Worn intake valve stems and guides.
6. Tapered or scored cylinder walls.
7. Faulty gaskets (valve cover, timing case, oil pan).
8. Leaking vacuum booster pump diaphragm.
9. Out-of-round and badly worn crankpin and crankshaft.
10. Oil too light for engine condition.
11. Oil pressure too high.
12. Oil level too high.
13. Late timing of intake valve due to stretched timing chain.
14. Distorted cylinder wall due to uneven tightening of cylinder head studs.
15. Excessive speed.

Lack of Power and Poor Acceleration

1. Low compression due to excessive blow-by.
2. Weak, broken or worn rings.
3. Carbon deposits on valve seats.
4. Badly carboned spark plugs.
5. Burned valves.
6. Fuel system not functioning properly.
7. Late ignition timing.

Low Fuel Mileage

1. Low compression due to excessive blow-by.
2. Increased internal friction due to worn bearings.
3. Poor valve condition.
4. Late valve timing due to worn timing chain.
5. Late ignition timing.
6. Worn or wrong size carburetor jets.

Engine Knocks

1. Main and/or connecting-rod bearing worn excessively, or bearing metal cracked or melted out allowing excess clearance.
2. Piston-pin bushing worn to allow excessive clearance.

3. Crankshaft end-play excessive due to worn flanges on thrust bearing.

Spark Knock (Detonation)

1. Heavy carbon deposits on piston heads, valve heads and cylinder head.
2. Overheated engine due to cooling system not functioning properly.
3. Fuel not suitable for spark timing and/or compression ratio (too low octane rating).

Low Oil Pressure

1. Main and connecting-rod bearings worn excessively or with bearing metal cracked or melted out, allowing abnormal oil flow through enlarged oil clearance space.
2. Worn oil pump.
3. Clogged or dirty oil screen.
4. Water in oil pan.

Engine Misses

1. Oil soaked or carboned spark plugs, due to excessive oil, thrown off by bearings or working past rings into combustion chamber.
2. Defects in ignition system.
3. Carburetor not functioning properly.
4. Air leakage between carburetor and engine.

Escaping Fumes

1. Excessive oil throw-off from worn or defective bearings resulting in carboned rings which allow blow-by, building up a positive pressure in the crankcase which forces oil vapors out of breather or oil filler pipe.
2. Blow-by from worn, weak or broken rings.

Failure to Respond to Corrective Adjustments

Engines with several or all of the above symptoms cannot be put into satisfactory operating condition by the cleaning and adjustment operations of the most scientific tune-up job. Worn bearings, rings in bad condition, scored or worn cylinders, burned, grooved or worn valves and other functioning parts must be replaced or reconditioned, as required.

Summary

The *power plant* consists of the *engine* and the *auxiliary systems*, (fuel, ignition, charging, cooling, starting).

When an *engine problem is diagnosed*, check the parts in a systematic order. Results of these tests will indicate the corrective steps needed. Obvious defects may indicate that mechanical engine work is needed.

To make a *compression test*, remove spark plugs and insert compression gauge fitting in cylinder No. 1 and take compression. Repeat test at other cylinders. Test should be made with engine at normal operating temperature. This test is primarily to show the differences in compression between cylinders, and secondarily to give actual compression pressure.

The *cylinder leakage test* will show the leakage path, whether through the intake valve, exhaust valve, rings, or head gasket.

The ability to *trace engine knocks by sound* and diagnose engine noises is important. The noises may develop due to normal wear or from the failure of engine parts. Do not make wild guesses as to the source of abnormal sounds.

It is advisable to use a *soundscope* to help locate the source of engine noises. The diagnostician should be able to distinguish between normal and abnormal noises.

Distinctive sounds are generator bearing noises, sparks at spark plugs, fuel pump operation, etc., which are normal. Defective action will give sounds that vary from normal. Abnormal sounds are "knocks," piston slap, etc. Shorting out a spark plug at idle speed will amplify piston-pin knocks. Broken rings make higher pitched knocks.

Engine valve timing is accomplished by the camshaft, driven by gears or a timing chain. The setting must be correct. A stretched chain could retard the valve timing and possibly allow the chain to jump one or more teeth.

Carbon knocks may occur due to carbon accumulations in cylinders, so that the pistons strike the carbon. The noise is most noticeable on deceleration. A good carbon solvent plus some fast highway driving will often help. The only sure remedy is to remove the head or heads and clean out the carbon.

Bearing noises and other knocks are distinctive. Camshaft bearings seldom give trouble. Connecting-rod and main bearing knocks may be reproduced by racing the engine momentarily and then closing the throttle. A medium knock comes from loose connecting-rod bearings, and a heavier knock from main bearings. A loose vibration damper may cause a heavy rumble or thump at the front of the engine.

Valve tappet noises are easily identified by their higher pitch and frequency.

An engine noise may be described as a squeak, rattle, thump, grind, knock, scrape or hiss.

Questions

1. Name six important engine components.
2. Name five auxiliary power plant systems.
3. How might engine troubles be classified?
4. How might troubles in the auxiliary systems be classified?
5. What is the first part to be checked in any engine diagnosis?
6. What kind of trouble does low compression indicate, if any?
7. At what engine temperature should compression be checked?
8. What test is preferred to the compression test?
9. Name five worn parts that may cause engine knocks.
10. What is the quickest and easiest way to localize engine noises?
11. Does an engine in good mechanical condition make any noises?
12. What can be done to improve worn pistons?
13. What should be done in cases where it is difficult to connect a vacuum gauge to an engine?
14. Name four vacuum gauge indications and state what they tell the observer.

15. Where in the engine would a loose piston-pin knock be located?

16. What kind of a noise will be made by a broken piston ring or ring land?

17. What could happen when a timing chain is excessively worn, and what would be the result on engine operation?

18. Would rod bearings worn enough to cause excessive oil consumption knock enough to call attention to this condition?

19. Mention five symptoms of poor engine condition.

20. What is the difference between a "carbon knock" and a "spark knock"?

CHAPTER TEN

Cooling System—Function, Maintenance and Troubles

A thorough knowledge of the cooling system is important in diagnosis and tune-up because what may appear to be a malfunctioning of this system may be the *symptom of trouble* in one of the other systems. Of course, if there is trouble in the cooling system, it must be diagnosed and corrected.

Function of the Cooling System

When fuel is burned in the cylinders of a gasoline engine, heat is generated — and only about 20% of the heat is converted into mechanical work. The other 80% of the heat must be dissipated in some way to prevent the temperature from exceeding a safe point.

The engine is cooled in several ways: approximately 13% if the heat is carried away by the air which blows over the engine; 40% is carried away in the hot exhaust gases; and 27% is eliminated in the cooling system.

As long as heat can be dissipated as fast as it is generated, there will be no temperature increase in the engine. If this balance is upset, and the heat is not dissipated with sufficient rapidity, there will be an increase in temperature. As the engine temperature goes up, the temperature *difference* between the coolant and the surrounding air will increase, causing a more rapid dissipation which may be enough to hold engine temperature at a safe level. However, if the amount of heat generated exceeds the heat-dissipating ability of the cooling system, the temperature will keep on rising to the boiling point, which means trouble.

In designing the cooling system, sufficient heat-dissipating capacity must be provided to keep the temperature of the engine at a safe operating point under all conditions of speed, load and atmospheric temperature. For example, the cooling system must be able to keep the coolant temperature below the boiling point when the engine is operated in air temperatures as high as 120°F.

Because of the large cooling capacity of the average cooling system, it is possible for it to be only partially operative and still keep the engine down to a satisfactory temperature. In average use, under moderate temperature conditions, the owner may be unaware that the cooling system is not in perfect condition. Should the car be driven at a sustained high speed in warm weather, it will overheat without previous warning. It is a safe estimate that at least 25% of the cars on the road over two years old are operating with cooling systems which have impaired cooling capacity.

Heating after Stopping Engine

When the engine is stopped after the car has been well warmed up, the temperature of the cooling liquid will immediately rise — possibly as much as 20°F. The reason for this is that when the engine stops operating, the fan, pump and motion of the car also stop. Once the air and coolant circulation have ceased, heat cannot be dissipated by these means. The heat already generated will continue to raise the temperature of the coolant and power plant until the radiation and normal convection cooling start to lower it, and it finally drops to meet the atmospheric temperature.

This is perfectly normal and should be remembered in cases of complaints of loss of volatile type anti-freeze liquids and engines that become hot after being driven hard and fast. If the cooling system is in bad condition, excessive heating after normal driving may be expected.

The cooling system consists of the water jacket around the cylinders, the water pump (or pumps), the tubing connecting the engine and the radiator, the radiator, thermostat and the car heater. Refer to Fig. 10.1.

Inspection and Maintenance

The importance of maintaining the cooling system as close as possible to new-car efficiency at all times should be understood. Even a modestly sized passenger car engine generates sufficient heat to keep a six-room house comfortable on a zero day. Complete failure of the cooling function for any reason means dangerous overheating of the engine in a few minutes. Proper cooling contributes more to continued engine operation and long life than is generally realized. A check for liquid flow is shown in Fig. 10.2.

Many expensive failures on the road are caused by simple irregularities that very often could have been detected and corrected by a few minutes close inspection. Inspection for cooling system liquid losses is extremely important, for when a vehicle is driven with insufficient liquid in the cooling system, the engine can

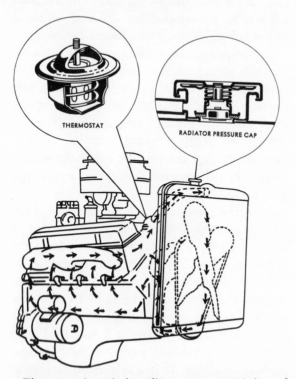

THERMOSTAT

RADIATOR PRESSURE CAP

Fig. 10.1 A typical cooling system, consisting of radiator, water jacket, water pump, thermostat, pressure radiator cap and connecting tubing. The thermostat and pressure radiator cap are enlarged.

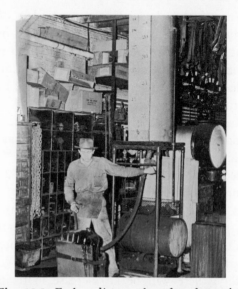

Fig. 10.2. Each radiator, when free from obstructions will have a specified flow. This can be checked with equipment as shown here, to get the gallons per minute through the core.

be quickly damaged from overheating. Contrary to the general belief, evaporation of water or anti-freeze solutions accounts for only a small part of liquid losses. At least half of all loss is due to leakage, while most of the remaining half is due to loss through the radiator overflow pipe from boiling, foaming, etc.

To detect small leaks, the inspection should be made with the cooling system cold. Leaks which may show dampness or even dripping when cold can easily escape detection when the engine is hot due to rapid evaporation. Note Fig. 10.3.

Certain parts of the cooling system are difficult to inspect for leakage, such as the rear of the engine water jacket, some drain plug locations, the front side of the radiator on some of the newer cars, the underside of the radiator bottom tank, and the water pump seal.

Letting the car stand overnight on a clean floor or over clean papers will show the general location of the leak. The common points of liquid leakage are: radiator, cylinder-head gasket joint and studs, water-pump shaft, hose connections, engine castings (cracked or porous), water-jacket freeze plugs, thermostat and pump housings, drain cocks and hot-water heater. Fig. 10.4 illustrates one common place for leakage.

Internal Leakage

While external leakage is a hazard, *internal leakage* of the cooling system, if neglected, may have even more serious consequences. Not only is there the danger of overheating due to low liquid level, but the possibility of water getting into the crankcase and contacting moving parts of the engine, may have extremely serious consequences. It is particularly dangerous if permanent anti-freeze gets into the oil pan.

Common points of internal leakage are: loose cylinder-head gasket joints, thread leakage of loose cylinder head studs or bolts and pores or cracks in the cylinder head or block.

Either water or anti-freeze solution leakage into the engine is detrimental to lubrication.

Mixed with the engine oil in sufficient quantities, both form sludge which may cause lubrication failure, sticky piston rings and valves, excessive wear and extensive engine damage. Permanent anti-freeze, in addition, can make a sticky coating on all internal parts, requiring dismantling and cleaning of the entire engine.

Checking for internal leakage is not as simple as finding external leaks. However, there are several tests which can detect internal leakage before it reaches a serious stage.

Testing with Engine Running

Start with the engine cold, first removing the fan belt from the drive pulley to prevent

Fig. 10.3. Inspecting radiators with a special flashlight to see if tubes are clogged and to check inside condition.

Fig. 10.4. When radiator hoses begin to soften and the rubber separates from the fabric, it is time to replace them. Particles of rubber getting loose on the inside often clog radiator tubes. It is far better to replace tubing before it fails than to lose the anti-freeze and possibly ruin an engine.

water-pump operation. Drain the system until the coolant level is exactly even with the top of the cylinder block Remove upper radiator hose, thermostat housing, and thermostat. Replace the thermostat housing and fill with water, (or with the housing removed, fill the water jacket completely).

With the engine in neutral, "gun" it several times, watching for bubbles in the water opening, both while gunning and when the engine drops back to idling speed. To detect smaller leaks, jack up the rear wheels of the car and run the engine at higher speed, in high gear, loading it gradually and intermittently by using the foot brake.

The appearance of bubbles or the sudden rise of the liquid indicates leakage of exhaust gas into the cooling system. Injecting a light oil into the carburetor while making the test sometimes helps to identify exhaust gas leakage by introducing smoke into the bursting bubbles. Make the test quickly, before boiling has time to start, because steam bubbles would give misleading results. Even a small leak should be corrected because it will eventually allow liquid to get into the engine if it is not already doing so.

Testing with Compressed Air

Using an adapter, which can be made from an old spark plug shell, apply air pressure — about 100 psi — through each spark plug hole in turn, with the piston on top dead center on the compression stroke. Air leakage from the cylinder will be indicated by air bubbles or by a rise of liquid level in the radiator or in the engine water outlet if the upper hose is disconnected. This is also a useful test for valve leakage.

Testing by Odor

The "smell" test, made at the radiator filler opening, is reported to be of value, since exhaust gas leakage into the cooling system seems to give the cooling liquid a distinctive odor.

Water Pump Leakage

Water pump leakage is a fairly common occurrence. The dripping from a pump seal may be visible with the engine stopped or idling, yet it may not show up at all with the engine running at moderately high speed because the suction of the running pump will draw air in and thus prevent the liquid from running out. This same condition exists at all points of leakage on the suction side of the water pump, including heater hose connections to the engine or car heater, lower hose, connection between pump and radiator, lower tank of the radiator, and even leaks in the lower portions of the radiator core.

A special test may be necessary for air suction into the cooling system, as water pump leakage cannot always be detected by inspection. A quick check for leaks on the suction side of the water pump can be made using a piece of rubber tubing and a glass bottle containing water.

To make the test, first adjust the liquid level in the radiator, allowing for expansion when hot. Be sure the radiator cap is tight. With pressure caps, block open the pressure valve or replace with a plain cap.

Attach a suitable length of hose to the lower end of the overflow pipe. All connections must be airtight. Run the engine in neutral gear at a safe high speed until the engine reaches a constant operating temperature. Without changing engine speed, put the free end of the rubber tubing into the bottle of water, avoiding kinks or sharp bends that might impede the flow of air. Watch for bubbles in the water bottle.

In the absence of exhaust gas leakage into the cooling system, a continuous flow of bubbles indicates that air is being sucked into the system. Any leak on the low-pressure side of the pump that will permit air to be drawn in at high speed will also eventually allow liquid leakage when the engine is idling or stopped. It is possible that the condition already allows such leakage.

Air which may be drawn in (or gas forced in from leaks) will be circulated with the cooling liquid, increasing the apparent volume of the coolant. This, of course, causes the level to rise in the radiator. Entrained air or gases in sufficient quantity will cause large overflow losses of liquid while the vehicle is being driven.

Mechanical Condition of Water Pump

The water pump, being a mechanical device with moving parts, is subject to failure, although it generally gives very little trouble. Since there is always the chance that the water pump may be the cause of heating system difficulties, it must not be overlooked.

Water pump bearings are of two kinds: (1) ball bearings, and (2) plain sleeve bearings. A common arrangement is to have a ball bearing on the pulley side of the pump and a plain sleeve bearing in the other bearing position. Note the water pump used by Chrysler in Fig. 10.5. Trouble can develop with either bearing, or with both. In some cases the pump shaft becomes worn, causing the pump to fail.

The pump seal is a critical part of the pump. Its function is to make a liquid-tight seal around the pump shaft where it enters the liquid compartment. Most of the later cars have pumps equipped with a packless seal. This consists of a carbon ring which seats against a bronze ring as the shaft rotates and carries with it the revolving portion of the seal, and the impeller.

If the seal should leak, the pump will have to be rebuilt or replaced. The seal will no longer prevent leakage if it becomes worn, warped, scored, corroded or broken.

Another trouble that occurs occasionally is a broken pin or key that locks the impeller on the shaft. When this happens, the shaft will turn normally, but the impeller will not turn at all, or is turned so slowly that coolant circulation is seriously affected. If overheating occurs and no other cause can be found, the water pump should be carefully checked. To do this

it may be necessary to remove and disassemble it. A disassembled pump is shown in Fig. 10.6.

Cooling System Thermostat

The thermostat is a temperature-sensitive, thermostatically-operated valve; its function is to trap the cooling liquid in the water jacket until the coolant reaches operating temperature. This causes the engine to reach a good running temperature in the shortest possible time, and it minimizes the "cold-running" time. Typical types of thermostats are shown in Fig. 10.7.

Without a thermostat in cold weather, as fast as the cooling water or anti-freeze solution

Fig. 10.5. Water pump used by Chrysler. This pump has two ball bearings; however, some pumps have one ball and one plain bearing. Notice the construction of the seal (*12, 13*).

Fig. 10.6. Disassembled water pump, showing its parts.

picks up a little heat it is lost at the radiator. In severe weather or on short runs, the engine will never reach a satisfactory running temperature. The bad effects of cold engine operation, such as excessive oil dilution, formation of cold sludge, water condensation, thickened oil, and poor lubrication, are well known, and will definitely shorten engine life. Therefore, it is quite important that the thermostat be kept in good operating condition at all times. Even in the summer time, it is advisable to have a thermostat in the system, to get the engine up to temperature as quickly as possible. Temperatures of 65° to 100°F. are warm compared to 0° to —30°F., but they are still far below good engine operating temperatures of 160° to 180°F.

Fig. 10.7. There are three types of thermostats in use, all of which perform the same function — control the minimum engine temperature. (Left) Capsule type. (Center) Sylphon bellows. (Right) Thermostatic spring type.

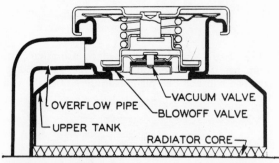

Fig. 10.8. Cross section of the pressure radiator cap which controls the pressure on the cooling system. The blow-off valve will be forced off its seat, allowing pressure to escape when it reaches its designed pressure. As the power plant cools, the vacuum valve allows air to enter the system when the pressure in the cooling system drops to that of the atmosphere and below.

The minimum thermostatic start-to-open temperature should be 150°F. — and 160°F. is better. Some car owners like to use 180°F. thermostats in the winter, when they have permanent anti-freeze in their cooling systems, to get more heat out of the car heater. Ordinarily, though, 160°F. is high enough, and this thermostat can be left in the car the entire year. The thermostat only controls the *minimum operating temperature* after warm-up.

Since overheating frequently damages the thermostat, it is a good idea when this occurs to check that the thermostat is still operating. A thermostat that is in place but is not performing its normal function is of no value. To test a thermostat, it is only necessary to immerse it in water, and heat the water, measuring the temperature with a thermometer having a scale that reads up to 212° to 220°F. Note the temperature at which the valve starts to open. This should be close to its rated temperature. The valve should be wide open when the temperature has risen another 15° to 20°F.

Pressurized Cooling Systems

Pressurization of the cooling system is accomplished by the use of a specially designed filler neck and a pressure-controlling cap. The pressure cap is equipped with a pressure-controlled built-in valve. It seals the cooling system off from the overflow pipe and the atmosphere, permitting the system to pressurize itself automatically as the coolant is heated above the atmospheric boiling point. Refer to Fig. 10.8. The greater the pressure, the higher the coolant temperature — and the greater the cooling effectiveness, due to the increased temperature difference between the coolant temperature and the outside air temperature.

The pressure-control valve also functions as a safety valve to keep the pressure within the desired safe limits. Some operate at 7 psi, some as high as 15 psi and in a few cases higher pressures may be used.

These pressure caps are equipped with a vacuum relief valve which opens automatically as the engine cools off and the internal pressure drops below atmospheric pressure. This prevents the formation of a vacuum in the cooling system which could otherwise cause the collapse of the rubber hoses. Fig. 10.9 shows a typical pressure radiator cap.

A pressurized cooling system has a much wider temperature operating range than an open system. It is perfectly safe and normal for late model cars equipped with the pressure cap to run at comparatively high temperatures when driving at high speed, climbing hills, hauling heavy loads, in heavy traffic or when the outside air temperatures are above 90° or 95°F. Even if the heat indicator needle gets over to the "hot" side, there is no cause for alarm *as long as the temperature does not exceed that for which the pressure cap is designed.*

In order to avoid overheating, there must be a balance between heat input in the cooling system and its heat-dissipating ability. If the temperature difference between coolant temperature and outside air temperature is increased by allowing the coolant temperature to go to a higher point, more heat can be dissipated at any given velocity of air through the radiator core.

It is a well-known fact that the boiling point of water will be increased if the pressure it is subjected to is increased. By permitting the pressure in the cooling system to rise 7 psi, the boiling point is increased 20°F., so that the coolant temperature can go to 232°F. (instead of the atmospheric boiling point of 212°F.) before it starts to boil. Therefore, with a 7 psi pressure cap, the cooling liquid will not boil at any temperature under 232°F.

With a 15 psi pressure cap, the temperature can go to 250°F. before the coolant will boil. With an adequate supply of good quality lubricant in the engine, no damage will result if the operating temperature gets up above 212°F., as long as cooling liquid is not lost because of boiling.

Inspecting Pressurized Systems

Whenever the water level is inspected, pressure caps, where used, should also be inspected. There should be no obvious nicks or breaks in the lower impact gasket or in the lower sealing seat in the filler neck. The cams on the out-turned flange of the filler neck must not be bent, and the in-turned ears on the cap that engage the cams must not be bent or worn to a point where they cannot retain the caps firmly on the filler neck. To pressurize the system

Fig. 10.10. Pressure testing the cooling system. The hand bulb pumps air into the system to force coolant out of any leaks there may be so that they can be identified. Pressure almost up to the pressure rating of the radiator cap is usually applied. Different fittings allow the tester to be adapted to any of the current radiator filler necks.

Fig. 10.9. A typical pressure cap. The rubber or neoprene gasket helps to make a tight seal against the pressure valve seat.

there must be a tight joint between the gasket on the bottom of the filler cap and the seat against which it seals. Fig. 10.10 explains one method of pressure testing a cooling system.

Caution must be used when removing the pressure cap when the system is under pressure. The sudden removal of a pressure cap will reduce the pressure and lower the boiling point. A coolant at a temperature of more than 212°F. would immediately start boiling. Severe scalding could result from the sudden release of pressure in the system. If steam is escaping from the overflow, do not touch the cap until the sound of escaping steam has stopped. Then turn the cap slowly until steam again rushes out of the overflow, but keep the cap against the safety stop on the filler neck. At this point the pressure valve is lifted away from the sealing seat, and the pressure is free to escape through the overflow tube. When steam once more stops escaping, the cap can be safely removed. Idling the engine for a few minutes before shutting off the ignition will help to reduce the excess temperature. Fig. 10.11 shows the instrument used in testing the pressure cap.

The correct cap must always be used on a pressurized cooling system, and a pressure system must always have a pressure cap. Do not substitute an atmospheric cap for a pressure cap, and do not use a pressure cap on a car which is not designed for pressurized cooling.

Causes of Overheating

There are only two basic causes of engine overheating: (1) excessive production of heat, and, (2) insufficient dissipation of heat.

The excessive production of heat is not nearly as common as the insufficient dissipation of heat. Excessive heat production results from, (1) inadequate lubrication, (2) late ignition timing, (3) inefficient combustion, (4) excessive loading.

Insufficient dissipation of heat results from, (1) loss of coolant, (2) loss of effective radiator surface, (3) reduction or loss of cooling air stream, (4) restriction of coolant circulation, (5) inadequate heat transfer from cylinders to coolant in the water jacket.

Diagnosis of Cooling System Troubles

As a guide for the quick and accurate diagnosis of cooling system troubles, indicated by overheating (and at times, overcooling), the following outline is given:

Low Liquid Level in Cooling System

    A. *Leakage from system.*

1. Water hose, radiator, car heater.
   a. Loose or defective hose clamps and fittings. (Refer to Fig. 10.12.)
   b. Defective rubber hose.
2. Radiator and hot-water heater.
   a. Cracked seams of core, tanks and overflow pipe.
   b. Broken joints in outlet or inlet fittings.
   c. Tanks or core worn through at points of support.
   d. Corrosion perforation of water tubes.
   e. Loose or defective drain-cock, plug or vent.
   f. Accidental damage.
3. Engine block water jacket.
   a. Loose or defective drain-cocks or plugs.
   b. Loose or corroded freeze plugs.

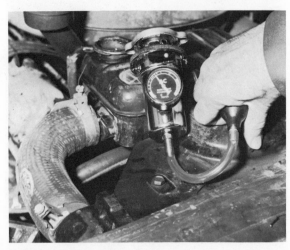

Fig. 10.11. Pressure testing a radiator cap. The same instrument with a different adapter is used to check the pressure cap. It can be pumped up to its rated pressure. (AC)

c. Loose cover plates or bad gasket.

d. Defective car heater shut-off valve.

e. Pump housing loose or gasket bad.

f. Warped block at cylinder-head joint.

g. Cracked or porous water jacket casting.

h. Cylinder head studs loose in block.

4. Cylinder head.

a. Defective or blown gasket.

b. Loose hold-down bolts or nuts.

c. Cracked, porous or corroded head casting.

d. Head casting warped at block joint.

e. Loose thermostat housing or defective gasket.

f. Loose heat indicator fitting.

g. Loose heater-hose nipple.

h. Corroded, broken or loose water manifold.

i. Loose or corroded freeze plugs.

5. Water-pump shaft seal.

a. Scored, worn or warped thrust seal.

b. Deteriorated or perforated shaft seal.

c. Thrust seal compression spring failure.

d. Scored or corroded shaft.

e. Worn or corroded bearings.

B. *Overflow loss of cooling liquid.*

1. Steam formation at hot spots in water jacket.

2. Air suction into cooling system.

3. Foaming of cooling liquid.

4. Exhaust gas leakage into cooling system.

5. Use of alcohol anti-freeze with high temperature thermostat.

6. Use of alcohol anti-freeze for high-altitude driving.

7. Loose radiator cap or cap missing.

8. Pressure valve in radiator cap stuck open.

9. Restricted flow in radiator core.

Obstructed or Inadequate Cooling Liquid Circulation

A. Rust-clogged radiator core. (Refer to Fig. 10.13.)

B. Rust-clogged water jacket passages.

C. Thermostat valve stuck in closed position.

D. Collapsed radiator hose or torn and loose rubber lining.

E. Slush-ice in radiator core (frozen).

F. Water-pump impeller loose on shaft.

G. Impeller blades corroded, worn or broken, housing corroded.

H. Failure or slippage of pump drive.

I. Shortage of liquid from incomplete filling of system.

J. Liquid capacity of system reduced by rust deposits.

Obstructed or Inadequate Air Circulation

A. Fan belt worn or loose.

B. Fan blades bent.

C. Radiator baffles out of place.

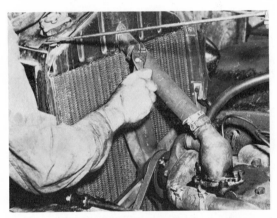

Fig. 10.12. All hose clamps (even hard-to-reach bottom clamps) must be tight, especially when permanent anti-freeze is used in the cooling system.

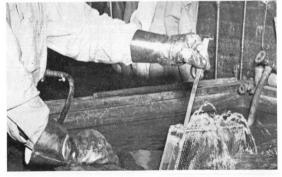

Fig. 10.13. The only sure way to clean out clogged radiator cores is to "rod out" the tubes as shown here. Upper or lower tank is removed and each tube opened up by a flat metal rod, which pokes out the obstructing scale, mud, hardened oil or grease.

D. Radiator air passages clogged with bugs, dirt, etc.
E. License plate or other obstruction in front of radiator.

External Causes of Heating

A. Engine timing delayed or over-advanced.
B. Improper fuel mixture.
C. Lubrication system clogged with oil-water sludge.
D. Lubrication failure from freezing of water on oil screen.
E. Oil break-down deposits in engine; valves and piston rings sticking.
F. Shortage of engine oil.
G. Clogged exhaust muffler or pipes.
H. Engine in bad mechanical condition.
I. Dragging brakes.
J. Excessive sustained high-speed driving.
K. Overloading of vehicle.
L. Traveling with a tail-wind with heavy load; not enough air through radiator.
M. Driving in deep sand, mud or snow.

Diagnosis of Overcooling

A. Thermostat.
   1. Not installed, or removed.
   2. Valve stuck open; fails to close.
   3. Valve opening temperature too low.
   4. Bypass valve stuck in closed position.
B. Stop-and-go driving at low engine speed and output.
C. Thermostat fails to maintain adequate engine operating temperature.

Protection of Cooling System

Every car that is in service should have its cooling system protected against corrosion and scale deposit by adding corrosion inhibitor to the cooling liquid. Most anti-freeze preparations incorporate an inhibitor which will keep the system clean for one winter season. When the anti-freeze is removed for the summer, a separate inhibitor treatment should be added to the coolant. This should be checked as part of the diagnosis and tune-up procedure. A leak-sealing compound can be used to correct minor cooling system leaks.

Summary

Trouble in the cooling system may be a *symptom of trouble* in one of the other power-plant systems which should be diagnosed and corrected.

In the *cooling system*, only about 20% of the heat generated by combustion in the engine cylinders is converted into engine power, and of the balance, 40% must be handled by the cooling system. As long as heat is dissipated at least as rapidly as it is generated the temperature will stay at or below the desired level.

A *partially operative cooling system* may keep the temperature down to a satisfactory point at moderate engine speeds and loads.

When the engine is stopped after normal operation, the *residual heat* without circulation of air and water will raise the coolant temperature, possibly enough to cause boiling.

The *cooling system* consists of the water jacket, water pump, tubing, radiator, thermostat, car heater and its tubing and automatic controls.

It is important to *maintain the cooling system* in good condition as its failure may lead to dangerous overheating of the engine. Inspection for liquid losses is most important. Most of the liquid loss is due to leakage and/or loss through the overflow pipe.

Inspect for leaks when the cooling system is cold. Let the car stand overnight with clean papers beneath so leaking liquid can be seen.

Internal leakage is a hazard as it may introduce water and permanent anti-freeze into the crankcase with serious consequences. This is also detrimental to lubrication. It may be detected by watching for bubbles in the radiator filler pipe.

Do not overlook the *water pump* when diagnosing cooling system troubles. The pump seal is usually the most critical part.

The *thermostat* is a temperature-sensitive, thermostatically-operated valve which traps the coolant in the water jacket until it reaches the temperature for which the thermostat is set. The average thermostat temperature is around 170°F. The thermostat only controls the *minimum operating temperature* after warm-up. Overheating may damage the thermostat.

Pressure cooling systems have a pressure-controlling radiator cap. A pressurized cooling system can operate at a higher temperature without boiling than an atmospheric system. For example at 7 psi, the boiling point is 232°F., which is 20° higher than the atmospheric boiling point of 212°F.

When *removing pressure caps* from hot engines, release the pressure *before* taking off the cap all the way. Always use the correct pressure cap for a given pressure system.

Two basic reasons for overheating are (1) excessive production of heat, and (2) insufficient dissipation of heat.

Protect the cooling system against corrosion and scale deposits.

Questions

1. Is malfunctioning of the cooling system necessarily an indication of cooling system trouble? Why or why not?
2. What proportion of the heat content of the fuel is converted into engine power?
3. What proportion of heat of combustion is dissipated by the cooling system?
4. What is the result when heat is dissipated as rapidly as it is generated?
5. How high can the atmospheric temperature be before a cooling system in good condition will fail to keep the engine to a safe temperature?
6. What happens to the coolant in a system when the engine is stopped after a period of normal operation?
7. What will quickly result if and when the cooling system fails?
8. What is the most important point to watch in maintaining the cooling system?
9. How would you try to detect cooling system leaks?
10. Why is it important to check for internal leaks?
11. What can result if permanent anti-freeze gets into the crankcase?
12. How would you detect internal leaks?
13. How does the water pump fail most frequently?
14. How would you check for leaks on the suction side of the coolant pump?
15. What is the function of the cooling system?
16. What is the minimum temperature at which a thermostat should be set, and what is a good average?
17. Why are pressurized cooling systems used?
18. How does the pressure radiator cap work?
19. At what pressures do pressurized cooling systems usually work?
20. Name two basic reasons for cooling system overheating.

SECTION IV

Working
Tools
of
Diagnosis
and
Tune-Up

CHAPTER ELEVEN

Electrical Test Instruments

Every serviceman knows that the modern automotive power plant is a complicated machine. However, this statement is a good starting point for a consideration of the many and varied instruments and accessories used in testing various power plant components.

Instrument Actuating Factors

The engine, its auxiliaries and accessories are subject to many types of trouble. Diagnosing problems and checking adjustments require the measurement of a number of electrical, physical and mechanical factors. These factors are:

Electrical current flow in amperes.
Electrical pressures in volts.
Electrical resistances in ohms.
Electrical capacities in microfarads.
Electrical impulses or intermittent currents.
Gaseous pressures, positive or negative (vacuum).
Exhaust gas composition.
Liquid volumes.
Liquid pressures.
Speeds.
Specific gravities of liquids.
Temperatures.
Spring tensions.
Precision dimensions.
Engine timing.

Only three of these factors can be measured, even approximately, by any of our human faculties — speed, temperatures, and spring tension. Fortunately, a variety of finely built, accurate, and convenient instruments are available. These are sensitive to various factors, such as electrical volume and pressure, electrical impulses, distances, capacities, and physical pressure, speed and temperature. With these instruments — the "working tools" of diagnosis and tune-up — measurements can be taken that will give information as to the actual performance of the power plant and its

Fig. 11.1. The modern testing department where diagnosis and tune-up are done will be well equipped with the working tools necessary for scientifically determining what the car needs.

components. Thus their functioning can be compared to established specifications. When properly applied, these instruments will point out deficiencies or deteriorations that need to be corrected to restore engine performance. A typical testing department is shown in Fig. 11.1.

The user of these instruments must be familiar with their working principles and applications. Each instrument gives some kind of an indication, usually by a needle moving across a scale. Except for those instruments which are pressure actuated, almost all testing devices utilize the d'Arsonval meter movement. The actuating electric current may be modified by resistors, shunts, condensers, chokes, coils, transformers, and special circuits so that the proper information will be given on the calibrated scale. However, most electrically actuated instruments depend upon the magnetizing effect of an electric current for their operation. For example, the ohmmeter, voltmeter, ammeter, condenser tester, coil tester, dwell meter, electric tachometer, and combustion analyzer, all use the d'Arsonval galvanometer movement.

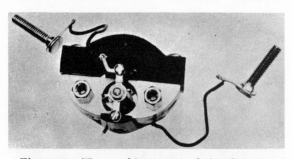

Fig. 11.2. The working parts of the d'Arsonval meter movement. The dark upper part is the Alnico magnet. This is a back view of the instrument showing the pole shoes and rear armature support.

Fig. 11.3. The armature coil, pivots, hair springs and pointer of the d'Arsonval meter movement.

d'Arsonval Meter Movement

The d'Arsonval meter movement is literally built like a watch and will operate on almost inconceivably small currents, which is one reason for its adaptability and versatility. It consists of a powerful magnet to which two pole shoes and an armature are attached. Centered accurately between the two pole shoes is a soft iron cylinder whose diameter is about 1/16" less than the space between the pole shoes. The armature consists of an aluminum frame 1/2" long, and 7/16" high and about 1/8" wide; it has tiny external flanges running around the edge, carrying from 40 to 200 or more turns of enameled copper wire nearly as fine as a human hair. The armature coil is free to rotate through an angle up to about 90 degrees.

Cemented to each end of the coil is a pivot support and a tiny hardened steel pivot. Attached to each pivot support is a fine hair spring. These two hair springs of spring bronze perform the double duty of (1) conducting the electric current to and from the coil and (2) returning the armature to its zero position. The pivot which supports the armature rides on jewelled bearings to reduce friction to a minimum. One end of the armature carries the indicating pointer which sweeps across the instrument scale when actuated by movement of the armature. The extent of this movement is determined by the relative magnitude of the current flowing through the coil. Refer to Fig. 11.2. The armature is shown in Fig. 11.3.

The strength of the magnet, the size of the copper wire and the number of turns of wire must be designed for the specific instrument application.

When an electric current is passed through the armature coil, the same forces are involved that make the starting motor operate, though on a much smaller scale. The current flowing in the coil makes it rotate in the powerful field of the permanent magnet. Since the magnetic strength of the armature is determined by the current, the movement of the armature will be large or small in relation to the strength of the current.

The instrument scale is calibrated in various units, such as amperes, volts, ohms, microhms, speeds in rpm and dwell angle. A disassembled movement is shown in Fig. 11.4, and an assembled unit in Fig. 11.5.

Instrument Applications

The application of these basic electrical instruments, either singly or in various combinations, enables the diagnostician and tune-up expert to locate hard-to-find troubles. After corrective work has been done, it provides a means of checking the performance of the engine and its auxiliaries against factory specifications.

The instruments available are made (1) for a single purpose in separate cases (2) with two or three instruments in one case (3) with one instrument so connected and modified that it can indicate several different items (4) as groups of instruments assembled together to give a number of related indications.

Individual Instruments

The following list covers most of the individual electrical instruments:

Voltmeter.

Ammeter.

Carbon-pile rheostat.

Ohmmeter.

Tachometer (speed indicator).

Dwell meter (cam angle meter).

Coil tester.

Condenser tester.

Combustion analyzer.

Armature tester (growler).

Power timing light.

Circuit tester (test light).

Oscilloscope.

Solenoid starter switch.

Electronic distributor tester.

Diode tester.

Each of these individual instruments will be briefly described in this chapter so that

its general operation and application will be better understood. Many experienced mechanics are a little afraid of diagnosis and tune-up instruments, mainly because they do not know what the instruments are supposed to do or how they do it. Electrical instruments merely respond to electrical currents or impulses. When properly connected and manipulated, the instrument indications can be interpreted in terms of power plant condition and state of adjustment. The connections and instrument controls

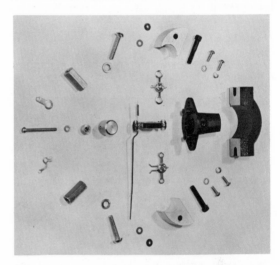

Fig. 11.4. Disassembled d'Arsonval meter movement showing the many parts that make up this valuable movement, which is the indicating unit on many test instruments. Designs of different makers will vary, but the operating principle is the same.

Fig. 11.5 Assembled movement of d'Arsonval meter movement removed from the case. Various housing designs are used for this instrument and for the other appliances used in connection with it.

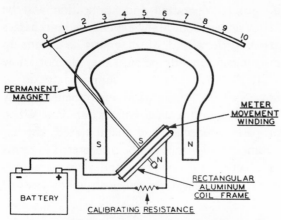

Fig. 11.6. Schematic diagram of voltmeter. The direction of current flow is such that the winding moves the pointer in proportion to voltage impressed on the coil.

Fig. 11.7. Allen volts-amperes meter, with fixed resistors which can be used for testing voltage regulator. The voltage range is 0-10, 0-20, 0-50, and the current range is 0-100, 0-200 amperes.

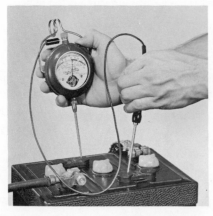

Fig. 11.8. Open-circuit voltage tester for testing the unloaded voltage of individual battery cells. It reads to .01 volt, and when used correctly will give a close indication of battery state of charge. It is essentially a voltmeter.

are not mystical, and a knowledge of power plant functions makes the interpretation of the readings easy to master.

Voltmeter

The *voltmeter*, as the name implies, is used for measuring voltage (electrical pressure), voltage drop, or voltage difference. For automotive use the instrument indicates (1) voltage drop in a circuit or the voltage drop of a single storage battery cell (which will be between 0 and 3 volts), or (2) battery or generator voltage (which will vary between 0-8, 0-15, or 0-28). Two or more scales are frequently found on one voltmeter, and these can be used as desired by turning the selector switch or pushing the correct button. The so-called "Open Circuit Voltage Tester" is a sensitive voltmeter used for testing battery cells when unconnected to electrical loads or charging means, and will read to 0.01 volt.

Essentially, the voltmeter consists of the d'Arsonval movement, plus a resistance in series with the wire leading to the armature. The size of this resistance is such that the total resistance of the instrument will usually be 100 ohms per volt. In especially sensitive instruments, the resistance may be as high or higher than 1000 ohms per volt.

The *voltmeter is always connected in parallel* with an electrical circuit. Because of its high internal resistance, only a small current flows through it. However, this small current will always be proportional to the voltage difference between the two points at which contact is made for checking the voltage. A schematic diagram is shown in Fig. 11.6.

Some voltmeters will indicate more than one range, such as 0 to 3 volts and 0 to 8, 0 to 18, or also 0 to 32 volts. These instruments connect resistances in series internally at various points to give the required resistance for the ranges desired. A multi-range voltmeter will have several scales on the face of the instrument, each one indicated or marked so that the voltage can be read directly. The range is selected by a switch on the front of the instrument. A combination volt-ammeter is shown in Fig. 11.7. An open circuit voltage tester is shown in Fig. 11.8.

Voltmeters, to be dependable, should have a fairly high standard of accuracy. Commercial instruments used for automotive work are guaranteed accurate within 2% of the full-scale reading.

Remember that the voltmeter is always connected *in parallel* with the unit circuit or portion of a circuit across which the voltage drop is to be measured. A voltmeter only allows an extremely small current to flow through it. Its reading will always indicate the voltage difference between the two points touched by the terminals of the meter leads.

Ammeter

The *ammeter* for automotive service work uses a d'Arsonval movement with a somewhat larger wire and fewer turns on the armature than a voltmeter. Commonly, the ammeter armature is in series with a resistor, so that in effect it is a millivoltmeter, which requires .050 volt (50 millivolts) for full-scale deflection of the pointer. The schematic diagram is shown in Fig. 11.9.

An important part of the ammeter is the shunt, which is calibrated to carry a specified current in amperes. The ends of the shunt are connected by electrical conductors to the meter movement, so that actually the armature reacts to the voltage drop across the shunt. However, the voltage drop will be proportional to the current flowing, in accordance with Ohm's law $E = IR$ (where E is voltage, I is amperes, and R is resistance in ohms). Therefore in any given circuit where the resistance is constant, the voltage will vary in proportion to the current. While voltage drop is actually measured, the scale of the instrument can be calibrated in amperes.

To illustrate this, suppose 10 amperes were passed through a shunt which has a resistance of exactly 1 ohm. A voltmeter connected across the shunt would indicate 10 volts. If 5 amperes were passed through the shunt, 5 volts would be indicated. Because of this relationship the meter scale can be calibrated in amperes instead of volts, and the number of amperes passed through the shunt will be indicated directly in amperes by the instrument. A combination volts-amperes tester is shown in Fig. 11.10.

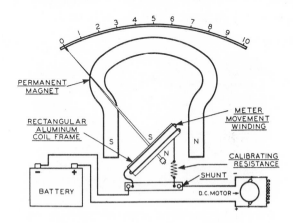

Fig. 11.9. Schematic diagram of ammeter movement. The d'Arsonval meter movement is very similar to the one used in the voltmeter. Notice that the meter leads are connected to each end of a shunt through which flows the current to be measured.

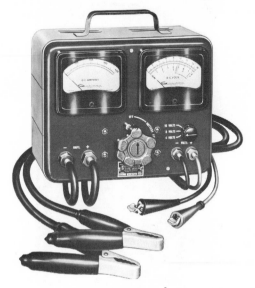

Fig. 11.10. Sun battery-starter tester (also volts-amperes tester) is very useful for testing batteries and starting loads. The ammeter has a capacity of 400 amperes. A carbon rheostat is included.

Actually the millivoltmeter used in ammeters is connected with a shunt having very low resistance. If a millivoltmeter has a calibration of 0 to 50 millivolts (.050 volt) a 50-ampere shunt to be used with it would have a resistance of .0010 ohm. The millivoltmeter scale will be marked 0 to 50 amperes, and it will indicate (in amperes) the current flowing through the shunt. The instrument capacity will be 50 amperes, though a current of twice this amount for a very short time will do no harm.

Fig. 11.11. Inside arrangement of Sun volts-amperes tester, showing the resistor, shunt, and switches. Much research, testing, skillful design and precision manufacturing are required to turn out accurate yet durable instruments such as this.

The current which a shunt must carry determines its size, because it is evident that enough metal must be supplied to prevent the shunt from becoming overheated. At the same time, its resistance must be high enough to allow a suitable amount of current to flow through the parallel circuit of the millivoltmeter so that it will give the desired indication. The inside of a volts-amperes tester is shown in Fig. 11.11.

Although the temperature of the shunt may be raised by the current, the resistance of the shunt must not increase appreciably with temperature change in order that the indications will be correct over a wide range of temperatures. To accomplish this, special metal alloys are used for shunts. One commonly used is called Manganin. A handy combination volts-amperes tester is shown in Fig. 11.12.

When small currents are to be measured, such as those which will flow in the field circuit of a generator, correspondingly small shunts are used. Thus, the multi-range ammeter will have scales of 0 to 6 amperes, 0 to 10 amperes, etc.

When very heavy currents are to be measured, it may not be practical to construct an

Fig. 11.12. Combination volts-amperes tester.

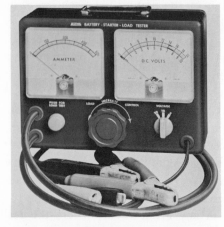

Fig. 11.13. King battery-starter load tester. This type of instrument is needed for testing batteries and starters. To check capacity, load the battery with three times (in amperes) its ampere-hour rating. In 15 seconds, the voltage should not drop below five on a 6-volt battery, or ten on a 12-volt. On this instrument the ammeter reads to 500 amperes and the voltmeter 0-2, 0-10, 0-20 volts.

instrument with a self-contained shunt because the instrument would be too bulky and unwieldy. It is more convenient in some cases to construct the shunt separately, providing it with suitable terminals for connection in a circuit and separate terminals for millivolt meter connections. However some battery-starter testers have a capacity up to 600 amperes, and the shunts are built into the instrument. Also included in the case is a carbon pile variable resistor so that it can be used as a variable loading device to put the desired load on the battery. Another make of battery-starter tester is shown in Fig. 11.13.

The *ammeter is always connected in series* with the circuit in which the current is to be measured. Within the ammeter, most of the current goes through the shunt; only a very small parallel current goes through the millivolt meter to give the indication. Remember, whenever an ammeter is used the circuit must be broken and the ammeter inserted into the circuit so that it is in series. The point at which the circuit is broken is not important, since the same amount of current flows through the entire circuit.

To check the accuracy of ammeter indications it is only necessary to put the ammeter in series with another ammeter known to be accurate or with a standard test instrument. With the two instruments in series, the current flowing through one also flows through the other and the indications should be the same. If they are different the shop instrument is probably in error as the standard instrument should be correct.

Battery Post Adapter

The *battery post adapter*, supplied by Sun Electric Corporation, is designed to make it easy and convenient to connect an ammeter in series with the insulated battery terminal. Refer to Fig. 11.14. The insulated battery cable (positive on all American cars since 1956) is loosened and disconnected from the battery. The adapter is slipped into place on the battery

post *C*, and the battery cable is then slipped into place on the tapered post of the adapter *P*. The two leads of an ammeter are connected to the binding post with the knurled nut *A* and to the straight post above the battery post *B*. See Fig. 11.15. Switch *D* is closed to start the engine; after it is running, the switch is opened putting the ammeter in series with the battery. This makes it convenient to start the engine with the battery, but still allows use of the ammeter by merely opening the switch.

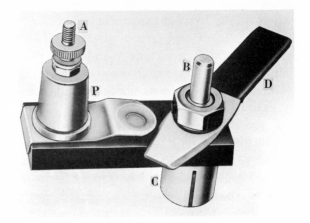

Fig. 11.14. Battery post adapter, useful for connecting an ammeter into the charging circuit. When the switch is closed, the ammeter is bypassed. The ammeter is connected to terminals *A* and *B*.

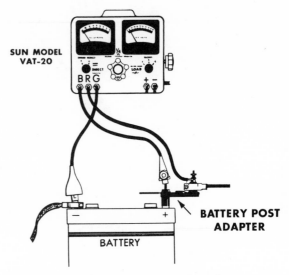

Fig. 11.15. Ammeter connected to battery post adapter.

Carbon Pile Resistor or Rheostat

The carbon pile resistor or rheostat consists of a group (or pile) of carbon plates. When these plates are in loose contact with one another, the resistance to electric current is high. As the plates are pressed more tightly together, the resistance decreases in proportion; when they are in complete contact, the resistance for this unit is at a minimum.

Carbon pile resistors are incorporated in some volt-ampere testers and in some battery-starter testers. Turning a hand screw or hand-wheel on the front of the instrument will vary the pressure of the carbon plates, which in turn will vary the resistance of the carbon pile. This makes a very convenient way of getting variable resistances to accomplish certain diagnosis or tune-up measurements.

Ohmmeter

The *ohmmeter* is designed to indicate directly the resistance of a circuit or part of a circuit, unit or appliance which is connected to the instrument. Ohm's Law, as previously considered, ($R=E/I$, where $R=$ ohms, $E=$ volts,

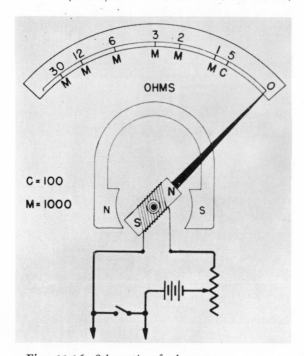

Fig. 11.16. Schematic of ohmmeter.

and $I=$ amperes) shows that if E is kept constant, the resistance will be inversely proportional to the current. That is, as the resistance in ohms increases, the current in amperes will decrease. Therefore, with a d'Arsonval meter movement properly connected inside the ohmmeter, with a constant voltage supplied by a battery within the instrument case, and with a scale calibrated in ohms, the meter dial can be calibrated directly in ohms.

One well-known coil tester has ohmmeter circuits built into it and will measure from 0 to 100,000 ohms, with accurate readings from about 500 to 10,000 ohms. The condenser tester manufactured by the same company also has ohmmeter circuits built into it which will measure in two ranges, from 0 to 1000 ohms and from 0 to 10 megohms. (A megohm is one million ohms.) Accurate readings can be made on this instrument from about 50,000 ohms to two megohms.

There are numerous valuable and helpful measurements of resistance other than those in connection with coils or condensers. Since the ohmmeter is not nearly as familiar to the average shop man or student as it should be, the information given here should be studied carefully.

Resistance describes the difficulty which an electrical conductor presents to the flow of current. Resistance may be due to the material composing the current path or to local spots of high resistance, such as loose or dirty connections or poor conducting materials interposed in the current path.

The basic internal ohmmeter circuit is simple, as shown in Fig. 11.16. It consists of the d'Arsonval meter movement, a calibrated resistance *R-1*, a variable resistance to adjust the battery voltage, a self-contained battery, two instrument leads and the instrument housing. The leads may be fitted either with spring clips or metal prods.

Before using the instrument, it is necessary to standardize the battery voltage. To do this, join the two leads together so that there is zero resistance outside of the instrument and *R-1* is the only resistance in the circuit. Then adjust the variable resistance to bring the indicating pointer to zero on the scale.

On some ohmmeters there are two or more resistances inside the instrument which will permit the use of different resistance ranges such as 0 to 1000, 0 to 100,000, or 0 to 10 megohms. The knob on the front of the case is turned to select the desired range.

The self-contained battery differentiates the ohmmeter from all other electrical measuring instruments; this instrument does not need an outside current source. In fact there should be no current whatever flowing in a circuit or unit being measured with the ohmmeter except that provided by the instrument battery, or the instrument might be damaged. Once the meter is calibrated, it is only necessary to make contact with the leads to the circuit, part or unit being checked, and then to read the indication on the dial.

Among the items that can be tested for continuity and level of resistance with the ohmmeter are light bulbs, sealed-beam head lamps, fuses, coils of different kinds, turn signal flashers, high-tension conductors and stop light switches. The ohmmeter can also be used to test resistor spark plugs, resistors, ignition coil secondary windings, and ignition ballast resistors.

Tachometer

The *tachometer* is a speed indicating instrument. It is used on the motor analyzer, the generator tester, and the distributor scope. It is also available as a separate instrument or in combination with the dwell-angle meter or cam-angle meter. The back view of a dwell-tachometer is shown in Fig. 11.17.

The tachometer operates on electric impulses picked up from the lead which runs from the coil to the distributor, or the distributor side of the coil. Each time the breaker points open there is a surge of voltage due to the interruption of the ignition current. By connecting the instrument in parallel with the breaker points, that voltage is conducted to the instrument circuits and flows through them to ground through the instrument ground lead.

The current picked up from the distributor operates a vibrating relay within the instrument which charges and discharges a condenser. The faster the engine goes the more frequently the condenser will be charged and discharged; thus the amount of current which flows through the inner circuits of the instrument will be proportionate to engine speed. When a millivolt meter is connected to the proper points of

Fig. 11.17. Back of Sun dwell-tach meter, showing the condensers, inductors and resistors. This instrument is used to modify the electric impulses picked up from the distributor.

Fig. 11.18. Hanson dwell angle-tachometer tester. This type uses a single meter movement to register either dwell or engine speed. One lead is connected to the distributor contact or the distributor side of the coil, and the other to ground. Observe the correct polarity.

this circuit, the current flowing through the instrument will move the pointer across the scale. With the scale properly calibrated in rpm, the desired speed indication can be obtained.

The natural damping effect of the meter armature will keep the needle from vibrating under the current impulses so that it will give a steady indication. A switch on the instrument is turned to the 4-lobe, 6-lobe, or 8-lobe position, depending upon the number of cylinders on the engine. A tachometer-dwell meter is shown in Fig. 11.18.

Dwell Meter (Cam Angle Meter)

The *dwell angle meter*, or the *cam angle meter* as it is sometimes called, indicates the angle through which the distributor shaft turns while the breaker points are closed. The angle from cam point to cam point is 60° for a six-cylinder engine and 45° for an eight-cylinder engine. This dwell angle is always less than these angles because it is necessary that the points break the ignition primary circuit in order to produce the high-tension ignition sparks. The dwell angle for a six-cylinder car will usually be between 34° to 38° and for an eight-cylinder car from 26° to 32°.

As is the case with the tachometer, the dwell angle meter is connected to the distributor or distributor side of the coil, and is actuated by impulses in the primary ignition circuit. However, the internal wiring and electrical devices are different and are differently arranged. The dwell meter shows the proportion of time that current is flowing — from zero indication with no current flowing to 100% of the time when there is no break in the current. The instrument scale is calibrated from 0° to 50°, covering the dwell angle for all engines from 4 cylinders to 12 cylinders. Another make dwell-tachometer is shown in Fig. 11.19.

In effect, the instrument measures the duration of the electrical impulses coming through the instrument from the distributor. This is shown on the scale as the actual degrees of dwell or the angle through which the distributor shaft turns while the points are closed.

Some dwell meters can be used to test continuity in addition to indicating dwell. This makes them convenient for testing such units as fuses, light bulbs, and stop light switches. A different design of dwell tachometers is shown in Fig. 11.20. The oscilloscope can also be used to check the angle of dwell.

Coil Tester

Most of the coil testers now offered for automotive service use are combined with a condenser tester. However, since the tests to check an ignition coil are somewhat different from the tests to check condenser condition, these instruments will be treated separately.

The purpose of a *coil tester* is to determine whether or not an ignition coil is in satisfactory condition. There are two general types of coil testers: (1) an instrument with built-in ohmmeter that will check the resistance of the primary and secondary windings; plus a small cathode ray tube that displays the coil-condenser section of the typical oscilloscope trace of a complete spark cycle, from the isolated coil only, and (2) an instrument that measures the resistance of the primary and secondary windings and places stress upon the insulation

Fig. 11.19. Allen dwell-tach meter. In this instrument a single d'Arsonval meter movement is used, with internal arrangement such that either dwell angle or engine rpm is indicated according to position of selector switch.

to check for insulation break-down. The cathode ray tester is quite new and is much superior to the resistance tester. It does not require reference to any specifications and it gives more definite and dependable results.

Coils operate at a temperature above that of the atmosphere. In order to test the coil under conditions similar to its working conditions, it should be heated to approximately operating temperature. Most of the coil testers have a provision for electrically bringing the coil to the desired temperature within a few minutes.

Built into a coil tester are important ohmmeter circuits. In addition to testing coils and condensers, this instrument can be used to measure resistances, provided the range of the ohmmeter circuit is sufficient. A desirable range is from zero to 100,000 ohms.

Many of the coil testing instruments have the dial marked *Good* or *Bad* so that in addition to the numerical readings, the tester will indicate whether the feature being checked is satisfactory. Remember that all three tests on a coil should be *Good* before it is considered satisfactory for further use.

The wave forms on the cathode ray tester will indicate (1) normal, (2) shorted, or (3) open. Instrument manufacturers supply easy-to-follow instructions so that anyone with some automotive experience, reading them carefully, will be able to use the tester to advantage. The Sun cathode ray coil tester is shown in Fig. 11.21. This is also a condenser tester.

Condenser Tester

The *condenser tester* is designed to test the three factors that will indicate whether a condenser is in sufficiently good condition to warrant its continued use, or should be replaced. These three factors are (1) series resistance (microhm test), (2) capacity (microfarad test), and (3) insulation (megohm test).

The series resistance test (microhm test) tells whether there is good conductivity through the condenser for alternating current. In an AC circuit, a condenser acts like a conductor (except for its capacitance effect, which can be ignored in automotive work). This will show up any high resistance points, broken

Fig. 11.20. Combined dwell meter and tachometer has a different scale for four-, six-, and eight-cylinder engines. This simplifies the internal circuitry. The bottom figures on each scale are dwell in degrees, while the top figures are speeds in rpm.

Fig. 11.21. The Sun coil tester which makes use of a cathode-ray tube and displays the "coil-condenser" portion of the usual oscilloscope trace. From this indication the condition of the coil may be determined. This combination instrument is also a condenser tester. In addition, the upper unit may be used as an ohmmeter from zero to 100,000 ohms.

wires, bad connections, or poor contacts. Since a microhm is one-millionth ohm, any addition to the usual resistance will be readily indicated.

The test for capacity indicates whether or not the condenser being tested has the correct capacity, or in other words, is the right size.

Fig. 11.22. A handy condenser tester which may also be used to make measurements of resistance as an ohmmeter. It may be used separately or as a panel instrument.

Fig. 11.23. Sun electronic distributor tester, connected with No. 1 spark plug. It is equipped with a power timing light, and may be used for initial advance timing as well as to measure total and automatic advance at different speeds.

Condenser capacity is measured in microfarads.

The insulation test (megohm test) indicates whether the insulation between the two sides of the condenser is of sufficient dielectric strength (resistance to electrical current flow) to safely withstand the highest voltage that may be impressed on it. During testing, the insulation is subjected to an emf of 500 volts, whereas in actual service the voltage seldom exceeds 250 volts.

The condenser tester also uses the d'Arsonval meter movement to give the indication. The circuits for the various tests are selected by turning a selector switch to megohm, microfarad, microhm or ohm. The circuits are modified by resistors, vibrators, and step-up coils, so that the meter will give the indication in suitable units of measurement.

In addition to the condenser tests, other checks may be made with this valuable instrument. Resistance tests from 1 ohm to 10 megohms are easily made on such items as gas gauges, relays, resistance units and suppressors. An instrument of this kind is shown in Fig. 11.22.

Electronic Distributor Tester

This instrument measures the operation of the distributor advance mechanism at any reasonable engine speed, without removing the distributor from the engine. It also provides a quick and convenient means of testing or adjusting initial ignition timing.

The electronic distributor tester consists of: (1) a timing light which can be used in the same way the conventional timing light is used, and (2) a meter which measures the spark advance (from the initial timing advance as the engine is speeded up) due to the automatic and vacuum spark advance incorporated in the ignition system. The meter movement is the d'Arsonval galvanometer. Fig. 11.23 shows one design of electronic distributor tester.

Initial ignition timing is a mechanical adjustment establishing the exact point in the engine cycle at which the plug will fire in each cylinder at the specified engine speed. Timing is established and specified by the engine manufacturer for the exact point in the engine cycle at which the fuel charge should be ignited. The strobe-light flash of the electronic distributor tester is simultaneous with the firing of No. 1 spark plug. When timing is properly set, the specified mark on the vibration damper or flywheel will appear to be aligned with the pointer when the strobe-light flash occurs. This test is performed at the specified timing speed, which is usually normal idle speed. A different design of tester is shown in Fig. 11.24. The timing light, which is plugged in, is not shown.

Correct timing under all speed and load conditions is extremely important to performance and economy. As engine speed is increased, the distributor advance mechanism causes each spark plug to fire earlier in the engine cycle. As a result, the timing mark moves away from the pointer as viewed with the stroboscopic timing light. With the electronic distributor tester, at a specified test speed the timing mark can be electrically realigned with the timing pointer by turning a knob on the face of the instrument. When the timing mark is once more aligned with the pointer, the meter will indicate the number of degrees the spark plugs are firing ahead of the initial timing.

The meter will indicate the total net advance of both the automatic and vacuum advances, which should be checked with the manufacturer's specifications. To get the mechanical advance, disconnect the vacuum line from the distributor and recheck. The difference from the combined reading will be the vacuum advance. To get the initial timing, in most cases it is necessary to disconnect the vacuum line from the distributor to eliminate any vacuum advance as the timing is being checked. The automatic advance does not cause any advance at idle speed. Fig. 11.25 shows another type of electronic distributor tester with its timing light.

Section 6, "The Ignition System," gives a detailed discussion of this important system. The

distributor tester used for testing the adjustment of a distributor when off the engine will be discussed in the next chapter.

Rectifier Diode Tester

One of the newest of the test instruments is the *diode tester* which is used to test the diodes and rectifiers used in automotive charging systems that have an alternator. This tester checks

Fig. 11.24. Allen ignition advance meter, which is the same as the electronic distributor tester. The high-tension pick-up and the timing light are not shown in this picture, but they are plugged into the appropriate sockets when the instrument is to be used.

Fig. 11.25. Marquette (Heyer) spark advance tester, which is similar to the ones shown in Figs. 11.23 and 11.24. The timing light is shown but connections are required to an AC source, to ground, and to a No. 1 spark plug.

the diodes for *shorts*, *opens*, or *good*. An outstanding advantage of this type of tester is its ability to check complete sets of diodes, (usually three positive and three negative) without having to isolate them individually. To

Fig. 11.26. Alternator diode tester furnished by Simpson Electric Company. The manufacturer states that diodes installed in the alternator and not isolated or disconnected can be accurately tested with this instrument. It can also be used to test zener diodes and power transistors. It must be connected to an AC source at 120 volts.

Fig. 11.27. Rectifier diode tester from Sun Electric Corporation. It works in the same manner as the one shown in Fig. 11.26, and is a handy, durable instrument.

isolate the diodes it is necessary to break the connection to the center electrode or antenna.

The instrument operates on 120 volts AC and has a power lead connected to a power supply, and two test leads. One test lead is black and fitted with a spring clip, and the other is red with a prod on the end. The black lead is negative and the red lead is positive in polarity. The polarity of the circuit in which a diode is used is determined by the color of the test lead touching the case or heat sink at the time the pointer on the instrument moves in a positive direction. The polarity of a diode is determined by its case, not its antenna. Fig. 11.26 illustrates a alternator diode tester.

The instrument is of value to detect diodes which are defective or damaged, as well as to check their polarity, as diodes with negative polarity are used in the ground circuit. To use the instrument it is only necessary to touch one of the leads to the antenna and the other to the heat sink if the diodes are in place in the heat sink. If the diodes are not installed, touch the other lead to the diode case.

When testing diodes, a reading of two amperes (or a little more) indicates that the diode is satisfactory. However, a reading of zero amperes indicates a shorted diode, and one ampere or less means that the diode is open circuited. In either case the diode must be replaced.

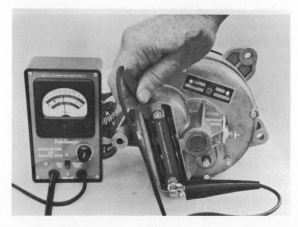

Fig. 11.28. Testing with a rectifier diode tester.

The diode tester, in common with the other meters discussed, makes use of the d'Arsonval meter movement, along with other circuitry. Another make of tester is shown in Figs. 11.27 and 11.28.

Diodes and their application in the alternator circuit will be discussed in greater detail in Chapter 18.

Combustion Analyzer

The *combustion analyzer* is designed to take a continuous sample of exhaust gases from the tail pipe and indicate on a dial the percentage of combustion efficiency and also the fuel-air ratio of the explosive mixture supplied by the carburetor.

The essential parts of the tester are: a gas pick-up unit which is inserted in the tail pipe and connected to the instrument by a rubber tube, or a wire; a motor-driven fan which draws in the gas sample; (on some instruments) a 1-millivolt d'Arsonval meter movement and the internal electric circuits.

The principle of operation is based on the fact that carbon dioxide (CO_2), which is an important component of engine exhaust gas, is heavier and has more heat-carrying ability than air. Incorporated in the internal circuit of the combustion analyzer is a *Wheatstone Bridge*. This consists of four resistors arranged diagramatically in diamond form, as shown in Fig. 11.29. A meter movement is connected as shown so that any inequalities in the four resistances will cause a current to flow through the meter. Two of the resistances have constant values; the third one is a platinum wire of a precise length, in a tube through which *air* is drawn; and the fourth is a corresponding platinum wire in a tube through which the *exhaust gas sample* is drawn. The platinum wires are heated somewhat by the current flow.

Platinum has the characteristic of changing its electrical resistance as its temperature changes. As the samples of air and exhaust gas are drawn through their respective tubes, the platinum wires will change resistance in proportion

to the heat-carrying ability of air and carbon dioxide, as the gases exert their respective cooling effects on the heated resistors. A difference in the two resistances will cause current

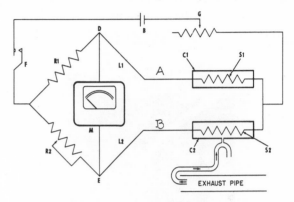

Fig. 11.29. Wheatstone bridge wiring diagram. This is the basis of the combustion analyzer or combustion tester. Resistance *R2* is adjustable to get the instrument in balance. When the current flowing through the *A* side and through the *B* side is the same, there will be no current flowing through the meter movement. The resistance *S1* is in contact with air, while resistance *S2* is in contact with the exhaust gas being tested. The difference in resistance between *S1* and *S2* will be proportional to combustion efficiency and will be indicated by current flowing through *M*.

Fig. 11.30. The Sun combustion analyzer or combustion tester makes use of a small motor-driven fan inside the instrument case to draw the gas sample through the instrument. The gas pick-up at the tail-pipe is connected to the tester by a hose. The fan insures a representative sample of gas. The indication is given in *air-fuel ratio* and *percent efficiency*.

to flow through the meter. By carefully calibrating the scale of the meter it can be made to indicate the "Percent of Combustion Efficiency" and also the "Air-Fuel Ratio" of the explosive mixture supplied to the engine by the carburetor. The scale has divisions from 60% to 100% combustion efficiency, and from 10.5:1,

to 15:1 air-fuel ratio. The 100% end of the scale is marked "Lean" and the other end "Rich." Figs. 11.30 and 11.31 show the Sun combustion tester.

As the engine is operated through different speed ranges, the combustion analyzer will respond to the different fuel mixtures supplied for idle, for high speed, and for conditions requiring use of the accelerator pump. This is true because the different conditions require variations in the air-fuel proportions, which in turn will result in different proportions of CO_2. As we have seen, varying proportions of this heavier gas will exert varying degrees of cooling effect, in turn affecting the indications of the instrument. Figs. 11.32 and 11.33 show the Marquette (Heyer) instrument. Fig. 11.34 shows the exhaust gas analyzer supplied by Snap-on Tools Corporation.

Armature Growler

The armature growler consists of a 110-volt AC magnet-winding around a laminated core with a "V" on top large enough to hold generator and starting motor armatures. In addition there is usually a test circuit equipped with a light; test-prods are so arranged that light will be produced when the prods touch metal or conductors that will carry current from one prod to the other. Some models also have an ammeter to measure the current which is induced in the armature coils when adjacent segments of the commutator are connected by contacts in series with the ammeter circuit.

Fig. 11.31. The gas pick-up used with the Sun combustion tester. A built-in condenser removes the water vapor.

Fig. 11.32. The Marquette gas analyzer makes use of an electric pick-up with the gas-cooled leg of the Wheatstone bridge at the tailpipe. The gas pick-up is connected with the instrument by a wire.

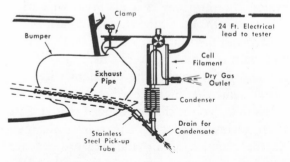

Fig. 11.33. The electric gas pick-up used by the combustion analyzer.

This instrument has the name *Growler* because a deep hum can be heard when an armature is placed in the V-groove. This is caused by the alternating current field in which the armature is resting.

The growler is used to test a generator or starting motor armature for shorts. When an armature is placed in the powerful alternating current magnetic field, a current will be induced in any shorted commutator coil due to the fluctuating magnetic field. To locate such a shorted coil, rotate the armature slowly in the growler V-groove while holding a hack saw blade or other thin piece of steel parallel to the armature. As shorted coils pass under the hack saw blade or strip of steel, it will be attracted to the armature and will vibrate. Refer to Fig. 11.35.

The testing circuit can be used with the test prods to check for grounds, open circuits, grounded brushes, and grounded or open field coils.

Power Timing Light

The power timing light is used to check the ignition timing by causing a bright flash of light to occur simultaneously with the surge of high-tension current (spark) in No. 1 cylinder. This flash is directed against the timing mark on the dynamic balancer or through a window in the flywheel housing which exposes timing marks on the flywheel.

When the intermittent flash is synchronized with the rotation of the timing mark, it gives the impression that the timing mark is standing still because the eye retains the image until the next flash occurs. This *stroboscopic action* also enables the operator to check the shifting position of the timing mark when the engine is speeded up and the automatic advance is actuated.

The power timing light has: a transformer; a vibrator; 2,600-volt discharge condensers; a 50,000 ohm filter-resistor and the gas-filled light tube. The electrical parts and circuit are so arranged that a high-voltage electrical charge is accumulated in the condenser which is "triggered" each time a sparking current is sent to No. 1 spark plug. This causes a brilliant white flash to occur each time No. 1 plug fires. When properly directed, the flash will illuminate the timing mark, and by stroboscopic action it will seem to stand still.

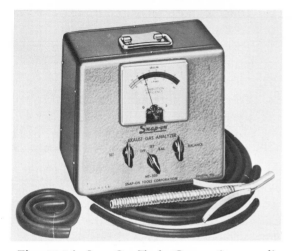

Fig. 11.34. Snap-On Tools Corporation supplies the exhaust gas analyzer shown here. It picks up the gas sample at the tail pipe and conducts it to the instrument through a rubber tube.

Fig. 11.35. Typical growler used for testing armatures. An AC ammeter is included for checking individual coil capacity. When the growler is in use, the armature is slowly rotated in the magnetic jaws by the operator and a steel strip is held against it. Any shorted coils will attract the strip and cause it to vibrate. Test prods are supplied for testing opens and grounds.

The timing light is connected by two wires to the battery circuit (the red wire to the positive side and the black wire to negative). A third, more heavily insulated wire goes to No. 1 spark plug. This device does not short out No. 1 spark plug and will have no effect on engine operation.

The timing light, as made by several manufacturers, has a handle and a barrel made of plastic, neoprene or rubber. The current timing lights are so designed that they can be used with either 6-volt or 12-volt batteries, adjusting automatically to the supplied voltage.

A timing light which uses no battery current and which is connected in parallel with No. 1 spark plug, is used in some shops. Its neon tube gives a red flash which is not as bright as the flash from the power timing light and limits its usefulness in brightly lighted places.

Power timing lights which are powered by 120-volt AC are also available. Their use eliminates the need for connection to a battery,

Fig. 11.36. This circuit tester is a simple, but very useful, device for picking out "hot" terminals and for testing fuses and windings for continuity and grounds.

Fig. 11.37. Another version of the circuit tester which can also be used as a trouble light by clamping one end on a live terminal and the other on a good ground.

but at the same time limits their application to locations where house current is available.

Circuit Tester (Test Light)

The *test light*, illustrated in Fig. 11.36, consists of a spring clamp, a length of primary wire, a lamp socket with a test prod attached and a 3 candle-power, single-contact taillight bulb. This very simple device is quite useful in locating electrical troubles and making simple electrical continuity tests. Fig. 11.37 shows another convenient form of test light.

Among the practical uses of the test light are:

1. To test fuses, both cartridge type and 110-volt screw type as used in chargers for battery service.
2. To test condensers for internal shorts.
3. To test coils for continuity of flow in the low-tension circuit.
4. To test for current at the coil and at the distributor.
5. To test opening and closing of distributor breaker points (ignition current on).
6. To test horn or starter relays.
7. To test all lamps for proper ground.
8. To pick out "hot" terminals under the dash for making connections for such accessories as heaters, additional lamps, and defrosting fans.
9. To locate breaks in wires.
10. To test for live or dead circuits.
11. To test filaments for breaks on sealed-beam lights.
12. To test circuits.
13. To pick out *B* terminal on unmarked voltage regulators.

To locate a break in a wire where one end of the wire is shown to be alive and the other end dead, one side of the tester shoud be grounded by clamping the spring clip to an oil pipe, cylinder head stud, or other grounded points. Then use a scratch awl to pierce the insulation at different points, checking the continuity at each point by testing the scratch awl with the test prod to see if there is current. Presence of current will be indicated by a light.

Oscilloscope

This valuable instrument is treated in detail in Chapter 13.

Solenoid Starter Switch

The *solenoid starter switch* is the last of the "working tools" to be discussed in this chapter. It is a push-button switch with two leads fitted with spring clips. To use the switch on the solenoid-equipped Bendix starter, clip one lead to the binding post to which the wire from the dash starting switch is connected. Clip the other lead to the terminal to which power is carried through the Bendix solenoid. The starter motor can then be energized to turn the engine over with either the dash starting device or the push-button. Refer to Fig. 11.38.

This switch is quite a convenience for making the cylinder leakage test and for many other operations in connection with engine service, diagnosis and tune-up.

Summary

Most of the important *electrical instruments used for automotive analysis* and correction, and the basic principles on which they operate, have been covered in this chapter. Understanding these principles and the basic designs of the various tune-up and test instruments should help the diagnostician to use them more effectively.

Most of the electrical instruments use a *d'Arsonval meter movement* to actuate the indicating pointer. This instrument is sensitive to very tiny electrical currents.

The *voltmeter* is used to measure electrical pressures and voltage drops in circuits due to resistance. *The voltmeter is always connected in parallel with the circuit or part of a circuit being tested.*

The *ammeter* is used to measure the amount of current which flows in a circuit. *The ammeter is always connected in series with the circuit being tested.* It can be inserted any place in the circuit as long as the current flowing in the circuit flows through the meter.

The *ohmmeter* is used to measure resistances, which may be only a few ohms or millions of ohms, depending upon the application. A characteristic of the ohmmeter is that it has a self-contained battery and must never be used on a circuit in which current is flowing or voltage is present.

The *dwell meter* or *cam angle meter* is used to measure the dwell angle, which is the angle through which the distributor shaft turns while the distributor points are closed. On systems with negative ground, it is connected with the positive instrument lead to the distributor side of the coil (or the distributor terminal) and to ground. On positive grounded systems, the lead connections are reversed.

The *tachometer* is a speed-indicating device which is very useful in making various tests at specified speeds and also for adjusting the carburetor idle speed. It is connected in the same manner as the dwell meter.

The *coil tester* is supplied in two designs: (1) a unit that uses a cathode-ray tube plus a built-in ohmmeter which will test the resistance of the primary and secondary coil windings, and (2) an instrument which measures the primary and secondary resistance and stresses the insulation to check for breakdown.

The *condenser tester* is often combined with the coil tester. It is used to test three factors which will indicate whether a condenser is usable. They are: (1) series resistance (microhm

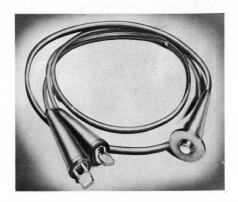

Fig. 11.38. Solenoid starter switch for turning over the engine from outside the car when making such tests as adjusting tappets or checking compression.

test), (2) capacity test (microfarad test) and (3) insulation test (megohm test).

The *electronic distributor tester* makes use of a timing light, but in addition it has the ability to adjust the "firing" of the timing light electronically. After the spark is advanced by the vacuum and automatic advances when the engine is speeded up, the electronic adjustment returns the light flash to the "idle setting" and at the same time measures and indicates the degrees of advance.

The *diode tester* is used to test the rectifying diodes used in alternators.

The *combustion analyzer* is designed to take a continuous sample of exhaust gases from the tail pipe and indicate the ratio of air and fuel in the combustible mixture sent to the engine from the carburetor. It is used to check the operation of the carburetor accelerating pump and various other carburetor circuits.

The *armature growler* is used to check whether a DC generator armature is shorted. It is usually supplied with a test light and prods for checking for opens and grounds.

The *power timing light* flashes each time No. 1 spark plug fires. This stroboscopic action seems to make the timing mark on the engine stand still so that ignition timing can be observed and adjusted as necessary.

The *circuit tester* or test light is used to check for continuity of fuses, light bulbs and other devices, and also to detect electrically alive terminals or conductors.

Questions

1. Name four electrical factors that actuate electrical test instruments.
2. What is the basic instrument movement used in many electrical test instruments?
3. Name eight commonly used electrical test instruments.
4. The voltmeter measures two characteristics of current flow in a circuit. Name them.
5. How is the voltmeter connected to measure voltage?
6. What is the main difference in construction between a voltmeter and ammeter?
7. How is an ammeter connected in a circuit?
8. Why is a carbon pile rheostat used?
9. What is the battery post adapter used for?
10. Where should the ammeter be inserted in a circuit to measure current flow?
11. What is the ohmmeter used for?
12. Is current flow required in a circuit when the ohmmeter is being used? Why?
13. What is the purpose of the tachometer?
14. What makes an electric tachometer operate?
15. What is the dwell meter used for?
16. What is meant by "dwell" or "cam angle"?
17. Name two kinds of coil testers.
18. For what three factors is a condenser tested?
19. What information does the electronic distributor tester give?
20. Can the electronic distributor tester be used to set initial spark advance?
21. For what three diode conditions does the diode tester test?
22. On what basic principle does the combustion analyzer work?
23. What information does the armature growler give?
24. What kind of action is it that makes the power timing light valuable?
25. What is the solenoid starting switch used for?

CHAPTER TWELVE

Mechanical Instruments and Instrument Combinations

Several instruments that are actuated by other than electrical means are quite important, while others are helpful tools but play relatively minor parts in the work of the diagnostician. Among the important working tools are the pressure testing instruments.

Numerous instrument combinations are available. The variations include: instruments using the same dial and pointer for two kinds of indications and tests; two instruments in the same case; a multipurpose instrument in a single case; motor analyzers which include a whole panel of instruments and, in some cases, an oscilloscope; and elaborate generator-regulator testers.

Pressure Testing Instruments

The *Bourdon-tube instrument movement,* illustrated in Fig. 12.1, is the movement used in the vacuum-pressure tester, the compression tester, the cylinder leakage tester, the fuel-pump pressure tester and most pressure and vacuum gauges.

The actuating element is a flattened tube bent into a portion of a circle. When pressure is applied to the inside of the tube it tends to straighten out. With one end anchored securely, the other moves, and by means of a linkage, operates a pointer on a dial. If vacuum is applied to the tube it tends to contract moving the free end in the opposite direction so that inches of vacuum may be indicated.

Vacuum-Pressure Gauge

The *vacuum-pressure gauge* indicates up to 24-25 inches of vacuum and low positive pressures up to 6 or 8 psi. It is supplied in many forms, some round, some square or rectangular,

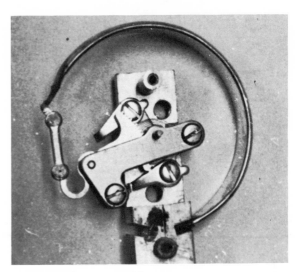

Fig. 12.1. Bourdon tube pressure gauge movement. The tube end moves upward, moving the gear sector; this in turn moves gear on pointer shaft.

and in many different sizes all using the Bourdon tube movement. One useful gauge is shown in Fig. 12.2, a panel type of instrument. It is conveniently used for measuring intake manifold vacuum, fuel pump suction, fuel pump pressure, and distributor vacuum when the distributor is mounted on the distributorscope for calibrating the vacuum advance. Many of the motor analyzers include a vacuum gauge in the instrument panel.

Compression Gauge (Compression Tester)

The *compression gauge* also makes use of the Bourdon tube movement. A common form

Fig. 12.2. Sun combined vacuum-pressure gauge for checking engine manifold vacuum, fuel pump suction, and fuel pump pressure (up to 6 lbs.).

Fig. 12.3. Sun compression gauge. This is also a Bourdon tube gauge, with a range up to 200 lbs. It is a very convenient, sturdy instrument.

is shown in Fig. 12.3. It is used for taking the cylinder compression pressure. It will measure pressures up to 200 psi or more, so that modern engine compression pressures can be checked.

The Bourdon tube is stiffer than the type used in the vacuum gauge. The gauge is fitted with a neoprene or rubber tip so it will readily make a tight connection with spark plug holes in engine cylinders. In some cases a screw fitting is provided which fits into the spark plug hole; in addition, some instruments have a heavy-duty tube which can be connected to those spark plug holes that are difficult to reach. A check valve holds the pressure until it is released.

When this instrument is properly used, quite accurate readings can be obtained. The purpose of these readings is two-fold: (1) the actual compression is checked, and (2) the variation in pressure between cylinders can be noted. A difference of more than 5 psi is normally an indication of possible valve trouble, unequal buildup of cylinder deposits or ring trouble.

While careful readings of the compression tester are accurate, the conditions within the cylinders may give misleading readings. For example, if there is some compression leakage past valves or rings, and at the same there are deposits in the cylinder, the deposits may increase the pressure enough to offset the leakage and give a normal, but misleading, indication. For this reason, and also because it gives information as to the *leakage paths* of cylinder pressure losses, the cylinder leakage tester is preferred for testing cylinder conditions.

Cylinder Leakage Tester

The *cylinder leakage tester* is a relatively new instrument that gives information on engine conditions that is difficult to obtain by any other means. Although compact, relatively inexpensive, and easy-to-use, this instrument provides important information.

The cylinder leakage tester consists of these parts: a pressure gauge with a Bourdon tube and a scale calibrated from 0 to 100 in *percent of pressure lost;* a pressure regulator which when properly set, maintains a pressure of 60 pounds within the instrument; and a carefully calibrated opening so sized that unobstructed flow of air through the instrument shows 100% pressure loss and no flow shows zero pressure loss. Figs. 12.4, 12.5 and 12.6 show this instrument and accessories.

The cylinder leakage tester is superior to the compression tester. While the compression tester merely indicates the amount of pressure in the cylinder, the cylinder leakage tester makes it easy to determine *where* any leakage is occurring. For example, if the exhaust valve leaks, air will escape through it to the exhaust pipe, tail pipe and muffler, and can be heard distinctly at the end of the tail pipe. If the intake valve leaks, air will leak into the intake manifold, and with the air cleaner removed from the carburetor, it can be heard distinctly at this point. If there is leakage past a piston and its rings, the hissing noise can be heard at the oil filler pipe; while if there should be leakage through a head gasket into the water jacket,

bubbles of air can be heard rising at the radiator filler pipe.

The tester is mounted in an attractively finished steel case, complete with accessories, and can readily be attached to any car in current use. It is also included in several instrument combinations (motor analyzers).

To use the leakage tester instrument, the spark plugs are removed. Set the No. 1 piston 2° to 3° before TDC on the compression stroke so that both valves will be completely closed.

Fig. 12.5. A disc to fit on top of the distributor shaft for use with the cylinder leakage tester. It makes it easy to turn the crankshaft just one-sixth or one-eighth turn to get the next cylinder in TDC position after the first one is properly positioned.

Fig. 12.4. Cylinder leakage tester. This particular instrument is part of the Sun Master Motor Tester. It may also be purchased as a separate instrument. It is valuable for pointing out leakage paths through the intake valve or the exhaust valve, past the rings, or through a defective head gasket.

Fig. 12.6. A whistle used to locate the TDC position of the first piston. It will blow while the piston is being brought to the top position, but will stop as soon as TDC is reached.

Fig. 12.7. Manometer used in connection with Sun distributor tester for checking and adjusting Ford-Mercury pressure-controlled distributors. The manometer is easily read to .01″ Hg.

Fig. 12.8. Anti-freeze tester operates on the same principle as the battery hydrometer, utilizing a weighted float whose stem height indicates the relative weight or specific gravity of the fluid. At least three different gravity anti-freeze fluids must be measured, at widely varying temperatures. Therefore a built-in thermometer is an important part of this instrument. A rotating drum carrying tables within the instrument may be turned to the correct table of safe temperatures.

This cylinder is then tested. Test the other cylinders, with the pistons in the TDC position on the compression stroke. Following the normal engine firing order is most convenient. If a small whistle is placed in the spark plug hole, it will cease to sound as the piston approaches TDC. Normal cylinder leakage will vary from 6% to possibly 15%. More variation than that indicates valves or rings should have attention.

Manometer

The *manometer* is a device for checking low pressures or vacuum by means of a column of mercury, oil or other liquid. The liquid is contained in a closed chamber into which an open-top glass tube fits. Pressure applied to this chamber will force a column of liquid up the tube. On the other hand, vacuum applied to the top of the glass tube will allow liquid to be forced up into the glass tube by atmospheric pressure in the chamber. When the manometer is used for measuring vacuum, the liquid reservoir must be open or vented to atmosphere. The height of the liquid in the tube indicates, on a properly calibrated scale, the amount of pressure or vacuum applied to the instrument. It is used principally in order to diagnose and set the full-vacuum-controlled distributor for correct vacuum advance, and advance due to speed conditions. Because this distributor adjustment requires very accurate settings, the manometer is designed to give measurements of vacuum which are correct within .01″ of mercury. This is approximately 1/200 of a pound, so the sensitivity of this instrument is evident. Fig. 12.7 shows a handy type of manometer.

One design is so constructed that it is easy to attach to the distributor scope or distributor tester made by Sun Electric Corporation.

Battery Hydrometer and Anti-Freeze Tester

The *hydrometer* and *anti-freeze tester* depend upon the same operating principle — measurement of the depth to which a weighted and calibrated float will sink. The higher the specific gravity of the liquid into which the float is inserted or which surrounds the float, the higher it will ride.

The battery hydrometer float is calibrated to indicate the specific gravity of the acid electrolyte used in storage batteries. This liquid will vary from about 1.1 to 1.3 times as heavy as water. In other words, this will read gravities of from 1.100 (read as 1100 gravity) up to 1.300 (read as gravity 1300). Refer to Fig. 12.8.

When the temperature of the battery is above or below 80°F., a correction must be made in the gravity reading. If the temperature is higher, add 1 point for each 3°, and; if the temperature is lower, subtract 1 point for each 3°. The best battery hydrometers have a thermometer built into them to show the electrolyte temperature. Refer to Fig. 12.9.

The anti-freeze tester is designed for two classes of liquid (1) alcohol solutions using either ethyl or methyl alcohol, or (2) ethylene glycol solutions or similar liquids. Anti-freeze testers use a float with a longer stem than that of the battery hydrometer because a wider range of fluid gravity must be checked. As temperatures of these liquids can range from 60° to 150° or more, the liquid temperature is a very important part of the specific gravity interpretation.

The float on most anti-freeze testers is calibrated as a series of letter designations. This reading, in conjunction with the indicated temperature, is used to determine the specific gravity in a table which gives the temperature down to which the anti-freeze mixture will protect against freezing.

The anti-freeze tester is not, strictly speaking, a diagnosis or tune-up instrument. However it is frequently used in the wintertime and those working in the automotive service field should be familiar with it.

Spark Plug Tester

The *spark plug tester* in common use consists of a receptacle into which the electrode end of a spark plug can be inserted and air pressure applied. A tester is shown in Fig. 12.10. With the end of the plug under pressure, a high-tension current equivalent to that applied to the plug on the car is brought to the plug. Air pressure is varied upward from about 60 psi. A plug which will fire regularly under an air pressure of approximately 90 psi is generally considered to be usable. A glass window

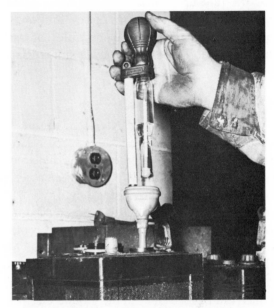

Fig. 12.9. Battery hydrometer with built-in thermometer which corrects variations from the standard temperature of 80°F.

Fig. 12.10. This generally used type of spark plug tester puts the plug under test in a chamber containing compressed air. The air pressure may be varied, and the pressure at which the plug ceases to fire regularly can be observed. This test is not considered conclusive, only indicative.

in the compression chamber in which the plug is firing permits the spark to be observed as the plug is under test. This type of spark plug test is indicative but is not conclusive.

It has been the general practice among tune-up men to discard all plugs on cars brought into them for tune-up service, on the general principle that new plugs will work properly while old ones may not. While this sells plugs for the tune-up man and usually accomplishes the desired result, it also causes millions of plugs that are good for many miles of satisfactory service to be thrown away unnecessarily every year.

Spark Plug Gap Gauge

The *spark plug gap gauge* is useful for checking and setting the correct space between the center electrode and the grounded electrode on spark plugs. It usually has either a set of blades or wires ranging in thickness from .015″ to .040″. The wire gauge is preferred because it will fit into the gap and follow the contour of a pitted ground or side electrode and give the correct gap. Many of the gauges have one or two notches of different sizes in the handle which can be used to bend the ground electrode. Some designs have a point strong enough to bend up the ground electrode after it has been pushed too far toward the center electrode.

This instrument is not too important, but it is extremely handy. It is of value more to the tune-up man setting spark plug gaps than to the diagnostician checking engine condition. All spark plugs, including new ones, should have the gap checked, and readjusted when necessary, before putting them in an engine.

Spring Tension Tester

The *spring tension tester* is nothing more than a small spring balance with a hook on one end. It is used to check the tension on the distributor breaker arm. The hook is put under the end of the breaker arm and the breaker point is pulled away from its contacting stationary point. Just as the breaker arm leaves the stationary point, the spring tension should be read. This should equal the number of ounces specified for the given car or distributor make. A handy type is shown in Fig. 12.11.

Since wrong spring tension is frequently a source of ignition system troubles, this test is important in both diagnostic and tune-up work.

Sound Scope (Stethoscope Type)

The stethoscope type of *sound scope* is useful in locating engine noises. It consists of a metal prod with one end in contact with a metal diaphragm which transmits sound waves up two tubes to the ears of the operator. It is much more sensitive to sounds around the engine, at the generator, and at the distributor, than is the human ear. Parts which make noise

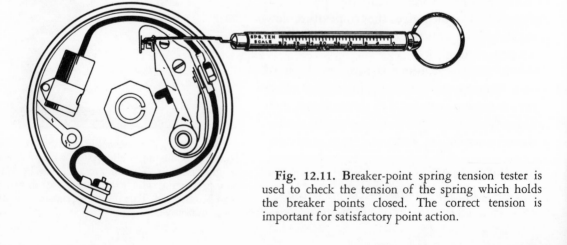

Fig. 12.11. Breaker-point spring tension tester is used to check the tension of the spring which holds the breaker points closed. The correct tension is important for satisfactory point action.

because of poor condition, excessive wear, or some other cause, can be localized by following the sound to the point of greatest intensity. This is illustrated in Fig. 12.12.

Sound scopes are made by several different companies and frequently will prove their value to the automotive diagnostician or tune-up man.

Fuel Pump Tester

In order to assure an adequate supply of fuel and a constant fuel level for all driving conditions, it is necessary that both fuel pump volume and pressure be within specifications. The only reliable test is one that is made under actual operating conditions: (1) with the pump supplying fuel to the carburetor and (2) with the pressure gauge located within six inches of and connected to the fuel line.

The *fuel pump tester* consists of (1) a connection to be attached to the carburetor and to be inserted in the main fuel line to the carburetor, and (2) a pressure gauge attached to the tester carburetor connection. On this connection there is also an outlet which can be opened so that fuel can flow into a calibrated jar that comes with the tester. When using the tester, first observe the pressure indicated by the pressure gauge; this should be in accordance with manufacturer's specifications. Then with the engine running on the fuel in the carburetor float bowl, allow the pumped fuel to discharge into the glass jar. Note the time it takes for one pint of fuel to be discharged; this should be no longer than 20 seconds for an eight-cylinder engine or 30 seconds for a six. A fuel-pump pressure testing set is shown in Fig. 12.13.

Cooling System Pressure Tester

It is desirable to test cooling systems under pressure for two reasons: (1) to verify that the radiator pressure cap releases at the specified pressure, and (2) to check the cooling system for leaks around the radiator core or tanks, in the connecting hoses, around the head gasket or gaskets, or around the block (cracks or leaking freeze plugs).

One very convenient *cooling system pressure tester* is made by the AC Spark Plug Division of General Motors. It consists of a cylindrical body to which a pressure gauge is attached, and also a hand bulb for building up pressure on the cooling system. The gauge reads up to 15 psi. The upper end of the body is closed

Fig. 12.12. Sound scope noise detector is a very useful aid in localizing sounds that may mean trouble. This instrument plus an understanding of the significance of various noises will help correct diagnosis.

Fig. 12.13. Fuel pump pressure testing set.

and the lower end is designed with the proper fittings to be attached to the filler neck of the radiator or to a radiator cap. By working the hand bulb, cooling system pressure can be built up to the desired point. This pressure is maintained while the system is checked for leaks, or while the pressure radiator cap is checked for its release pressure. Fig. 12.14 illustrates a convenient cooling system and pressure radiator cap tester.

Insulated High-Tension Pliers

In making certain tests with the oscilloscope or tests on the secondary or high-tension circuit

Fig. 12.14. Cooling system and pressure radiator cap tester.

Fig. 12.15. The insulated spark plug pliers are used to pull off a spark plug cable without injury or shock to the operator, for the purpose of stressing the ignition coil and primary ignition system to test the coil. Several instruments such as the volts-ignition tester are used for this test.

it is desirable to pull off spark plug wires while the engine is running. *High tension pliers* were designed to make this operation safe and free from electric shocks. The pliers are insulated with vulcanized fiber or similar material. Fig. 12.15 shows the pliers being used to remove a spark plug cable. The ignition coil is being tested.

Instrument Combinations

In Chapter 11 and the preceding portion of this chapter the individual testing instruments have been described. As a matter of convenience and also to impress the buyer of automotive service, there is a growing tendency to mount a number of instruments in a stand or cabinet. These larger instrument combinations are called motor analyzers, motor testers, tune-up testers, or similar names.

Commonly used instrument combinations are:

        Volts-amperes tester
        Battery-starter tester
        Tach-dwell meter
        Multi-purpose instruments
        Motor analyzer
        Generator and regulator tester
        Distributorscope or distributor tester
        Generator test bench

The various makers of instruments may combine single instruments in different ways, but a very common combination is the voltmeter and ammeter. The volts-amperes tester is often mounted on a stand with casters so it can easily be moved. Two ranges or capacities are provided in different instruments, one range designed for testing the generating system and ignition system while the other, with a much higher capacity is designed for testing the battery and starter.

Volts-Amperes Tester

The voltmeter will usually have scales of 0-2, 0-8 and 0-16 volts. A $\frac{1}{4}$-ohm resistor is sometimes built in, along with a variable resistance. The ammeter will have a capacity of up to 100 amperes. Among the tests which this unit can conveniently make are:

Circuit resistance tests (voltage drop)
  a. Insulated side
  b. Ground side
Ignition system voltage (engine running)
Generator output voltage (voltage regulator)
Generator output current (current regulator)
Voltage drop, regulator ground
Cut-out relay test

Battery-Starter Tester

This combination is similar to the volts-amperes tester, except that the ammeter has a range of 0-400 amperes and a carbon-plate rheostat is built into the unit so that battery capacity tests may be made and starting-motor current draw may be checked. To test battery capacity, a load equal to three times the battery ampere-hour rating (in amperes) is placed on the battery for at least 15 seconds. Battery voltage should not drop below 10 volts on a good 12-volt battery or 5 volts on a good 6-volt battery.

The voltmeter scales will usually be 0-3 or 4, 0-8, and 0-16 volts. In some cases the carbon-plate rheostat will not be built in, but will be furnished as a separate unit. When it is built in, a control knob is located on the front of the instrument to control the pressure on the carbon plates. Among the tests which can be made with this unit are:

Battery capacity
Battery voltage
Starter current draw
Battery leakage
Starter ground circuit resistance

Fig. 12.16 shows a combination volts-amperes and battery-starter tester.

Tach-Dwell Meter

The tachometer and the dwell meter have been discussed separately in Chapter 11. They are so often combined in one case that it is customary to speak of the *tach-dwell meter*.

This combination may have a single dial, with scales for both speed indications and indications of dwell angle, or it may be equipped with separate dials, making use of two d'Arsonval meter movements.

These instruments are available in a case which is readily portable as a unit in a motor analyzer or motor tester, which is a combination of a number of instruments in a fairly large cabinet mounted on casters.

Multipurpose Instruments

Several instruments will give two, three or more different kinds of indications. For example, the Simpson Meter shown in Fig. 12.17 will indicate (1) dwell angle, (2) speeds, (tachometer), (3) ignition output, and (4) secondary current. The instrument hung below is a battery loader with carbon-pile rheostat and voltmeter for testing batteries. A convenient stand such as this is supplied by several of the instrument makers. On this instrument the indicating scale is rotated when the selector knob

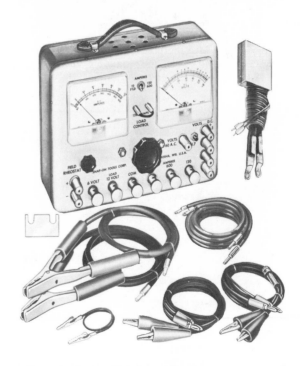

Fig. 12.16. Combination volts-amperes tester and battery-starter tester supplied by Snap-On Corporation.

is turned to bring the appropriate scale into view.

Fig. 12.18 shows a generating system tester, which gives indications of (1) generator output (amperes), (2) cut-out relay voltage, (3) voltage regulator voltage, and (4) current regulator setting in amperes. After making the indicated connections to battery terminal, battery wire, generator field, armature terminal and

Fig. 12.17. Multipurpose instrument supplied by Simpson Electric Company indicates dwell angle, speed (tachometer), ignition output, and secondary current.

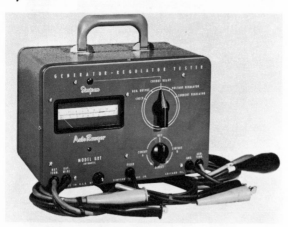

Fig. 12.18. Another multipurpose instrument supplied by Simpson Electric Company to check generator output, cut-out relay, voltage regulator, and current regulator. Turning the selector knob brings the correct scale into view.

ground, the tests can be made in a matter of seconds.

An interesting combination supplied by Allen is the vacuum-pressure gauge and combustion analyzer shown in Fig. 12.19 with a stand. Where considerable carburetor work is done, this type of equipment is very handy.

Motor Testers or Motor Analyzers

Various instrument combinations are called *motor testers or motor analyzers*. Some include three or four instruments, part of which may be dual- or multipurpose units, while more elaborate combinations include an oscilloscope. Generally the more elaborate equipment has greater utility, but the organization of the shop may be such that separate instruments are more functional.

Fig. 12.20 illustrates an Ignition Analyzer test set supplied by Snap-On Tools Corporation. It contains an alternator regulator tester, with scales for 0-20 volts, 0-100 amperes and 0-500 ohms; a tach-dwell meter; an amperes-ignition meter, with scales for 0-60 and 0-150 amperes and 0-100,000 ohms. This set is primarily a coil

Fig. 12.19. Combination vacuum-pressure gauge and combustion analyzer, supplied by Allen Electric and Equipment Company. The stand is an added convenience.

and condenser tester but can also be used to detect faults in the ignition system such as fouled or misfiring plugs. Ballast resistors can be checked, and ammeter and ohmmeter indications can be obtained.

The master analyzer supplied by Snap-On, shown in Fig. 12.21, contains the ignition analyzer which was included in the set shown in Fig. 12.20; a volts-amperes meter with 0-18 volts and 0-70 amperes; a tach-dwell meter; a vacuum-pressure gauge, with 0-26 inches vacuum and 0-10 psi; and the Anal-O-Scope oscilloscope. The set is mounted in a spacious cabinet, on large-size casters for easy movement around the shop. Additional accessories may be stored in the lower cabinet.

A different grouping of instruments is shown on the Allen test set illustrated in Fig. 12.22. The left-hand instrument is a combination of a voltmeter with scales for 0-10, 0-20 and 0-40 volts; electronic distributor tester or ignition advance meter; a tachometer with three scales, 0-800, 0-1600, and 0-6000; a combination ammeter 0-100 amperes and dynamic compression indicator; and the Allen oscilloscope.

The dynamic compression is only relative. The indication is obtained by selectively shorting out one cylinder at a time in the oscilloscope circuitry and observing the loss of speed on the dynamic compression scale which reads from 0-250. If the reading is approximately the

same for all cylinders, it can be assumed that each cylinder is developing about the same amount of power. A noticeable difference between cylinders indicates that corrective work should be done. The set is mounted in a roomy

Fig. 12.21. Analyzer supplied by Snap-On Tools Corporation includes the ignition analyzer shown in Fig. 12.20, a volts-amperes meter, a tach-dwell tester, a vacuum-pressure gauge and an oscilloscope.

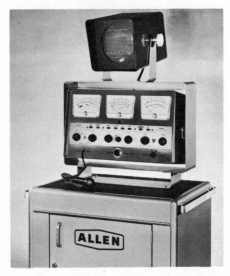

Fig. 12.22. Another grouping of instruments is shown in this test set by Allen. It contains a combination voltmeter and electronic distributor tester, tachometer, combination ammeter and dynamic compression tester (cylinder balance meter) and the Allen oscilloscope.

Fig. 12.20. Ignition analyzer test set furnished by Snap-On Tools Corporation. It includes an alternator regulator tester, ammeter, ohmmeter, tach-dwell meter, and amperes-ignition tester.

Fig. 12.23. The engine analyzer, furnished by Marquette Manufacturing Company (formerly supplied by Heyer), is very fast and convenient to use for making overall engine checks. It contains a vacuum gauge and combustion analyzer, voltmeter and tachometer, plus a spark advance meter (electronic distributor tester) and oscilloscope.

cabinet on large casters. A timing light is included in the equipment to go with the electronic distributor or ignition advance tester.

The Marquette offering is shown in Fig. 12.23. The Dyna-Vision oscilloscope is mounted above the lower units. The left unit is the vacuum gauge and combustion analyzer. The middle unit controls the oscilloscope, while the upper right-hand unit is a combined tachometer and voltmeter 0-16 volts. The spark advance meter is enclosed in the lower case. Fig. 12.24 shows the latest Marquette Engine Analyzer which has added speed and convenience.

One of the fine new motor testers is the Sun 820 Electronic Engine Tester, Fig. 12.25. At the upper left of the case is a voltmeter-ohmmeter combination instrument and a dwell meter-condenser tester instrument. At the right is a tachometer with several ranges and a combustion efficiency meter. In the center is an improved oscilloscope. A timing light is included in the tester equipment which has a

Fig. 12.24. This latest engine analyzer by Marquette is quite advanced. It has a combined voltmeter, spark advance meter, cylinder balance meter, and tachometer. The two windows at the left of the oscilloscope, by means of a roller chart, can be made to show a pattern to match almost any trace the scope will show, with its interpretation. At the right of the scope a roller chart gives all the current tune-up specifications. Only four leads need to be connected to get all the needed information. The scope is used to check dwell.

Fig. 12.25. Electronic Engine Tester, Model 820, supplied by Sun Electric Corporation. The instruments included are: oscilloscope, voltmeter, ohmmeter, dwell meter, tachometer, condenser and coil tester, combustion efficiency tester, vacuum gauge, cylinder leakage tester, timing advance control, and cylinder balance tester.

spark advance indicator built into the light body. This simplifies checking ignition advance and setting ignition timing.

A cylinder leakage tester and vacuum gauge are located below the oscilloscope. The tester is completely AC powered and incorporates the latest in transistorized voltage-regulated circuitry which automatically compensates for line voltage variation.

The instruments are mounted on a wide cabinet which gives ample storage space for such accessories as wires and cables. Large casters make it easy to wheel the tester from place to place in the shop.

In Fig. 12.26 the Sun 320 Electronic Engine Tester is shown. It is similar to the 820, but is somewhat smaller and lower priced.

Application of the Motor Testers

Motor testers mounted on casters can be taken to an automobile easily. There are two general ways in which the instruments are used. One is to make certain specific diagnostic tests in the effort to locate defective units, parts or accessories. The other way is to make an overall checkup by connecting most or all of the instruments and then going through a planned routine to check the adjustment and/or performance of all the various systems of the power plant. This will include tests of the ignition system, generating system, fuel system, and starting system. Many individual tests can be made on each system when such tests will give helpful information.

A student or beginner in tune-up and diagnostic work will usually be quite impressed by the array of instruments, but he should remember that the whole panel is made up of individual instruments which must be used one at a time. If he is familiar with the individual instruments, he should have no difficulty with the motor tester.

More and more motor analyzer units include an oscilloscope, for this instrument gives considerable information about the ignition system. The problem for the service man is to be able to interpret the meaning of the traces shown on the scope screen. Remember that the scope included in the analyzer is exactly the same as an individual instrument and may be used by itself or in conjunction with other appropriate instruments.

The Distributor Tester

The *distributorscope, distributor tester, or synchroscope*, as it is variously called, is the preferred instrument for testing and adjusting ignition distributors. Defects in distributor operation will be quickly and readily exposed. After new points are installed, they can be easily aligned and their spacing adjusted to give the specified dwell angle.

Mechanical advance and vacuum advance can be accurately checked at specified speeds and vacuums, respectively. The indications can then be compared with manufacturer's specifications to see how closely to the correct advance curves the distributor performs. If it is necessary to make corrections, the new settings can be checked in the same way.

The distributor testers manufactured by Sun and Allen drive the shaft of the distributor and also rotate a brilliant indicating arrow at the same speed. Each time the breaker points open, a surge of high-tension current is sent to the

Fig. 12.26. Model 320 is similar to the 820, but has smaller instruments and a lower selling price.

neon tube which illuminates the arrow, and it appears, as it rotates, in four, six or eight positions around the circumference of the protractor, depending upon the number of cylinders.

Fig. 12.27. The Sun Distributorscope (distributor tester). This type of instrument is preferred for testing and adjusting the distributor. The instruments at left and right are tachometer, dwell meter, condenser tester, and vacuum gauge. The distributor is mounted and driven at the center; such things as spark advance and cam variation are indicated on the center protractor.

The arrows will be equally spaced around the 360° of the protractor ring if the breaker cam in the distributor is accurate. The positions of the arrows on the protractor will appear to move in the direction of distributor rotation with an increase of distributor shaft speed, due to the mechanical advance in the distributor. As vacuum from the built-in vacuum pump is applied to the vacuum advance, the arrow positions will again be affected. Thus the actual performance may be compared with specifications. A scroll, giving all the needed specifications for the various cars and engines likely to be encountered, is supplied with each instrument. Fig. 12.27 illustrates the Sun Distributor Tester.

As part of the distributor tester, Sun incorporates on the panel these separate instruments: tachometer, dwell meter, condenser tester and vacuum gauge. On the Allen, a tachometer, dwell meter, and vacuum gauge are supplied. It is essential that means be provided for measuring speed (in either engine or distributor rpm), dwell or cam angle, and vacuum. Any other instruments included are "plus" equipment. Fig. 12.28 shows the Allen Synchroscope panel and 12.29 shows the complete unit.

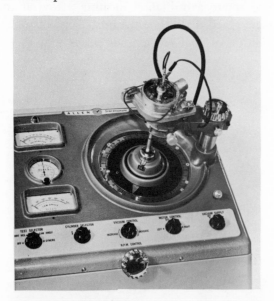

Fig. 12.28. The distributor tester (Synchroscope) as furnished by Allen. Close-up view shows the control panel and instruments.

Fig. 12.29. The complete Allen Synchroscope showing the cabinet base which is available with most of the units of this type on the market.

On the Marquette distributor tester a different operating method is used to give the desired indications. First, a disc is set for the angle between the lobes of the distributor cam; then the distributor rotation is started, and the pattern displayed on the disc shows at once whether there is perfect cam action. A "gunsight" makes it easy to adjust the precision protractorscope to the exact image. An amplifier reads the spark advance to $\frac{1}{4}$ of 1° accuracy. Three separate instruments are supplied: tachometer, dwell meter and vacuum gauge. This distributor tester is shown in Fig. 12.30.

The Snap-On distributor tester presents the information in still a different manner. Instead of using the opening of the breaker points and the moment of spark occurrence to show what the distributor is doing, this instrument uses the dwell period. From the moment the points close until they open, segments around the protractor are illuminated. Degrees, from 0° to 180° are marked on each half of the protractor. By rotating the protractor by hand to set 0° at one end of a dwell segment, the dwell degrees can be read on the protractor. The uniformity of the lengths of the dwell segments indicates wear or lack of wear on the distributor cam. Note Fig. 12.31. All the distributor testers shown here are supplied with attractive, roomy base cabinets.

The distributor drive is set to one side, leaving the protractor free of obstruction and readily visible. Since the dwell indication is shown directly on the protractor, no dwell meter is required. Therefore the only separate units furnished are the tachometer and vacuum gauge. Each of the four distributor testers shown is equipped with a vacuum pump for supplying vacuum to the vacuum advance.

On every tune-up job, and when there is difficulty with the ignition system that may be from the distributor (other than a cracked or dirty cap or bad rotor), remove the distributor, check it and adjust it while it is on the distributor tester. While this is not generally done, it is the only good practice.

The distributor tester is actually very easy to use. With the distributor in place on the instrument, replace points and condenser if needed. Then run the machine to set the dwell correctly and check point resistance. Proceed to check cam action for accuracy, dwell variation, and

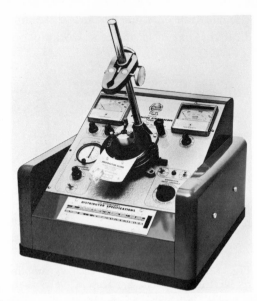

Fig. 12.30. The Marquette Distributor Stroboscope does not use the protractor; instead it uses initial settings to correspond with the engine being tested. (See text description.)

Fig. 12.31. The Snap-On Distrib-U-Scope has the distributor mounted to one side with the firing pattern shown on the center protractor. It can be furnished with or without a base.

automatic advance, referring to the specifications which will be obtained from the chart furnished with the tester. Next, running the engine at the specified speed, check the amount of vacuum advance at different degrees of vacuum. Where there are variations from specification for automatic (or mechanical) advance and/or vacuum advance, work on the distributor is indicated. Only a distributor working on the

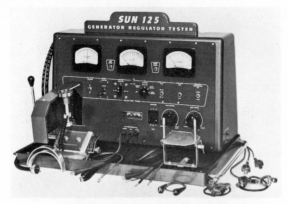

Fig. 12.32. Generator test bench as supplied by Sun Electric Corporation. This is very useful if the volume of generator, alternator, and regulator work is sufficient.

Fig. 12.33. Generator-regulator test bench furnished by Allen. It, like the others, is designed to test both DC generators and alternators with their regulators.

correct advance curves will give the engine performance it should give. The only way a distributor can be thoroughly tested and checked is on the proper equipment.

Generator-Regulator Test Bench

The volts-amperes testers equipped with field rheostats and 1/4- to 1/2-ohm resistors can do a good job of checking the generating system on the car. However, if a lot of generator and regulator work is done it pays to have a good generator-regulator test bench available for testing these parts off of the car.

There are several different makes available at different prices. Three of them are shown: the Sun, the Allen and the King. Since the generator and regulator work as a team, it is important that they be tested together under actual working conditions; that is what these instruments make possible.

The Sun Generator-Regulator Tester (Fig. 12.32) is a heavy-duty piece of equipment with ample power to drive the largest passenger car and light truck generators and test them under full load output. A table is provided, for mounting the voltage regulator. It is adjustable for angle to match angle of installation in the automobile.

In the instrument panel there is an ammeter for DC field current, a voltmeter with scales for 10, 20 or 40 volts, and a DC output ammeter with scale reading up to 100 amperes. Selector switches on the instrument panel allow tests to be made of field current, cut-out relay, voltage limiter, current limiter and double contact voltage regulator. The motor runs at constant speed, but the generator output can be varied by adjusting the field current control on the panel.

A "Big Job" generator-regulator tester is available for testing big bus and truck generators and their regulators, with up to six control units. It is a good investment for shops working on the larger and heavier equipment, even though it costs over three times the price of the smaller unit.

The Allen Generator-Regulator Tester (Fig. 12.33) drives the generator at the side of the tester by a coupling to a shaft. The regulator is located on a platform at the side. Three meters are furnished in the panel: a field ammeter, output volts voltmeter, and output ammeter. Panel controls allow substantially the same tests as the Sun tester.

The King Alternator-Generator-Regulator Tester (Fig. 12.34) mounts the generator at the front of the unit and uses a belt generator drive. On the instrument panel are two separate instruments: a dual range ammeter with scales for field current, 0-7.5 amperes and output, 0-225 amperes; and a voltmeter with three scales, 0-10, 20, and 50 volts. The King tester is not quite as versatile as the Sun tester, but it is somewhat simpler to operate.

All three of the testers mentioned may be used to test alternators and their regulators. Since there is no provision for testing the diodes separately, a diode tester should be used for this purpose. Field current and alternator output, however, can be readily checked, as well as the voltage regulator. Most of the alternators do not make use of a current regulator or a cut-out relay.

The generator-regulator testers may be purchased with or without the base cabinet.

Test-instrument manufacturers supply excellent instruction books and pamphlets, and most have provision for teaching the use of their equipment. Operating instructions and the basic information that may be obtained by careful study of this book, along with some practical experience, should qualify a man for tune-up and diagnostic work.

In addition to the motor tester, it is convenient to have a volt-amperes tester and a battery-starter tester on separate stands for making tests on the generating system and the battery and starting system.

Separate instruments which will make the required tests will do just as well as an elaborate panel mounted on an attractive cabinet.

However, they are not as convenient to use nor do they make as lasting an impression on your customers.

In many cases the tachometer and dwell meter are combined in a single case and the same d'Arsonval meter movement is used for both indications. This works satisfactorily except that the speed and dwell angle indications cannot be taken together and must be taken alternately. For this reason it is preferred to have separate tachometer and dwell angle meters. A similar condition is present in other multipurpose meters; that is, only one reading can be taken at one time. This should be kept in mind when selecting instrument equipment, giving consideration also to the comparative cost of the separate instruments.

The generator-regulator tester is an expensive piece of equipment but its purchase is amply justified where enough suitable work is done.

A great many shops go without suitable instrument equipment because they think it is too expensive. It is costly; however, it pays handsome dividends in the hands of capable

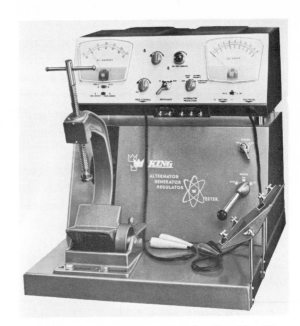

Fig. 12.34. Generator test bench offered by King. It is designed particularly to be convenient to use with alternators and their regulators. It is a sturdy machine.

men, and the use of instruments is imperative in diagnosing and tuning recent automotive power plants. Equipment purchase should be looked upon as an income-producing investment, not as an expense.

Summary

The *Bourdon tube* is used in a number of pressure type instruments, such as the vacuum-pressure gauge, compression tester and cylinder leakage tester.

The *cylinder leakage tester* is preferred to the compression tester because it will indicate where the leakage path or paths occur.

The *manometer* is a device for measuring small amounts of vacuum or pressure by means of a column of liquid in a tube.

Both the *battery hydrometer* and *anti-freeze tester* operate by measuring the depth to which a weighted float of glass or plastic will sink in a liquid whose specific gravity is to be tested.

The *spark plug tester* causes a spark plug to fire under air pressure on the assumption that if it will fire under air pressure it will fire under cylinder compression in an engine.

The *spring tension tester* is a small spring balance used to check the breaker arm spring tension in a distributor to see that it is according to specifications.

The *sound scope* is useful in locating the source of engine noises. It is made something like a stethoscope.

The *fuel pump tester* tests the fuel pump pressure and volume of delivery in a given time under operating conditions and will pinpoint a defective fuel pump.

The *cooling system pressure tester* is designed to (1) test radiator pressure caps, and (2) to put a cooling system under pressure to help disclose any leaks.

High-tension insulated pliers enable an operator to remove a high-tension spark plug cable without injury or inconvenience in the course of making certain ignition tests.

Combinations of two or three instruments in a single case, multipurpose instruments and combinations of instruments in a panel are referred to as *motor testers* or *motor analyzers*.

A common combination is the *volts-amperes tester*, primarily used for testing generating systems, plus the usual applications of the voltmeter and/or the ammeter in circuit and unit testing.

The *battery-starter tester* is similar to the volts-amperes tester except that the ammeter has a much larger capacity and usually has a carbon-pile rheostat built into the instrument case.

The *tach-dwell meter* is a common combination which may have a single dual-purpose meter movement or two separate movements.

Multipurpose instruments may give two, three or more different indications from a single meter movement.

Motor testers or *motor analyzers* are available in a variety of combinations with from three or four instruments to eight or more. An oscilloscope is often included.

Motor testers may be used to make specific tests with the individual instruments, or all the instruments may be connected to make an overall test or diagnosis of the power plant.

The *distributor tester* is used to test a distributor off of the car. It will check dwell, operation and mechanical and vacuum advance as well as other characteristics.

The *generator-regulator tester* is valuable equipment when the volume of work justifies the expense of buying it. Several are described and illustrated.

Any *instruments on hand should be used* and need not be duplicated, though the motor analyzer is convenient and makes an excellent impression on the customer. Instrument equipment is an income-producing investment and is necessary to cope with today's service requirements.

Questions

1. Name the instrument movement that actuates most pressure gauges.
2. What is the difference between a vacuum gauge and a pressure gauge?
3. What is a manometer?
4. What two important kinds of information does the compression tester give?
5. What does the cylinder leakage tester do and why is it more valuable than the compression tester?
6. On what principle does a battery hydrometer work and what information does it give?
7. What information does a spark plug tester give?
8. What information does an anti-freeze tester give?
9. Why is a spring tension tester used?
10. Of what value is a sound scope in engine work?
11. What two kinds of information will a fuel pump tester give?
12. What two functions will a cooling system pressure tester perform?
13. Why are high-tension insulated pliers used?
14. Name three two-instrument combinations.
15. Name a multipurpose instrument.
16. What do you understand from the term *motor analyzer?*
17. What is meant by *dynamic compression?*
18. What is the most elaborate of the motor testers illustrated and described?
19. What is the function of the distributor tester?
20. When does a generator-regulator tester prove to be valuable?

CHAPTER THIRTEEN

Automotive Oscilloscope

The automotive oscilloscope is the newest of the diagnostic tools available for checking the condition of the ignition system on an engine. The idea of using the oscilloscope for this purpose dates back to 1941, when the Socony-Mobil Oil Company started experimental work and development on the instrument, and patented the so-called "raster sweep." This displayed a graph or trace for each cylinder separately, one above the other, on the screen of the cathode-ray tube.

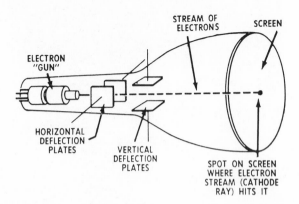

Fig. 13.1. Cathode-ray tube used in the oscilloscope. Note the deflection plates which bend the stream of electrons in accordance with the electrical impulses sent to the plates, and thus draw the "trace" on the screen.

Basic Operation

The cathode-ray tube of the oscilloscope is the same type of tube used in television sets. An electron gun within the tube shoots a stream of electrons at the fluorescent screen at the front of the tube. When this electron stream strikes the screen, a small spot of light results. Inside the tube are two sets of metal plates; the two plates in a horizontal position are called the vertical deflection plates, and those in a vertical position are called the horizontal deflection plates.

When the horizontal deflection plates are given appropriate electrical charges from the circuits of the oscilloscope, they will bend the electron beam so it will sweep across in a horizontal direction inside the tube. This makes the beam, which appears as a spot of light on the screen, trace a brilliant line across the screen from left to right, and then retrace its path faintly, from right to left. The movement of the spot or point of light is so rapid that it appears to the eye as a solid line.

When the instrument is connected to an ignition system on a running engine, the vertical deflection plates will receive electrical charges through the circuits of the oscilloscope. These charges are proportional to the instantaneous changes in voltage in the ignition system. The varying charges bend the electron beam vertically as it sweeps from left to right, so that the point of light actually *traces a graph* on the cathode-ray tube screen. The pattern drawn will correspond to the electric charge in the ignition system. More specifically, the pattern represents the intensity and time of the detailed voltage changes that take place in the ignition system. Every instant of each complete cylinder ignition spark cycle is shown, starting with the opening of the distributor contact points. The tube is shown in Fig. 13.1.

To understand and use the oscilloscope, it is first necessary to understand the significance of the basic *trace* (or pattern lines) that appears on the oscilloscope screen. Otherwise the indications are meaningless. When the traces are understood, more information about the ignition system of any engine, and what is happening in that system, can be obtained (and more quickly) than by the use of the conventional testing instruments. This is not to say that the oscilloscope will completely replace the usual testing instruments, but it is an additional tool that is very valuable in diagnosis work.

Advantages

The science of oscillography represents the electronics industry's influence on automotive performance diagnosis. It is a modern and very practical approach to faster and more thorough engine analysis.

Through simple and easily accessible connections, the entire ignition system can be tested. This is an area type test, which means that an entire system, circuit, or series of components is tested in operation — similar to testing a chain by placing a given weight on the end of it. If the chain will sustain the weight, each link must be satisfactory.

If a tested system shows trouble, the flaw must then be isolated by closer pattern interpretation or additional testing with other equipment.

In addition to simplicity of operation and speed of testing (3 to 10 minutes), the 'scope has another great advantage: the complete ignition operation is pictured, including the actual spark inside the combustion chamber. This gives a mechanic the first comprehensive test of spark plugs in operation. He can also obtain indications of abnormal combustion chamber temperature or pressure and fuel-air ratio.

The oscilloscope provides a simple quality-control test for a novice, and a precision measuring device for the experienced technician.

A Single-Cycle Trace

The basic wave form or trace of a single cycle may be obtained from either the primary circuit or the secondary circuit of the ignition system. The *primary trace* is not quite as sensitive or informative as the *secondary system trace*, although, otherwise, both are similar.

In Fig. 13.2 the upper trace is a typical wave form of the primary circuit relative voltage through one complete firing cycle. It starts with

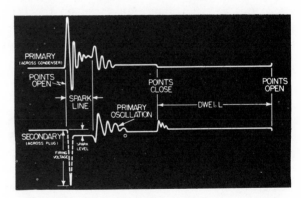

Fig. 13.2. The basic traces shown on the oscilloscope screen. The upper trace is the primary trace obtained by connecting the pick-up leads across the distributor breaker points, i.e., to the distributor side of the coil or the distributor terminal and to ground. The lower trace is the typical secondary trace. The dotted line indicates the rise and fall of the voltage which initiates the spark. This is shown as a straight vertical line unless the trace is much expanded horizontally. Notice the spark line which shows the oscillations in the primary, the coil-condenser zone (marked "primary oscillation"), the points close signal, the dwell zone, and the points open signal. Here, on both traces, positive voltage is shown above the base line and negative voltage below.

the initiation of the spark as the breaker points in the distributor open and continues through the cycle until the points open again. This trace is obtained by connecting across the distributor breaker points. As the distributor breaker points open and the spark starts to arc across the spark plug gap, the primary voltage increases rapidly. High-frequency oscillations then take place in the primary circuit and continue for the actual duration of the spark. At 2000 rpm, the duration of the spark will be approximately one thousandth of a second, and the entire spark cycle will take place within one-hundredth of a second on a six-cylinder engine.

As soon as the spark is extinguished or ceases to exist as an arc across the spark plug electrodes, lower frequency oscillations take place in the circuit due to rising voltage in the system. The resulting kick-back in the coil and condenser appears in both primary and secondary, from the transformer effect between these coils.

The oscillations end in a straight line, and the height of that line above the base line corresponds to the voltage impressed on the primary circuit across the open points. The *points close* signal is quite definite and easy to see. After the points close, primary voltage drops down, substantially to zero, and shows as a straight line up to the point of the next distributor contact-point opening and the next spark. When the next spark occurs, the cycle starts all over again with the next cylinder.

Thus, it can be seen that the trace from a single cylinder shows: (1) a definite *spark zone* which gives a picture of spark action, (2) a *coil-condenser zone* which shows the quality of the action of these parts, (3) a *points close* signal which indicates the beginning of the dwell period, and (4) the *dwell zone* which shows the relative length of the dwell period, preceding the *points-open* signal.

On the lower trace in Fig. 13.2, notice the sharp increase in secondary voltage when the spark occurs. This is followed in the normal pattern by a straight horizontal line representing the duration of the spark. In the primary circuit there is an oscillating (alternating) current resulting in a high-frequency oscillation in the trace at this time, but in the secondary circuit the normal spark shows that there is direct current during the duration of the spark. This part of the secondary trace is one of the most important, since deviations here will tell of deficiencies or defects in the high-tension portion of the ignition circuit, particularly in the part between the distributor and the plugs, and including the spark plugs.

The portion of the primary trace marked *spark line* also represents the action of the condenser. Defects in the condenser will affect the form of this portion of the trace. Refer to Fig. 13.2.

The *coil-condenser* zone of the secondary is very much like that of the primary trace. This is followed by the *points close* signal. While in the primary trace there is a smooth drop to zero voltage, oscillations are seen in the secondary. These oscillations give valuable information about the distributor breaker points.

The *dwell zone* is just about the same in both the primary and the secondary traces. An important feature of the dwell zone is that the end of the dwell line will also give information about the breaker points. If there is any abnormal arcing between the points when they open to initiate the spark, there will be a "hash" (irregular splashes) at the end of the dwell zone. On those oscilloscopes which can exhibit superimposed traces of all cylinders, the expanded trace will show this arcing fault clearly. When it is shown, new breaker points are indicated. Where the superimposed traces cannot be shown, watching the expanded traces of several of the individual cylinder traces will serve to check the points for arcing.

Both the primary and secondary traces are mentioned because together they give a clear picture of the condenser condition. Oscilloscopes currently available can show both the primary and secondary traces, although the secondary trace is more commonly used for checking the ignition system.

Fig. 13.3 shows a typical trace as shown on the Sunscope. In comparing this with Fig. 13.2 it can be seen that the only difference between the two traces is that the Sunscope shows the initial voltage line (as the spark first jumps the spark plug gap) as a straight vertical line, whereas Fig. 13.2 shows it as a rapid rise and fall. Also the Sun trace shows negative voltage above the base line, while the basic trace shows it below the base line. The Sun trace is a true-voltage diagram showing the voltage variations in the high-tension ignition circuit without appreciable distortion.

The traces from the other oscilloscopes available to the automotive service trade will be discussed later in this chapter. Regardless of the trace presented, however, it will have the four basic zones: (1) spark zone, (2) coil-condenser zone, (3) points close signal, and (4) dwell zone.

Analysis of Ignition System Action

At the top of Fig. 13.2 is shown the primary pattern or trace and at the bottom the secondary pattern. These traces or patterns show *voltage* in the vertical direction and *time* in the horizontal direction, going from left to right. Positive voltage is up, and negative voltage is down.

The primary signal is obtained by connecting across the breaker points; that is, from the distributor terminal or the distributor side of the coil to ground. At the time when the points are closed, they short out the condenser so that no voltage is impressed on the condenser. While the breaker points are closed, current flows in the primary ignition circuit. When the points open, the magnetic field in the coil collapses, producing a very high negative secondary voltage. This voltage must first overcome the electrical resistance across the spark plug gap to form the spark; then it must maintain the spark. A much higher voltage is required to start the spark than to maintain it the additional fraction of a second it is needed.

In the primary trace, the initiation of the spark is shown by the first high positive peak, and the duration of the spark is shown by the high-frequency oscillations. In the secondary trace, the initiation of the spark is shown by the dotted line and the duration of the spark by the straight horizontal portion of the spark zone.

It is a characteristic of the coil to try to maintain current flow after the points are open. When the points are opened, the current has no place to flow but into the condenser. Thus the condenser becomes charged and its voltage increases. Soon the condenser becomes charged to a voltage higher than that of the battery or any other portion of the circuit, so the current flows in the reverse direction. The current again has no place to go but around the circuit to the other plate of the condenser, charging it up in the opposite direction. This process continues, giving an oscillatory current and voltage in the primary. Due to dissipation of energy in the spark and in the resistance of the primary circuit, these oscillations die out rather rapidly, as shown by their decreasing amplitude on the trace.

It was noted that when the points open, a high negative secondary voltage is built up which causes the spark plug to fire. From 3,000 to 15,000 volts is necessary to initiate or start the spark, whereas only from 1,500 to 3,000 volts is required to maintain the spark. On engines with high compression ratios, spark plugs

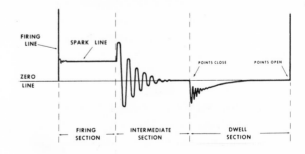

Fig. 13.3. Single cylinder trace as shown on the Sunscope. On this presentation, negative voltage is shown above the base line. The "intermediate section" is the coil-condenser zone.

in poor condition or excessive resistance in the high-tension circuit may require an initial voltage as high as 20,000 to 25,000 volts.

The spark level as shown in the secondary trace is rather flat, and the spark lasts for an appreciable period of time, as shown by the horizontal length of the line. The actual duration is measured in thousandths of a second, and the full length of the trace of a single sparking cycle represents only approximately 0.01 second with the engine running at 2000 rpm. The time represented at other speeds will be proportional. The arc of the spark acts as a voltage regulator, which is the reason the secondary spark line stays relatively flat, indicating direct current voltage in the secondary circuit for the duration of the spark. The voltage across the spark plug electrodes is shown by the relative distance from the base line in the spark line.

After a certain period of spark duration, there is not sufficient energy remaining in the ignition system to maintain the spark further, so it dies out or is extinguished. At this time the *coil-condenser zone* in the oscilloscope traces begins. Since the spark plug load is now open-circuited, the voltage in the coil increases. Thus in the secondary trace the voltage increases in the negative direction. This rather sharp increase is transferred back into the primary, through the transformer action of the coil, shock exciting the primary so that corresponding oscillations, but with opposite polarity, occur in this circuit.

The oscillations in the coil-condenser zone are of lower frequency than those shown in the primary trace in the spark zone; that is, the "waves" will be farther apart. There should be at least five waves, gradually decreasing in amplitude. Because of the resistance in the primary ignition circuit, the oscillations die out rather rapidly. Since the coil acts as a fairly good transformer for this particular frequency, the same low-frequency oscillation appears in both the secondary and primary.

After the low-frequency oscillations die out, only battery voltage appears across the condenser. *When the points close,* the condenser is shorted out so that there is a rapid change across the condenser from battery voltage to zero. Because of the rapidity of this change, the secondary circuit of the ignition system gets shock excited, so that a short duration high-frequency signal is obtained and shows in the secondary trace. This high-frequency oscillation is referred to as the *point close signal*. The points close signal in the primary trace is shown as a smooth drop in primary voltage, but in the secondary trace, oscillations occur, though smaller in amplitude than the coil-condenser oscillations.

At the end of the dwell period, shown as a straight line in both primary and secondary traces, the points open and the entire firing cycle is repeated.

The oscilloscope traces the variations in voltage which actually occur in the primary and secondary ignition circuits. Due to the speed with which the light beam of the cathode-ray tube moves, these traces appear as pictures shown on the screen of the tube. There is a choice of showing either the primary trace or the secondary on several of the oscilloscopes available.

The secondary system trace is somewhat more sensitive, and more troubles can be detected from its signal than from the trace of the primary. However, the trace of the primary gives considerable information and the oscilloscope which can show both secondary and primary is a valuable diagnostic tool.

Types of Trace Presentation

There are two general types of trace presentation used by the makers of automotive oscilloscopes: (1) the parade sweep, and (2) the raster sweep.

The parade sweep shows the traces for all cylinders of an engine on the one line. By means of the instrument controls, the trace of a single cylinder can be made to take up the whole screen of the cathode-ray tube, or each cylinder trace can be shortened enough to show all cylinders at once. Also, on most of the instruments, the different cylinders can be paraded across the screen one or two at a time. The wider each trace can be shown, the more detailed information it will give, except for comparisons with the other cylinders when at least half of the cylinders should be shown at one time. On the Sunscope, provision is made for showing a single cylinder trace above the parade sweep so that a good cylinder can be compared readily with the others. The parade sweep is shown in Fig. 13.4.

The raster sweep, used exclusively by DuMont, shows each cylinder trace on a separate line, one below the other in firing order. In this type of presentation, all cylinder traces may be shown simultaneously, nearly the full width of the screen. By means of a control, these can be stretched to show more details of any portion.

On the raster sweep, the spark initial firing line, which is shown as a high vertical line on the other scopes, is omitted because if shown it would run into the traces of the other cylinders. The DuMont engineers do not consider it of major importance, since the information it provides can be obtained easily by other tests. The level of the spark line, compared with the base line, the length of the line, and the amplitude of the coil-condenser oscillations will give some indication of the relative initial spark voltage. The raster sweep is shown in Figs. 13.5, 6, 7, 8, 9, and 10.

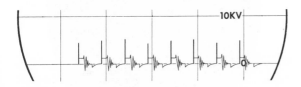

Fig. 13.4. Parade sweep of the Sunscope, showing the trace of all eight cylinders. Notice that the firing line, spark zone, coil-condenser zone, points close signal and dwell can readily be identified and the cylinders compared.

The ignition signal occurs constantly, but there is only a limited screen on which to display it. In order to be of value, the signal must be repeated. If this is done for every engine

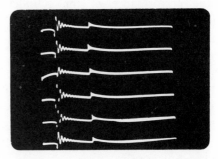

Fig. 13.5. Raster sweep or traces as shown on the DuMont Enginscope. The individual cylinder lines appear in the engine firing order. Notice that the third line down (cylinder No. 3) has the spark line bent, indicating resistance in this cylinder circuit.

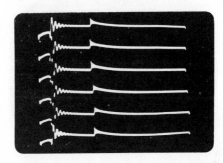

Fig. 13.6. Raster sweep as shown on the DuMont Enginscope, with all cylinders showing high resistance in the spark line. This would indicate that the cause is either in the distributor rotor, in the high tension lead from coil to distributor, or in the coil tower HT connection.

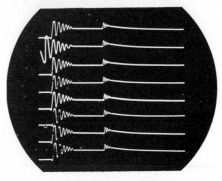

Fig. 13.7. Eight-cylinder display showing the appearance of a misfiring cylinder on No. 8 (second line) caused by a bad wire (open) or a plug which is open.

cycle, and the pattern is shown starting with the operation of No. 1 cylinder, then each cylinder will be shown in the same order as the engine firing order. Each cylinder trace indicates the performance of the cylinder each time it operates and occasional "misses" will be noticeable.

Three Basic Questions

When making an oscilloscope examination of an ignition system, there are three basic questions which should be asked, the answers to which will give the initial information needed in making a diagnosis:

1. Is the oscilloscope picture normal in all respects and in all cylinders?

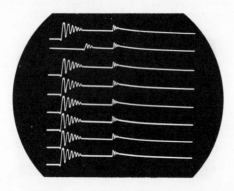

Fig. 13.8. Eight-cylinder display showing the effect of a shorted wire or plug on No. 8 (second line). Notice the long spark line and reduced coil-condenser oscillations. The location of the defect is plainly indicated.

2. If a defect is indicated, is it common to all or less than all cylinders?

3. In what event or zone does the defect occur?

If the pattern is normal, then apparently no trouble exists.

However, if the pattern is other than normal, the answers to questions two and three will give clues to the trouble, both its location and its nature. For example, if one or more, but less than all cylinders, are affected, the trouble will generally be found between the distributor rotor and the spark plugs (including the plugs). The spark zone of the trace will show a variance from cylinder to cylinder. This is true because individual circuits lead from the distributor cap to the spark plugs, and one or more can be affected without affecting the others.

If the trouble affects all of the cylinders in the same way, it will have to be between the coil primary and the distributor rotor, with two possible exceptions: (1) the spark jumping to the primary pigtail in the distributor, or (2) a worn cam lobe on the distributor cam, which could affect the dwell pattern and the spark line. Trouble in the points —such as point bounce, burned points, or high resistance — will show up in the points close signal. Trouble in the points which causes arcing will show in the points open signal.

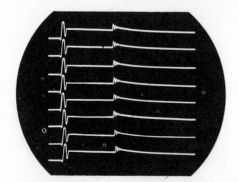

Fig. 13.9. Eight-cylinder display showing only a few "wiggles" in the coil-condenser zone. This indicates a defective condenser, as there should always be five or more waves at this point if the ignition system is functioning normally.

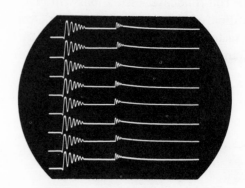

Fig. 13.10. Typical display of the raster sweep, with an ignition system in good condition. On the DuMont instrument the firing lines cannot be shown as they would all run together. Notice how clearly each of the zones can be seen.

From this it can be seen that the answers to the questions will immediately give helpful information. The next step is to interpret the meaning of the several different variations from a normal pattern.

Significance of Trace Variations

The factors that cause below normal or defective operation in the ignition system are:

1. Resistance in the high tension system.
2. Excessive spark plug gap.
3. Shorted plugs.
4. High-tension electric leakage.
5. Cross firing.
6. Defective coil.
7. Defective condenser.
8. Breaker points in bad condition.
9. Excessive dwell.
10. Too little dwell.
11. Low primary voltage.
12. Worn distributor shaft bearings.
13. Unusually worn distributor cams.
14. Reversed polarity.
15. Variations in cylinder to cylinder timing.

Spark Zone Indications

Any defective operation of the system will affect the traces as shown in the oscilloscope screen. One of the most generally affected zones on the trace is the spark zone. The length of the line, any bending of the line, and its relative level in respect to the base line, are all significant. The spark zone is affected by:

1. Resistance in the high-tension conductors or their contacts.
2. The spark plug gap.
3. Shorted plug or plug circuit.
4. High-tension leakage.
5. Cross firing.
6. Low primary voltage.
7. Defective distributor rotor or cap.

The length of the spark line is inversely proportional to the size of the spark gap — the larger the spark gap, the shorter the spark line; and the smaller the gap, the longer the spark line. The spark line is somewhat longer for six-cylinder engines than for eights because the dwell is longer on sixes.

An open circuit in the spark plug circuit, due to a wire entirely removed or some other circumstance that provides a gap too big to be jumped by the highest available voltage in the secondary circuit, will provide infinite resistance. Under this condition there will be no spark line and the coil-condenser oscillations will have greatly increased amplitude, thus, indicating the open circuit.

It is possible to have open circuits in the secondary circuit which would have the effect of stopping all current flow if the voltage were quite low. However, if the voltage is great enough to jump the gap, the "open circuit" actually only has the effect of increasing the voltage required. The spark line will be affected in the same way so that an excessive spark gap will be indicated.

Low primary voltage will affect the relative length of the spark line, but will not affect its level (which is a function of the required high-tension voltage) or the amplitude of the coil-condenser oscillation. Low primary voltage may be due to a low battery or high resistance in the primary circuit, either at the ignition switch or a loose or corroded connection.

When a plug is shorted there will be a long spark line with a lower voltage, because the only spark gap in the high-tension circuit is at the end of the rotor. In a normal circuit with good plugs, there are two gaps — the plug gap and the distributor gap between the rotor end and the contact in the distributor cap. Because of the low energy level with a shorted plug, the amplitude of the coil-condenser oscillations will be much smaller than normal.

Resistance in the high-tension circuit will cause the spark line, or lines, to have a distinct curvature. When the trace shows negative voltage below the line, as on the DuMont instrument, the spark line will bend up. Where the negative voltage is above the base line, high resistance will cause the line to bend down from

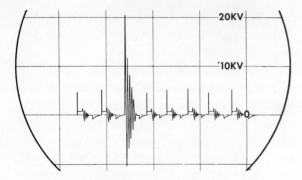

Fig. 13.11. Sunscope trace showing the effect of an open wire or plug on the third cylinder in the firing order. This indicates that the available voltage is 20 KV (kilovolts or thousands of volts). Projection below the base line should be at least half of the length above; otherwise it indicates that the insulation has broken down.

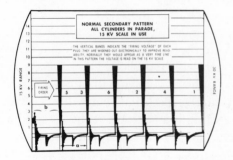

Fig. 13.12. Parade sweep as shown on the Heyer Dyna-Chek. This shows the firing lines or "spikes" exaggerated both as to height and width. The zones can be easily identified and comparison of the firing lines is easily made. The required voltage can be measured in KV.

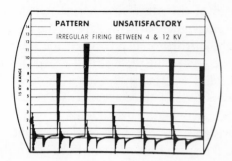

Fig. 13.13. Irregular pattern indicates high resistance or even open plug (high firing line) and shorted plug (low firing line). With a system in good condition the overall firing voltage will be proportional to spark plug gap, compression pressure and fuel-air mixture density.

the initial firing point toward the coil-condenser oscillations.

Coil-Condenser Zone and the Points Close Signal Indications

The coil-condenser zone is affected by (1) the coil and condenser, (2) low primary voltage, (3) open circuit in the high-tension circuit, and (4) shorted plugs. Electrically, the coil circuit begins at the battery side of the coil primary terminal and ends at the center tower of the distributor cap. A defective coil will reduce the amplitude of the coil-condenser oscillations, while a bad condenser will produce a line that is almost straight. Low voltage in the primary will reduce the energy in the ignition system and cause low amplitude in the coil-condenser zone.

The condition of the breaker points will appear in the points close signal and perhaps also at the points open end of the dwell line. The points close signal on the expanded cylinder trace should show clearly defined small oscillations. The first oscillation should always be the largest unless there is trouble or prospective trouble in the points. Excessive point resistance will cause the first oscillation to be lower than the following ones. Low amplitude of the points close signal can indicate a coil starting to fail, which will also affect the number of coil-condenser oscillations. There should always be five or more waves if the coil and condenser are in good condition. A bad condenser will affect the coil-condenser zone by almost eliminating the oscillations, but will not affect the points close signal.

If the points-close signal is too close to the coil-condenser zone, the breaker points are too close together and the dwell period is excessive. If the points close signal is too far away from the coil-condenser zone, the dwell is too small and the point gap is excessive.

Dwell Zone Indications

Most of the oscilloscopes for automotive service have a scale on the screen to measure the dwell. When a single cylinder trace is adjusted to just the length of the scale, by means of the width control, the dwell can then be read either in degrees or percent of dwell. On a six-cylinder engine, 100% dwell will be 60°, while on an eight cylinder, 100% will be 45°. Thus, if the dwell should read 55%, which is a common figure, this would be 55% of 60° or 33° for six cylinders. It would be approximately 27° for an eight-cylinder engine.

Worn distributor shaft bearings will allow shaft wobble or side play and will change the position of the dwell for the different cylinders. A bent distributor shaft will cause the same trace, but in a regular pattern. With the parade sweep, this is not too easy to observe; but with the raster sweep, the comparison from trace to trace is quite obvious. The corresponding spark lines will also show change of relative length due to change in the spark gap at the end of the rotor.

An unequally worn distributor cam will, in general, change the length of the dwell zone. These conditions show up plainly where the traces can be superimposed, with the trace expanded.

Reversed polarity of the high-tension system will cause the trace to appear on the opposite side of the base line from the normal pattern position. This condition can be corrected by changing polarity if the battery has been put in wrong or by reversing the coil connections.

The illustrations in this section (Figs. 13.5-13.21) show how the various defects in the ignition system affect the oscilloscope traces as they appear on the screen of the cathode-ray tube. The DuMont traces are presented because the raster sweep enables an easy comparison to be made, so the defects in the ignition system will be readily apparent to one who is being introduced to the oscilloscope. These illustrations and the captions should be carefully examined to observe the indications of abnormal behavior in the ignition system.

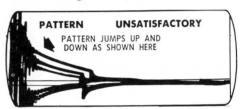

Fig. 13.15. Superimposed secondary trace shown on Dyna-Chek. When the pattern jumps up and down as illustrated, it is a sure indication of an open in the secondary winding inside the coil.

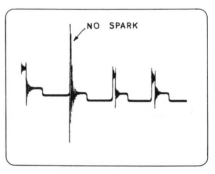

Fig. 13.16. Primary trace as shown in the Heath Ignition Analyzer. Four cylinders are shown, with the second cylinder having an open spark circuit. Note that this is quite similar to the open spark circuit shown in Fig. 13.11.

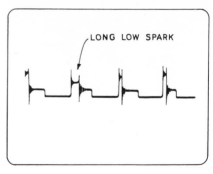

Fig. 13.17. Primary trace showing partially shorted plug circuit on the second cylinder in the firing order. Note the long spark zone at lower level. Low resistance in the secondary lowers the level and increases the length.

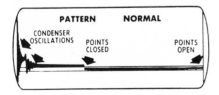

Fig. 13.14. Primary circuit trace as shown on the Heyer Dyna-Chek. On this trace the spark zone is indicated by the left arrow, and the coil-condenser zone by the next arrow showing "condenser oscillations."

Oscilloscope Controls

The controls on the automotive oscilloscope are similar to those on a television set. Except for the *off-on* switch used to control the required 115-volt AC supply, the controls are used to adjust: (1) the vertical location or the height of the trace, (2) the horizontal position of the trace, (3) the width of the trace and, with the parade sweep, the number of cylinder

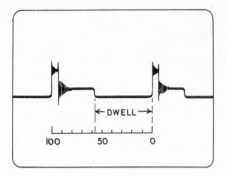

Fig. 13.18. Trace of a single cylinder (primary) showing how dwell may be measured. The length of a single-cylinder trace can be controlled so that it is just the length of the scale which gives dwell in percent of degrees (60° for 6-cylinder or 45° for 8-cylinder engines). Dwell shown is 57% (24° for 8-cylinder, 32° for 6-cylinder). Some scopes read directly in degrees.

traces shown on the screen, (4) the trigger or stability control, and (5) the left-hand starting position.

The number of control knobs will vary from three to ten, but actually only a few of the controls need to be manipulated when using the instrument; the others, once set, need little further adjusting. The purpose of each control is clearly marked, so that using the oscilloscope is not at all difficult.

The Marquette (Heyer) Oscilloscope has a main control knob which can be turned to show: (1) primary trace, one cylinder only, (2) primary trace, all cylinders superimposed, (3) secondary trace, one cylinder only, (4) secondary trace, all cylinders superimposed, and (5) secondary trace, all cylinders on parade.

It is essential to understand: (1) the significance of the trace that appears on the screen of the cathode-ray tube, and (2) the function and action of the ignition system.

Descriptions of Available Oscilloscopes

At the time this is written there are six oscilloscopes offered to the automotive industry. The automotive type is specified because oscilloscopes are used for many purposes, and those used for automotive work are especially adapted.

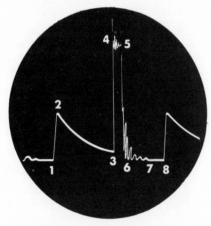

Fig. 13.19. Specialized primary trace shown by Snap-On Anal-O-Scope, picked up by connecting across the ignition coil. *1-2* is points closed signal; *2-3* is dwell zone; *3* is points open; *3-4* is firing line; *4-5* is spark zone, representing spark duration; *5*, spark is extinguished; *6-7* is coil-condenser oscillations; *6-8* is coil-condenser zone; *1-8* is one sparking cycle, for one cylinder.

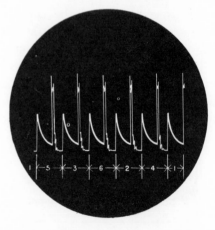

Fig. 13.20. Parade sweep on Anal-O-Scope screen shows six-cylinder engine. While at first glance these traces seem different from the basic traces shown on the other oscilloscopes, actually it is easy to distinguish the same zones and signals.

Any oscilloscope must have provision for picking up the desired signal from the ignition system — from the primary circuit, from the secondary (high-tension) circuit, or from both. There must also be a "trigger" pick-up, which is a connection to one of the spark plug wires to start off the succession of individual traces. The traces will then appear in the same order as the engine firing order, beginning with the cylinder to which the trigger pick-up is connected (usually No. 1 cylinder).

Some of the instruments require a good ground on the engine or chassis. The connections to the ignition system may be made (1) by clamps over the high-tension wires, giving what is called a "capacitive pick-up"; (2) by spring clips to one or more of the coil or distributor terminals; and (3) by inserting connecting links in series with high-tension conductors and tapping off signals.

Regardless of the particular form of the trace that is obtained on the screen of the cathode-ray tube, or the type of connections made with the ignition system, the same analysis of the basic trace must be made. If this basic trace and its zones are understood, any of the oscilloscopes can be used to advantage.

Sunscope

The oscilloscope shown in Fig. 13.22 is made by the Sun Electric Corporation. It presents a normal high-tension trace similar to the basic trace shown in Fig. 13.2, with spark zone, coil-condenser zone, points close signal, and dwell zone.

The scale on the screen is calibrated in kilo-volts (thousands of volts) so that the height of the initial spark line, or spark firing line, will indicate the voltage required to ionize the spark gap at the spark plugs and initiate the spark. Immediately after the spark has jumped the gap, the voltage required to sustain the spark drops down to a much lower value. This is shown by the straight horizontal spark line, unless resistance in the high-tension system causes it to be bent.

The firing line, indicating the initial voltage required to cause the spark to jump the spark plug gap, is clearly shown for each cylinder.

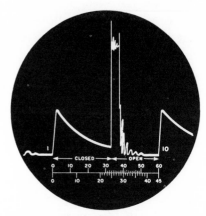

Fig. 13.21. Showing how dwell is measured on the Anal-O-Scope. The scales are calibrated in degrees, 0-60° for sixes, and 0-45° for eights. The length of one spark cycle (points close to points close on one cylinder) is adjusted to the length of the scale. The length of the dwell zone is then measured on the scale.

Fig. 13.22. Sunscope oscilloscope made by Sun Electric Corporation. Connections to the engine are made by inserting left pick-up in series with high-tension coil-distributor lead, and right pick-up (trigger) in series with last spark plug in firing order. The controls give great flexibility for maximum information and sensitivity. It is also furnished mounted in the Master Motor Tester. Screen is 7″ diameter.

Where there is an open circuit in a spark plug circuit (as when a spark plug wire is removed, disconnected, or broken), this line will be much higher, indicating the "available voltage." Subtracting the "required voltage" from the "available voltage" will show the "ignition reserve." However, to get the true value of the ignition reserve, it should be observed with the engine under load, since it takes considerably more voltage to fire under load than when the engine is idling or operating without load. The distance the firing line extends *below* the base line should be equal to one-half or more of the length of the firing line above the base line, to indicate that the insulation on the secondary circuit conductors is satisfactory. If the line deviates from normal, the insulation is defective and the conductors should be replaced.

The Sunscope has more controls than most of the other instruments, providing good flexibility in the indications which appear on the screen. The trace can be enlarged, either vertically or horizontally, for close examination of indicated ignition system defects. With another

Fig. 13.23. DuMont EnginScope, made by Allen B. DuMont Laboratories, Inc., Division of Fairchild Camera and Instrument Corp. This instrument features the raster sweep which shows a separate trace for each cylinder. Capacitive pick-ups are used; one long-jawed clip is clamped over the HT coil-distributor lead and the other over No. 1 spark plug lead. The screen is 5″ diameter. The IgnitionScope is similar in appearance, but somewhat smaller, with the tachometer omitted.

pick-up connected across the breaker points, primary traces can be shown separately or superimposed. The secondary traces can also be superimposed.

A feature of the Sunscope that is valuable for comparison purposes is the provision for showing one or two cylinder traces above the traces of other cylinders. The upper trace (s) is held while the traces on the lower line are paraded across the screen.

This instrument has a seven-inch screen. The new Sun oscilloscopes maintain a constant width of trace with changes in engine speed.

DuMont EnginScope and Ignitionscope

The DuMont automotive oscilloscope shown in Fig. 13.23 is furnished in two models, the EnginScope and the Ignitionscope. These are the only oscilloscopes which offer the raster sweep, showing each cylinder trace simultaneously on a separate line, one above the other, on a five-inch screen. Each cylinder pattern is the full effective width of the screen; comparison of the traces with each other is quite easy.

The EnginScope has some valuable and exclusive features. One of these is the circuit in the instrument which automatically compensates for different engine speeds to maintain a desirable constant trace length. Since the trace on most other automotive oscilloscopes shows time-voltage relationships, as the cycle time decreases with higher engine speed, the traces get shorter. Another feature is the built-in tachometer, so that engine speed can be indicated without an outside instrument. This instrument is extremely sensitive and will show up some ignition and cylinder conditions that otherwise might not be found.

Provision is also made for connecting transducers to pick up various engine signals and show the appropriate trace or pattern. (A *transducer* is a device for picking up such signals as vibrations, pressure differences, impulses, and noises, and converting them to equivalent electrical signals which will appear as patterns on the oscilloscope screen.) Valve action, for example, can be checked in this way.

The Ignitionscope is a simplified, less-expensive version of the EnginScope. It does not have the constant-trace-length provision; the tachometer is omitted, and transducers cannot be used with it.

Snap-On Anal-O-Scope

The Snap-On Anal-O-Scope (Fig. 13.24) picks up its signal for the trace pattern differently from any of the other instruments. Two connections are made across the primary of the coil and a third to ground. As with other instruments, the trigger pick-up is to one of the spark plugs.

Picking up the signal from across the coil primary terminals results in a trace form that is quite different in appearance from the basic forms for primary and secondary voltage variations, in these respective circuits. However, the wave form displayed by the Anal-O-Scope does show clearly the four basic trace zones.

This trace does not represent the circuit voltage variations in either the primary or the secondary, as is done in the other automotive oscilloscopes. Due to the unique signal pick-up connections, the trace on the screen of the Anal-O-Scope shows changes in voltage in the coil primary winding during each ignition cycle as it is affected by each phase of the cycle. The maker of this instrument claims extreme sensitivity to ignition troubles and easy interpretation of the trouble signals.

One outstanding feature is the built-in power pack, which enables the instrument to be used with the car battery as a current source instead of 115-volt alternating current. This permits convenient road testing. A power timing light is included with the oscilloscope, along with a set of spark plug extensions and insulated pliers for testing ignition reserve voltage. Another feature is the "ignition load" which permits bleeding off ignition primary current gradually to check the capacity of the primary ignition circuit.

Room is provided in the back of the instrument cabinet for the timing light, connecting wires, and accessories.

Marquette (Heyer) Dyna-Vision Projector

The Dyna-Vision Projector, by the Marquette Manufacturing Company, is designed to be mounted on a stand with other testing instruments. It consists of a vertical projector case containing the controls and chassis with its tubes and circuitry and an 8½" television tube (cathode-ray tube) mounted in a metal housing on top of the case. Refer to Fig. 13.25.

The screen of the cathode-ray tube has a scale calibrated 0-15 KV and 0-30 KV.

Connections are made to both high-tension and primary circuits. One pick-up lead is inserted in series with the wire from coil to distributor, at either end. Another link is inserted in series with one of the spark plugs for the trigger pick-up. The connections to the primary circuit are made by clipping two leads to the distributor side of the coil or to the distributor terminal and to ground, *i.e.*, across the breaker points.

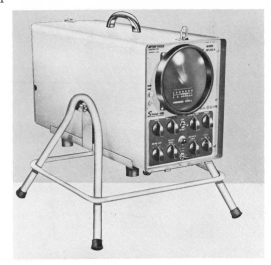

Fig. 13.24. Anal-O-Scope furnished by Snap-On Tools Corporation. This scope shows a trace taken from across the primary coil terminals, giving it a distinctive form, yet having the definite zones of the sparking cycle. Timing light, built-in power pack and other accessories are included. Screen is 5" diameter.

The instrument has only three controls: (1) horizontal speed, (2) horizontal hold, and (3) the pattern selector. However, the pattern selector will produce: (1) any one of three primary traces, (2) any one of four high-tension traces, and (3) an engine valve pattern, using an accessory unit and a transducer.

The primary traces are: (1) any single cylinder, (2) all cylinders superimposed, and (3) pattern for adjusting dwell. The high-tension patterns are (1) any single cylinder pattern, (2) all cylinders superimposed, (3) all cylinders firing voltage (15 KV scale) and (4) all cylinders firing voltage (30 KV scale). The engine valve trace will show the pattern of valve action and will indicate valve condition.

The primary trace shown on the screen is the same as the basic primary pattern previously discussed. The secondary or high-tension pattern is much like the basic high-tension pattern except that the circuitry used emphasizes the height of the firing line and its width at the top.

The superimposed traces of all cylinders shows differences in the various cylinders clearly, especially on the expanded traces; however the traces of all cylinders separately are needed for identification of defective cylinders.

Another valuable feature of the Marquette (Heyer) Dyna-Vision control panel is a knob which enables the operator to short out electronically one cylinder at a time so that the loss in engine speed may be observed on the tachometer. A comparison of the different cylinder losses will give a cylinder balance.

Heathkit Ignition Analyzer

The Heathkit Ignition Analyzer is made by the Heath Company. It is supplied in kit form, to be assembled by the purchaser. Everything that is needed to assemble the instrument is provided except a roll of rosin core solder. The components are all of excellent quality, and the instruction book which is furnished is complete, clear, and easy to follow. The assembly can be made in from twelve to sixteen hours in most cases. The price is about one-sixth that of other commercially available sets. The Heath oscilloscope may also be purchased completely assembled.

The trace shown by this instrument is taken across the distributor breaker points, and therefore is the low-tension or primary trace. In this trace, the spark zone shows the initial rise in voltage as the breaker points open and the high-frequency oscillations which take place for the duration of the spark. Thus the spark line will actually be the center line of the high-frequency oscillations, which corresponds to the straight spark line as shown by the basic undistorted high-tension trace. Variations due to high resistance in the high-tension circuit which cause the spark line to be bent, will also cause the center line of the high-frequency oscillation to be bent in a corresponding manner. The height above the base line and the length of the spark duration are important points to be noted in the trace and have the same significance as the height and length of the high-tension trace. Reference to the illustrations of the Heath traces will show this clearly, Fig. 13.26.

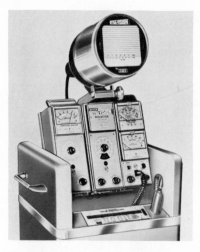

Fig. 13.25. Dyna-Vision oscilloscope made by Marquette Mfg. Co. The center unit contains the oscilloscope chassis and controls, with an 8½" cathode ray tube. The left unit is a combustion analyzer; the right unit is a combination tachometer, spark advance meter and voltmeter. The oscilloscope features three controls, and will show both primary and secondary traces.

The connections are made by clipping the leads either to the distributor side of the coil or the distributor terminal, and to ground; the trigger pick-up is clamped over one of the spark plug leads. If it is attached to No. 1 cylinder head, the traces will appear in the same order as the engine firing order, starting with No. 1.

A fourth connection is supplied, a clip with long jaws, which is attached to the cable from coil to distributor, to provide an inductive pick-up to give a secondary trace. A switch makes it easy to change from the primary to the secondary trace. Removing this clip from the coil to distributor cable and replacing it with the trigger lead from No. 1 spark plug will give a superimposed primary trace of all cylinders.

For road testing an engine, which is quite desirable at times, a small power pack can be used to supply the 115-volt AC needed. The overall dimensions of 6½″ x 11″ x 20″ make the instrument compact enough to use it readily inside an automobile.

In common with all the oscilloscopes using the parade sweep, this instrument shows the trace of a single cylinder filling the full width of the screen, as well as from two to the full six or eight cylinders at once. With all cylinders shown, the different zones of the traces can be compared. With all shown, the traces of each cylinder are small and it is difficult to observe some of the differences, but decided variations from normal show up clearly.

Depending upon the manner of making connections across the breaker points, the trace can be made to appear with positive voltage above the base line or below it. If the trace appears below the base, reversing the connections of the oscilloscope across the points will reverse the position of the trace.

For those who may not be willing to make the fairly substantial investment in one of the factory-built oscilloscopes, the Heathscope is recommended. It can be purchased at a very low price, and can be assembled by anyone who can follow simple directions and can solder wires and terminals.

This instrument has its limitations and it will not do quite as much as the more expensive oscilloscope, but it will give very valuable information in diagnosis and trouble shooting.

Allen Scope

The Allen Scope (Fig. 13.27) is made by the Allen Electric and Equipment Company. It is readily portable, as the dimensions are 9″ high, 11¼″ wide, and 16″ long.

There are two connections to the ignition system, one to pick up the trace signal and the

Fig. 13.26. Heath Ignition Analyzer, supplied at a very modest price to be assembled by the purchaser. This instrument shows the typical primary trace on a screen 3″ x 4″. Connections are easily made by clips across the breaker points, with capacitive coupling to spark plug wire for trigger.

Fig. 13.27. Allen Scope made by Allen Electric and Equipment Company. It is very compact, being 9″ high, 11¼″ wide, and 16″ long, with a screen approximately 4″ x 5″. It shows the secondary trace and uses the capacitive type of pick-up for signal and trigger. Four controls make it very easy to use.

other to pick up the trigger signal. The trace signal pick-up lead is merely clamped over the high-tension lead from coil to distributor, while the trigger pick-up is clamped over a spark plug wire. This will present the basic high tension trace pattern. As there are only four controls, the instrument is very easy to use.

The Allen Scope is supplied in several different models. In addition to the one illustrated, a unit mounted above a group of test instruments is available. This test unit enables a test for "dynamic compression" to be made which is similar to the Marquette (Heyer) cylinder balance test.

Information and Instructions

Each of the oscilloscopes described here has an instruction book with charts and drawings, giving information on the specific connections to be made and the tests to be conducted. Information is also given on the interpretation of variations from the normal trace pattern.

This interpretation will be made considerably easier if the analysis of the ignition system and the action of the primary and secondary circuits are understood. No matter which oscilloscope is used, the four zones — spark zone, coil-condenser zone, points close signal, and dwell zone — will appear in the trace pattern. Knowledge of the parts of each circuit to which each zone applies will help to identify trouble.

Remember to ask these questions when observing the traces of all the cylinders:
1. Is the pattern normal?
2. If not normal, is the trouble in all or less than all cylinders?
3. In what part of the trace does the trouble appear?

Observation of the nature of the variations from normal will give an indication of the nature of the trouble.

The oscilloscope is a very valuable testing and diagnostic tool. However, it should be considered as an additional tool, not as a replacement of the other valuable testing instruments which are still needed as much as ever for tune-up, diagnosis, and checking corrective work.

Summary

The *automotive oscilloscope* is the newest diagnostic tool for checking the ignition system.

The *cathode-ray tube* is similar to the television tube and projects the trace of the ignition spark cycle on its screen.

The *entire ignition system* can be tested as an area test. A trace may be obtained from either the primary circuit or the secondary circuit. The duration of the ignition spark is about one thousandth of a second and an entire spark cycle will take around one hundredth of a second at 2000 rpm, in a six-cylinder engine.

In the *ignition cycle*, as the distributor breaker points open, the spark jumps across the spark plug electrodes. After the spark is extinguished there are low-frequency oscillations in the coil and condenser which show up in both the primary and secondary circuits from the transformer effect of the two coil windings.

The *oscillations* end in a straight line above the base corresponding to the primary voltage. The points close signal is definite and easy to see, and the voltage drops to substantially zero. When the next spark occurs, the cycle starts over again.

In a *spark cycle*, there are four zones: *spark zone*, *coil-condenser zone*, *points close signal*, *dwell zone*, and *points open signal*.

The *superimposed traces* of all cylinders will show arcing breaking points.

The *oscilloscope trace* is a "time-voltage" diagram, showing voltage in the vertical direction and time horizontally. The *primary trace* is obtained by connecting across the breaker points. In the primary trace there are oscillations during the spark occurrence. In the *secondary trace* the spark zone is a straight or slightly curved line. The next portion of the trace shows the oscillations in the coil-condenser circuit.

The *voltage across the spark plug electrodes* is shown by the relative distance from the base line to the spark line. It takes 3,000 to 15,000 volts to fire a spark plug, but only 1,500 to 3,000 volts to maintain it.

When the *spark is extinguished*, the spark plug is open-circuited and the voltage in the coil increases, starting the coil-condenser oscillations.

When the *points close*, the condenser is shorted out so there is a rapid change across the condenser from battery voltage to zero, giving the high-frequency oscillations which we call the "points close signal."

There are two general types of *trace presentation*: (1) *parade sweep*, and (2) the *raster sweep*. The parade sweep shows all cylinders side by side, while the raster sweep shows the cylinders one above the other in substantially parallel lines.

Answering *three basic questions* will give important diagnostic information: (1) Is the trace normal in all cylinders? (2) Is the defect (if any) common to all or less than all cylinders? (3) In what portion of the spark cycle does the defect occur? Trouble from the coil primary to the distributor rotor affects all cylinders. Trouble from the distributor cap to the spark plugs may affect only an individual cylinder.

Below-normal or defective operation in the ignition system will affect the scope trace.

Most of the automotive oscilloscopes have a scale to measure dwell and may be used as a dwell meter. Dwell is sometimes given in percent which is the ratio of actual dwell to 100% dwell.

Oscilloscope controls are similar to those on a television set, such as vertical location, width of traces with parade sweep, trigger or stability control, and left-hand starting position. The Marquette (Heyer) controls the whole display with one knob.

Questions

1. What kind of tube is used to display the oscilloscope trace?
2. The scope trace is a curve or chart representing variations in what factor?
3. What two kinds of traces can be shown on most oscilloscopes?
4. Mention the first two important portions or "zones" of the oscilloscope trace.
5. Mention a following event, a zone, and final event in the spark cycle.
6. What voltage is generally necessary to initiate the spark in an ignition system in good condition?
7. What voltage will maintain the spark for its normal duration after it has jumped across the spark plug electrodes?
8. How long does the complete spark cycle take?
9. How long is spark duration normally?
10. What is meant by "parade sweep"?
11. What is meant by "raster sweep"?
12. What factors in the ignition system will affect the spark zone in the trace?
13. What factors will affect the coil-condenser zone?
14. What factors will affect the points close signal?
15. What does the length of the dwell zone indicate?
16. What are the three basic questions that should be asked when checking an ignition system with the oscilloscope?
17. What happens to the firing line when a plug circuit is open?
18. What happens to the firing line when a plug is shorted?
19. Mention four items that will affect the trace.
20. Name five manufacturers of automotive oscilloscope equipment.
21. What oscilloscope has a different type of trace than the others?
22. What is meant by "cylinder balance" and "dynamic compression"?
23. In what order on the oscilloscope screen do the cylinder traces appear?
24. Is the ignition condenser charged before or after the breaker points open?
25. What happens to the condenser when the breaker points close?

SECTION V

Generation
and
Storage
of
Electricity

CHAPTER FOURTEEN

The Storage Battery

The storage battery is an important unit closely linked to the operation of the generator and its controls, the starting system, and the ignition system. It is essential for the service man to have a basic and comprehensive knowledge of this unit. He should know battery construction, rating, functioning, operation, servicing, testing and trouble shooting. This chapter provides information which is practical and applicable to automotive service. Remember that no diagnosis can be complete without an analysis of battery condition.

An extremely important fact, too frequently overlooked, is that there is only one fully serviceable battery — a fully charged battery! For starting in cold weather, for proper charging by the car generator, for best results from the ignition system, for freedom from sulphation, and for longest battery life, a battery that is kept fully charged will give by far the best results.

Batteries in good condition can be kept fully charged provided the charging system, which includes the generator and generator control (voltage regulator), is in good condition; and provided that the car is run for a sufficient time at or above the minimum charging speed.

The Storage Battery

The Association of American Battery Manufacturers defines the storage battery as follows: "the lead acid storage battery is an electrochemical device for storing energy in chemical form so that it can be released as electricity." In other words, the storage battery is a device within which a reversible chemical process takes place. This process is activated in one direction when an electrical direct current is passed through the battery. It is reversed when an external circuit, connected to the terminals of the battery, is closed, permitting the flow of electricity from the battery. The external effect is exactly the same as if the battery stored electricity when being charged and surrendered electricity when being discharged. However, it is actually chemical energy and not electrical energy which is stored.

Parts of a Battery

The basic group of parts in battery construction is the *cell*. One storage battery cell has an emf of approximately 2 volts so that a 6-volt battery requires the use of three 2-volt cells connected in series. A 12-volt battery

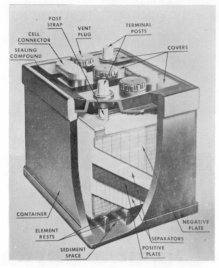

Fig. 14.1. The construction of an automotive lead-acid battery. Notice the ribs at the bottom for supporting the plates.

Fig. 14.2 (Top, left) positive plate with part of active material removed to show grid structure. (Bottom, left) negative plate. (Top, right) wood separator showing ribs and grooves on one face, other face smooth. (Lower, right) positive plate with some of the active material washed away. Glass fiber retainer mat (right) retards shedding of positive plate material.

requires the use of six cells connected in series. Fig. 14.1 shows battery construction.

The most important battery cell parts are the plates, both the positive and negative. The cell voltage depends on the presence of the charged *positive* and *negative plates* and the liquid covering them, the *electrolyte*. The number of plates in the cell does not determine the voltage. A cell consisting of one charged positive plate and one charged negative plate would still have a voltage of approximately 2 volts. Plate details are shown in Fig. 14.2.

The *amount of current* the cell can produce, however, is governed by the number of square inches of plate surface in the cell. Therefore more plates will mean more current capacity at the cell electromotive force of 2 volts. This is an important point to remember.

In order to keep the plates of different polarity from contacting each other they are held apart by separators made of specially treated wood, porous rubber or other suitable materials. Note in Fig. 14.3 how fiber glass is used. The required number of positive plates in any given cell is assembled together by means of a plate strap to which the individual plates are welded, forming a positive plate group. The positive plates are so spaced that between each two positive plates a negative plate and two separators can be inserted. The negative group is assembled in the same way, although there is one more negative plate than positive plate so that a negative plate will always be on the outside of the assembled cell unit. After the groups are assembled they are slipped together, making up what might be pictured as a rather complicated sandwich consisting of a negative plate, separator, positive plate, separator, negative plate, etc. The post straps to which the corners of the plates are welded are so positioned that they will be at opposite corners when the total unit is inserted in the cell compartment of the case. Refer to Fig. 14.4.

The battery case for a 6-volt battery has three compartments, one for each cell. It is necessary to connect the individual cells in series to build up the required 6 volts emf. Cast lead bars, called cell connectors, are used for this purpose. *Terminal posts*, one at cell No. 1 and the other on the opposite polarity group of cell No. 3 or No. 6, provide for external connections.

Cell covers seal the cells to keep out dirt and other foreign matter and to prevent evaporation of the liquid. A threaded opening and vent plug in each cell cover provide a means of filling or inspecting the electrolyte level.

In order for the plates to go through the reversible chemical reaction, it is necessary to have a liquid electrolyte. In a fully charged battery, the electrolyte usually contains about 38% sulphuric acid by weight, or about 27% by volume, with the balance pure water. The sulphuric acid supplies one of the constituents which makes possible the chemical reaction that stores the chemical energy and releases the electrical energy. It also is a carrier for the electric current inside the battery between the positive and negative plates through the separators.

Most batteries are equipped with a type of vent plug or inside level indicator which also acts to control the liquid level in the battery cell when liquid is added. Batteries require the addition of water from time to time, but it is undesirable to add too much.

Battery Plates

The foundation of each battery plate, whether negative or positive, consists of a grid cast from a lead alloy containing about 8% antimony. These grids serve to conduct the current to and from the active materials in the plates and to hold this material in place. The antimony in the alloy stiffens and strengthens the soft lead and makes the grids less susceptible to corrosion. It also helps to cast the fine details of the structure of the grids and enables the battery weight to be kept to a minimum.

The open spaces in the grids are packed full of a paste made from various lead oxides and then dried. This oxide paste is called the "active

material." In some cases the same material is used for the positive and negative plates making them so-called "neutral plates," and in other cases a different mixture of oxide is used for each.

After the plates have dried, they are assembled in positive groups and corresponding negative groups and "formed." The forming

Fig. 14.3. Batteries made with glass fiber separators, which combine glass fiber and plastic, will give long battery life when used with high-grade plates and a rubber case.

Fig. 14.4. Group of plates lifted from battery case to show the arrangement of the plates and separators. A negative plate is always on the outside of the group. A group can be lifted out by cutting the connecting strap and removing the compound.

operation consists of inserting the groups in a weak sulphuric acid solution and passing an electric current through them for 30 to 50 hours. This causes formation of lead peroxide on the positive plates and a spongy pure metallic lead on the negative plates. The formed positive plates are a dark red or brown in color, while the negative plates are dull gray.

Chemical Reaction

In order to understand the chemical reaction that takes place in the charging and recharging of the storage battery, it is necessary to know something about the electrolyte and the sulphuric acid it contains.

Sulphuric acid is made up of 2 atoms of hydrogen, 1 atom of sulphur, and 4 atoms of oxygen, with the chemical formula H_2SO_4. Of the three chemical elements the sulphur and the oxygen are much more closely bound together than to the hydrogen. Sulphuric acid, H_2SO_4, can be considered as being made of H_2O (water) and SO_3 (sulphate). Added together, these form H_2SO_4.

When any one or more of the electric loading circuits (such as lamps, fan, radio or ignition) connect the two terminals of the battery with the switch closed, the SO_3 part of the acid combines with the lead peroxide active material on the positive plates and with the sponge lead on the negative plates. Both combinations form lead sulphate. This process continues until the greater part of the active material on both plates has been converted to lead sulphate, and the amount of acid in the electrolyte is much reduced. The electrolyte becomes progressively weaker because for every molecule of SO_3 that combines with the plate material a molecule of water (H_2O) is left. At this time the battery is said to have run down. Fig. 14.5 shows how the charging and discharging take place.

There is an energy potential in a charged storage battery which can be compared to compressed air confined in a tank. Opening a valve in the air tank will allow the air to discharge rapidly. Likewise, providing a current path from one terminal of the storage battery to the other will permit electricity to flow. With a current path provided, the chemical reaction described immediately starts to take place; electrical energy is formed from the released chemical energy, producing electrical current.

When a battery has been partially or fully discharged it is necessary to charge it again. This means that instead of current flowing *from* the battery, current flow must be supplied *to* the battery from an outside source, either a generator in the car or direct current from some other power source, such as a battery charger. Passage of current through the battery causes a reverse in chemical reactions. The SO_3, which combines with the positive and negative plates on *discharge*, is separated from them when the battery is *charged*. This restores the original lead peroxide and sponge lead on the positive and negative plates, and the SO_3 combines with the H_2O to form H_2SO_4 (sulphuric acid) once more.

The battery is fully charged when most of the active material on the positive plates has been converted back to lead peroxide and almost all of the SO_3 has been removed from the negative plate. Once again, it is ready to reverse the chemical process and give out current when a current path is provided. This reversible process can be repeated hundreds of times until the battery finally fails. Fig. 14.6 illustrates this reversing process.

Sulphation

The various uses of the term *sulphation* in connection with storage batteries may lead to a certain amount of confusion. Actually *sulphation* means the formation of lead sulphate on plates. Sulphate forms as a natural part of the process of discharge. It is finely crystalline and can easily be reduced and separated from the lead and lead peroxide when the charging current is passed through it. Sulphation considered in this way is a necessary part of the operation of the battery and is not a source of trouble.

CHEMICAL ACTION IN BATTERY

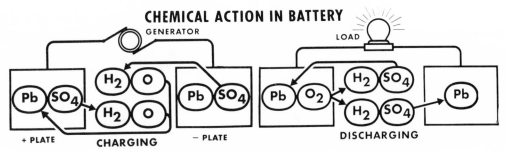

Fig. 14.5. In discharging, the Pb (lead) and SO_4 combine to form lead sulphate, while the H_2 combines with the O_2 to form water, lowering the specific gravity of the electrolyte. When charging, the Pb and O_2 recombine to form lead peroxide. (DR)

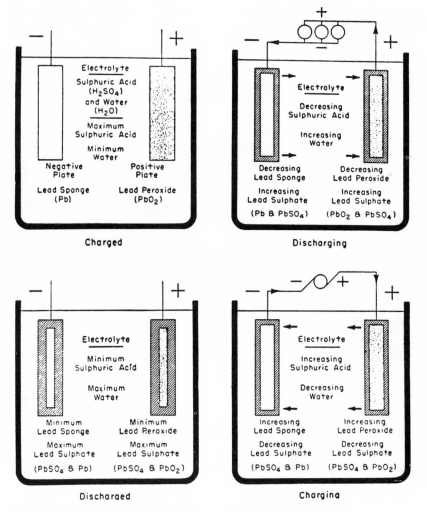

Fig. 14.6. Battery condition as it is charging, charged, discharging, and discharged. (Ex)

Sulphation, as often used by those working with batteries, refers to lead sulphate which may be formed as a result of local action, self-discharge of the plates or plates standing in a discharged condition for a long time. This sulphate appears as much larger and more bulky crystals.

The severest form of sulphation results in large crystals or a crust of lead sulphate which form on the plates from neglect or misuse. Discharged batteries standing unused for some length of time gradually lose the balance of their charge. In fact no battery should stand over a week or two without receiving some charging current. If it stands for a month or longer without attention, the battery will self-discharge almost completely. In this condition large, bulky crystals of sulphate form and can clog the pores of the active materials. Due to its expansive characteristics it will partially push the active material out of the grids and may cause them to buckle. Sulphated batteries may have so much internal expansion that the cases will be bulged and cracked. Fig. 14.7 shows the appearance of sulphated plates.

When extensive sulphation exists in a battery, the electrolyte will naturally be deficient in acid. However *acid should never be added within the battery*. If the condition is not beyond correction, the acid strength will reappear when the battery is charged. Sulphate formed when the battery stands in a discharged state for some time seems to harden and become more dense, and noticeably increases the internal resistance of the battery. Because hard sulphate is so difficult to break up, a battery in this condition is likely ruined. Fig. 14.8 shows the effect of sulphation on battery cases.

Specific Gravity

The electrolyte liquid is 1.285 to 1.300 times as heavy as an equal volume of water when both liquids are at the same temperature. In other words, the battery electrolyte has a *specific gravity* of 1.285 to 1.300. The term *specific gravity* is frequently referred to as *gravity*.

In the discharging process, the acid in the electrolyte is broken up into H_2O (water) and SO_3 (sulphate) with the sulphate forming lead sulphate on the positive and negative plates, thus reducing acid content in the electrolyte. With decreasing amounts of acid in the electrolyte, the specific gravity also decreases. Since

Fig. 14.7. Excessive sulphation on positive plates will ruin the plates and cause battery failure.

Fig. 14.8. Battery cases badly warped due to excessive sulphation. The straightedge at the battery end emphasizes the distortion.

the decrease in the amount of acid is proportionate to the amount of discharge of the battery, the approximate amount of charge left in the battery can easily be determined.

A hydrometer is used to measure the specific gravity of the electrolyte. The liquid from the battery is simply drawn into the instrument and a reading taken. For further information on the operation of the hydrometer refer to Chapter 12, "Battery Hydrometer."

The specific gravity of storage batteries for automotive service will properly range from 1.250 to 1.260 for the so-called "stay-full batteries" and 1.280 to 1.300 with an average of 1.285 for standard batteries. These figures are generally considered to indicate a fully charged battery. The gravity readings are stated as "twelve eighty-five" or "thirteen hundred," etc. Fig. 14.9 shows a good type of hydrometer with thermometer.

The following table illustrates the range of specific gravity for a cell at various stages of charge at a temperature of 80°F.

Table 3
Relationship of Specific Gravity and State of Charge of Lead-Acid Cells

Specific Gravity	Charge
1.280	100%
1.250	75%
1.220	50%
1.190	25%
1.160	Little useful capacity
1.130	Discharged

The specific gravity of the electrolyte in any cell is a measure of how much unused sulphuric acid remains in the solution, and this is an indication of the approximate capacity which is still available in a normal cell. For the most dependable indication the liquid level in a cell should be at normal height when the hydrometer reading is taken, and the electrolyte should be thoroughly mixed with any water which may have just been added. The hydrometer reading therefore should never be taken immediately after water has been added. The water should be thoroughly mixed with the electrolyte either by charging for at least one-half hour or by standing for two hours.

The hydrometer barrel and float must be rinsed with clear water each time the hydrometer is used. If the calibrated scale inside the float appears wet, it is an indication that the float has been cracked and leaks; a new float should be inserted in the barrel or a new hydrometer purchased.

Temperature Correction

The battery temperature of cars may vary from possibly 0°F. to as much as 120°F. or even higher. The specific gravity of the electrolyte depends upon the temperature as well as the acid concentration. The standard reference point for gravity is 80°F., and therefore a correction must be added for temperatures above 80°F. or subtracted for temperatures below that.

Acid volume expands when it is heated and shrinks when it is cool. When acid is expanded, it will be less dense than normal and therefore will not raise the hydrometer float to as high a level as it should, causing the reading to be low. The reverse happens when the acid is cool. This error due to temperature is well known and can be easily allowed for if the temperature

Fig. 14.9. Measuring the specific gravity of the electrolyte is one of the standard ways of checking battery state of charge. This hydrometer has a built-in thermometer for making temperature corrections.

of the acid which surrounds the float is known. Before reading the temperature or the float level, the electrolyte should be drawn in and out of the hydrometer barrel several times so that the barrel will assume the temperature of the liquid. Some hydrometers have a small thermometer and a correction scale built into them so that correction can readily be made. This type is highly recommended for diagnostic work. Note Fig. 14.10.

The temperature correction amounts to .004 specific gravity (referred to by shop men as 4 "points") for each 10°F. change in temperature from the reference point of 80°F.

It is advisable to check the temperature of the electrolyte if the battery is much colder or warmer than room temperature. For example, during cold weather a partially discharged battery might be overlooked if you relied on the hydrometer reading alone. This might read 1.270 indicating a nearly charged battery if it were at the normal temperature of 80°F.; but when the temperature correction is applied, the actual value might be only 1.246 which corresponds to a 75% charged battery. A partially discharged battery such as this should not be installed in a car during severe winter weather since it is liable to fail.

On the other hand, a low gravity reading of a battery at high temperature may be misinterpreted as failure of the battery to take its full charge. Application of the temperature correction will show the battery to be fully charged.

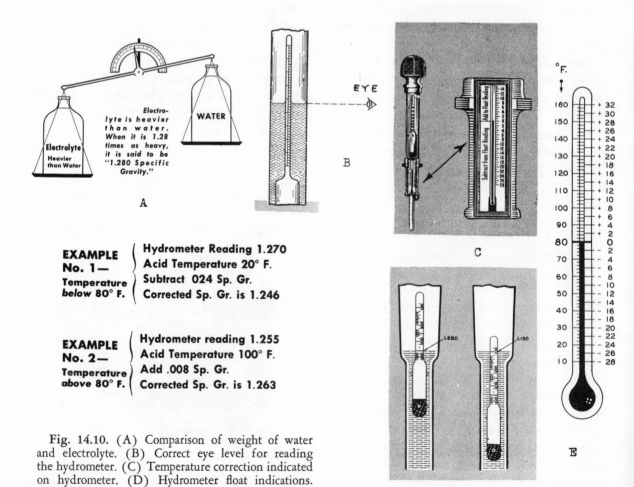

EXAMPLE No. 1— *Temperature below 80° F.*

Hydrometer Reading 1.270
Acid Temperature 20° F.
Subtract .024 Sp. Gr.
Corrected Sp. Gr. is 1.246

EXAMPLE No. 2— *Temperature above 80° F.*

Hydrometer reading 1.255
Acid Temperature 100° F.
Add .008 Sp. Gr.
Corrected Sp. Gr. is 1.263

Fig. 14.10. (A) Comparison of weight of water and electrolyte. (B) Correct eye level for reading the hydrometer. (C) Temperature correction indicated on hydrometer. (D) Hydrometer float indications. (E) Amount of temperature correction.

Gravity readings may be misleading if taken just after a battery has been discharged at a high rate such as after excessive use for cranking the engine. A heavy discharge weakens the acid in and near the plates, and until this weak acid has had time to diffuse with the remaining stronger acid in the cells, gravity reading of acids taken at the top of the cells will be too high and indicate a higher state of charge than really exists. The acid will slowly mix if the battery stands idle for several hours. The mixing will be more rapid if the battery is charged and the acid is mixed by diffusion and by the bubbles which are formed during the charging process. Fig. 14.11 shows the relation between state of charge and specific gravity.

Battery Rating and Capacity

Since storage batteries are made in a variety of sizes, from a small motorcycle battery to a large truck battery, some standardized method to indicate battery size or capacity is necessary. The capacity of a battery depends upon the number and size of plates per cell as well as upon the amount of acid present. The cranking capacity of a battery is therefore proportional to the positive *plate area*. For this reason automotive starting and lighting batteries are built with thin plates to provide a large plate area in order that the acid may have quick access to as much active material as possible. Automotive batteries are limited in capacity by the amount of acid contained in the cells.

The unit generally used for indicating battery capacity is the *ampere-hour*. The number of ampere-hours is determined by multiplying the time in hours by the number of amperes that will flow for a given period.

As this total amount of energy that a battery will produce will vary somewhat with the rapidity with which the energy is taken from the battery, it is necessary to specify some period of time over which the discharge occurs. The battery industry has worked out several accepted standards of performance which have also been accepted by and approved by the Association of American Battery Manufacturers, the Society of Automotive Engineers, and the Bureau of Standards of the United States Government.

The most commonly used rating in automotive practice is the *20-hour rating*. The 20-hour rating indicates the ability of the battery to discharge a small amount of current for a continuous period of 20 hours. To test the 20-hour rating, the fully charged battery is brought to a temperature of 80°F. and is discharged at a rate equal to one-twentieth of the 20-hour capacity in ampere-hours. For example, a 6-volt battery rated by the maker at 120 ampere-hours capacity would be discharged at one-twentieth of 120 (6 amperes) until the final or terminal voltage reached 5.25 volts (1.75 volts per cell).

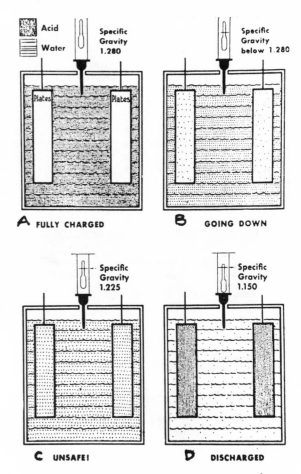

Fig. 14.11. Variations in specific gravity as battery becomes discharged. Note the different levels of the hydrometer float as the gravity drops.

A 12-volt battery rated at 60 ampere-hours would be discharged at 3 amperes for 20 hours and should not fall below 10.5 volts at the end of this time.

Any automotive battery in good condition and fully charged should deliver approximately

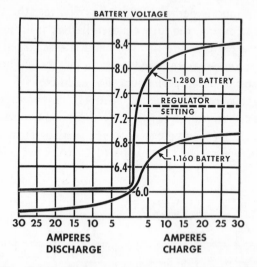

Fig. 14.12. Difference between voltage when discharging and charging. The chart also shows the difference between a fully charged battery and one with gravity of 1.160. The *Charging Voltage* is the voltage necessary to get a given number of amperes through the battery. Notice that at 7.4 volts the voltage regulator prevents the flow of more than about 3 amperes into a charged battery, while a low battery will take full generator output. (DR)

Fig. 14.13. Quick-discharge tester, also called break-down tester. It will draw a current of from 160 to 250 amperes from each cell in turn. Voltage should not drop below 1.7 volts per cell, at the end of 15 seconds.

one-twentieth of its rated ampere-hour capacity on the 20-hour basis for a period of 20 hours and still have a voltage of 5.25 (or 10.5 volts) at the end of this time. Most automotive batteries, especially those used for passenger car service, will have a 20-hour rating of from 90 to 120 ampere-hours for 6-volt or 45 to 70 ampere-hours for 12-volt units.

Fig. 14.12 shows the difference between voltage when charging and discharging.

High Capacity Unit

The characteristic of the lead-acid storage battery which makes it so valuable for automotive service is its ability to deliver an extremely heavy current for a short time, as well as a small current for a long period. It is not uncommon in wintertime cranking service for a moderately sized battery to deliver 300 to 400 amperes or more. A current as high as 700 amperes can be taken for a short period from 6-volt (or half this current from 12-volt) batteries. Batteries are also rated in another way which gives an indication of the cranking ability of a fully charged battery at low temperature. This rating is called the *300 amperes at 0°F*. rating. The rating is expressed in two ways: (1) by the terminal voltage of a fully charged six-volt battery taken 5 seconds after the start of discharge at a rate of 300 amperes with an initial electrolyte temperature of 0°F., (2) by the number of minutes required for a six-volt battery to reach a terminal voltage of 3.0 volts when discharged at 300 amperes with an initial electrolyte temperature of 0°F. Terminal voltages for 12-volt batteries will be twice this amount and current in amperes half as much. Fig. 14.13 shows a quick discharge tester. Notice that the temperature at which the rate is given is 0°F. It is important that a battery give its best possible performance at low temperatures because the heaviest demand is put on the battery when it has to start a cold engine in the wintertime.

It is very important to remember that the number of ampere-hours which can be realized from any given capacity of storage battery is cut down materially as the temperature drops and as the rate of discharge increases. In other words, a battery rated at 100 ampere-hours will give a current of five amperes for a period of 20 hours at an initial temperature of 80°F. However, if that same battery were discharged at 300 amperes it will produce only 32 ampere-hours at the same temperature. If the 300-ampere rate of discharge should take place when the battery is at 0°F. it would only yield 14 ampere-hours. This would mean that the battery would become discharged in 2.8 minutes, if the rate were continued until the battery reached a terminal voltage of 3.0 volts. The following table will give the ampere-hours that should be delivered by a 100 ampere-hour 6-volt battery, fully charged, with temperatures of 80°F. and 0°F. respectively.

Table 4
Relationship of Temperature and
Capacity of Lead-Acid Cell

Amperes	Ampere-Hours (80°F.)	Ampere-Hours (0°F.)
5	100	76
25	75	46
50	62	37
100	50	32
300	32	14
500	26	12

12-volt batteries will have half of above values for 50 ampere-hour battery.

From this table it can be seen that a battery can easily be run down under conditions of very heavy current draw and low temperature. When a complaint of a defective battery is received, it may be that the battery is in perfectly good condition, but excessive use under adverse conditions requires that it be recharged.

Not only is the number of ampere-hours greatly reduced at low temperatures, but the available cranking effort from a fully charged battery is also reduced. A battery at 0°F. is capable of delivering only 40% of the power it could deliver at the same state of charge at 80°F.

Battery Output

It is important that the correct terminology be used when referring to battery capacity and performance. *Amperes* refers to the amount of current that is drawn from the battery and has no connection with its rating. *Ampere-hours* is the term generally used to describe the capacity of a passenger car battery and the complete term should be used when referring to battery capacity. The ampere-hours that can be delivered by a battery will depend upon the rate at which the discharge takes place, and will vary from 100% to 26% or even lower if heavier current rates are used.

Battery rating in ampere-hours will depend on the size of the plates and the number of plates in each cell. There will always be an uneven number in each cell because the negative plates are always on the outside.

The number of plates per cell will ordinarily be 7, 9, 11, 13, 15, 17, or 19. Batteries are sometimes listed giving the number of plates per battery which would be on a corresponding basis. Numerous thin plates will not have as long a life as heavier plates, but they do make a more active battery. Thus they will provide more current for starting in cold weather and are generally preferred for passenger cars.

Batteries for cranking diesel engines are required to deliver high amperage. In addition to the passenger car ratings, such batteries are frequently described according to the number of amperes they will deliver for 1.5 minutes at 0°F. with a terminal voltage of 1 volt per cell.

12-Volt Batteries

As the voltage per cell in the lead-acid storage battery is approximately 2 volts, 12-volt batteries require six cells. In order to keep the dimensions close to those of 6-volt batteries, 12-volt units have about half the number of plates per cell. The electrical output per battery, compared with a 6-volt battery, will be about the same, but with one-half the amperage at twice the voltage.

Therefore, remember when working with 12-volt batteries, that generator voltage will be approximately doubled, from 7.4-7.6 volts to 14.3-14.8 volts. Power should be measured in *watts*. The number of watts is found by multiplying volts times amperes. This will give a logical basis for comparing the power requirements of 6-volt and 12-volt units.

The ampere-hour rating of 12-volt batteries is about half of the usual 6-volt rating, and the 12-volt units will not give the heavy ampere flow that can be drawn from 6-volt batteries. However, with higher voltage and the provision for offsetting the battery voltage drop due to the starting load, which is affected by the ignition system series resistor, starting is generally easier with the higher voltage. The change from 6 volts to 12 volts was completed on all American-built automobiles with the introduction of the 1956 models.

Dry-Charged Batteries

Dry-charged batteries have become popular in the last few years because factory-fresh batteries can be delivered to customers regardless of the length of storage after manufacture (up to about two years).

When the dry-charged batteries are made, the plates are dried after forming. The negative plates must be dried in a non-oxidizing atmosphere, such as carbon-dioxide or super-heated steam, to prevent them from being oxidized. The positive plates, being made largely from lead oxide, will not oxidize further at atmospheric temperature. The dried plates are assembled into groups, fitted with separators and put into battery cases. A wick or restrictor is put into the vent hole in the filler caps to keep out moisture, and is removed when the battery is activated.

To put the battery into service, electrolyte supplied by the battery maker is poured into the cells to the proper level. This electrolyte will be of 1.265 specific gravity at 80°F. After filling, the battery should be allowed to stand long enough to cool off; then the liquid level can be adjusted with the same electrolyte, if necessary. The battery will have 60% to 75% of full charge. It is preferable, though not necessary, to bring the battery up to full charge with a slow charger.

A dry battery in good condition before being activated should show no voltage at all across its terminals. If there is any voltage, the battery should be activated at once and charged.

It is the general practice to pour the prepared electrolyte into the battery and then put the battery into a customer's car immediately. While this will work most of the time, it is not good practice and will result in a certain proportion of complaints. The desirable procedure is to fill the battery at least half an hour before placing it in the automobile. A booster charge should then be given for 15 or 20 minutes at approximately 25 amperes for 12-volt batteries. The temperature should not exceed 125°F.

Summary

The *storage battery* is such an important item in automotive operation that a comprehensive knowledge of it is essential.

There is only one *fully serviceable battery* — a fully charged battery.

The storage battery is an *electrochemical device* for storing energy in chemical form so it can be released as electricity. The reversible process has the same effect as storing electricity.

The *cell is the basic group of parts*, with two volts per cell. A battery consists of three cells for a 6-volt battery or six cells for a 12-volt battery.

A *cell* consists of a group of positive and negative plates kept apart by separators. The amount of current a cell will give depends upon the number and size of the plates. Plates of like polarity are connected together by means of plate straps. The battery case has a compartment for each cell. The plates must be immersed in electrolyte of suitable strength.

The foundation of each *battery plate* is a grid of lead alloy containing about 8%

antimony. The spaces in the grids are packed full of lead oxide paste and then dried. After drying they are assembled into positive and negative groups and "formed" by passing direct current through them. Formed positive plates are dark red or brown in color while the negative plates are dull grey.

The *electrolyte* is sulphuric acid (H_2SO_4) which can be considered as being composed of water (H_2O) and sulphate (SO_3). When current is produced by the battery the active material on the plates begins to combine with the SO_3 of the electrolyte to form lead sulphate on the plates and release water to the electrolyte.

The *energy in a battery* can be compared to a tank of compressed air. The pressure (electrical or air) is ready to escape as soon as a path is provided.

When a battery is *discharged* it must be recharged.

Sulphation means the formation of lead sulphate on the positive and negative plates. There are two kinds of sulphate, (1) normal harmless sulphate formed as a result of useful battery discharge, and (2) hard sulphate with large crystals formed as a result of self-discharge and standing idle for long periods. The hard sulphate will ruin a battery and is difficult to remove.

The weight ratio to an equal volume of water is called *specific gravity*. The electrolyte is 1.285 to 1.300 times as heavy as an equal volume of water at 80°F. The gravity decreases as the battery becomes discharged. It is measured by a hydrometer, and is an indication of the battery state of charge.

The *specific gravity will increase as the temperature falls* below 80°F. and will decrease with temperatures above 80°F. at the rate of .004 (four "points") for each 10° of temperature change above or below 80°F.

Battery capacity depends on the size and number of plates per cell. Cranking capacity is proportional to positive plate area. Capacity is measured in ampere-hours which is number of amperes that will flow in a circuit for 20 hours

(20-hour rate), with a minimum terminal voltage of 1.75 volts per cell. The actual battery output will vary with the rate of current flow. There will be fewer ampere-hours capacity at high discharge rates such as operating the cranking motor.

Its *ability to deliver heavy current* makes the storage battery very valuable. While a 12-volt battery has twice the voltage of a six-volt with the same ampere-hour rating, it will be able to deliver only half the number of amperes. The number of ampere-hours delivered and available cranking effort are much reduced at low temperatures.

Ampere-hours refers to battery capacity rating while *amperes* refers to actual current flow drawn from the battery. There is always an uneven number of plates in a battery with negative plates on the outside. More thin plates per cell will have shorter life, but will make a more active battery.

12-volt batteries usually have about half the plates of a corresponding 6-volt battery. The voltage regulator is usually set for approximately twice the 6-volt setting. The change from the 6- to the 12-volt electrical system was completed with the 1956 models.

In *dry-charged batteries*, the plates after forming are dried, assembled into groups and fitted with separators. When the batteries are to be used they are filled with 1.265 gravity electrolyte at 80°F. (rated strength). They will generally have 60% - 75% of full charge. The batteries should be brought up to full charge with a slow charger.

Questions

1. What kind of a battery is fully dependable?
2. Define a storage battery.
3. Name the three basic parts of a storage battery cell.
4. How does the number of plates per cell affect cell voltage?
5. How does the number of plates per cell affect current capacity?

6. Why are separators used in a storage battery cell?

7. Why is there always an uneven number of plates in a cell?

8. Does a storage battery store electricity? Explain.

9. What is the forming operation in making a storage battery?

10. Give the chemical make-up of sulphuric acid.

11. What is meant by sulphation in a storage battery?

12. What is the specific gravity of a charged storage battery?

13. In the discharging process of the battery the electrolyte is broken up into what two substances?

14. What instrument is used to measure the concentration of battery acid?

15. What is the specific gravity of a half-charged storage battery cell?

16. Why should temperature be considered when checking battery gravity?

17. What unit of measurement is used to indicate battery capacity?

18. What time period is battery rating usually based on?

19. What is the difference between *amperes* and *ampere-hours*?

20. What is the voltage per storage battery cell?

21. How is battery power figured in watts?

22. What is the difference between dry-charged and wet batteries?

23. How should dry-charged batteries be activated?

24. How much voltage should a six-cell dry-charged battery show on a test before being activated?

25. Is a dry-charged battery usually ready for immediate installation and use upon being filled with electrolyte? Explain.

CHAPTER FIFTEEN

Storage Battery — Care and Servicing

The charging current for storage batteries must be direct current; therefore current from the usual power lines cannot be used without a device to rectify the current from AC to DC and transform the voltage to the required pressure for charging. The rectifying means may be motor-generator sets, tungar tube type rectifiers, dry-disc rectifiers, or diode rectifiers.

Charging Batteries

There are two general methods of charging used storage batteries: (1) constant current charging at a low rate and (2) high rate charging.

The *constant current* method of charging is the oldest and most common method of charging batteries where the internal cell condition is not known and where a diagnosis of trouble is being made. It is also the safest method since batteries cannot be injured when the charging current is held to approximately 6 amperes. When any kind of a charging device is used, the *positive* lead of the charger should always be connected to the *positive* terminal on the battery, and the *negative* lead to the *negative* battery terminal. The constant current charging method can be used with from one to six batteries in a series on small units, and from six to twelve batteries on larger units.

The batteries are connected in series, with the negative terminal of one battery connected to the positive terminal of the next battery, etc. The positive terminal of the first battery is connected to the charger positive terminal and the negative of the last battery in the series is connected to the negative terminal of the charger. The positive terminal of the battery is usually marked with a plus sign or "P" or "Pos," and it has a slightly larger post diameter ($11/16''$) than the negative terminal ($5/8''$). If it is difficult to tell which is the positive terminal of a battery from inspection, a voltmeter connected across the terminals of any cell can be used. The needle of the instrument will move toward that instrument terminal connected to the positive post of the battery.

When batteries are being charged, the charging rate should be so regulated that the temperature of electrolyte will not exceed $125°F$. Electrolyte will expand and the liquid level rise due to heat; displacement of the liquid by gas bubbles forming at the plate may take place while the battery is on charge. Therefore the vent opening should be kept tightly closed so that acid will not be forced out of the cell.

Hydrometer readings of each cell should be taken as the battery approaches the fully charged state. A battery is considered fully charged when the cells are all gassing freely and the gravity ceases to rise for three consecutive readings taken an hour apart. Most batteries can be recharged at the 6-ampere rate in 12 to 16 hours, which will add from 65 to 88 ampere-hours (for 6 volts) figuring an ampere-hour efficiency of 90%. Some batteries may require 24 hours or longer, and if so no harm will be done, as long as they are not left in the charging circuit for over three hours after reaching a constant specific gravity. A badly sulphated battery will require longer to receive its charge than a battery in normal condition.

Fig. 15.1. Portable fast charger. This type can be readily moved from place to place or can be taken to cars where the battery has failed and where 110 volts AC is available.

Fig. 15.2. Using a fast charger in a busy service station. Only batteries in good condition should be fast charged, and an understanding of batteries is necessary to determine those that are suitable.

The low-rate, constant current method of charging is the best and safest for lead-acid batteries, but it is not as convenient and profitable as the high-rate battery charging. This latter method has largely replaced the low-rate charging, especially in service shops and service stations.

High-Rate Charger

High-rate battery charges (Fig. 15.1) have become popular because of their ability to boost the battery charge rapidly without removing it from the car. This eliminates the need to have rental batteries available and also saves the labor involved in removing the battery from the car, installing a rental, removing the rental and installing the original battery. Since the same charging fee is asked for high-rate charging as for slow charging, the high-rate method is preferred by many shops and service stations. Batteries may be charged once or twice at the high rate without damage, as long as the electrolyte temperature of any cell does not exceed 125°F. and as long as excessive bubbling and loss of electrolyte does not take place. Sulphated batteries heat excessively under high charging currents. Batteries with even a moderate amount of sulphation can be damaged beyond repair by this method.

High-rate chargers usually supply an initial charging rate of 50 to 100 amperes, though there is little advantage in charging at a higher rate than 80 amperes. This should gradually be tapered off as the battery voltage rises due to the amount of charge it has received, and after a period of from 30 minutes to an hour, the rate should be reduced to 10 to 15 amperes for the final period. For 12-volt batteries, 25 to 50 amperes should be the initial rate.

A high-rate charger cannot be expected to bring a battery to full charge within the half hour to an hour that it is usually applied. But they do add enough charge to the battery so that it can continue to give service consistent with its condition and its state of charge. High-rate chargers can damage or ruin the battery if the safeguards provided by the manufacturer are ignored or circumvented or if the operating instructions supplied with the charger are not carefully followed. It is important that the duration of fast charge be accurately determined for any given battery so that severe overcharging will not damage it. Note Fig. 15.2. The fast-charging time can be determined from the following table. The "stay-full" batteries are fully charged at 1.260 gravity, and therefore the table should be modified proportionately for them.

Table 5
Fast-Charging Periods for Lead-Acid Cells

Gravity and Charge	Fast Charging Time
1.265 - 1.300 Fully charged	Do not charge
1.235 - 1.260 ¾ charged	Charge at slow rate
1.205 - 1.230 ½ charged	Fast charge 30 min.
1.170 - 1.200 ¼ charged	Fast charge 45 min.
1.140 - 1.165 Barely operative	Fast charge 60 min.
1.110 - 1.135 Discharged	Fast charge 60 min.

Some chargers control the charging action with a thermostat control that shuts off the fast-charge current when the temperature reaches 100° to 125°F.

All fast charger manufacturers and battery men agree that when the gravity readings of the individual cells differ by more than 40 to 50 points or when the open-circuit voltage readings differ by more than .04 to .05 volt, the battery is defective and doomed to early failure.

Testing Before High-Rate Charging

There are two important items that should be determined before fast charging: (1) the difference in cell condition, if any and (2) the state of charge of the battery.

In case the battery charge is so low that the capacity test cannot be made, make the "three-minute charge test" recommended by Sun Electric Corporation. To do this, put the battery on a fast charge of 70 to 80 amperes (35 to 40 amperes for 12 volts) for just three minutes. At the end of this time, with the battery still on charge, check the individual cell voltages. If

these are uneven by 0.1 volt or more, the battery is defective. Fig. 15.3 illustrates a voltage tester being used.

If the voltage remains under 7.75 volts (15.5 volts) for the three minutes, and the cell voltages are even within 0.1 volt, the battery is good. If the battery voltage rises above 7.75 or 15.5 volts during the three-minute test period, but the cell voltages remain even, the battery is either sulphated or has lost active material from the plates.

Once it is determined whether the battery is good or bad, the next procedure can be decided upon. If the battery is apparently good, the hydrometer should be used to check the state of the charge, and the battery put on a charger as necessary. A fully charged battery is required before any corrective work can be done on the electrical system. If the car battery is not fully charged, another battery should be substituted.

A sulphated battery will have a higher internal resistance than is normal. This can be quickly seen when such a battery is put on a high-rate charger; it will be impossible to get the charging current up to the usual 70 to 80 (35 to 40) amperes at the allowable maximum voltage of approximately 7.75 (15.5) volts. If with this voltage the current only gets up to about 50 (25) amperes, it is a good sign

Fig. 15.3. The open-circuit voltage tester is used to check the voltage of battery cells, with no load on the battery. It is calibrated in both volts (reading to .01 volt) and percent of charge. It is especially useful in spotting differences in cell voltages.

that the battery is sulphated. The three-minute charge test should be made on all batteries, as the fast charge will finish the destruction of batteries in this condition, with the possibility that the operator will be held responsible by the car owner.

The final and completely accurate check on a battery is to give it a charge and see if it will hold the charge for a reasonable length of time. Well-charged batteries in good condition, standing unused, will lose gravity at the rate of about .001 (1 point) per day over a 30-day period. Temperatures affect the rate of self-discharge; gravity will be lost at the rate of .003 (3 points) per day at 100°F. and .0005 (½ point) at 50°F. In tropical regions, batteries using 1.225 gravity electrolyte will work better and have a longer life than batteries having higher gravity. Batteries with the higher 1.285 gravity are used in cold portions of the country to prevent freezing.

Batteries Can Freeze

A *discharged battery* which originally had 1.285 gravity when fully charged will freeze at about 10° above zero. However, if kept above ¾ discharged (or ¼ charged), these batteries will usually avoid freezing. With tropical batteries (1.225 full-charge gravity) the gravity would drop down about 65 points lower when the battery was discharged. This would bring

the freezing point up so high there would be constant danger of frozen batteries. As a practical method of protection, the higher gravity is generally used except in climates where it is warm throughout the year and there is no danger of the temperature dropping to the freezing point.

In making battery diagnosis in warm climates, remember that the gravity may originally have been 1.225. For this reason, other tests should be made in addition to checking gravity. If they indicate the battery is in good condition, it is certainly safe to assume that it will be satisfactory for starting and lighting purposes.

In general, the best way to determine the state of charge in a battery is to use the battery hydrometer. Refer to Fig. 15.4 for gravity tables.

Analyzing Battery Condition

The overall battery performance will be no better than that of the weakest cell of the three or six which are connected in series. It seldom happens that all cells will remain continuously in the same condition; therefore, in checking battery condition, the only procedure of significant value is to check each cell individually. In general, as long as the tests on each cell are about the same, it can be considered that the battery is in fairly good condition. The important indications of impending

State of Charge	Standard Sp. Gr. as Used in Temperate Climates	Specific Gravity in Cells Built with Extra Water Capacity	Specific Gravity as Used in Tropical Climates
Fully charged	1.280	1.260	1.225
75% charged	1.230	1.220	1.180
50% charged	1.180	1.170	1.135
25% charged	1.130	1.120	1.090
Discharged	1.080	1.070	1.045

State of Charge as Indicated by Specific Gravity When Discharged at 20-Hour Rate.

Table I

Desired Specific Gravity	Approximate Number of Parts of Pure Water to Which Must Be Added One Part of 1.835 Specific Gravity Sulphuric Acid, by Volume
1.100	9.8 parts water by volume
1.200	4.3 parts water by volume
1.300	2.5 parts water by volume
1.400	1.6 parts water by volume

Table II

Specific Gravity (Corrected to 80° F.)	Freezing Temperature Degrees Fahrenheit
1.280	−90° F.
1.250	−62° F.
1.200	−16° F.
1.150	+ 5° F.
1.100	+19° F.

Table III

Fig. 15.4. Table I gives electrolyte gravities for standard, stay-full, and tropical batteries in different states of charge. Table II gives proportions of water and acid for different gravities. Table III gives the freezing points of various gravity electrolytes. (AABM)

failure are those which show differences in gravity or voltage in the cells. With the one-piece plastic tops now being more widely adopted, it is not practical to measure the individual cell voltages.

There are routine checks which all battery men agree are quite dependable and will give an accurate picture of battery condition. Refer to Fig. 15.5. The most generally used test and the one considered to be most reliable is the specific gravity test. This should be made with a hydrometer which is accurate and preferably has a thermometer built into it so that the temperature of the electrolyte can be readily determined. Remember the correction for temperature variations above or below 80°F. should be made in arriving at correct gravity indication. The gravity reading has value in two ways: (1) to indicate difference between cells and (2) to indicate the degree of battery charge. Variations of more than 25 to 40 points in cell readings indicate that the cell with the lower reading is approaching failure. The relationship between the gravity reading and the amount of charge is shown in the table in Chapter 14, page 165. Gravity reading will range from 1.250 to 1.260 for the stay-full battery and from 1.280 to 1.300 for the standard battery. A good average value for the standard battery is 1.285. Tropical batteries may have a fully charged gravity as low as 1.225.

A check used in conjunction with the gravity test is the high-rate discharge test or capacity test. This can be made in several ways. With the volt-amperes tester equipped with a current loading device (a carbon pile), the battery can be discharged at a rate of three times its ampere-hour rating, for 15 seconds; after this it should indicate not less than 1.6 volts per cell. The high-rate discharge tester for testing one cell at a time usually has a shunt that will carry from 200 to 300 amperes and a voltmeter with a 3-volt scale. When this is connected across one cell at a time for 15 seconds, the voltage in any cell should not fall below 1.6 volts. On cells in 12-volt batteries the high-rate discharge current should be 150 to 225 amperes (three times ampere-hour rating). Note the connection diagram in Fig. 15.6 for testing with a battery starter tester.

With plastic one-piece tops, a load of three times the ampere-hour rating should be put on the battery, and the battery voltage should be compared with a total of 1.6 volts per cell.

Treating Sulphated Batteries

All discharged batteries may be said to be sulphated because in the normal process of discharge the active material on both positive and negative plates is converted into lead sulphate. Whether a discharged sulphated battery can be recharged depends upon both the way it is sulphated and how long it has been in the discharged condition. A long period of disuse in a discharged condition permits the

Fig. 15.5. Testing the battery: battery-starter tester to test battery capacity, and hydrometer to indicate state of charge.

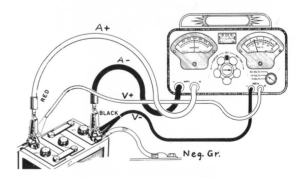

Fig. 15.6. Connection diagram for testing a battery with a battery-starter tester. This model has a built-in carbon-pile rheostat which permits a current of three times (in amperes) the ampere-hour rating of a battery. The voltmeter gives the battery voltage, which should not drop below 4.8 (or 9.6) volts at the end of 15 seconds.

formation of large crystals of sulphate that are difficult to change back to the original constituents by passing a charging current through them.

Sulphation should be suspected when battery cells that show little difference in gravity fail to charge, or when during high-rate discharge the voltage falls to a lower-than-normal point.

A sulphated battery has a high internal resistance. Thus the charging current will not be up to normal under full voltage. Such a battery will also heat up rapidly.

In some cases where the sulphation is not too severe, charging at a low rate for twenty-four to thirty-six hours, then discharging and recharging may bring up the capacity to a fairly satisfactory point.

Discharging and recharging a battery is *cycling* the battery. This will, in some cases, help a sulphated battery to get back into usable condition. To cycle at battery, first connect a lamp load or a fixed resistor of sufficient capacity to reduce the battery emf to zero voltage. The load should not exceed 30 amperes. Allow the battery to stand for six hours or more after discharge; then recharge at half the slow rate, which would be 3 to 4 amperes, until fully charged. If one cycling does not restore reasonably normal capacity, it is doubtful if further cycling will accomplish anything of value, and it would be best to replace the battery.

Sulphated batteries that are a year or more old may be in such deteriorated condition that they are not worth the effort required to save

Fig. 15.7. Cracked battery case caused by expanding of large crystal sulphate on plates.

them. However, one should certainly try to restore new batteries that have been sulphated due to neglect.

Battery Deterioration and Damage

Deterioration of a storage battery may be due to mechanical, electrical, or chemical causes or combinations of two or three of these factors.

Mechanical damage may be from a cracked case (Fig. 15.7), post strap, or post; wear on separators due to vibration when in use; and shedding of active material from the positive plates. The active material is relatively soft, and as time passes both vibration and the reaction incidental to charging and discharging cause some of this material to be loosened from the plates and to drop to the bottom of the battery case where it accumulates as mud.

The negative and positive plate groups rest on ridges formed on the bottom of the hard rubber or composition battery cases. When the space between these ribs is filled with mud from loosened active material from the positive plates, the mud can contact both the positive and negative plates and cause a short. The cell will be dead and the battery useless for further automotive purposes when this occurs.

Batteries which are subject to considerable vibration may in time wear through the separators from the motion of the plates on each side. This will also short out a cell if the negative and positive plates come in contact. Separator failure may also occur from tiny knots, cracks, or checks in the separators and these will frequently cause the cell to short out.

Loss of water resulting in a liquid level below the tops of the plates might also be considered mechanical deterioration. If a battery is allowed to stand for some time with a low liquid level, the exposed parts of the plate may become badly sulphated or oxidized. Even after the battery is filled to the proper level, this exposed portion will not be usable.

Long continued overcharging, which may be the result of a defective voltage regulator or carelessness in charging batteries, is always accompanied by oxidation of the grids. This reduces the metallic cross-section of the grid wires and weakens these plates so that they are easily broken under slight pressure or from vibration. Overcharging can only be corrected by adjusting the charging rate to meet driving conditions. Oxidation of the grids is reportedly a common cause of battery failure.

Any foreign materials, especially metallic materials, that get into the battery will cause rapid deterioration of the cells.

Chunky shedding of the active materials may be caused by too high a charging rate on sulphated plates. It might also be caused by the battery freezing while in a discharged condition. Chunky shedding may also be due to excessive vibration caused by the battery being loose in the holddown frame.

Buckling of the positive plates may be caused by plates standing in an undercharged state for some time. It may also be the result of excessive charging, especially after plates have previously become badly sulphated by standing in an undercharged condition. Plates buckled by sulphation may expand so that the case will be bulged or cracked.

The most common cause of battery failure, though not necessarily the end of battery life, is discharged batteries due to some cause outside the battery itself. For example, the cut-out relay points will sometimes stick, permitting the battery to run down. Leaving the ignition turned on overnight or longer will frequently run the battery down. The same result will occur when lights, radio, heater fan, or other electrical appliances are left on. Wires with worn insulation will sometimes contact a grounded part of the car and run the battery down. Moisture allowed to collect on top of the battery may permit a trickle of current from terminal to terminal and weaken the battery charge or in some cases even cause it to be discharged.

A cause of battery failure that occurs occasionally is stuck contacts in the stop-light switch. If a battery runs down without apparent cause, test the stop-light switch for continuity of current flow with a test light or ohmmeter.

Excessive use of the battery, such as using it to run the starter to drive the car for more than a few feet, may overheat the battery to such an extent that it will be ruined. Unless it is an extreme emergency, the starter should never be used to drive the car.

Whenever a battery is charged some free hydrogen and oxygen are given off at the surface of the plates. These gases are highly flammable and a spark near the battery may cause an explosion. One or more of the cell covers may rupture and someone who is near the battery could well be injured by flying acid. Sparks from lighted cigars or cigarettes or acetylene flames should be kept away from batteries unless the vent cap has been removed and a little blast of air has been blown into each battery cell to remove possible explosive gases.

Repairing Batteries

Except for minor repairs or replacement of broken parts, extensive battery repairs are seldom justified because of the high cost of parts and labor compared to the cost of replacement with a new battery.

Present-day storage batteries of reputable makes are designed and constructed so that with reasonable care they usually will not require any repairs during their normal life, barring accidents such as breaking or cracking a cell cover.

Service and Care of Batteries

Water is one of the four essential chemicals of a lead-acid storage battery, and under normal conditions of operation it is the only component of the battery which is lost because of charging or use. It should be replaced before the liquid level falls to the top of the separators. If the water is not replaced and the plates are exposed, the acid will reach a dangerously high concentration which may char and disintegrate the wood separators, attack the grid metal of the plates, and possibly sulphate the plates. Sulphuric acid need never be added to a cell unless some has been lost due to spilling or cracks in the case.

The holddown frame, if not properly adjusted, may allow the battery to vibrate and bounce, causing undue wear on the plate groups and accelerating the loss of active materials. For this reason, the holddown frame should be tightened to hold the battery firmly.

On the other hand, if the holddown frame is too tight, it may distort or crack the container and loosen the sealing compound allowing the loss of acid from the cells, particularly the end cells.

The starting motor should never be used for more than thirty seconds at any one time without allowing at least an equal period for the battery to recover between successive periods of operation.

Some of the batteries now in use have automatic self-leveling devices for controlling the liquid level when water is added to the battery. These devices generally consist of a means for trapping air in the battery after the water has reached its proper height so that additional water will only fill the vent opening to the top and will not bring the level above the desired point. When the vent plug is removed for the purpose of filling the battery nothing else should be taken out. Lead washers or rubber parts that are part of the self-leveling automatic devices must not be removed.

The newer types of batteries which have been advertised as not requiring water more than twice a year, the so-called "stay full" type, have merely lowered the ridges on the bottom for supporting the plates, giving more room at the top for liquid. These batteries may require as much as an inch of water above the level of the separators instead of the customary 3/8". They are equipped with leveling devices so that the correct liquid level will be reached when filled up to the top of the vent. When properly filled these batteries will have a gravity, as previously mentioned, of 1.260. This gravity is lower than usual so that if the large amount of water left at the top of the plates is evaporated, the gravity will not exceed the normal 1.280.

Water for automotive batteries should be either distilled water or a good grade of drinking water which has a low degree of hardness. Battery water should be kept in covered containers made of glass, hard rubber or lead.

A battery that requires excessive amounts of water indicates a defective voltage regulator which permits overcharging of the battery. Also, the battery may be approaching failure and should be given a capacity test.

Service Procedure

On cars coming in for diagnosis and correction on the electrical equipment of the car, it is a good idea to clean the battery top with a stiff bristled brush. Be careful not to scatter any of the oxides or dirt from the top of the battery onto other parts of the engine and its accessories. After brushing, the top of the battery should be wiped with a cloth moistened in an ammonia or baking soda solution. This will neutralize any traces of acid that may be on or around the battery. Water should be added if needed.

The battery cables should be inspected and replaced if they are in bad condition. Refer to

No. 0 Gauge   No.1 Gauge

No.2 Gauge   No.3 Gauge   No.4 Gauge

Fig. 15.8. Since battery cables must carry extremely heavy starting currents with a minimum loss of voltage, they should be No. 0 or No. 1 gauge. No. 0 (32 lb. copper per 100 ft.) will carry two and one-half times as much current as No. 4. No. 1 (25 lb./100 ft.) will carry two times as much current as No. 4. The above are actual cable sizes. Note that the outside size is the same in each case.

Fig. 15.8 for battery cable size. The tapered terminal posts should also be checked to see that they are not deformed or broken. They then should be cleaned with a wire brush or one of the tools made for cleaning battery posts and cable terminals. Note Figs. 15.9 and 15.10.

The tests which were previously discussed should be made on the battery. If they indicate a need for charging, the battery should be given a boost on a fast charger or put on a slow charger, depending upon the time available and the shop equipment.

Other than cleaning the battery, adding water, testing it, and charging it, there is not much that can be done in the shop in the way of servicing batteries.

Owners should be instructed to maintain the water level in the battery or to bring it to the shop periodically for this service. They should be told to bring the battery into the shop for testing, charging, or possible replacement if it shows any indication of sluggishness or lack of cranking ability. Car owners should also be warned of the bad effect of permitting batteries to stand unused for a long period of time without keeping the batteries well charged.

Summary

Storage batteries require direct current for charging, and therefore a rectifier must be used to utilize AC for this purpose. Two methods of charging may be used: (1) constant current at a low rate, and (2) high rate charging.

When charging always connect the positive charging lead to the positive battery terminal and negative charging lead to the negative battery terminal. When batteries are being charged in series, connect the negative lead of one battery to the positive lead of the next battery. The charging temperature should not exceed 125°F. to avoid damage to the batteries.

A *battery on charge is considered fully charged* when all cells are gassing freely with no gravity increase for three successive hourly readings. The low-rate charging method is best for batteries.

High-rate chargers have become popular because of their rapid action, convenience and elimination of battery loans. A rate of 50 to 100 amperes is used for 6-volt batteries, and 25 to 50 amperes for 12-volt batteries. High-rate charging can damage a battery if it is not properly done.

When *checking a battery* consider (1) the difference in cell condition, and (2) battery state of charge.

Make the *three-minute charge test* when the state of charge is too low to make a test.

Sulphated batteries have higher internal resistance than those in good condition. On high-rate charge it will be impossible to get

Fig. 15.9. Whenever a battery is serviced, the cables should be removed and any corrosion eliminated. A tool of this kind, with an internal wire brush, is handy, quick, and efficient for this job.

Fig. 15.10. Removing corroded battery cable terminals is sometimes a difficult job. This tool will remove stubborn cables without damage to either cable or battery post.

the required charging current through the battery at the usual charging voltage.

The *final and complete check* on a battery is to see if it will hold a charge for a reasonable length of time.

A *discharged battery can freeze* at 10°F. Batteries one-fourth or more charged will not freeze ordinarily. To check the state of charge use a battery hydrometer.

Overall battery performance will be no better than that of the weakest of the three or six cells in series. Check the condition of each cell in doubtful batteries. The *specific gravity test* is the one most commonly used. Remember to make the correction for temperatures above or below 80°F.

Variation in cell readings of over 25 to 40 points of gravity indicates that the low-reading cell is approaching failure. A good average for a fully charged battery is 1.285.

The *high discharge or capacity test* is often used in conjunction with the gravity test. With the battery loaded to three times its ampere-hour rating for 15 seconds the voltage should not drop below 1.6 volts per cell. On 12-volt batteries the high-rate discharge should be 150 to 225 amperes (three times the ampere-hour rating).

All *discharged batteries are said to be sulphated*. Long disuse of a battery in a discharged condition permits large crystals of sulphate to form. This makes such a high internal resistance that it is difficult to get sufficient charging current through the battery.

Discharging and recharging the battery is *cycling* it. This sometimes helps a sulphated battery.

Mechanical damage describes such conditions as: a cracked battery case, wear on separators, loss of active material, loss of liquid and dried plates, sulphation crystallization, accumulation of mud at the bottom of cells which shorts plates, breakage of plates or connections, and shedding of active material. Batteries are often discharged due to an external cause

such as a defective stop-light switch or cut-out relay.

Questions

1. Can storage batteries be charged from AC power lines? How?
2. Name two general methods of charging storage batteries.
3. In what way is a charger connected to a battery?
4. In what way are batteries connected in series?
5. What is the maximum temperature a battery should be allowed to reach while being charged?
6. When is a battery on charge considered to be fully charged?
7. Which is the best charging method for batteries?
8. When charging at the high rate, what is the ampere range for 6-volt batteries?
9. What can a high-rate charger be expected to do?
10. What difference in cell gravities would indicate approaching battery failure?
11. What two checks should be made on a battery before fast charging?
12. What is a characteristic of sulphated batteries?
13. At what temperature will a sulphated battery freeze?
14. What is the normal gravity for a fully charged battery?
15. What is the most generally used battery test?
16. What would be your recommendation when one cell is found to have failed?
17. What is a good additional test to make on a battery?
18. How is this test made?
19. What is meant by cycling a battery?
20. In case sulphation is not too severe, how would you try to charge a battery?
21. Name three kinds of mechanical battery deterioration.

22. What effect would excessive overcharging have on a battery?

23. What effect would an excessively high charging rate have on a sulphated battery?

24. What might cause buckling of battery plates?

25. Name two possible causes of a run-down battery.

CHAPTER SIXTEEN

The Charging Circuit— Generator and Cut-Out Relay

The charging circuit consists of generator, generator controls, wiring and battery. On some cars an ammeter on the dash panel indicates what the generator is doing; on others, an indicator light acts as an alarm when the generator is not functioning. The charging circuit is a complete generating and energy-storage system which furnishes electric current for lights, starting, ignition, heater fan, electric windshield wiper, radio, and many other accessories.

The generating circuit (including the battery) supplies current when desired. When the engine is in operation, the *generator* supplies current to carry the electrical load, and also keeps the battery in a properly charged condition. The amount of current diverted to the battery depends upon the degree of battery charge and upon the amount of the electrical load.

The battery has been discussed in detail in Chapters 14 and 15, and so will only be mentioned incidentally in this chapter.

Generator Function and Safeguards

The generator is a machine which converts mechanical energy from the engine into electrical energy. The generator restores to the battery the current used in cranking the engine, and it also supplies current to operate the lights, ignition, radio, etc. As previously explained, when electricity flows through a wire, a certain amount of heat is created. Therefore, most automotive generators are ventilated by means of a fan on the drive pulley which draws a current of air through the generator. This carries away the heat produced in the generator, and prevents overheating and possible damage. Because this system also permits the generator output to be increased to higher values without danger

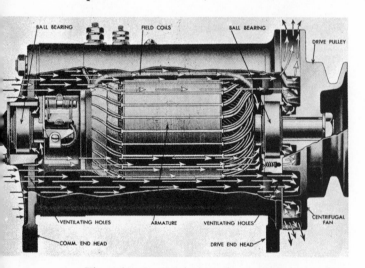

Fig. 16.1. Sectional view of a ventilated generator. Air is drawn through holes in commutator-end head and passes over and around internal parts to cool them. It is the excellent ventilation which makes possible the high output generators for automotive use.

of overheating, all ventilated generators carry higher output ratings than non-ventilated units of the same size. Refer to Fig. 16.1.

Generator Construction

For many years the generator has been the two-brush controlled, direct-current type. The 1961 Chrysler-built cars were equipped with a relatively new type of generator, *the alternator*, which produces alternating current. By the use of silicon diode rectifiers, this alternating current is converted to the necessary direct current.

The use of the alternator has increased because of certain definite advantages, and it has displaced the DC generating system entirely on new cars. However, there are over sixty million automobiles in service equipped with the direct current generator, and it will be many years before it becomes obsolete. It is very necessary that the direct current generator and its controls be well understood since diagnosis, adjustment and repair will be required on them for some time to come.

Both this chapter and Chapter 17 are devoted to the DC system. Chapter 18 will cover the operation of the AC generating system.

The major parts of the DC generator are the armature (with its commutator), the field, and the brushes. The armature is supported on bearings so that it can rotate freely. The field coil windings create a magnetic field which the armature conductors cut as the armature rotates. This induces an electric current in the armature windings which flows from them to the armature commutator and brushes, and then to the output conductor. The current is then carried to the point where it will be utilized. Part of the current is fed into the generator field winding so that the magnetic field is built up and maintained at the proper strength.

DC generators have two principal circuits, the armature circuit and the field circuit. The principal parts of the automotive generator are the frame, which provides a rigid housing for the entire unit and forms part of the magnetic circuit; two or four field poles (depending upon

the design and capacity of the generator) made of soft steel machined very accurately to fit the inner circumference of the frame; the field coils; the commutator-end head; the drive-end head; and the armature. The basic generator parts are shown in Fig. 16.2.

The soft steel used in the field poles is of such composition that after it has once been magnetized it will retain a small amount of residual magnetism and act as a very weak permanent magnet. It is important that the pole pieces be rigidly attached to the field frame by screws or bolts as they are subjected to considerable force when the generator is in operation.

The joints between the pole pieces and the frame should be clean and have a full area of contact to the frame so that there will be minimum resistance to the passage of the magnetic lines of force. The lines of magnetic force start in the field poles, flow from pole to pole through the armature, and around through the field frame.

The air gaps between each pole piece and the armature core should be as nearly the same as possible so there will be uniform magnetic pull upon the armature core and uniform resistance to the passage of magnetic lines through the air gaps. Since even a small air gap offers

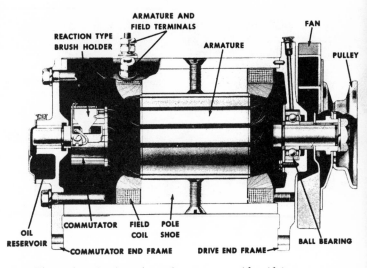

Fig. 16.2. Section through generator, identifying the various parts. (DR)

considerable resistance to the flow of magnetism, it is essential that this gap be kept down to the smallest practicable amount. For example, the air gap for a 4½″ generator, a commonly used size, should be .029″ minimum to .040″ maximum. The air gap that is established by the designer must allow for normal bearing wear and the unavoidable variations in assembly.

The field coils consist of many turns of fine wire. For example, one type of 6-volt generator has 210 turns of No. 19 wire for each field coil (approximately 420 feet of wire). These field coils are connected in series with each other so that the polarity of the coils alternates, *i.e.* the first one would have a north pole and the second a south pole, continuing to alternate if there are more than two poles.

The field coils are held in place by the pole pieces. The shape of the pole shoes is an important factor in reducing magnetic noises and losses within the generator. The poles are made from a rolled steel section cut to length and formed in a press to give the desired pole-face contour. Fig. 16.3 shows an exploded view of a generator.

The end plates of the generator are called the heads, one being the commutator-end head and the other being the drive-end head. These plates are made of stamped steel, or cast frame, and on them are mounted the bearings for the ends of the armature shaft. The brush holders and brushes are mounted on the commutator-end head. The drive-end head is frequently fitted with a ball bearing to carry the weight of the armature as well as the tension of the belt which drives the generator. The commutator end is always at the opposite end from the driving pulley.

Armature

The armature is an assembly which consists of the shaft, the core, the commutator, and the armature winding.

The armature core has two functions (1) it serves as a carrier for the conductors of the armature winding and (2) it completes the magnetic circuit of the field. The core is made up of soft steel laminations whose outer circumference is slotted to carry the armature windings.

As the armature rotates, the magnetic field is cut by the core as well as the armature conductors. This sets up *eddy currents* in the metal of the core. If the core were made of solid steel, these eddy currents would be very large and would absorb a considerable amount of the energy supplied to drive the generator and would also cause the temperature of the core to be increased, possibly to the danger point. In order to reduce these energy losses, the armature core is made up of laminations of soft steel, each layer approximately .035″ in thickness.

The surfaces of these laminations are treated to form an oxidized coating which serves as an insulation between the laminations, thereby reducing the eddy current, maintaining a safely low operating temperature, and increasing the efficiency of the generator.

Armature cores should never be filed nor turned on the external surface since such treatment would cause burrs between the laminations and would result in short circuits between them.

Fig. 16.3. Exploded view of a generator showing the parts in correct relationship to each other. (AL)

Armature windings are made up of coils consisting of a number of turns of insulated copper wire. In some generators the coils are wound in the slots either by hand or machine. Other armatures have form-wound coils which are wound separately and then bent into the proper shape to fit into the armature slots. An armature is usually identified by a part number stamped on its core. Fig. 16.2 shows the armature in place in the generator.

The connecting leads of each armature coil are mechanically wedged into slots in the commutator bar risers, after which they are soldered to make mechanically strong joints with low electrical resistance.

It is important that these connections be made mechanically strong to withstand the stresses of the centrifugal force at high armature speed and also have low electrical resistance to minimize electrical losses. At high engine speeds, armatures on 4½″ and 5″ generators will sometimes reach a speed of 8000 rpm.

Commutator

The commutator is an extremely important part of the armature. It must be made with a high degree of mechanical accuracy and must have satisfactory electrical characteristics. For a two-pole generator, the ends of each armature circuit are connected to opposite commutator bars. As it turns, each brush is connected first to one end of the revolving armature, and then to the other end, making the change just at the instant the voltage in the coils is reversing. This causes the voltage supplied to the external armature circuit always to be in the same direction, in other words, to be direct current. The commutator changes the alternating current generated within the armature to direct current as it leaves the brushes. These rotating "reverse-switches'" are composed of segments of copper rigidly held together and separated by insulation (usually mica). It is important that the commutators be turned so they are very accurately concentric with the armature shaft bearing surfaces. A high-grade armature will

maintain a tolerance of .0003″ concentricity for the commutator brush surface in relation to the shaft bearing surfaces. In order to maintain this close tolerance, commutators are ground with high-speed wheels. Fig. 16.4 shows how the commutator is checked for concentricity.

The armature coils are connected to each other in many combinations depending upon the desired voltage and ampere capacity. Armature design is highly technical and their manufacture is a precision process which has been developed over a long period of years.

Generator Operation

The generator functions on the principle that current will be induced in any conductor which is part of a closed circuit when the conductor is moved through a magnetic field so that it cuts the lines of magnetic force. The conductors of the generator armature are so connected to each other and to the commutator that when the brushes are placed on the commutator, any flow of current induced in the conductors can be carried away from the armature through the brushes. Because the field circuit is in parallel with the armature, part of this current will flow through the field winding to build up and maintain the magnetic field in which the conductors are moved.

Fig. 16.4. Dial indicator used to check generator commutator when placed on V-blocks. (AL)

Two separate magnetic fields are actually involved. The conductors on the armature move through a powerful magnetic field and have a current flow through them which builds up an armature magnetic field. There will be some interference as the two magnetic fields (armature and field) cross each other. This will cause distortion of the magnetic lines of force flowing in the field.

In order for current to be induced, a conductor must move across a magnetic field *at right angles to the lines of force*. The amount of current which will be induced in any conductor that is part of a closed circuit is determined by: (1) the strength of the magnetic field through which the conductor moves, and (2) the speed at which the conductor moves, or the *rate* at which the lines of force are cut. Remember that it takes mechanical force to move a conductor through a magnetic field; considerable power is required to drive a generator. Fig. 16.5 illustrates how current flow is induced.

To describe further how a generator operates, one turn of an armature generator will be described. In Fig. 16.5, if the armature loop is rotated in a clockwise direction, the current will be induced in the left-hand side of the loop, *flowing away from the operator*. In the right side of the loop, current will flow toward the operator. The current which is induced will flow to the right-hand segment of the two-segment commutator and to the right-hand brush. From there most of it flows through the external circuit and the connected electrical load. Then it flows through the left-hand brush and the left-hand segment of the commutator and back into the loop. The remainder of the induced current flows through the field windings which are assembled around the two magnetic pole shoes. This current flow is such that it strengthens the magnetic field between the two pole shoes.

The commutator segments keep the current flowing in the external electrical circuit in the same direction, regardless of the relative positions of the two sides of the loop with respect to the north and south magnetic poles. Refer again to Fig. 16.5. When, for instance, the left-hand side of the loop has rotated 180° it will be moving in the opposite direction with respect to the magnetic field; but since the commutator segment to which it is connected has also rotated 180°, this current will be fed to

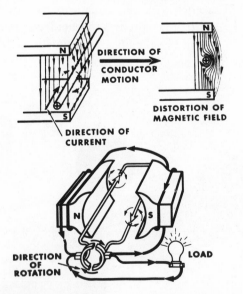

Fig. 16.5. (Top) The principles of current generation illustrated by a closed circuit conductor cutting lines of force in a magnetic field. (Bottom) A commutator rectifying the current to give direct current. (DR)

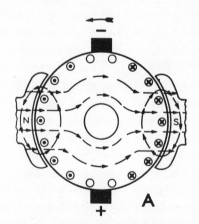

Fig. 16.6. A two-pole generator with brushes located at no-load neutral point between field poles. Armature magnetic lines are concentrated in the poles and that part of the armature under the poles.

the right-hand brush so that it still continues to flow in the same direction in the external circuit. However, if slip rings were used to which each half of the single coil were connected and with which brushes were in contact, the current output would be alternating instead of direct.

The armature in the actual generator has many conductors placed in insulated slots on the outer circumference, and the field windings have many turns of wire to give them the right magnetic strength. Fig. 16.6 shows the flow of magnetic lines of force and how they are cut by the armature conductors.

Shunt-Type Generator

On the shunt-wound generator, the field windings are shunted or *in parallel across the generator armature* so that generator voltage is impressed upon them and a small part of the current induced in the armature conductors flows through them to build up the magnetic field and permit adequate generator output.

This type of circuit provides a very convenient means of controlling the generator output because varying amounts of resistance can be readily inserted into the generator field circuit. This will cause variations in the field current and consequently in the magnetic field strength; the final result will be to provide the necessary variations in the generator output, in accordance with electrical load and battery state of charge.

Generator Regulation

The desired control of generator output is supplied by an external means. The control in general use includes contact points and resistance units so arranged that when the points open, resistance is inserted into the generator field circuit. This reduces the field circuit current and the generator output. If the points are opened and closed at the correct rate of speed and remain closed the correct percentage of time, the generator output can be readily varied from the specified maximum to a low output of a few amperes. The device which performs

this control function is called a *generator regulator* or *generator control*, although it is more commonly referred to as a "voltage regulator." Since the entire control unit is made up of three parts (the cut-out relay, voltage regulator or limiter, and current regulator or limiter), it will be referred to in this book as the *generator regulator* or generator control. Its operation will be discussed in detail in a later section. Any generator connected in a battery circuit must be equipped with a cut-out relay, regardless of the means of output control.

Generators of the *shunt type* are connected internally in two different ways. The two methods of connection are referred to as the standard-duty type and the heavy-duty type, or the *A*-circuit and the *B*-circuit, respectively. Refer to Fig. 16.7.

The difference between the two types of generator circuits is mainly in the part of the field circuit in which the resistance is inserted. In the standard-duty type, the resistance is inserted between the field and ground when

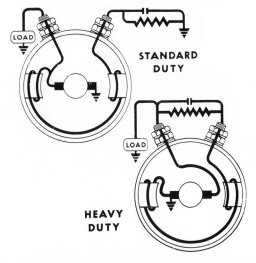

TWO TYPES OF GENERATOR CIRCUITS

Fig. 16.7. The standard duty circuit *(A circuit)* supplies the field current from the "hot" brush which is grounded through the generator control (voltage regulator). The heavy duty circuit (*B* circuit) supplies field current through the generator control, and is grounded inside the generator. Ford cars use the heavy duty circuit. (DR)

the generator regulator points open. The opposite end of the generator field circuit is connected to the insulated brush within the regulator. The field current flows from the live or insulated brush of the generator through the field circuit and is grounded through the generator control.

In the heavy-duty type, the generator regulator inserts resistance between the field and the insulated side of the circuit. The opposite end of the field circuit is directly connected to ground inside the generator. In other words, current is supplied to the field circuit from the generator control. To summarize, in the standard-duty unit the field is grounded through the generator regulator, while in the heavy-duty type the current is sent to the field coils *from* the voltage regulator and grounded inside the generator. Ford generators are connected in accordance with the heavy-duty circuit.

Cut-Out Relay

With all DC automotive generators a cut-out relay must be used. The cut-out relay might be

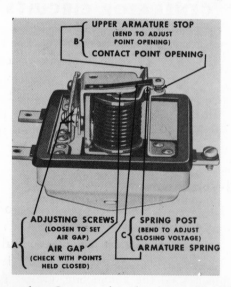

Fig. 16.8. Cut-out relay showing points where adjustment may be made when necessary. The contact points are closed by the voltage winding when specified voltage is attained by the generator. They are held closed by the current winding until the voltage drops below battery voltage. The current coil can be seen; the voltage winding is underneath. (DR)

considered as a one-way electrical check valve — a magnetic switch which opens and closes the circuit between the generator and the battery. When the generator is operating at or above the minimum charging speed, the cut-out relay connects the generator to the battery. When the generator slows down or stops so that its output voltage is below battery voltage, the cut-out relay opens the circuit to prevent the battery from discharging current back to and through the generator. A cut-out relay is shown in Fig. 16.8.

The cut-out relay has two coils wound around a magnetic core of soft iron. One of the coils is a *voltage coil* consisting of many turns of very fine wire, so that its magnetic effect is proportional to the *voltage impressed on the coil*. The other coil is a *current coil* with few turns of heavy wire, so that its magnetic effect is proportional to the *current flowing through the coil*. The voltage coil is connected in parallel with the generator so that at all times it will have generator voltage impressed on it; only a tiny current will flow, but in proportion to generator voltage. The current coil is in series with the generator output conductor so that all generator output must flow through it when the generator is producing current.

Above the winding core is a flat steel armature, pivoted at one end and held away from the core by spring tension when the unit is not operating. There is a contact point assembled on one end of the armature. Meeting with this point is a stationary contact point which is connected through wiring to the battery.

When the generator begins to operate, voltage is built up and forces current through the voltage relay winding. This creates a magnetic field in the winding core. When the voltage reaches the value for which the relay is set, the magnetism becomes strong enough to overcome the armature spring tension and the armature makes contact with the stationary point; this closes the circuit between the generator and the battery. Current now flows from the generator to the battery and *also passes through the current winding* adding magnetism to assist the voltage coil in holding the points closed.

When the generator slows up sufficiently or stops and the generator voltage falls below battery voltage, current will begin to flow in a reverse direction — from the battery back to the generator. This reverses the direction of the current flow in the relay current winding, with the result that the magnetic field of the current winding is also reversed. However, the magnetic field of the voltage winding is always in the same direction since the same side of this winding is always connected to ground. Therefore, when the current winding magnetic field reverses, the magnetic fields of the two windings *oppose each other*. As a result, the magnetic force which pulls on the armature is reduced so much that it can no longer hold the points closed. The armature is pulled away from the winding core by its spring tension. The points are separated and the circuit between generator and the battery is broken.

Current will always flow from a point of higher voltage to a point of lower voltage in a complete circuit, so it is necessary to have a device such as a cut-out relay to prevent the battery from discharging through the generator when battery voltage is higher than generator voltage.

Charging System Voltage

For many years the standard emf for the charging system and the ignition system has been 6 volts. This voltage has been quite satisfactory for engines having compression ratios of between 6:1 and 7:1. However, the type of ignition system in current use, and the high-output, high-compression engines that are powering the latest automobiles put a severe strain on the capability of the 6-volt system. In the effort to get improved performance and to minimize ignition and starting difficulties, a change from 6 volts to 12 volts has been adopted by the automobile manufacturers. The three

main reasons for making the change to 12 volts are: (1) better ignition performance, (2) higher generator output, and (3) faster cranking speed.

The new engines require higher voltages to produce the necessary sparking at the plugs. Primarily, the breakdown voltage required at the spark plug gap (that is, the sparking voltage) is determined by the gas pressure around the plug at the time the spark occurs. This pressure has been increased throughout the speed range by higher compression ratios, and further increased through the medium- and high-speed ranges by better breathing of the engine.

Tests made on a single-cylinder, variable-ratio engine, with plug gaps set at .040", indicate that there is a 10% increase in breakdown voltage for each full ratio change in the range of compression ratios from 7:1 to 12:1. Other spark plug gaps show slightly different increases, but the .040" gap was selected as being in the middle range spark plug gaps in use.

12-Volt Coil

A 12-volt ignition coil can be made in the same size package as the 6-volt coil. The 12-volt coil has some operating advantages when used in series with an external ballast resistor. This coil permits an increase in energy input of approximately 50% to 100%, with the greater proportionate increase at the higher speeds, where it is needed more.

12-Volt Generator

The 6-volt generators still in use on passenger cars have a maximum output of around 45 amperes, which at 6 volts, is equivalent to 270 watts. With the increased use of electrical appliances on the automobile, greater generator capacity is needed.

A change to 12 volts gives an increase in electrical power output of about 33%. With an output of 40 amperes at 12 volts, the power is 480 watts. Since the power is measured in watts rather than amperes, the increase can readily be understood.

A generator of the same external size as the 6-volt unit, with more armature and field-winding turns of smaller wire, will produce the increased power. An important advantage of the 12-volt generator is its ability to get up to its controlled voltage at lower car speeds than that required for the 6-volt generator.

12-Volt Cranking Motor

It is quite important that the external size of the cranking motor (starter) be kept at its present dimensions; therefore the better cranking ability of the 12-volt motor is advantageous. It has been found that redesigning the cranking motor to operate on 12 volts enables it to turn over the engine from 50% faster at —10°F. to almost twice as fast at 70°F. Refer to Fig. 16.9.

The starting motor must operate at a lower current in amperes because the current capacity of the 12-volt storage battery is less, even though its ampere-hour capacity is greater. More turns of smaller wire in the motor will provide for the necessary lower current.

12-Volt Battery

The 6-volt battery commonly used with larger 8-cylinder engines was the 17-plate, 3-cell type,

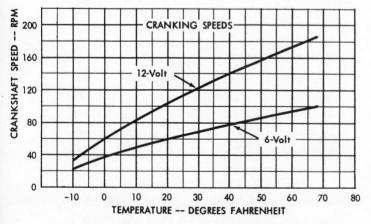

Fig. 16.9. Available cranking speeds at various temperatures with 6-volt and 12-volt motors.

with a 20-hour rating of 110 ampere-hours. The equivalent 12-volt battery has a rating of 50 to 70 ampere-hours. It is furnished in a case which is only slightly larger than the 6-volt case — same length, $\frac{1}{4}''$ less height, and $\frac{1}{4}''$ more width. At 12 volts, 65 ampere-hours represent an increase of almost 20% over a capacity of 110 ampere-hours at 6 volts.

The combination of the 12-volt cranking motor and greater storage battery capacity is what accomplishes the higher cranking speed. Refer again to Fig. 16.9.

An understanding of the importance and action of the battery in the generating system helps in visualizing the operation of the generator and generator regulator.

Relationship of Generator, Regulator, and Battery

These three units — generator, regulator, battery — work together as a team, each one affecting the others. See Fig. 16.10. The generator supplies the electric current used by the vehicle's electrical system — at all times when the engine is operating above the minimum speed that causes the generator voltage to close the cut-out relay contacts. The battery acts as a reservoir to receive all the current put out by the generator in excess (if any) of that used to operate the ignition, lights, radio, heater fan motor, electric windshield wiper, etc. The generator regulator (which includes the cut-out relay, the voltage regulator or voltage limiter, and the current regulator or current limiter) acts to keep the generator voltage and current at or below safe values.

Whenever the generator sends charging current to the battery, the battery voltage opposes the generator voltage, since all battery charging current has to flow through the battery in a direction opposite to battery discharging current. In other words, there is a battery counter voltage or counter emf (electromotive force). It is only the difference in voltage between generator voltage and battery counter emf that causes any charging current to flow through the battery.

In 6-volt systems, a common setting for the voltage regulator is 7.4 volts, while for 12-volt systems, the controlled voltage is approximately 14.5 to 14.8 volts. In general, all the voltage values for 12-volt systems are twice those pertaining to 6-volt systems. However, current flow values in amperes will be less for 12 volts. This is true because with 12 volts one-half the amperes will produce the same watts of power as a 6-volt circuit. However, the generator, cranking motor, and battery are somewhat more powerful on 12-volt systems than on 6-volt systems, and therefore the amperes specified are generally somewhat more than half of the 6-volt values. The smaller current flow is also the reason why much smaller wires are used with 12 volts than with 6 volts.

The automotive diagnostician cannot disregard 6-volt systems, because there are still many in use in automobiles, trucks, farm tractors, small engines, generating plants, and engines driving pumps, air compressors, etc.

Whenever an automotive generator is in operation, its output is balanced between voltage and current. For example, if there is relatively small demand for current, the voltage will be just as high as the voltage limiter will permit. This would be the case when there is a high state of charge in the battery and there are few electrical load items turned on other than the ignition system.

Now, suppose the battery is well charged and the lights, radio, heater fan motor, etc., are turned on in addition to the ignition system. This may place a load of more than 50% of its capacity on the generator and will tend to lower the generator voltage. The voltage could drop low enough that it would be below the limit set by the voltage regulator.

A battery in a low state of charge will put an additional load on the generator; if all the appliances are turned on too, the load may be great enough to take the control away from the voltage regulator and bring the current

limiter into action. Since only one of the generator control units acts at a time, the generator output at a specific time will be controlled by either the voltage limiter or the current limiter but never by both.

Temperature Effects

Temperature affects both the generator and the battery. When the generator is cold the resistance of all its wiring is at a minimum, but as it warms up to operating temperature its normal resistance increases. Therefore a cold generator will put out more current and voltage than one that is warmed up. The voltage limiter will also allow a somewhat higher voltage when it is cold. Thus, the very low temperature accounts for the high-voltage effects on distributor breaker points in extremely cold weather.

The battery has a lower resistance when it is cold. However, its chemical actions are made much more sluggish by the low temperature. Therefore, although its actual counter emf is low, its effective counter emf is high due to the higher voltage it takes to bring about useful charging action in the battery plates. Thus the charging action in cold weather is limited and the current available for operating the cranking motor is much less than in warm weather. For this reason it is quite important to have the engine, generating system, ignition system and starting system all in good operating condition on cars which are to be operated in severe weather.

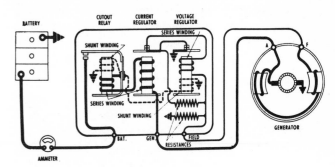

Fig. 16.10. Schematic drawing of charging circuit used on current model cars, showing battery, generator, and three-unit generator control.

As the battery warms up to use, it will take an increasing amount of charge. For example, a half-charged, 6-volt battery at 0°F. and 7.4 controlled charging voltage would only be able to pass approximately 2 amperes; while a 12-volt, half-charged battery, at the same temperature, with 14.6 volts from the generator, would only pass approximately 1 ampere. However, at 80°F. and the battery at half-charge, both 6-volt and 12-volt units will be able to take all the excess current the generator can produce, although for only a brief time.

With a cold regulator set at 14.6 volts at 124°F. (the specified adjusting temperature), the regulated voltage will be 16.0 volts at 45°F., dropping to 14.2 volts at 165°F. Therefore, it will be apparent that the output of the generator will vary considerably with changes in battery state of charge, battery temperature, regulator temperature, regulator setting, and connected load (number of appliances on).

Motorists apparently think that their generator will bring a low-charged battery up to charge. However, unless the car is being driven on a cross-country trip where the generator operates for a number of hours day after day, this seldom happens. As the battery receives charging current, the outer surface of the active material in the battery plates becomes fully charged before the inner material is penetrated. This builds up the counter battery voltage (counter emf) in greater proportion than the battery charge as a whole is built up. The voltage regulator, working at normal operating temperature, will maintain the generator voltage at the value for which it is set. With a high counter emf in the battery, the voltage difference between the generator and battery is so small that only a limited amount of current can be forced through the battery to charge it. The result is that, in most cases, the battery just barely maintains its state of charge, with little gain and often a gradual loss.

Actually the generating system is designed, not to charge the battery, but merely to replace the amount of energy used for operating the cranking motor, and the ignition system, lights, or radio, during the brief periods when the engine may not be running or is running under the minimum speed at which the generator produces current.

This emphasizes the importance of checking the battery periodically and giving it a booster charge when needed; the only truly dependable and effective battery is one that is fully charged.

Summary

The *charging circuit* is a complete generating and energy storing system which furnishes current for all car requirements.

The *generator* is a machine which converts mechanical energy from the automotive power plant into electrical energy. When current flows through wires, some energy is used up in creating heat.

The *alternator* has replaced the DC generator on new cars because of its advantages, but because there are some sixty million cars on the road with DC generators, the DC system must be understood.

The **DC generator** consists essentially of armature, fields, and brushes. It has two main circuits, (1) armature circuit, and (2) field circuit. A small amount of residual magnetism is retained and acts as a weak permanent magnet.

The **air gaps between the pole shoes and the armature** must be uniform in size. Even a small air gap has considerable resistance to the flow of magnetic lines of force.

Field coils consist of many turns of fine wire and are held in place by pole pieces. The end plates of the generator are called heads and carry armature bearings.

The *armature* is an assembly of shaft, core, commutator and armature windings. As the armature rotates, the armature conductors cut magnetic lines of force of the field and current is generated.

The *commutator* must be accurately made and should be concentric with the armature shaft within .0003″. It changes the initial alternating current into DC at the commutator.

The *armature winding* consists of many conductors placed in insulated slots around a soft laminated iron core which is assembled onto the armature shaft.

The *armature conductors* are connected together and to the commutator. Two magnetic fields are involved: (1) field and (2) armature magnetic field.

When a *conductor moves* across a magnetic field and cuts magnetic lines of force, current is generated. The amount of current depends on the strength of the magnetic field and the speed with which the lines are cut.

A *shunt-type generator* has field windings shunted or *in parallel* with the armature, and part of the armature current is used to supply the field current. This provides a convenient method of controlling generator output — inserting a varying resistance in the field circuit.

Generator regulation is provided by the generator control in which sets of contact points cut a resistance in and out of the field circuit. The generator control consists of cut-out relay, voltage regulator or limiter, and current regulator or limiter.

Shunt generators are connected in two ways: (1) standard-duty, or *A*-circuit, and (2) heavy-duty or *B*-circuit. The *A*-circuit is grounded in the regulator and the *B*-circuit is grounded inside the generator.

The *cut-out relay* must be used with all DC generators. It may be considered as a one-way electrical check valve.

Charging system voltage for many years has been 6 volts, but in 1956 the final change was made to 12 volts for better ignition performance, higher generator output, and faster cranking speed. The required sparking voltage at the spark plugs is a function of compression pressure which has been increased on the later model cars.

The *12-volt coil* is in the same size package as the 6-volt. The 12-volt coil used with a ballast resistor increases energy output over 50%, permitting higher engine speeds.

The *12-volt generator* is used because the 6-volt generators now in use have a maximum output of around 45 amperes, equivalent to 270 watts; while at 12 volts and 40 amperes, the output is 480 watts.

The *12-volt cranking motor* must be kept the same size as the 6-volt motor. By redesigning it to operate on 12 volts, 50% greater cranking speed is attained.

The *12-volt batteries* equivalent to the previous 6-volt units have a rating of 50 to 70 ampere-hours and are furnished in a case only slightly larger. Such a battery gives an increase of watts amounting to almost 20% in capacity.

The *generator, regulator and battery* work together as a team. It is only the difference between generator voltage and battery counter electromotive force that causes current to flow through the battery. Battery cemf controls the regulator, and the regulator controls the generator output.

At *low temperatures*, the battery rapidly loses capacity, and the generator has less internal resistance when cold. The regulator and generator must always be at operating temperature when the regulator is adjusted.

Questions

1. Of what does the charging circuit consist?
2. Define the term *generator*.
3. What is a side effect of electric current flowing through wires?
4. What important change has recently been made in automotive generator design?
5. Of what does the automotive generator essentially consist?
6. What are the two principal generator circuits?
7. Of what does the DC generator armature consist?
8. What are the two functions of the armature?

9. What happens when the armature conductors cut the lines of magnetic force of the field?
10. What is the function of the commutator?
11. What are the two magnetic fields in the generator?
12. What two factors govern generator output?
13. What would be the result if slip rings were used instead of a commutator in the DC generator?
14. What is the difference between the standard-duty or *A*-circuit and the heavy-duty or *B*-circuit?
15. How are the fields connected in relation to the armature on the shunt generator?
16. How is the voltage output of the generator regulated?
17. How is the current (amperes) controlled or limited?
18. What is the function of the cut-out relay and to what may it be likened?
19. What is a good average setting for the voltage regulator in a 6-volt system?
20. What advantages were gained by changing from 6 to 12 volts?
21. What is a good average setting for the voltage regulator in a 12-volt system?
22. What is used in conjunction with the coil in most 12-volt systems?
23. How does the output (in watts) of the average 6-volt system compare with the output (in watts) of the average 12-volt system?
24. What is the gain in cranking speed with 12-volt systems?
25. What is the usual 12-volt battery rating in ampere-hours?
26. Why should the relationship of the generator, regulator and battery be understood?
27. If the battery state of charge is low what effect does this have upon the generator?
28. What effect does low temperature have upon the battery?
29. What effect does low temperature have upon the generator?
30. At what temperature should the regulator be adjusted?

CHAPTER SEVENTEEN

The Charging Circuit— Generator Controls, Battery Considerations and Charging Signal

Years ago only a small generator output was required, since the electrical demand of the current-using equipment on the automotive vehicle was small. The third-brush generator, designed to supply approximately 10 to 15 amperes, met the requirements satisfactorily. The output was easily adjusted to meet the varying conditions of operation by adjusting the third-brush position. This particular method of control gradually reduces output as rotation speed of the armature is increased.

With the addition of more electrical equipment, sealed-beam lights requiring more current, and with higher vehicle speeds, the third-brush generator became less satisfactory. The third-brush generator output could be increased to handle the higher electrical load, but the tapering-off effect of this generator still reduced output at higher speeds, regardless of need for current. Furthermore, at low speeds only a small output was obtained; thus at the two extremes of speed, where more and more driving was being done, the small generator output was insufficient to meet the demands of the electrical system.

Development of Generator Controls

These considerations caused the adoption of the shunt generator. This type of generator reaches its specified maximum at lower speeds than the third-brush unit, and it can maintain this output through the speed range generator.

The increase of generator output brought with it a new necessity — controlling the generator output so that battery overcharge and high voltage could be prevented.

The storage battery in the generator circuit gradually increases its voltage as the point of full charge is approached. Thus with an uncontrolled generator output, the generator voltage would continue to increase as the battery came up to charge in order to maintain a high charging rate in the battery. Not only would this overcharge the battery, but it would also cause an excessively high voltage in the electrical system which would burn out electrical equipment and shorten the life of breaker points and other electrical units. Therefore, to avoid all these conditions, some means of regulating the generator output had to be used with the shunt generator. Regulating the generator meant holding the current output below a predetermined safe maximum, limiting the generator voltage to the desired value, and reducing the generator output as the battery reached full charge.

Various types of controls or regulators have been used. One method used in the past, and still in use on some equipment such as farm tractors, is merely a *generator field resistance switch* incorporated in the lighting switch. When the lights are turned on, the field resistance switch contacts are closed, shorting out the resistance so that the generator field is directly grounded and full generator output is available to handle the electrical load of lights. When the lights are turned off, the field resistance switch is opened so that the resistance is inserted into the generator field reducing the generator output to a lower value. There is usually an intermediate position on the switch at which the lights may be turned off without reducing the generator output. This permits recharging a low battery or supplying current for added electrical accessories such as a radio or additional light. Fig. 17.1 shows the development of the generator control.

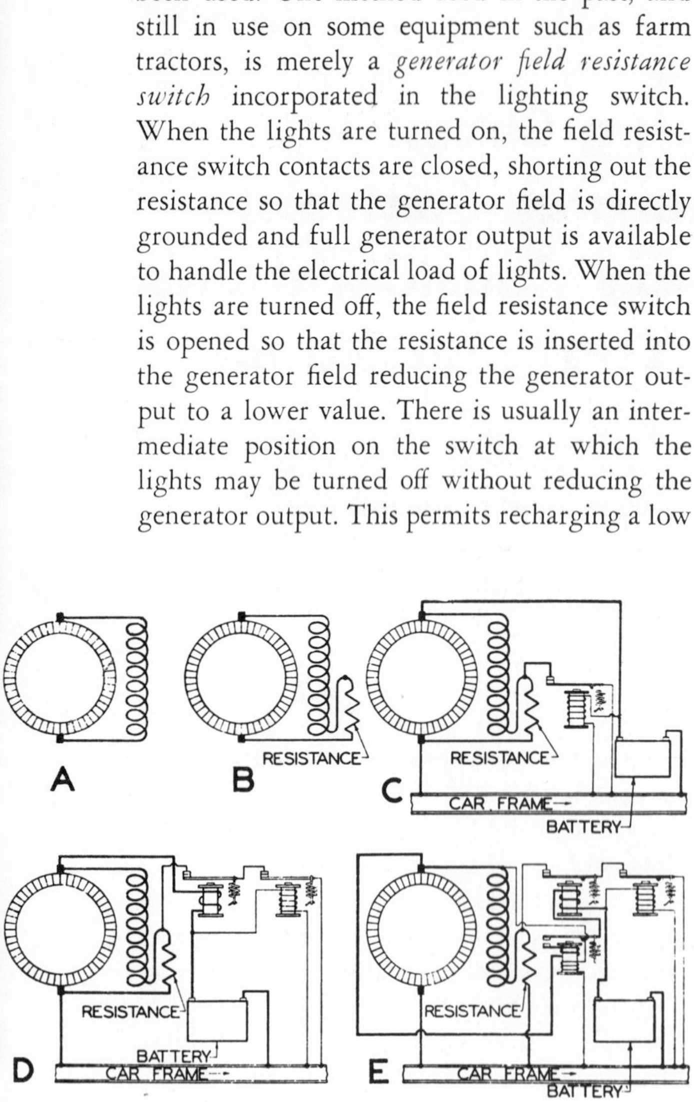

Step-Voltage Control

One of the first successful attempts to control the third-brush generator output was by means of a magnetic switch giving what was called *step-voltage control.*

The step-voltage control magnetically operates a switch which inserts or removes the resistance from the generator field circuit, thus performing magnetically the same function performed on tractors by hand in operating the light switch.

The step-voltage control consists of a shunt winding made up of many turns of fine wire, *i.e.*, a voltage coil. The winding is shunted across the generator so that generator voltage is impressed on it. Remember that on the voltage coil, the magnetic force will be proportional to voltage. Above the voltage winding core is an armature held away from the core by tension of a spring. In this position the two contact points, one on the armature and the other stationary, are in contact so that the generator field is directly grounded. Refer to Fig. 17.2.

Fig. 17.1. Shunt generator and VRB regulator. (A) There is no control of voltage. (B) A resistance is introduced which will cut down generator output. (C) The resistance is controlled by a vibrating voltage regulator. (D) A current limiter (or current regulator) is added to limit the maximum amperes the generator is allowed to put out. (E) A cut-out relay is added which completes the three-unit generator control.

Fig. 17.2. Cover removed from a two-charge regulator. (Left) Cut-out relay. (Right) Two-charge regulator which cuts resistance in and out depending upon the generator voltage.

As the battery approaches a charged condition, a higher voltage is required to force current into it and generator voltage increases as required to continue to push current into the battery. This increasing voltage reaches a value sufficient to operate the voltage control winding to create a magnetic field strong enough to overcome the armature spring tension. The armature is pulled toward the winding core, separating the contact points. When the points open, resistance is inserted into the generator field circuit, reducing the amount of current, the field magnetic flux, and the generator output.

As long as the battery remains in a charged condition and the circuit voltage is high, the resistance remains in the generator field circuit and the generator continues to operate at a reduced output. However, when the battery becomes partly discharged or when the electrical accessories are turned on so that the circuit voltage drops below a predetermined value, the lowered voltage becomes insufficient to hold the points open. Once the points are closed the field is directly grounded and generator output is increased.

This arrangement gives, in effect, partial generator control. The full generator capacity output will be required when the battery and line voltage are low, and the reduced generator output will be required when the battery and line voltage are high. The step-voltage control is not, however, true voltage regulation since after it inserts the resistance into the generator field, it cannot act to make any further cut in generator output. This minimum output is maintained even though conditions warrant its further reduction. Therefore it is easily possible, even with the resistance in the generator field, to overcharge a battery. The step-voltage control, for example, may reduce generator output from 20 amperes maximum to 12 amperes maximum, but under certain conditions the 12 amperes could still overcharge a battery.

The step-voltage control is in use on some generator applications and is a valuable control method. Applications which require that a high output be obtained at low generator speeds and applications where equipment operates for long intervals after starting, may successfully use the step-voltage control. General automotive applications, however, which have widely varying speed and electrical loads, require a different type of generator output control.

Vibrating Voltage Regulator

The vibrating voltage regulator or limiter is designed to prevent the voltage in the circuit from ever exceeding a predetermined safe value regardless of the generator speed and the condition of charge of the battery. This device was first used with the third-brush generator along with the necessary cut-out relay.

The voltage regulator is a magnetic switch consisting of two windings, a set of points and a resistor. One of the windings is a voltage winding consisting of many turns of fine wire connected across the circuit so that line voltage is impressed on it when the cut-out relay is closed. The other winding, a current winding, is composed of a few turns of heavy wire. The generator field current flows directly to ground whenever the regulator points are closed.

Above the core upon which these windings are assembled there is an armature on which is a contact point, positioned opposite a stationary point. (*Armature* in this connection is a hinged lever which is operated by magnetic force.) Spring tension holds the points together when the regulator is not operating. This permits the full amount of field current to flow through the field winding. As the battery approaches a charged condition the battery terminal voltage and the line voltage increase and continue to increase slightly as long as the charging rate continues high. This is an inherent characteristic of batteries. When the voltage reaches the value for which the voltage regulator is set, the magnetism of the voltage winding plus the magnetism of the current winding (carrying the field current) has increased to a value sufficient to overcome armature spring tension. The armature is then pulled toward the core and the points separate. Fig. 17.3 is a diagram of the three-unit control.

The instant the points separate, the field current has to flow to ground through a resistance. With the resistance inserted into the generator field circuit, the generator voltage and current output drop off. The result is that the magnetic field strength of the voltage regulator quickly drops too low to retain the armature in the "down" position. The armature is pulled up by its spring tension, the points again close, directly grounding the field circuit, and the generator voltage and current output increase. Magnetism is again produced in the regulator voltage and current windings, and the increased voltage strengthens the voltage-winding magnetic field aided by the current coil field, so that the magnetism once again reaches a value sufficient to open the contact points and reinsert the resistance into the generator field circuit, completing *one cycle* of regulator action. Note that this action only starts when the generator voltage reaches the voltage setting. This control has no effect on

voltages below its predetermined setting; it only prevents the voltage from rising *above* this value. Thus, in effect, the control is a *voltage limiter*!

In order to understand how the vibrating regulator works, the above cycle should be carefully studied. This complete cycle is performed from 50 to 200 times per second, which would be from 3000 to 12000 times per minute. It thus holds the generator voltage to a safe value.

Prevents Battery Overcharge

As the battery specific gravity continues to increase with the battery charge, the voltage regulator prevents battery overcharge by maintaining a constant voltage, thus reducing generator output. When the battery reaches a fully charged condition the voltage regulator will have reduced the charging rate to a few amperes, depending upon battery temperature. This is true because the battery voltage gradually increases as it reaches a point of full, or nearly full, charge; this point is reached when the difference between the controlled generator charging voltage and the battery counter voltage is so small that a current of only a few amperes can be forced through the battery. With a fully charged battery this amount of current is just sufficient to replace the current that is given up by the battery under the ordinary starting, ignition, and lighting load.

This characteristic of increasing battery voltage with increased charge and constant generator voltage when properly controlled is an important factor in making our present charging circuit work satisfactorily.

A few examples will probably help to clarify this process. With a discharged battery of 1.160 specific gravity, a voltage of only about 14.4 volts is required to force a charging rate of 30 amperes through the battery. However, as the battery begins to come up to charge it requires increased voltage to maintain a continued high charging rate. If the generator voltage is held at a predetermined value, then as the battery

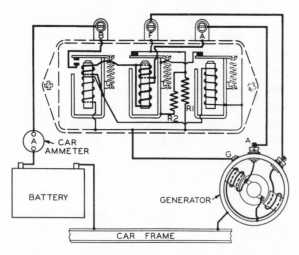

Fig. 17.3. Autolite VRP regulator with three units. (Left to right) Cut-out relay, current limiter, voltage regulator. Note the terminal markings: *B* (battery), *F* (field), *A* (armature output). Delco-Remy uses the letter *G* instead of *A*.

comes up to charge the difference between generator voltage and battery countervoltage will be less able to force a charge into the battery, with the result that the charging rate must taper off. This is desirable since otherwise a battery would be continually overcharged, greatly shortening its life.

The voltage regulator in operation actually holds the voltage at some definite value such as 14.3 volts. At this voltage, a battery with a gravity of 1.190 will take a maximum of about 30 amperes. When the battery reaches 1.220 gravity, the ampere charging rate will drop to about 20 amperes. As the battery reaches a gravity of 1.255, 1.260, or 1.270, the charging rate falls off still further until finally at a gravity of 1.280 there is only a charge of 3 to 6 amperes going into the battery as long as the voltage regulator limits the voltage to 14.3 volts.

As the battery comes up to charge, the regulator maintains a constant voltage by keeping the resistance in the generator field circuit a larger percentage of the operating time. Therefore, with the average field current decreased, generator output or charging rate will also decrease, dropping to lower values as the battery approaches a charged condition. In this way the voltage regulator operates to protect the entire circuit in the car from receiving high voltage with possible consequent damage, and prevents damage to the battery from overcharging. Fig. 17.4 shows a generator control with double-contact voltage limiter. The second contact directly grounds out the field current.

Current Regulator

Since the shunt generator does not of itself have any current limiting effect, it is necessary to have a device to prevent excessive current output that might damage the generator windings. For example, if the battery has a low state of charge and a heavy load due to a large number of current-using appliances being on at one time, the demand for current could exceed the generator capacity.

The current-limiting device is called a *current regulator*. In the equipment in use today it is assembled on the same base with the voltage regulator and the cut-out relay. (Autolite prefers to call the cut-out relay by the name of "circuit breaker.") The current regulator sets a maximum current limit which is consistent with safe generator capacity.

The current regulator is constructed in much the same manner as the voltage regulator. However, it has only one winding (a current coil) through which the entire generator output flows. Above the winding core is an armature with a pair of contact points held together by spring tension when the current regulator is not operating. Fig. 17.5 shows how adjustment of the voltage and current limits is made.

When the generator output increases to the value for which the current regulator is set, the magnetism of the current winding is sufficient to overcome the armature spring tension. The armature is pulled toward the winding core so that the points are separated. The generator

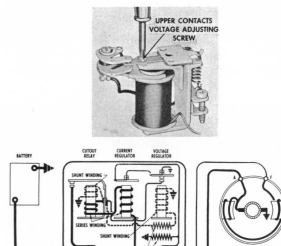

Fig. 17.4. (Above) How upper contact of Delco-Remy Double-Contact Voltage Regulator is adjusted. (Below) Wiring diagram of "600" series DR regulator. In this type, the field is shorted out when the upper contacts are working; therefore, when testing the generator, where this equipment is used, never ground the field unless the field connection to the regulator is broken.

field current must then flow through a resistance, and generator output is cut in the same way it is reduced by the voltage regulator when this is in action. This reduces the strength of the magnetic field and the points again close, directly grounding the generator field circuit so that the output increases. This cycle is repeated 50 to 200 times per second and the action limits the generator output to the value for which the regulator is set. A Delco-Remy generator control is shown in Fig. 17.6.

The voltage regulator and the current regulator never operate at the same time. If the electrical load requirements are large and the battery charge is low, the voltage will not be sufficient to cause the voltage regulator to operate. The generator output is consequently increased until it reaches the value for which the current regulator is set. Then the current regulator will operate to protect the generator from overload. A heavier current demand from the generator will keep the voltage low enough that it may not reach the point for which the voltage regulator is set. However, as the battery gradually increases its charge, it will require a higher voltage to force current through it. This will bring the generator voltage up to a point where the voltage regulator will become operative. This switch to the voltage regulator will also occur if the electrical load is reduced, such as turning off the radio or head lights. This reduces the generator output required

below the value required to operate the current regulator, and the generator will then be completely under the control of the voltage regulator.

Two resistances are used on many current and voltage regulators. When the current regulator points open, they are connected into the generator field circuit in parallel to give a lower value of resistance. When the voltage regulator points open, only one resistance is inserted into the generator field. This provides a higher value of resistance. This is desirable because it takes a higher value of resistance to reduce the output to a few amperes than to merely prevent the generator's output from increasing beyond a safe maximum for the generator. In other words, it takes more resistance to hold the voltage down to the point for which the regulator is set than it does to keep the current output within the safe capacity of the generator.

The type of regulator used for controlling current and for controlling voltage is not new. These units are adaptations of the Terrill regulator which has been in general use to control the voltage and power in lighting transmission systems for over fifty years.

Battery Considerations

Battery charging or overcharging is usually considered in amperes only, which is incorrect. Time is an important factor, as ampere-hours is really the measurement of battery capacity.

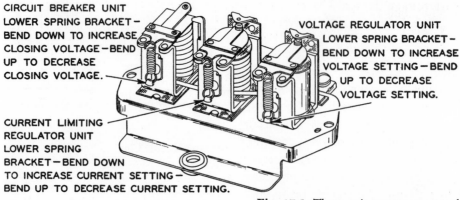

CIRCUIT BREAKER UNIT
LOWER SPRING BRACKET—
BEND DOWN TO INCREASE
CLOSING VOLTAGE—BEND
UP TO DECREASE
CLOSING VOLTAGE.

VOLTAGE REGULATOR UNIT
LOWER SPRING BRACKET—
BEND DOWN TO INCREASE
VOLTAGE SETTING—BEND
UP TO DECREASE
VOLTAGE SETTING.

CURRENT LIMITING
REGULATOR UNIT
LOWER SPRING
BRACKET—BEND DOWN
TO INCREASE CURRENT SETTING—
BEND UP TO DECREASE CURRENT SETTING.

Fig. 17.5. Three-unit generator control with spring hangers, showing how to adjust for voltage and current.

This should be kept in mind when referring to battery charge or discharge.

One of the difficulties in charging batteries over a wide variation in battery conditions is that the battery is primarily a chemical unit having characteristics which are not easy to control.

Regulators are manufactured to maintain a voltage within plus or minus .15 volt which places these units in the class of precision instruments. However, battery charging voltage, over the wide range of operating temperatures, is not maintained anywhere near these close limits.

There are a number of undesirable characteristics of the present-day battery as a unit of the charging circuit. For example, there is a lack of uniformity of the terminal charge voltage for batteries of different makes. Two well-known 90 ampere-hour batteries showed a difference of .4 volts when tested at a 15-ampere charging rate at 0°F.

There was also a difference in terminal charge voltage for batteries of the same make, but of different capacities. One make has a difference of .53 volts at 0°F. between a 45 ampere-hour battery and a 75 ampere-hour battery.

The battery charge voltage varies with the temperature. One prominent make of battery has an increase of 1.2 volts as the temperature increases from zero to 120°F. This is a 10% increase.

A considerable number of batteries had a reduction in charging voltage due to aging, apparently caused by antimony dissolving from the positive grids and being deposited on the negative plates. Very little consideration has been given to this condition in servicing the electrical system.

Some points mentioned previously in connection with battery voltages, must be considered in more detail as they relate to the operation of the voltage regulator and the generator in maintaining battery charge. Battery charge voltage (or charging voltage) is the minimum voltage that must be impressed on the battery in order to force charging current through the battery. Battery counter voltage, or counter-electromotive force (cemf), is the voltage that opposes the charging voltage. To get any charging current through the battery, the voltage of the generator current sent to the battery must be above the battery voltage. In accordance with Ohm's Law, the amount of current in amperes that passes through the battery to charge it will be proportional to the *difference* between the voltage of the generator current and the battery counter voltage.

A very important characteristic is its variation in counter voltage with changes in two factors (1) temperature, and (2) state of charge. (Refer to the chart of battery cemf variations, Fig. 17.7.)

Battery Temperature and State of Charge

As battery temperature drops, the counter voltage *increases* at a rapid rate. On the other hand, battery voltage *decreases* with drops in temperature. This is because the reversible chemical actions involved in charging and discharging slow up considerably as the battery gets colder.

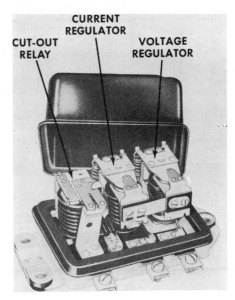

Fig. 17.6. Delco-Remy three-unit regulator, with double springs on voltage regulator and current limiter.

As the state of charge increases, the battery counter voltage *increases*. Therefore, the greater the amount of charging current that is to be passed through the battery, the higher the voltage of the charging current must be, Fig. 17.8.

As examples of the effects of these two conditions, consider the following: To get a current of 15 amperes through a 6-volt, fully charged battery, the voltage would have to be 8.9 volts at 0°F., 7.8 volts at 80°F., and 7.2 volts at 120°F.

To pass a current of 15 amperes through a battery with one-half charge would require 8.6 volts at 0°F., 6.7 volts at 80°F., and only 6.4 volts at 120°F.

With the voltage regulator set at 7.4 volts, a fully charged battery at 0°F. would only take about 1 ampere, at 80°F. about 3.5 amperes and at 120°F. 20 amperes.

A one-half charged battery with a regulator setting of 7.4 volts would take about 2 amperes at 0°F., but at 80°F. and higher, it would take full generator output without getting up to 7.4 volts.

From all this it is plain to see that *the battery regulates the charging system by its changes in counter voltage*! Fig. 17.9 shows the relation between battery voltage and charging rates.

The location of a battery in a vehicle will affect battery charge voltage. For instance, in one location a battery will run comparatively cool, closely approaching atmospheric temperature, while in another location underneath the hood some batteries have been found to operate at electrolyte temperatures as high as 185°F. The operating voltage and the temperature compensation specifications for a vehicle manufacturer using one make of batteries will be different from those of a manufacturer using another make. If the original equipment battery is replaced by one of a different make, size, or classification, the regulator may need to be adjusted to compensate for the difference in voltage due to battery differences.

Temperature Compensation

Most automotive vehicles are operated under a wide variation in atmospheric temperatures.

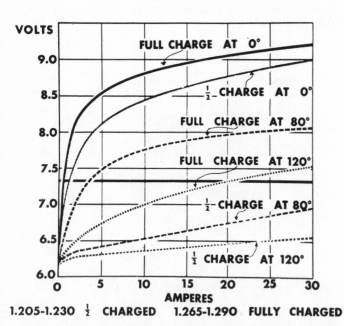

Fig. 17.7. Variations in cemf (battery counter-electromotive force) with different temperatures and states of charge. Temperature has a very important effect on battery charging rate. (DR)

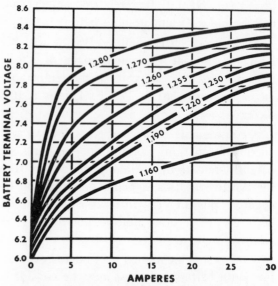

Fig. 17.8. Variations in charging voltage necessary to force given current through the battery with different states of charge. Note that at 7.4 volts (the usual regulated voltage), a fully charged battery will only take a few amperes, while a battery with low charge will take full generator output. (DR)

The resistance of the generator and regulator windings, in addition to the battery terminal voltage, will vary with the temperature. Therefore some form of temperature compensation is necessary.

For Autolite voltage regulators this is accomplished by a magnetic bypass. A nickel and iron magnetic shunt is inserted in the magnetic circuit of the voltage regulator. The metal used for this shunt is a poor conductor of magnetic lines of force at high temperature and a good conductor at low temperature. Therefore at low temperatures there will be greater magnetic force which will compensate for the low temperature. Refer to Fig. 17.10.

The composition and the cross section of the metal may be varied to produce desired compensation. There is a variation in the specifications of the car manufacturers of from .4 of a volt to .9 volt compensation between 0°F. and 140°F.

The degree of compensation is very accurately developed by the designing engineers, but in servicing regulators the regulator armature core gap must be accurately adjusted or the compensation will not follow specifications.

Less core gap increases the compensation, while greater core gap decreases it. This is the principal reason for very close tolerances in manufacturing core gap gauges.

Cut-out relays or circuit breakers and some current regulators use bi-metal hinges for temperature compensation. Variation in the core gap affects this compensation also. The compensation for cut-out relays is generally a straight line curve, but in some types they are over-compensated to provide for a reduction in closing voltage with higher temperature.

If the voltage regulator and the cut-out relay are not accurately calibrated, there is a possibility when operating under high temperatures that the operating voltage of the voltage regulator unit will be reduced to a value below the closing voltage of the cut-out relay so that the cut-out relay will not close. The generator will operate on open circuit and the battery will not

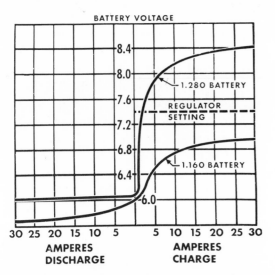

Fig. 17.9. Variations in battery voltage between charge and discharge of a 1.280 gravity battery and a 1.160 gravity battery. Curves to right of center line show ampere charge for different charging voltages. At left is the effect on voltage of different ampere loads on the battery. (DR)

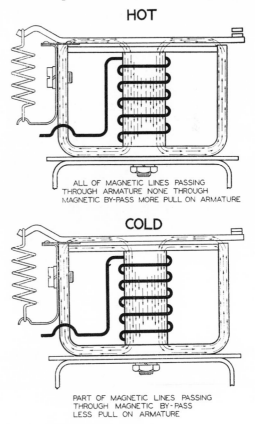

Fig. 17.10. One method of temperature control on voltage regulator.

be charged. Because temperature compensation is important in the calibration of regulators, service-manual calibration figures are given in degrees from 50° to 110°F. Therefore a thermometer is necessary to measure the air temperatures surrounding the units when they are calibrated to permit the correct figures to be selected from the manual.

Contact Points and Polarity

Most regulator contacts have dissimilar contact metals on the two points. It is important that the contacts be installed in their proper relation according to the polarity of the system in which they are used. Reversing the polarity or using the regulator of the wrong polarity will result in a short contact life and will require changing or servicing the regulator.

On some Autolite regulators designed to operate with a positive ground, the two-piece contacts should be on the armature and the single-piece contacts should be stationary. This relationship is reversed for systems with negative grounds.

The contact points are usually designed to have a slight wiping action when they open and close. For this reason a very fine file should be used when servicing contacts (No. 6 American-Swiss-Cut Equaling File), and the filing should

be done parallel with the length of the armature. Crossfiling causes a mechanical locking action of the regulator contacts, resulting in very erratic operation.

If the contact points are filed, they should be cleaned with a lintless tape soaked in carbon tetrachloride, and then wiped again with a dry piece of the same material. Oil or dirt on the contact surfaces of voltage regulators results in a high operative voltage and in a majority of cases the regulators will be found to be operating at higher levels than specified. Therefore, in cases where the voltage is higher than it should be, first try cleaning the points to restore their operation to normal.

A headphone of not less than 2000 ohms resistance, connected from regulator *field* or *F* terminal to ground, can be used to listen to the action of the contacts. The sound of the vibrations should be uniform and regular. Irregularity indicates trouble, sometimes in the regulator, but usually is caused by poor contacts in the charging circuit, or arcing of the generator brushes.

Dash Charging Signal

Prior to 1955, most cars had an ammeter on the dash to indicate when current was flowing into or out of the battery. Recently the ammeter has been omitted on most car models and a signal light installed. This will light when the ignition switch is turned on and will remain lit as long as the generator is not producing current, whether the engine is or is not running. As soon as the generator starts to put out current the light is extinguished.

One side of the lamp circuit is connected to a conductor that has current from the battery flowing in it when the ignition switch is turned on. The other side of the lamp circuit is connected to the output conductor from the generator.

When the generator is not generating current, the side of the circuit connected to the battery, through the ignition switch, will be alive while

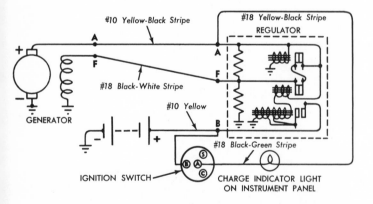

Fig. 17.11. One form of indicator light circuit. When the ignition key is turned to close the ignition circuit, contact *A* is connected to the battery and the light will glow, being grounded through the generator. When generator voltage approximates battery voltage, the light goes out.

the other side, connected to the generator, will act as a ground; and the signal lamp will light. As soon as the generator starts to produce current, both sides of the lamp will have voltage with a differential between battery and generator voltage insufficient to light the lamp. If there happened to be high resistance in the ignition switch or connections in the battery side of the circuit, there could be enough voltage difference to make the light glow dimly. When this happens, corrective measures should be taken. Refer to Fig. 17.11.

Summary

The early electrical demand on the automobile was met by the *three-brush generator*, but this soon became inadequate. The *shunt generator* was adopted to furnish the needed electrical current. This required some means to keep voltage and current within safe limits.

Storage battery voltage increases with state of charge so that the voltage limiter is needed to avoid excessive voltage. Various types of regulation have been used, including the step-voltage control and the vibrating voltage regulator or limiter.

The *voltage regulator* is a magnetic switch with a voltage winding and a current winding, a set of contact points and a resistor. A vibrating armature alternately cuts the resistor in and out of the field circuit.

When the battery reaches a charged condition the *voltage limiter* reduces the generator charging current to a few amperes. Just enough current is produced to replace the starting current, and idle load for lights, ignition, etc.

The voltage regulator or limiter holds the generator voltage to the point for which it is set, such as 14.3 volts. The control is provided through varying the field current. The control prevents battery overcharging.

The *current regulator* must be used with the shunt generator since it does not have any current-limiting effect. The current regulator or limiter is similar to the voltage regulator except that its winding is a current coil.

The *voltage regulator and current regulator* never operate at the same time. Only one or the other will operate.

Battery charging or overcharging is often considered in terms of *amperes only*. However, *ampere-hours* is the correct measurement of battery capacity. Battery charging conditions vary widely. Batteries of different makes may vary in voltage.

Battery charge voltage varies with temperature. Battery charge voltage is the minimum voltage that must be impressed on a battery to force a charging current through it. Battery counter voltage or cemf opposes charging voltage.

Generator voltage must be above battery cemf and the amount of charging current will be proportional to the difference between generator voltage and battery cemf.

As *battery temperature drops*, its cemf increases at a rapid rate and voltage drops. As state of charge increases, counter voltage increases. The battery regulates the charging system by its changes in cemf.

As most automotive vehicles are operated under widely varying temperature conditions *compensation for temperature* is necessary. A thermometer should be used to check the surrounding air temperature when the voltage regulator is adjusted.

Contact point polarity is important since many regulator contacts have dissimilar metals on the points and therefore must be operated with the correct polarity to prevent electrical erosion and possible sticking. Contact points, if filed, must be carefully cleaned.

A *dash charging signal* is used on many automobiles to replace the dash ammeter. Its wiring circuit is shown in Fig. 17.9.

Questions

1. How were the early generators controlled?
2. What type of DC generator is now used?
3. What was one of the first successful attempts to control third-brush generator output?

4. How is voltage controlled in present types of DC generators?
5. What does the control unit do?
6. How is current controlled in the DC generator?
7. What happens to battery voltage as the battery charge builds up?
8. How does this affect the battery charging current from the generator?
9. What is an average setting for voltage from a 12-volt generator?
10. What is a "voltage coil"?
11. What is a "current coil"?
12. How is a voltage limiter adjusted?
13. Under what conditions will a voltage limiter and current limiter operate simultaneously?
14. What effect does resistance in the field circuit have on generator output?
15. How is battery capacity stated?
16. What effect does low temperature have on a battery?
17. What is battery counter electromotive force (cemf)?
18. What happens to the cemf as the battery charge increases?
19. What effect does the battery have on the charging system?
20. What device is currently being used on many late model cars instead of the dash ammeter?

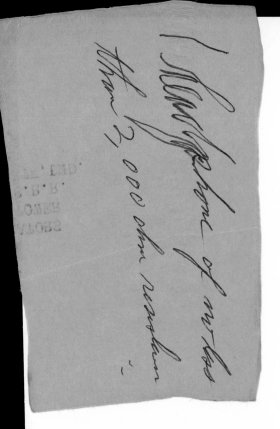

CHAPTER EIGHTEEN

Alternating Current Charging Circuits

Alternating current generators, *or alternators*, have been used for many years to supply rectified alternating current (DC) in trucks, police cars, cars with two-way telephone or radio and buses. However, the application of the alternating generator as standard equipment for passenger car use is relatively new. First introduced on the 1961 Chrysler automobiles as standard equipment, there are now six suppliers of alternators: Chrysler, Leece Neville, Delco-Remy Division of General Motors Corporation (Delcotron), Electric Autolite (Prestolite), Motorola, and Ford.

The alternator has several advantages:

1. It provides substantial current at engine idle speed.
2. It provides increased maximum output.
3. Its construction is simpler, and it is more durable than the conventional DC generator.

Electromagnetic Induction

Magnetism and electricity are very closely related. When electric current passes through a wire, a magnetic field is created around the wire; and if a wire carrying current is wound into a coil, a magnetic field with N and S poles is created, just as in a bar magnet.

If an iron core is placed inside such a coil, the magnetic field becomes much stronger, because iron conducts magnetic lines of force much more readily than air. Such an arrangement, called an electromagnet, is used in generators to create a strong magnetic field. Many turns of wire carrying current are wound around soft iron cores, called pole pieces.

If a wire conductor is moved so it cuts lines of force or if a magnet is moved so that lines of force cut across a wire conductor, a voltage will be induced in the conductor. This is called *electromagnetic induction*. The voltage will cause a current to flow when the conductor is part of a closed circuit. Refer to Fig. 18.1. The direction of current flow is determined by the direction of the lines of force and the direction of motion of the magnetic field with respect to the conductor.

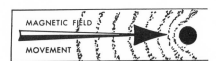

Fig. 18.1. If a magnetic field cuts across a conductor which is part of a closed circuit, a voltage is generated. The arrow indicates the direction of movement of a magnetic field.

209

In a DC generator, the magnetic field is stationary and the conductors in the armature are moved so as to cut across the magnetic lines of force. However, in an AC generator, a strong magnetic field is moved so that the lines of force cut across stationary conductors.

AC Generator Operating Principles

Voltage will be induced in a conductor if a magnetic field is moved across it. An example would be a bar magnet rotating on a horizontal axis inside a loop of wire, so the ends of the magnet with their respective *N* and *S* magnetic fields, swing past first one side of the coil and then the other.

In Fig. 18.2, note the rotating magnet with the *S* pole of the magnet directly under the top portion of the loop of wire, and the *N* pole directly over the bottom portion. There will be an induced voltage which will cause current to flow in the direction shown by the arrows. As current flows from positive to negative through the external or load circuit, the end of the loop of wire marked *A* will be positive polarity (+) and the other end, marked *B*, will be negative (—).

When the magnet has moved through one-half revolution, the *N* pole will have moved to a position directly under the top conductor of the loop, and the *S* pole directly over the bottom of conductor. The induced voltage at this time will now cause current to flow in the opposite direction. Therefore, the *A* end of the

wire will become negative polarity (—) and the *B* end, positive (+). This means that the polarity of the ends of the wire has changed. After the magnet makes a second one-half revolution, the bar magnet will be back to its starting point and the polarity will have again reversed.

The current flow through the external circuit, indicated by the lamp and leads to the lamp, will be first in one direction and then in the other. This is an alternating current, produced by an AC generator. Actually such a generator as illustrated, with a single loop of wire and a simple bar magnet, would only produce a very weak current.

Increasing Current Supply

By placing the loop of wire and the magnet inside an iron frame, performance is much improved. The iron frame provides a support for the loop of wire and also acts as a good conducting path for the magnetic lines of force. The number of lines of force which will flow from pole to pole is greatly increased; thus, there will be more lines of force cutting the conductor, which is located between the bar magnet and the frame. This is illustrated in Fig. 18.3.

The amount of voltage induced in a conductor is proportional to the number of lines of force which cut the conductor per second. Doubling the number of lines of force will

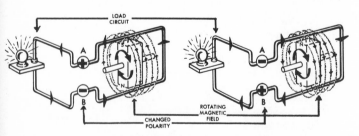

Fig. 18.2. Changes in polarity of current are dependent upon changes in polarity of magnetic lines of force which cut conductors. (Left) *S* lines are cutting top of wire loop. (Right) *N* lines are cutting top of loop. Polarity is indicated at *A* and *B*.

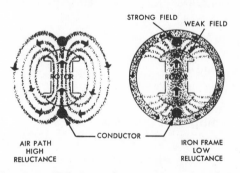

Fig. 18.3. When conductors are stationed in air, the lines of magnetic force must travel through air which has a high resistance to magnetism; but when conductors are within an iron frame, there is a much greater magnetic flow and a stronger magnetic field.

cause voltage to be doubled. Also, if the speed at which the magnet turns is increased, the voltage will increase since the number of lines cut per second will be greater. Conversely, decreasing either the speed of rotation or the number of lines of force cut per second will cause the voltage to decrease.

The rotating magnet in an AC generator is the field magnet and is called the *rotor*. The conductors (corresponding to the loop of wire and the outside frame) constitute the *stator*. This corresponds to the armature in the conventional DC generator.

Sine Curve

Fig. 18.4 illustrates different positions of the rotor as it rotates at constant speed. The top portion of the drawing shows a curve proportional to the magnitude of the voltage which is generated in the loop of wire as the magnet rotates. This voltage curve is the so-called "sine curve" and is typical of alternating current. It shows the generated voltage or electrical pressure in the stator; this voltage can be measured

at the terminals just as voltage can be measured across a battery.

With the rotor in *position 1*, there is zero voltage being generated in the loop of wire because there are no magnetic lines of force cutting across the conductor. As the rotor turns and approaches *position 2*, the voltage begins to build up because the magnetic field starts to cut across the conductor. When the rotor reaches *position 2*, the generated voltage is at its maximum, which is shown by the high peak of the voltage curve. This is when the magnet bar is directly under the loop of wire, which is thus being cut by the heaviest concentration of magnetic lines of force.

As the rotor turns from *position 2* to *position 3*, the voltage decreases until at *position 3* it drops to zero. Now, as the rotor turns from *position 3* to *position 4* the N pole of the rotor is passing under the top position of the wire loop and the S pole of the rotor is over the bottom position. This causes a voltage equal to the maximum in *position 2* but of the opposite polarity, shown by the part of the voltage below

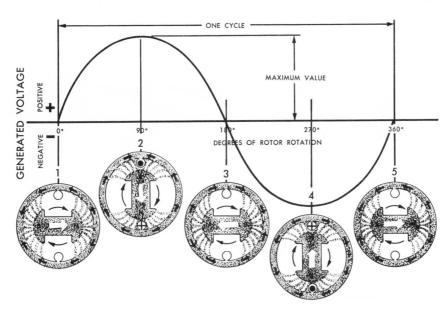

Fig. 18.4. Generation of one alternating current cycle. Different positions of the field rotor generate different voltages as illustrated by the sine curve indicating positive and negative voltage values.

the zero line. When the rotor turns to *position 5*, the voltage again becomes zero, indicated by the voltage curve at the zero line.

The voltage curve in Fig. 18.4 represents one complete turn of the rotor, which constitutes one AC cycle. If the rotor should turn at 60 rotations per second, there would be 60 *cycles* per second (120 alternations). The number of *cycles per second* is called the *frequency*. Generator speed in automotive applications varies considerably, and therefore the AC frequency also varies, but this is unimportant since the current is rectified into DC for use in automotive circuits. Sixty-cycle AC is illustrated in Fig. 18.5.

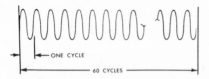

Fig. 18.5. Sixty AC cycles. The first wave is one cycle.

A single loop of wire was used in the stator of the illustration of the AC generator. In the actual device, three separate windings are used in the stator, each consisting of many conductors. Each of the three windings is called a *phase*, and the unit is called a *three-phase generator*. Connection of the three phases may be in the form of a "Y" connection; or in the form of a triangle, called a *delta* connection. See Fig. 18.6. In both the *Y* and *delta* connections, the stator is connected to *diodes* to convert the alternating current to direct current.

The molecular composition of a *diode* is such that it will allow current to flow in one direction only. The diode is frequently represented by the symbol shown in Fig. 18.7. The direction of current flow is indicated by the arrow. When a diode is connected in a circuit carrying an AC voltage, current will flow as shown in circuit *A* of Fig. 18.7, but will not flow in circuit *B*. Note the opposite polarity in circuits *A* and *B*.

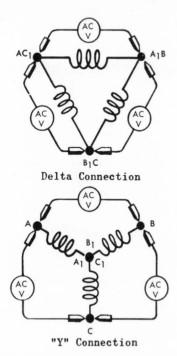

Fig. 18.6. In a three-phase generator there are three stator windings which may be "delta" or "Y" connected. Most automotive AC generators are Y connected.

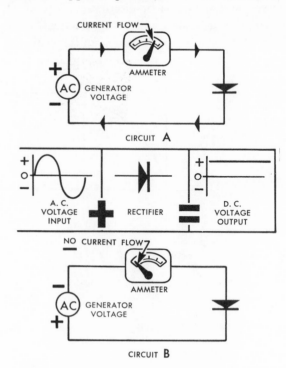

Fig. 18.7. A diode will only permit current to flow in one direction. Circuit *A* shows current flowing through a positive diode when the polarity is positive. In circuit *B* when the polarity is negative, no current will flow. The broad arrow is the diode symbol.

AC Generating System

An automotive AC generating system consists of the generating unit, the rectifier unit and a generator control. The battery is connected to the system, and in a way may be considered as part of the system. The early AC systems made use of copper sulphite rectifiers for 6-volt battery charging, but with the general adoption of 12-volt systems, selenium rectifiers of the same general type were used.

A relatively short time ago, the silicon diode was developed to replace the selenium rectifier. *Each phase* requires a positive and a negative diode to give full wave rectification, or a total of six diodes. The diodes are made in small housings, either cylindrical or with flanges. They are mounted in so-called "heat sinks," made with cooling flanges to help dissipate the heat (diodes get rather hot when the generator is delivering a fairly heavy current). Fan blades on the generator rotor furnish air for cooling both the diode and the stator windings. The use of diodes for rectifying the AC current makes it possible to install an AC system in the same space under the hood required by the conventional DC system. One design of the diode is shown in Fig. 18.8.

Diodes have polarity, either positive or negative. The polarity is determined by the polarity of the diode case, not the antenna or pigtail. Inside, the only difference between the positive and negative diodes is the way the two metal wafers, which compose each diode, are connected respectively to the case and the antenna. It is very important that diodes of the correct polarity be used in each diode position because they act as electrical check valves; wrong polarity would permit current to flow in the wrong direction.

AC generators or alternators do not require current limiters. Due to high self-induction at high speeds, they are self-limiting as to current output. However, a voltage limiter is required to control the strength of the field current.

The advantage of the alternator is that a heavy current can be delivered at low speed (up to 60 or even 70 amperes maximum), with 15 or more amperes at curb idle speed. With this system the only time the battery is called upon for current is for starting the engine, as the generator supplies current requirements most of the time, even at idle speed. A valuable result is that the battery is always well charged as long as it is in reasonably good condition.

Field current, usually only about 2 amperes, is supplied to the field winding through slip rings and brushes. With no commutator segments, there is no sparking, and rotor speed

Fig. 18.9. Typical alternator rotor, which supplies the rotating magnetic field. The lines of magnetic force from this field cut the conductors in the stator and generate electrical current.

Fig. 18.8. Diodes of the type used in the Delco-Remy AC generator, one negative and one positive. The hex flange is ⅝ inch across the flats.

is limited only by the allowable speed of the ball bearings which are usually on the driving end of the unit. The field rotor has from 8 to 12 poles, alternately positive and negative. The field winding is somewhat in the shape of a doughnut, nested inside the pole pieces. A typical alternator rotor is illustrated in Fig. 18.9.

With the alternator, no cut-out relay is needed as the diodes prevent current flowing from the battery to ground through the generator. The diodes will operate up to 300°F. without damage or loss of efficiency. However, the polarity of the battery must never be reversed, as this will quickly ruin the diodes. When the battery is installed with the correct polarity, its voltage is opposed to the diodes and no current will flow through them. However, if the polarity of the battery should be reversed, current can flow in the direction permitted by the diodes and a condition equivalent

Fig. 18.10. Leece-Neville AC generator with external rectifier and generator regulator. The external rectifier is now being replaced by six diodes mounted in the generator.

Fig. 18.11. Heavy duty Leece-Neville alternator mounted on generator test bench.

to a short circuit though the diodes is set up. The weakest point in the circuit will quickly burn out.

Leece-Neville Equipment

The Leece-Neville Company developed and introduced an alternating current generator in 1946. The company furnishes alternators for passenger cars and light trucks with outputs of 40 to 60 amperes. As with most alternators, they can be furnished with a voltage regulator plus a field relay which closes the field circuit when the ignition switch is turned on and a charging safety signal relay which causes a lamp to light when the engine is running and the generator is not putting out current. The voltage regulator or voltage limiter, a double-contact type, is similar in design to those used with other makes.

The earlier alternators, before the development of the diode, made use of selenium plate rectifiers which were rather bulky and developed considerable heat. With the advent of the diodes, the plate rectifier became obsolete. The diodes in the present alternator designs are contained inside the alternator, making it possible for alternators to fit into the space formerly required by the DC generator. Fig. 18.10 shows a typical plate rectifier. Conversion kits are available for converting plate rectifier installation to the diode type. Fig. 18.11 is a heavy-duty Leece-Neville alternator.

Delco-Remy Equipment — Delcotron

For some years Delco-Remy has been supplying heavy duty alternators for trucks and police cars. Recently a new design was introduced, called the Delcotron, for use in passenger automobiles and light trucks. It is somewhat similar in appearance to the other makes of alternators. Several capacities are available, ranging from 42 to 62 amperes. For convenience, connections to the diodes are made by screws instead of soldering to the antenna, so that the diodes can be easily isolated. The connection to the case generally is made by pressing the diodes into place. Connections to the field and indicating lamp relay are made by slip joints.

The Delcotron is used on all General Motors Corporation cars since 1963 with possibly one or two exceptions on certain models.

Chrysler AC Generator

Chrysler was the first automobile manufacturer to supply an alternator as standard equipment on passenger cars. Chrysler has been using only one unit in the voltage regulator — a double-contact voltage limiter. The field current is turned on when the ignition switch is closed. The charging signal is connected to one of the three alternator phases and to the battery, without a relay being used.

The generator housing is die-cast aluminum, made in two similar parts which join the stator in a plane at right angles to the generator shaft. The field is the rotor, with a 2-ampere field current supplied through slip rings. Fan blades at each end of the rotor force air through the unit for cooling both the windings and the diode heat sinks.

As in the Leece-Neville and Delco-Remy generators, six diodes are used to provide full wave rectification. The positive diodes are pressed into an aluminum casting which in turn is bolted to the end plate, while the negative diodes are pressed into the end plate itself. If any of the positive diodes need replacing it is best to replace the unit — the whole set of three and the aluminum casting. If one or more of the negative diodes should fail, either the whole end plate must be replaced or special tools must be used to press out the defective diode(s). If the special tools are available, the negative diodes can be pressed out of the negative heat sink and new ones pressed in.

In size the Chrysler generator is about 1½ inches larger than the conventional DC unit and about 2 inches shorter. With the small single-unit voltage regulator, the generator and regulator occupy less space under the hood than the conventional DC system. Fig. 18.12 shows the Chrysler alternator and control, while Fig. 18.13 shows the disassembled alternator.

Electric Autolite (Prestolite)

While the Electrical Autolite Company has not changed its name, the name Autolite as applied to electrical equipment has been sold to Ford Motor Company. Therefore, products now made and sold by Electric Autolite will carry the name Prestolite.

Prestolite alternators and regulators are offered as direct replacements on most late model cars. Three basic alternators are offered, two 5-inch diameter units and one 6⅝-inches in diameter. The principal components of the alternators are delta-connected stator, eight-pole

Fig. 18.12. Chrysler alternator. At upper right can be seen the negative diode heat sink. Two positive diodes are located below the rotor shaft and one above. At right is single-unit voltage regulator with cover removed.

Fig. 18.13. Chrysler alternator with end plates removed. The stator winding and laminations are shown at left, with diode connections. The rotor is at right.

rotor, slip ring end frame and six diode rectifiers mounted in separate positive and negative heat sinks. Cold output is 8 to 25 amperes for the 5-inch units and 25 to 31 amperes for the 6⅝-inch alternator.

Two different regulators are supplied with Prestolite alternators. One has a single unit which is a double-contact voltage limiter; the other contains a voltage limiter, charger indicator relay, and a circuit breaker which protects the diodes and wiring harness from possible reversed battery polarity. The circuit breaker is exclusive with Prestolite.

Motorola System

The Motorola alternator and regulator is specifically designed to replace the DC equipment on most U.S. cars built since 1959. It

Fig. 18.14. Motorola alternator with its fully transistorized regulator. This regulator is not adjustable, but is preset at the factory. If it fails in service, it must be replaced.

has also been adopted as standard equipment on Rambler and American Motors Cars beginning with the 1963 models.

The general design is similar to other AC generators in that it uses a rotor, stator, two end frames and six diodes to rectify the alternating current. Three models are offered with capacities of 30, 40 and 45 amperes, respectively. Each model will produce 8 to 15 amperes at engine idle. In addition to the six rectifying diodes, the 30-ampere unit has an isolation diode and the two larger sizes have two isolation diodes.

The outstanding feature of the Motorola alternator system is its all-electric voltage regulator. This sealed and transistorized unit controls the alternator charging rate by sensing the battery voltage and its requirements for charge. It has no relays or vibrating contacts and does not require adjustment. Its electronic parts do not cause any radio or TV interference. Fig. 18.14 shows the Motorola alternator and fully transistorized regulator.

Ford Alternator

The Ford alternator is supplied for Ford-built cars only. A feature of this design is that all connections to the generator are made by means of a connector block. Thus by means of a single terminal block the generator output, field, ground wire, and charge signal are all connected to the alternator. The stator is "Y"

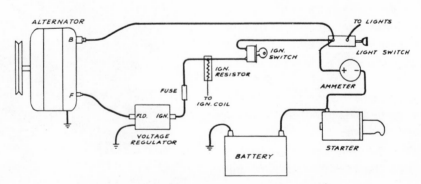

Fig. 18.15. Wiring diagram of Chrysler AC charging circuit. Notice that the ignition switch turns on the field current.

connected, and there is a voltage limiter and a field relay in the voltage regulator.

The output is rated at 35 to 40 amperes with up to 15 amperes at engine idle speed. The general design is similar to other alternators mentioned, in that it has six diodes, a rotor field and a stator. The field current is supplied by means of slip rings and brushes.

Trouble Shooting the AC System

In general the same troubles that affect the conventional DC generating system will cause the AC system to fail — loose wire connections, broken wires, loose fan belt, worn rotor bearings, wrong regulator adjustment, internal shorts, opens, or grounds. However, the AC system has eliminated one fairly common cause of failure — the commutator and brushes. The only sliding electrical contacts are two brushes and slip rings to supply current to the field winding. This field current is only 2 to 2.75 amperes, or possibly as much as 5 amperes on the larger sizes.

On the Chrysler system, Fig. 18.15, the ignition switch closes the field circuit that is grounded in the generator, making it comparable to the *B* or heavy-duty DC generator circuit. On the other makes of alternators the field circuit is closed by means of a field relay. Remember that on all the makes of alternators the output circuit is "hot" with full battery voltage to the output terminal, except that on the Motorola unit an isolation diode is inserted in the circuit.

In case there is no charging current delivered by the generating system and none of the possible troubles mentioned above exist, the failure may be due to (1) one or more defective diodes, (2) field circuit failure, (3) regulator failure, (4) open, shorted, or grounded stator.

To locate the cause of trouble on an alternator system, a volt-ampere tester, such as the Sun Electric VAT-20 (or equivalent) is needed, with meter ranges as shown at the top of the following column.

DC ammeter	0-60 amperes
DC ammeter	0-5 amperes
DC voltmeter	1-16 volts
Rheostat	40 ohm, 3-ampere capacity
Carbon pile	45-ampere capacity
Diode tester	(Sun, Simpson or equivalent)
Test lamp	12-volt DC
Ohmmeter	Not absolutely necessary but helpful

First connect the ammeter into the output circuit. It is helpful to use the Sun Battery Post Adapter, shown in Fig. 18.16, which only requires opening the circuit at the battery yet allows full battery current to be used for engine starting. With the engine not operating, no current flow should be indicated. If current flow is indicated it will be through defective diodes.

Next, turn on the ignition. This causes the field circuit to be closed so that the normal current of 2.3 to 4.5 amperes (depending on unit size) will flow. Start the engine and let it and

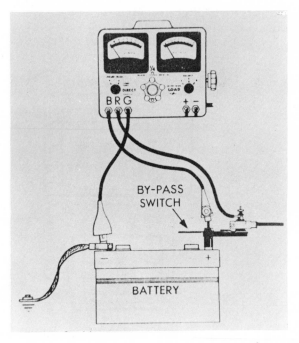

Fig. 18.16. Application of the battery post adapter. When the switch is closed, full battery power may be used for starting the engine. When the switch is opened, the ammeter is put in series with the charging circuit for testing alternator output.

the generator operate long enough to reach normal operating temperature. At approximately 2200 rpm, normal rated output should be delivered. It may be necessary to load the alternator by using the carbon pile, connected from ammeter (—) to battery (—) to get the unit to put out the current. If there is no output or if output is below normal, further testing will have to be done. Fig. 18.17 shows the Chrysler diagram which is similar to the others.

Diodes

The best way to test diodes is with one of the relatively new diode testers. With this instrument it is not necessary to disconnect or isolate a diode in order to test it. However, the end plate must be removed on most models to expose the diodes for testing, but this takes only a few minutes.

If the diodes are isolated by disconnecting their antenna, they can be tested with an ohmmeter showing 4 to 10 ohms in a forward direction and infinity in the reverse direction. A 12-volt test light, lighting in one direction only, can also be used. Fig. 18.18 shows a diode tester in use.

Preparation for Tests:

1. Disassemble alternator, if necessary, to make both sides of each diode accessible.
2. Attach tester power lead to 110-volt supply. If necessary use an adapter plug to adequately ground the tester.

Insulated Diode Test Procedure:

1. Insulated diodes are usually positive diodes. Connect test lead clip to the alternator "BAT" or "G" terminal or to the insulated heat sink.
2. Touch the test lead prod to the metal lead wire or antenna of each insulated heat sink diode.

A meter reading of 2 amperes or more for each diode and readings alike within two scale divisions indicate diodes are satisfactory. Meter pointer deflection to the positive side indicates a positive heat sink; to the negative side, a negative heat sink.

A meter reading of less than 2 amperes on two diodes and 0 amperes on the third diode indicates that the latter diode is shorted. Remove this shorted diode from the circuit and retest the remaining diodes for a meter reading of 2 amperes or more.

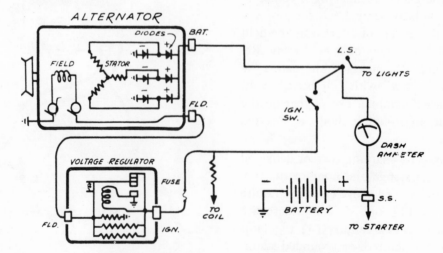

Fig. 18.17. Schematic diagram of Chrysler AC charging circuit. This shows the connections of the diodes very clearly. Note the connections of the double contact voltage regulator or voltage limiter, which shorts out the field entirely when on lower contacts.

A meter reading of 2 amperes or more for two diodes and 1 ampere or less for the third diode indicates that the latter diode is open-circuited.

Grounded Diode Test Procedure:

1. Connect the test lead clip to the end frame or to the grounded heat sink.
2. Touch the test lead probe to the metal lead wire or antenna of each of the grounded diodes.

A meter reading of 2 amperes or more for each diode and readings alike within two scale divisions indicates that diodes are satisfactory.

A meter reading of less than 2 amperes on two diodes and 0 amperes on the third diode indicates that the latter diode is shorted. Remove this diode and retest the remaining diodes for a meter reading of 2 amperes or more.

A meter reading of 2 amperes or more for two diodes and 1 ampere or less for the third diode indicates that the third diode is open-circuited.

Individual Diode Test and Polarity Identification:

Connect the test lead *clip* to the *diode case.* Touch the test *prod* to the diode lead or antenna. A meter reading of 2 amperes or more indicates a good diode. Remember that the *case* of the diode determines its polarity, so that when the clip is on the case and the prod touches the lead, the meter will indicate the diode polarity.

Field Circuit

To check the field circuit, an ohmmeter may be used. The resistance from the generator "Fld" terminal to ground should be from 4.4 to 5 ohms. If the circuit tests "open," it will be necessary to remove the end plate so the slip rings are exposed and to test the field winding in the rotor from slip ring to slip ring with the ohmmeter. This will check both continuity and resistance. Low resistance will indicate shorted turns. A test light or a voltmeter can be used to check for grounded winding. If the field coil

is good and there is an open field circuit, check the connections up to the slip ring brushes. By-pass the regulator to check the field circuit by jumping from the "Ign" terminal on the regulator to the "Fld" terminal on the generator. Insert a field rheostat in the field circuit before starting the engine and cut the field in gradually with the engine running. If the field circuit is good and other parts are satisfactory, at 2200 rpm the generator output should be at least at the level of rated amperes.

Regulator

The voltage regulator is the double-contact type. It must be adjusted to close tolerances. No compensation should be made for driving conditions as the alternator is charging at all times. A low regulator setting will cause the battery to gradually lose its charge, while a high setting will cause it to overheat and overcharge, also shortening the service life of the vehicle electrical equipment.

If the field circuit is closed with the regulator bypassed but open with the regulator in the circuit, the regulator contact points are defective. The regulator should be adjusted to give 13.65 volts minimum to 14.65 volts maximum at 80°F. when operating on the upper contacts. Lower contact operation, at high speed with

Fig. 18.18. Diode tester used for testing diodes in a stator. It is not necessary to isolate the diodes to make the test for continuity, open, or short.

light load, should not be more than 0.7 volt higher.

The Motorola regulator and one model of the Delcotron are fully transistorized. These are not adjustable, so if they are defective they must be replaced. The regulators of other manufacturers are similar to the conventional double-contact type and can be adjusted by changing the armature spring tension.

Stator

While the stator circuits are generally quite free from trouble, it is always possible that a short, open or ground might occur. To test the windings, it will be necessary to cut the leads that connect to the point between the two diodes in each phase; however, a test for grounded coils can be quickly made without cutting any wires. Use a voltmeter or test light in series with a battery, the winding, and the stator laminations.

If the leads should be cut, refer to them as *A*, *B*, and *C*. Check from *A* to *B*, *A* to *C*, and *B* to *C* for current flow with an ammeter or for resistance with an ohmmeter. The readings on each phase should be the same. If they vary the stator should be replaced.

Using the Sun volts-amperes tester the generating system can be tested in a matter of a few minutes. It is not necessary to polarize this generator at any time as field polarity is not important.

Precautions

1. Always disconnect the ground strap of the battery whenever a charger is connected to avoid damage to the diodes.
2. Always take special care to see that the battery is connected with the negative side grounded. Reversed polarity will rapidly ruin the diodes by allowing excessive current flow through them.
3. Never ground any part of the charging system circuit.
4. Never polarize the generator as this will only cause damage to the system.
5. If the regulator is bypassed, be sure to have a field rheostat in the field circuit and to have minimum field current flowing when the engine is started.
6. Never run the alternator on open circuit or open any portion of the circuit while the system is in operation.

Summary

The *alternating current generator* or alternator, supplying rectified alternating current, has been used for many years. In 1961 Chrysler introduced the alternator as standard equipment on its passenger cars and it is now being supplied on most makes. The advantages of the alternator are: (1) heavier current at idle and low speeds, (2) higher maximum output and (3) relative simplicity.

In the alternator a *rotating magnetic field* cuts conductors which are part of a closed circuit. As the magnetic lines of force from the positive and negative magnetic poles of the rotor cut across the stator windings in turn, alternating current is produced.

The *voltage is proportional* to the number of lines of force cut per second. The rotating magnet or field is called the *rotor*. The part corresponding to the DC armature is called the *stator*, and is kept in a stationary position.

The *AC generating system* consists of the generator, rectifier, and generator control or voltage regulator. The battery may be considered as part of the generating system.

AC generators *do not require current limiters*, though a voltage regulator or limiter is needed. An advantage of the alternator is the heavy current that can be produced at low speed. The field current of approximately 2 amperes is applied through slip rings. The rotor has 8 to 12 poles. No cut-out relay is needed. Care must be used to see that battery polarity is not reversed.

Diodes, one positive and one negative, are required to rectify each of the three alternator phases. Diodes have polarity, either positive or negative, and must be mounted in *heat sinks*.

Leece-Neville was the first company to manufacture the alternator. Delco-Remy supplies the Delcotron. Chrysler was the first auto company to provide the alternator as standard equipment. Electric Autolite (Prestolite), Motorola and Ford also supply alternators.

Many of the same *troubles* that affect the DC generating system will cause the AC system to fail, but the AC system eliminates commutator and brush troubles.

To *test the AC system*, use a DC ammeter of 0-60 amperes capacity for output and 0-5 amperes (for the field), and a DC voltmeter. Also use a 40-ohm rheostat, 3-ampere capacity carbon pile, diode tester and ohmmeter. Remember that the output terminal on the alternator is "hot" at all times.

Connect the *ammeter* into the output circuit. Check for field current. At 2200 rpm, rated output should be delivered. If no output or below normal output, test further.

Diodes are best tested with one of the available diode testers. If disconnected and isolated they can be tested with a test light or ohmmeter.

The *field circuit* may be checked with an ohmmeter. Normal resistance is 4.4 to 5 ohms. If circuit is open, expose slip rings and check them. Bypass regulator to check field.

The *regulator* is the double-contact type. It can be adjusted by changing the spring tension.

To test the *stator windings*, it is necessary to isolate each phase, which may then be checked with an ammeter or ohmmeter. A grounded stator may be tested with test light or ohmmeter.

A most important *precaution* is never to attempt to polarize the alternator.

Questions

1. When was the alternator first introduced in passenger cars as standard equipment?
2. What is the basic principle on which the alternator works?
3. What is the main structural difference between the DC generator and alternator?
4. How does the resistance of air compare with that of iron?
5. The amount of voltage induced in a conductor is proportional to what?
6. A single alternating current cycle is represented by a *sine curve*. What do the vertical distances above and below the base line represent?
7. The number of AC cycles per second is not constant but varies with engine speed. Why is this unimportant in the automotive generating system?
8. What are the three connected windings of the stator called?
9. The AC generating system consists of what?
10. Why do most alternators not require current limiters?
11. What will reverse polarity do to diodes?
12. What is the function of the diodes?
13. Why are diodes mounted in heat sinks?
14. What part of a diode determines its polarity?
15. Why is a cut-out relay not needed with an alternator?
16. Name five suppliers of alternators.
17. How does the physical size of the average alternator compare with the DC generator?
18. What should be kept in mind about the output terminal of the alternator?
19. When there is no current output, name five possible troubles that might exist with either a DC or an AC system.
20. In case of no current output name four possible alternator troubles that might be responsible.
21. How would you test the alternator output?
22. How would you test the field circuit for continuity?
23. Name two ways in which diodes may be tested.
24. If the field circuit is closed with the regulator bypassed, but open with the regulator in the circuit, what does this indicate?
25. Why should the alternator *not be polarized*?

CHAPTER NINETEEN

The Charging Circuit—Maintenance and Troubles

Properly maintaining the generator circuit to prevent trouble is just as important as correcting trouble after it occurs. However, the automotive diagnostician is concerned with both maintenance and correction and must have an adequate knowledge to perform either function. Since the wiring, the generator and/or the generator control may become defective, these will be considered in order.

Wiring

The information given in this section applies to both the DC and AC systems. With both 6-volt and 12-volt systems in current use, the allowable voltage drops are given for both, with the first mentioned value referring to 6-volt sytems.

The wiring between generator, regulator, ammeter where used, and battery may have loose connections, breaks (especially where the wires are clamped to the terminals) frayed or damaged insulation or corrosion. The wiring should be inspected periodically and any defective wiring replaced or repaired.

Inspect the battery ground strap, the generator mountings and regulator ground connection to make sure all are tight and free from corrosion. If necessary, remove the regulator and generator mounting screws and the

battery cables, and clean the mounting faces on each unit and on the engine or frame. Be sure to tighten the mounting and ground screws properly. Refer to Fig. 19.1 for possible troubles that will be detected by visual inspection.

Disconnect the lead from the cut-out relay or regulator "Battery" terminal and connect an ammeter between the terminal and lead. Operate the generator at a medium speed and turn on the lights or accessories to use about one-half of the maximum generator charging rate. With a low-reading voltmeter measure the voltage drop between the points given in the following paragraphs.

Separately Mounted Regulator

1. Generator A terminal to battery terminal; maximum drop of .5 (1.0) volt.
    1a. Generator A terminal to regulator A terminal; .1 (.2) volt maximum drop.
    1b. Regulator A terminal to regulator B terminal; .1 (.2) volt maximum drop.
    1c. Regulator B terminal to ammeter terminal; .1 (.2) volt maximum drop.
    1d. Across the two ammeter terminals; .1 (.2) volt maximum drop.
    1e. Ammeter terminal to battery post; .1 (.2) volt maximum drop.

Some of the newer cars do not have an ammeter, but instead have an indicator light which is connected to the battery at one end and to the output side of the generator circuit at the other end. Refer to Chapter 17.

2. Generator F terminal to regulator F terminal; .05 (0.1) volt maximum drop.

3. Generator frame to battery ground post; .04 (.08) volt maximum drop.

   3a. Generator frame to car frame; .02 (.04) volt maximum drop.

   3b. Battery post to car frame; .02 (.04) volt maximum drop.

   3c. Regulator base to car frame; .02 (.04) volt maximum drop.

4. Generator frame to regulator base; .04 (.08) volt maximum drop.

If the voltage drop on any of the overall tests above is greater than the maximum specified, the drop should be checked at each connection as specified to locate the cause of the excessive drop. If a connection is at fault, the terminals should be carefully cleaned and inspected. If connections are good, check the wire for partial breaks. If no apparent cause

can be detected, replace the wire with one of larger size. If the voltage lost in the regulator or ammeter is more than the specified maximum, consult the manufacturer's manual for the proper inspection and repair procedure.

When installing new wires in the charging circuit, be sure they have sufficient capacity to carry all of the generator output and have water-proof and abrasion-resistant insulation. If in doubt about the size of the wire, refer to a chart giving wire sizes. (Table 8 in Chapter 28 gives wire sizes needed for lighting circuits.)

Install metal terminals of the correct size for the wire and screws, making sure they are clamped and soldered to reduce resistance and make strong mechanical connections. Clamp or bind the lead to the frame or some other part of the chassis to prevent vibration of the wires which may cause breaks. Avoid sharp bends and always use an insulating grommet when running the wires through a hole in sheet metal.

When a ground lead is installed between a generator and regulator it should be the same size as the output lead.

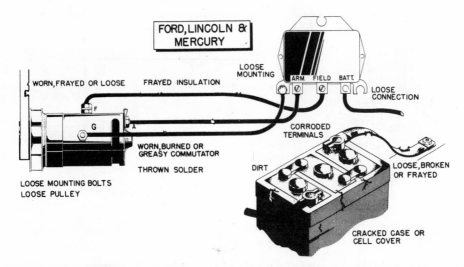

Fig. 19.1. When checking for trouble in the charging system, a visual inspection should first be made. Check for such things as a worn, loose or frayed belt, frayed insulation, loose mounting bolts, loose or corroded connections and terminals.

Generator Service

The generator, being a machine and requiring rotation for its operation, gets the hardest service of any of the units in the charging circuit. The following list gives most of the possible generator troubles.

Shorted field.	Worn, rough commutator.
Open field.	Grounded commutator.
Grounded field.	Dirty commutator.
Shorted armature.	Thrown solder, commutator riser.
Grounded armature.	Worn shaft bearings.
Open armature.	Bent armature shaft.
Grounded "hot" brush holder.	Broken brush leads.
Broken brush spring.	Grounded *A* or *F* terminal.
Worn brushes.	Defective internal connections.
Broken brush holder.	Loose belt.

Some of these troubles are mechanical and can be easily located by the inspection. The others are electrical and can be found by simple tests or inspection. Fig. 19.2 shows a section through a DC generator. Fig. 19.3 shows a disassembled generator so its parts may be seen.

The usual procedure of the car owner is to run the generating system until something fails and then have it repaired. However, the best insurance for maximum service from generators with a minimum of trouble is to follow a regular inspection and maintenance procedure. Periodic lubrication, inspection of the brushes and commutator, and checking of brush spring tension are essential. In addition, disassembly and thorough overhauling of the generator at periodic intervals is desirable as a safeguard against road failures from accumulations of dust and grease and from the normal wear of parts. This is particularly important for commercial vehicles since they must operate on schedules. Besides the generator

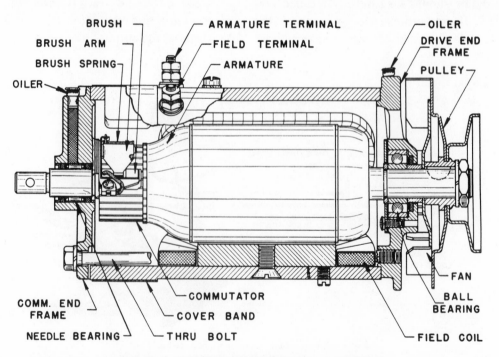

Fig. 19.2. The generator is the heart of the charging system. There are numerous spots where trouble can develop in this unit — brushes, armature, commutator, wires, bearings, and connections.

itself, the external circuit between the generator, regulator, and battery must be kept in good condition because defective wiring or bad connections will prevent normal generator and regulator action.

Lubrication

Bearings provided with hinge cap oilers or oil reservoirs should have 8 to 10 drops of medium weight engine oil at vehicle lubrication periods. Generators with grease cups and ball bearings should have these cups turned down one full turn every 5,000 miles. The grease cups should be kept filled with a suitable ball bearing lubricant. On tractor, marine or stationary applications, lubricate every 100 hours of operation.

Avoid excessive lubrication since this might cause lubricant to be forced out onto the commutator where it would gum and cause poor commutation. Such a condition results in reduced generator output and increased commutator brush wear.

Important. Never lubricate the commutator and do not lubricate the generator while it is in operation. Be sure to keep all lubricants clean and in closed containers.

Inspection

At periodic intervals the generator should be inspected to determine its condition. The frequency with which this should be done will be determined by the type and design of the generator as well as the type of service for which it is used. High-speed operation, excessive dust or dirt, high temperatures, and operation at or near full output most of the time, are all factors which increase wear.

If the commutator is dirty, it may be cleaned with a strip of No. 00 sandpaper. Never use emery cloth to clean the commutator because particles of the emery may be imbedded in the copper and cause rapid brush wear. Hold the sandpaper against the commutator with a wood stick while the generator is in operation, and move it back and forth across the commutator. Gum and dirt will be sanded off in a few seconds. Blow all dust from the generator after the commutator has been cleaned.

Inspect the brushes, and if cracked, oil soaked or worn to less than one-half of their

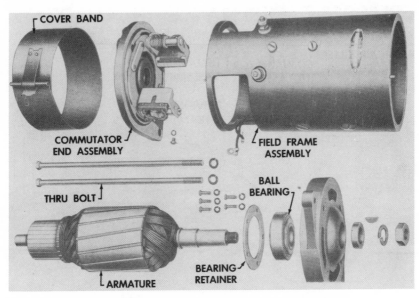

Fig. 19.3. Disassembled two-brush, shunt-type generator. (DR)

normal length, they should be replaced. If the generator brush holders are dirty or if the commutator and brushes are worn, the generator should be removed for an overhaul. Fig. 19.4 illustrates a badly worn commutator.

If the commutator is rough, out-of-round or has high mica between the commutator segments, the generator should be disassembled so that the commutator can be turned down in a lathe and the mica undercut.

If the brushes are worn down to less than half of their original length, they should be replaced. Seat new brushes to make sure they

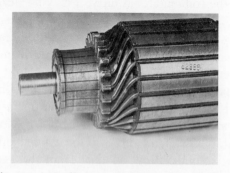

Fig. 19.4. Badly worn commutator. This can be corrected by turning it in a lathe. The pulley end of the shaft is held in an accurate chuck and the opposite end in a brass jaw chuck.

are in good contact with the commutator. A convenient means for seating brushes is a brush seating or bedding stone. This is a soft grade of material that disintegrates when held against a revolving commutator. The particles carried under the brushes, and contacting faces conform to the contour of the commutator in a few seconds. Blow all dust from the generator after the brushes are seated.

The brush tension must be correct. Excessive tension will cause rapid brush and commutator wear, while low tension will cause arcing and burning of the brushes and commutator.

Check the generator belt to make sure it is in good condition and has the correct tension. Low belt tension will permit belt slippage with resulting rapid belt wear and low or erratic generator output. Excessive belt tension will cause rapid belt and bearing wear. The belt tension should be adjusted in accordance with the specifications of the engine or vehicle manufacturer. It is usually measured by the amount of pull it takes to deflect the belt 1″ between the longest unsupported length, between pulleys.

PERMISSIBLE RESISTANCE IN CHARGING CIRCUITS – VR TYPE REGULATORS

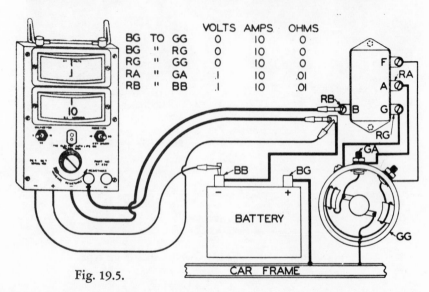

			VOLTS	AMPS	OHMS
BG	TO	GG	0	10	0
BG	"	RG	0	10	0
RG	"	GG	0	10	0
RA	"	GA	.1	10	.01
RB	"	BB	.1	10	.01

Fig. 19.5.

Checking Resistance

The maximum output of a shunt generator is determined by the setting of the current regulator used with it. It should be remembered that the generator control is so intimately connected with generator operation that each unit must be considered when trouble in the generator develops. Permissible resistance in charging circuits with voltage regulators is shown in Fig. 19.5.

The charging circuit is very sensitive to resistance. Resistance in the ground connection of the regulator causes the greatest trouble. Most regulators are grounded by screws which attach the regulator base to the vehicle body. Resistance anywhere between the regulator base and the generator frame that causes voltage drop in excess of .01 volt tends to increase the operating voltage of the regulator.

Extensive tests have been made showing the effect of resistance in this part of the circuit. On one of the popular type regulators on a 6-volt system, a resistance of .147 ohms increased the operating voltage .22 volts at 10 amperes charging current. At 20 amperes the voltage was increased .3 volts. This increase in voltage is sufficient to bring the generator output to maximum with a fully charged battery, usually resulting in the destruction of the battery within a very short time because of overcharging.

High resistance is comparatively easy to locate without instruments by a check which was developed for the United States Army. If the dash ammeter shows that the generator is operating at a steady, high output, a jumper wire (16 gauge or larger) is temporarily attached to the generator frame and the regulator base. If the ammeter reading increases it is an indication that excessive resistance exists somewhere between the regulator and the generator frame.

Another method to detect high resistance is shown in Fig. 19.6.

Resistance in the charging circuit when a shunt-type generator is used results in a reduction of the generator output. Tests show that with a discharged battery, under which condi-

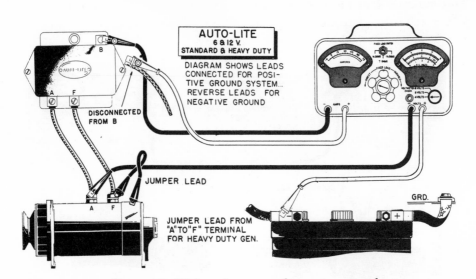

Fig. 19.6. High resistance, a frequent cause of trouble in the charging circuit, can be located by checking voltage drops. For insulated side of the circuit, connect the voltmeter and ammeter as shown. Run the engine to get output of 20 amperes. The voltmeter reading should not exceed .8 volt.

tion the normal output of the generator should be 35 amperes, the addition of .2 ohm resistance in the charging circuit reduced the generator output to 3 amperes, which is the normal output with a fully charged battery.

High resistance can develop at various points if circuit connections are not clean and tight.

Quick Checks

If the generator regulator system does not perform according to specifications; that is, if the generator does not produce the proper output or produces excessive output, the trouble can sometimes be isolated to the generator itself by following a quick check procedure. Refer to Fig. 19.7. In analyzing complaints of generator regulator operation any of several basic conditions may be found.

1. *Fully charged battery and low charging rate.* This indicates normal generator regulator operation. Regulator settings may be checked as discussed later in the section on regulator troubles.
2. *Fully charged battery and a high charging rate.* This indicates that the voltage regulator is not reducing generator output as

it should. A high charging rate to a fully charged battery will damage the battery and the accompanying high voltage is harmful to all electrical units.

This operating condition results from:

a. Improper voltage regulator settings.
b. Defective voltage regulator unit.
c. Grounded generator field circuit (either generator, regulator or wiring).
d. Poor ground connection at regulator.
e. High temperature which reduces the resistance of the battery so that it will accept the high charging rate even though the voltage regulator setting is normal.

If the trouble is not due to high temperature, determine the cause by disconnecting the lead from the generator *F* terminal, with the generator operating at medium speed. If the output remains high, the generator field is grounded in the generator. If the output drops off, the regulator is at fault and it should be checked for high voltage setting or poor ground.

3. *Low battery and high charging rate.* This is normal generator regulator action. The regulator settings may be checked as described in the following sections covering generator troubles.

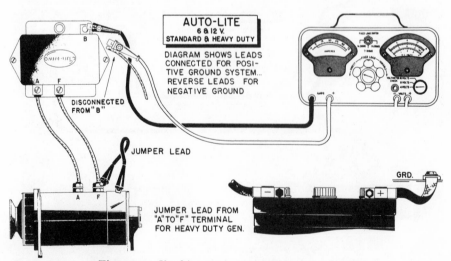

Fig. 19.7. Checking generator output is an important test. Insert the ammeter in the circuit, and run the engine at increasing speed until full rated output is reached at correct speed. If rated output is not attained, the generator needs servicing. (Sun)

4. *Low battery and low charging rate.* This condition could be due to:

   a. Loose connections, frayed or damaged wires.

   b. Defective battery.

   c. High circuit resistance.

   d. Low regulator settings.

   e. Oxidized regulator contact points.

   f. Defects in the generator.

If the condition is not caused by poor connections or damaged wires, further checks must be made. To determine whether the generator or the regulator is at fault, momentarily ground the *F* terminal of the regulator and increase generator speed. (On Ford-built cars use a jumper from *B* to *F*.) If the output does not increase, the generator is probably at fault and it should be checked. If the generator output increases, the trouble is due to: (1) low voltage or current regulator setting, (2) oxidized regulator contact points which insert excessive resistance into the regulator field circuit, or (3) open circuit in the generator field within the regulator at the connection or in the regulator windings.

5. *Burned resistances, windings or contacts.* This results from open circuit operation, open resistance units, or high resistance in the charging circuit. Where burned resistances, windings or contacts are found, always check the wiring before installing a new regulator. Otherwise the trouble may be repeated.

6. *Burned cut-out relay contact points.* This may be due to reversed generator polarity. Generator polarity must be corrected after any check of the regulator or generator or after disconnecting or reconnecting the leads. This is done by polarizing the generator.

The generator is polarized by momentarily jumping the *B* terminal to the *A* terminal on the generator control. This puts a brief surge of current through the generator windings and magnetizes the metal so that it will have the correct polarity. The exceptions are the heavy-duty generators as used on Fords. If the generator is of this type, which has the field windings grounded inside the generator, jumping from the *B* terminal to the *F* terminal will send a brief surge of current to the field and give the correct polarity; or disconnect the generator lead from the field terminal and touch the lead to the battery terminal on the regulator.

Be sure to determine the type of generator before attempting to repolarize it, because using the wrong procedure maintains the reversed generator polarity which will cause serious damage to the electrical equipment. (Generator type can easily be checked by inspecting the insulated brush. If the lead to the field is taken off the insulated brush, the field is then grounded through the regulator. If however, there is only one connection coming from the insulated brush, the generator is grounded internally and receives its field current through the voltage regulator or generator control.)

No Output Checks

If the generator has no output, check the commutator brushes and internal connections. Sticky brushes, dirty or gummy commutator, or poor connections may prevent the generator from producing any output. Solder which is thrown indicates that the generator has been overloaded by allowing it to produce excessive output; it then overheated and melted the solder at the commutator riser bar. Thrown solder often leads to an open circuit and burned commutator bars. Refer to Fig. 19.8.

Fig. 19.8. Armature which became overheated and "threw" the solder from the connections to the commutator. Armature in this condition must be replaced.

If the brushes are satisfactorily seated, making good contact with the commutator and the cause of trouble is not apparent, use a set of test points and a test lamp to locate the trouble. Before making this test, disconnect the leads from the generator terminals.

The test points and test lamp may utilize 110 volts AC current with the lamp in series with one of the test points, or a similar tester with battery power may be used. In the latter case, one test point will be connected to one side of the battery, and the lamp in series with the other test point will be connected with the other side of the battery.

It should be remembered that 110 volts will often go through a poor contact that 6- or 12-volt current will not go through so that indications from the 110-volt test may be taken as more conclusive. The following steps should be taken when making a generator check:

Step 1. To check for internal ground, raise the grounded brush from the commutator and insulate with a piece of cardboard. Check for ground with the test points from the generator main brush or the *A* terminal to the generator frame. If the generator is of the type where the field is internally grounded to the field frame, disconnect the field ground lead before making the test. A lighted lamp indicates that the generator is internally grounded. The location of the ground can be found by raising the insulated brush from the commutator and

Fig. 19.9. Testing the field circuit for opens or grounds. The two ends of the field must be ungrounded. If the lamp lights when the ends are touched, there is an internal ground.

checking the brush holders, armature, or commutator, and field separately. Note Fig. 19.9.

If a grounded field is found in a generator internally grounded to the generator frame, the regulator contact points may have been burned by an excessive field current. Burned regulator points should be cleaned or replaced, as required.

Step 2. If the generator field is not grounded, check the field for an open circuit with a test lamp. The lamp should light when one test point is placed on the regulator field terminal or grounded field lead and the other is placed on the brush holder to which the field is connected. If it does not light the circuit is open. If the open is due to a broken lead or bad connection it can be repaired, but if it is inside one of the field coils, the coil must be replaced.

On the type of generator which has the field grounded internally, put the two test points on the generator frame and the field contact respectively. If the lamp lights, the field connection is good; but if it does not light, the circuit is open.

Step 3. If the field is not open, check for a short circuit by connecting a battery of the specified voltage (6 or 12 volts), and an ammeter in series with the field circuit. Proceed with care because the shorted field may draw excessive current which might damage the ammeter. If the field is not within the specifications, new field coils will be required. Generator specifications can be obtained from the service manuals of the manufacturers of generators.

Step 4. If the trouble has not yet been located, check the armature for open and short circuits. Open circuits in the armature are usually obvious since the open-circuited commutator bars become burned from arcing each time they pass under the generator brushes. If the bars are not too badly burned and the open circuit can be repaired, the armature can usually be saved. In addition to repairing the armature, the regulator must be readjusted in order to bring generator output down to specifications to prevent overloading.

The armature should be visually inspected for mechanical defects such as a worn or bent shaft, worn commutator, scored core laminations, and to see that all windings are properly in place in the core slots and are correctly connected and soldered to the commutator. Resolder if necessary, being careful not to short between the bars.

Check the armature for grounds by touching the shaft with one point of the test prods and each commutator bar in turn with the other point. Discard the armature if it is grounded as indicated by the lamp lighting. See Fig. 19.10.

If the commutator surface is rough, burned, or out-of-round, or if the mica extends beyond the surface of the copper, it should be turned. Mount the armature by its bearing journals (not by the turning points on the end of the shaft if there are such points). Take light cuts until the commutator is completely cleaned up. Sand it with 00 or 000 sandpaper. Mount the armature with its bearing seats on "V" blocks and place a dial indicator against the commutator. Rotate the armature slowly and read the total indicator movement. There should not be a run-out of more than .0005". See Fig. 19.11. Undercut the mica insulation to a depth of $1/32''$ to $3/64''$, as shown in Fig. 19.12. Care should be taken to remove all of the mica without making the slot excessively wide.

The saw used for undercutting should be approximately .002" wider than the insulation between the bars to insure complete cutting of the insulation. See Fig. 19.13. After undercutting, clean off any burrs left on the edges of the bars with a narrow scraper that can be drawn the full length of the undercut groove.

Fig. 19.11. When turning the commutator, do not cut into the riser, and remove just enough metal to clean the metal to a straight cylindrical surface. Polish it with fine sandpaper, and check it for accuracy with a dial indicator.

Fig. 19.12. After turning the commutator, the mica separating the copper bars must be undercut. A machine of this type does the job quickly and easily.

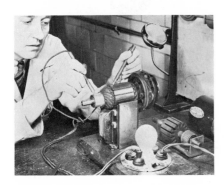

Fig. 19.10. Checking armature for grounds. Test prods touch commutator and armature laminations or shaft. If the lamp lights, the commutator is grounded.

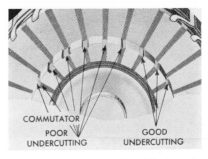

Fig. 19.13. Samples of good and bad undercutting. Good undercutting is .002" wider than mica, accurately centered, 1/32" to 3/64" deep, and without burrs.

Finally, check the armature for short and open circuits with a growler and test prods. Place the armature in the growler and slowly rotate it while holding a thin strip of steel such as a hack saw blade above the armature coils. The steel strip will vibrate and be attracted to the armature when it is above the area of the armature core in which short-circuited armature coils are located. If the short circuit is obvious, the coils can often be repaired so that the armature can be sawed; otherwise they will have to be replaced and the defective armature rewound. See Fig. 19.14.

Fig. 19.14. Using the growler to detect shorted armature coils. The armature is slowly rotated in the growler magnetic field. Any shorted coils will be indicated by attraction of the strip of steel (see arrow).

Fig. 19.15. Testing the commutator-end head and brush holders for shorts or grounds. The lamp is in series with the test prods. When the circuit is completed, the lamp will light. If it lights when it should not, unwanted ground is present.

Low Output Checks

If the generator produces a low or unsteady output, the following factors might be the cause:

1. A loose drive belt slips and drives the generator erratically.
2. Brushes which stick in their holders or low tensions on brush springs prevent good contact in the brushes and the commutator. This will also cause arcing and burning of the brushes and commutator.
3. A commutator which is dirty, out-of-round, or has high mica insulating sheets between the commutator segments must be turned and the mica undercut. Burned commutator bars indicate an open circuit condition in the armature.

In the generator which has the field circuit externally grounded, accidental internal grounding of the field circuit would prevent normal regulation so that excessive current might be produced. Such an internally grounded field circuit can be located by the use of test points connected between the F terminal and the generator frame. Before the test is made, disconnect the lead from the F terminal, and raise the brush to which the field lead is connected from the commutator. If the test lamp lights, the field is internally grounded. If the field has become grounded because the field lead insulation has been worn, simply re-insulate the lead. When the ground has occurred at the field shoes, repair can be made easily by removing the field coils, re-insulating and re-installing them. A ground at the F terminal studs can be repaired by installing new insulating washers or bushings. Testing for shorts and grounds is shown in Fig. 19.15.

If the generator is of the type which has the field circuit internally grounded, about the only cause of excessive output (with the leads disconnected from the generator's F terminal) would be a short between the field circuit and the insulated main circuit. This can be corrected by relocating and re-insulating the leads.

A noisy generator may be caused by a loose mounting, a loose pulley, worn or dirty bearings or improperly seated brushes. Sometimes a squeal is caused by the belt. Dirty bearings may sometimes be saved by cleaning and lubrication, but worn bearings should be replaced. Brushes can be seated as previously explained.

Generator Control Checks and Adjustments

There are several different kinds of generator control units as earlier discussed: (1) cut-out relay, (2) three-unit regulator controls including cut-out relay, voltage regulator and current regulator, (3) the heavy-duty three-unit control including the same three units with a different field current connection, and (4) heavy-duty four-unit controls. Examples of these controls are shown in Figs. 19.16 and 19.17.

The test specifications and precise adjustment of these control units are given in the manufacturer's service manuals. Therefore, this section is limited to the principles of adjustment and testing.

Delco-Remy and Auto-Lite supply most of the original equipment generator controls. A number of manufacturers supply replacement units, but the specifications follow closely those of Delco-Remy and Auto-Lite so that checking and adjustment methods follow those specified by the original equipment makers.

The preceding pages have explained how to localize trouble in the generator circuit, either in the generator or the generator control, and how to correct it if it is in the generator. If the trouble is in the generator control (or voltage regulator) different checks and adjustments must be made.

The three units in the generator control, (1) cut-out relay, (2) voltage regulator, and (3) current limiter, each require separate checking and adjusting.

These adjustments can be made either on the engine or vehicle, or with the generator and regulator mounted on the test bench.

Do not attempt to adjust the regulator unless its operation is thoroughly understood and accurate meters are available. Even a slight error in the setting of the unit may cause improper functioning and result in either run-down or overcharged batteries.

Make sure the units are connected correctly and check the ground polarity of the battery to see that it agrees with the specified car polarity. Check the regulator specifications for the correct polarity, as regulators must not be used on systems with a polarity opposite to that for which they were designed.

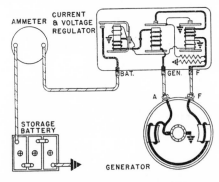

Fig. 19.16. Wiring diagram of single-core current and voltage regulator with two-brush shunt generator. The unit on the left is the cut-out relay. (DR)

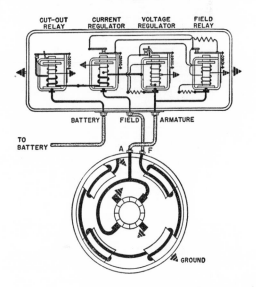

Fig. 19.17. Wiring diagram of Delco-Remy four-unit regulator used in connection with a four-pole, four-brush generator. The fourth unit is the field relay.

Check the part numbers stamped on the name-plate of the generator and regulator to make sure the correct regulator is installed. Regulators are designed for use with a generator having a specified field current, output, internal connections, and speed range. They will not function properly if an incorrect substitute is made.

Measure the specific gravity and voltage of the battery. An old battery, one which is partially charged or one which has been subjected to excessive heat, will cause a high charging rate. A battery subjected to excessive cold, hard plates, high resistance separators or sulfation, will cause a low charging rate. If the battery is not up to specifications, temporarily substitute a battery of the same type and capacity, fully charged and in good condition. The generator should be functioning properly.

Cut-Out Relay

The cut-out relay is the end unit with the heavy wire winding and contact points which

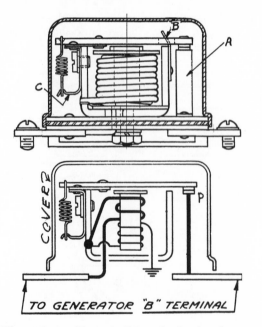

Fig. 19.18. (Lower) Internal circuit of cut-out relay. The current goes from current coil to armature, to upper contact point. (Upper) Showing the adjustments: *C* for spring tension (closing voltage); *B* for air gap; *A* for contact point gap.

close when the armature moves downward. Its internal circuit is shown in Fig. 19.18. To check it, connect an ammeter in series with the regulator *B* terminal and the lead removed from this terminal. Connect an accurate voltmeter from the regulator *A* or *GEN* terminal to the regulator base. It is also advisable to place a reliable thermometer near the regulator, *i.e.*, about 2 inches from the regulator cover but not touching the regulator. It is necessary to check that the closing voltage is at the correct value. Slowly increase generator speed and note the relay closing voltage. This can be noted by watching the ammeter and getting the voltage reading just as the ammeter indicates that current flow is started. Decrease generator speed and make sure that the cut-out relay contact points open.

On Delco-Remy units, adjust the closing voltage by turning the adjusting screw. Turn it clockwise to increase the spring tension and closing voltage, and counterclockwise to decrease the closing voltage.

On Auto-Lite units, adjust the closing voltage by bending the lower spring hanger. Increasing the tension raises the closing voltage and decreasing the tension lowers it. The closing voltage and the opening voltage or current should be within the specified limits. Refer to Figs. 19.19, 19.20, and 19.21.

An accurate method of noting the exact instant of opening or closing of the cut-out

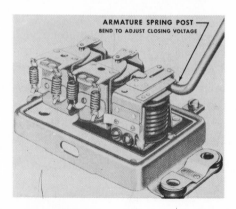

Fig. 19.19. Adjustment of cut-out relay closing voltage.

relay is to connect a headphone with a resistance of 2,000 ohms or higher to the battery and armature terminals of the regulator. When the contacts open or close a click will be heard.

Voltage Regulator

The voltage regulator, or, as it is sometimes called, the voltage limiter, is the end unit with fine wire winding. Connect the ammeter the same way as for checking the cut-out relay, *i.e.*, with the ammeter in series between the *B* terminal and the voltmeter connected from the *B* terminal to ground, preferably the regulator base. Note Fig. 19.22.

Run the generator at one-half maximum output for 15 minutes to make sure the regulator

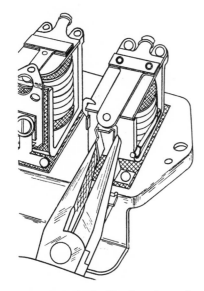

Fig. 19.20. Method of adjusting the spring tension on cut-out relay with adjustable spring hanger. Bending down increases spring tension and raises closing voltage.

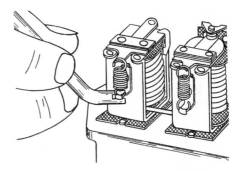

Fig. 19.21. Method of adjusting contact point gap on some Autolite models of cut-out relays. Squeezing the sides of the stationary point support increases the gap.

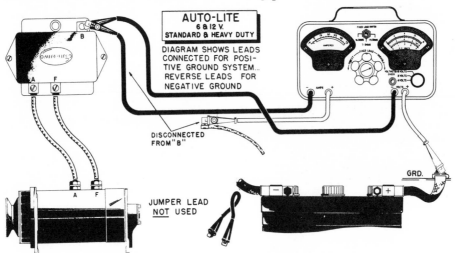

Fig. 19.22. To test the Autolite voltage regulator, make connections as shown, which will put the ammeter in series with the battery circuit. Load the generator by lights, etc., to one-half the rated load. Speed the engine up to 1500 rpm. The voltmeter will indicate V.R. setting. The volts-amperes tester shown here has a built-in resistor which can be used to load the generator. (Sun)

is at normal operating temperature. The cover should be on the unit during this warm-up period and when taking readings. Stop the engine; then bring it up to approximately 2500 generator rpm. Adjust the amperage to one-half maximum output by turning on lights or accessories and then note the voltmeter reading. This reading should be within the specified limits. If not, either adjust the armature spring tension by bending the hanger at the lower end of the armature spring (as shown in Fig. 19.23) or by setting the adjusting nut.

LOWER SPRING HANGER
BEND DOWN TO INCREASE SETTING
BEND UP TO LOWER SETTING

Fig. 19.23. Adjusting voltage regulator setting. (DR)

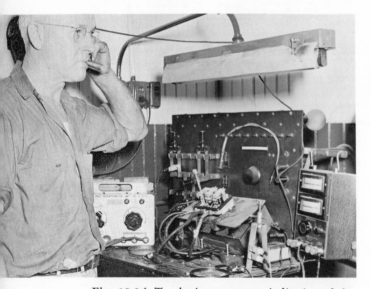

Fig. 19.24. To obtain an accurate indication of the operation of the voltage regulator, connect a headphone of 2000 ohms resistance or higher between *F* terminal and ground. This will pick up the sound of the opening and closing of the contacts. The sound should be regular and clear without any irregularities or missing.

After each adjustment, stop the engine; then restart it, bring it up to speed and adjust the current before taking a reading.

To obtain a quick, correct and easy indication of the operation of the voltage regulator unit, connect a headphone with a resistance of 2,000 ohms or higher from the *F* terminal and ground. This will pick up the sound of the opening and closing of the regulator contact, Fig. 19.24. The clicks should be regular and clear. If not, remove the regulator cover and inspect the contacts. These should be flat, not excessively burned, and should be aligned to make full-face contact. If the contacts are burned, dirty or rough, file them with a #6 American-Swiss-cut equalling file. Move the file parallel and lengthwise to the armature as cross-filing may form grooves which would tend to cause sticking and erratic operation. File just enough so that the contacts present a full surface to each other. It is not necessary to remove every trace of burning. After filing, dampen a piece of linen or lintless bond tape in carbon tetrachloride and draw the tape between the contacts. Repeat this with a dry piece of tape, using a clean piece for each set of contacts.

If the voltage control unit is made with two springs, increase the tension on only one of them. If one is weaker than the other, make the adjustment on the weaker springs.

Delco-Remy recommends two other methods of checking and adjusting the voltage on the voltage control unit. These are the fixed resistance method and the variable resistance method.

For the *fixed resistance method*, a fixed resistance unit is substituted for the external charging circuit by disconnecting the battery lead at the regulator and connecting the resistance between the regulator *BAT* or *B* terminal and ground. In other words, a ¾-ohm resistor is substituted for a 6-volt battery. A test voltmeter is connected in parallel with the fixed resistance, which must be capable of carrying 10 amperes without any change of resistance as temperature changes. Use 1½ ohms for 12-volt units. Refer to Figs. 19.25 and 19.26.

With the generator operating at a speed at which it would normally produce its rated output, and with the regulator at operating temperature, note the voltage setting. The cover must be in place. If the setting is different from that specified, it should be adjusted.

If the adjusting screw is turned clockwise beyond the normal adjustment range, the spring support may fail to return when pressure is relieved. In such a case, turn the screw counterclockwise until sufficient clearance develops between the screw head and the spring support; then bend the spring support carefully upward with small pliers until contact is made with the screw head. Final setting of the unit should always be approached by increasing the spring tension — never by reducing it. If the setting is too high, adjust the unit below the required value and then raise it to the exact setting by increasing the spring tension. Bend the lower spring hanger if there is no adjusting screw.

After each adjustment and before taking voltage readings, replace the regulator cover, reduce generator speed until the relay points open, and bring the generator back to speed again to make the test.

To use the *variable resistance method*, connect the ammeter into the charging circuit at the *BAT* terminal on the regulator with a 1/4-ohm variable resistance in series. Connect the

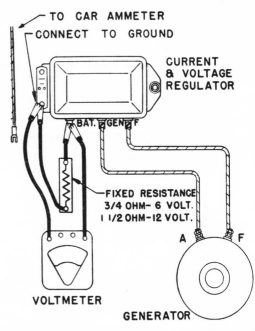

Fig. 19.25. Delco-Remy recommends using a resistance in series with the BAT terminal to ground, in place of using the battery, in checking the voltage regulator. This eliminates variable battery charge conditions.

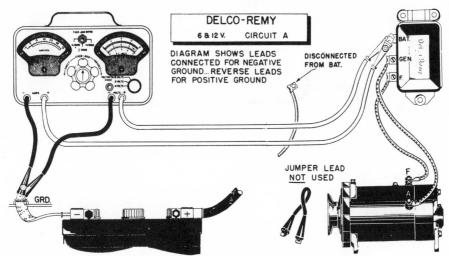

Fig. 19.26. For testing the Delco-Remy voltage regulator, a fixed 3/4 ohm resistor is used in place of the battery. Connections are made as shown. This is similar to the Autolite test except for battery polarity and use of a fixed resistor.

voltmeter from the regulator *BAT* terminal to ground. Increase the generator speed to where it would normally produce the rated output. If less than 8 amperes is obtained, turn on the lights to permit increased generator output. Cut in resistance until the output is reduced to 8-10 amperes. Operate until the regulator reaches operating temperature. Retard generator speed until the relay points open, then bring generator back to speed and note the voltage setting. The voltage reading must be taken with the regulator at operating temperature, with 8-10 amperes flowing, and with the cover in place.

The adjustment is made as previously explained in the fixed resistance method.

If the battery temperature is excessive, battery overcharge is apt to occur even though regular settings are normal. In this case it is permissible to reduce the voltage regulator setting.

Current Regulator

To check the current regulator setting, the voltage regulator must be prevented from operating, since both cannot operate at one time. Four methods of preventing voltage regulator operation are available. Regardless of the method used, an ammeter must be connected into the charging circuit at the regulator *BAT* terminal. The first method should be used for preliminary checks whenever possible since it does not require removal of the regulator cover.

1. *Quick-check method.* Insert a screwdriver blade through the oblong hole in the base of Delco-Remy regulators until a contact is made with the shield around the resistor. Be sure to keep the screwdriver at right angles to the base and hold it firmly in place during the check so that the blade simultaneously touches the regulator base and the shield. This temporarily cuts out the voltage regulator unit. Turn on lights and accessories to prevent high voltage during the test. With the ammeter connected as described, and with the regulator at operating temperature, run the generator at 50% above rated output speed and note the current setting. If it is necessary to adjust this, remove the cover and

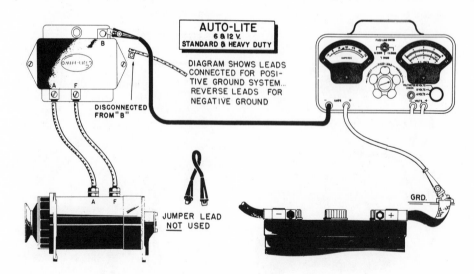

Fig. 19.27. Connections used for making test of Autolite current regulator. With the instrument shown, a variable resistance is used to load the generator, in place of the battery. Run the engine at 2000 rpm. The ammeter will show the current regulator setting.

adjust in the same manner as the voltage regulator by turning the adjusting screw clockwise to increase current setting or counterclockwise to decrease it, or by bending the lower spring hanger. Refer to Figs. 19.27 and 19.28.

2. *Jumper Lead Method.* Remove the regulator cover and connect a jumper lead across the voltage regulator contact points. Turn on lights and accessories to prevent high voltage during the tests. With the generator operating at 50% above rated output speed and with the regulator at operating temperature, note the current setting.

3. *Battery Discharge Method.* Partly discharge the battery by cranking the engine for 30 seconds continuously. Immediately after cranking, start the engine, turn on the lights and accessories, and note the current setting with the engine operating at 50% above the rated output speed.

4. *Load Method.* If a load approximating the regulator setting is placed across the battery during the time that the current regulator setting is being checked, voltage will not increase sufficiently to cause the voltage regulator to operate. This load may consist of a carbon pile or a bank of lights. Note Fig. 19.29.

In using any of these methods, the adjustment is carried out in the same way, *i.e.*, by turning the adjusting screw or by bending the lower spring hanger. Increasing the tension by bending the hanger down will increase the current setting. Decreasing the tension by bending the hanger upward will decrease the current setting.

After each adjustment, stop the engine. Then restart it, and bring the engine up to speed and take an ammeter reading. Be sure the cover is on the unit before reading the meter.

Many of the current regulators are temperature compensated, and in some cases this will mean that the reading will vary depending upon conditions.

The current regulator operation can be checked by use of the headphone in a manner similar to that described for the voltage regulator. The headphone is connected to the regulator *F* terminal and ground and picks up the sound of the opening and closing of the contacts. This is possible because the regulator operates on the field circuit of the generator.

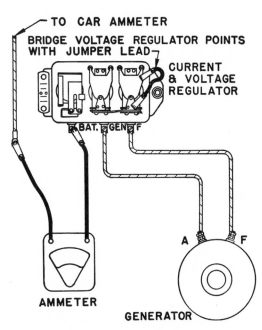

Fig. 19.28. Connections for testing the current regulator. Turn on the lights and radio to prevent high voltage. Increase the engine speed until the output is constant. The ammeter indicates the current regulator setting. (DR)

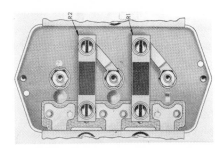

Fig. 19.29. Carbon resistor used in connection with voltage and current regulators. Both resistors are in parallel in the circuit when the current regulator is controlling generator output. (AL)

Adjustment Versus Replacement

When a car is brought into the shop for service on a generator control unit that is not operating as it should, the tendency too often is to simply remove the old unit and replace it with a new or rebuilt unit. Many thousands of new units are thus put on unnecessarily. A knowledge of correct action and simple adjusting methods would make it possible for the old regulator to give many thousands of miles of additional service. The competent diagnostician and tune-up man will specify adjustment and correction rather than replacement, except in cases where parts are so badly worn or deteriorated that there is no alternative except replacement.

Other Regulator Troubles

Aside from wear of contact points due to normal use, here are some of the things to look for in checking the generator regulator:

1. Evidence of burning or abnormally high temperature in the coils, contacts, insulation, contact springs, external terminals, or any other points.
2. Loose connections which result from poor soldering.
3. Loose nuts on the bottom of the magnet coils; loose rivets or screws. All nuts and screws must have lock washers.
4. Loose contacts.
5. Misalignment of contacts.
6. Armature stops rubbing against or interfering with the cut-out relay armature.
7. Bent armature, either at the contact or hinge end. The armature should be perfectly straight from one end to the other.
8. Field yoke bent.
9. Bent or distorted armature hinges.
10. Reversed bi-metal hinges on the cut-out relay unit and temperature compensated current regulator unit. (When correctly installed, the brass side must be up.)
11. Stripped or crossed threads on any screw or nut.
12. Corrosion due to salt or acid.
13. Evidence of water having been inside outer covering.
14. Incorrect, bent or distorted armature springs. In case of doubt, it is recommended that the springs be replaced.
15. Broken or altered carbon resistors.
16. Broken gaskets.
17. Incorrect wiring connections between units.
18. Reversed armature springs. On regulators using different armature springs, the sizes are specified.
19. Broken or corroded ground.

The Alternator

Refer to Chapter 18 for making checks and trouble shooting on the alternator. Most of the troubles and checks made on the DC voltage regulator or voltage limiter apply to the same unit in the alternator circuit. This circuit does not require a cut-out relay or a current limiter.

In the alternator there is no commutator with its wear and possible troubles, and no brushes. Current output is checked in the same way as with the DC generator. Field circuit continuity may be checked with an ohmmeter. The diodes seldom fail unless abused, though there may be failures from time to time. Diodes should be tested with one of the available diode testers; if they are isolated from each other, they can be tested with an ohmmeter or a test light and 12-volt battery.

Never try to polarize an alternator as this is unnecessary and may possibly cause diodes to fail.

Summary

Properly maintaining and checking the *generator circuit* to prevent trouble is as important as correcting it after it occurs. The wiring, generator and/or generator control may become defective.

The *wiring* between generator regulator and battery may have high resistance connections. Tighten and clean as necessary.

Connect an ammeter in the generator circuit. With a voltmeter, *measure the voltage drops*, and compare with the allowable voltage drops.

Many of the newer cars do not have an ammeter but instead have *indicator lights* to show when the generator is not working.

When the *voltage drop is excessive*, locate the trouble spot by testing. Be sure any new wires have ample capacity and use proper metal terminals.

The *generator* gets the hardest service of any unit in the charging circuit. Some troubles are mechanical and some are electrical. A list of possible troubles is given.

Car owners usually run the generator system until something fails. *Inspection* of brushes and commutator is important. In addition to the generator, the external circuit must be kept in good condition.

Attention should be paid to *generator lubrication* on units which require it. Never oil excessively.

At periodic intervals the generator should be *inspected*. A dirty commutator may be cleaned with 00 sandpaper.

If *brush holders are dirty* or if the commutator and brushes are worn, the generator should be removed for an overhaul. Brush tension should be correct. Rough, out-of-round commutators should be turned and undercut. *Worn brushes* should be replaced.

Maximum output is governed by the setting of the *current regulator*. Both generator and generator control must be considered when trouble develops in the generator circuit.

The point of greatest trouble is *resistance in the ground connection* of the regulator, which should be under .01 volt.

The *increase in resistance* between the regulator base and ground will increase the operating voltage. It can be located by running a jumper from the generator frame to the regulator base with an ammeter in the circuit. Resistance in the charging circuit causes reduction in generator output.

If the generating system does not perform properly it may require checking of the generator to locate the cause of the trouble.

Quick checks of generator and regulator

1. Fully charged battery and low charging rate — normal.
2. Fully charged battery and high charging rate — indicates that voltage limiter is not acting to reduce current output.
3. Low battery and high charging rate — normal.
4. Low battery and low charging rate — locate cause of trouble. To determine whether generator or regulator is at fault, momentarily ground the *F* terminal.
5. Burned resistances, wiring, and contacts — check wiring before installing a new regulator.
6. Burned cut-out relay contact points — check generator polarity and polarize if necessary.

Check *commutator, brushes and internal connections*. Use a test light to check for grounds and opens. Check commutator and armature. Causes of low or unsteady output may be a loose drive belt, sticking brushes, low spring tension, or dirty or out-of-round commutator.

There are two types of *generator connections*: field grounded at regulator, and field grounded inside of generator.

There are four types of *generator controls*: (1) cut-out relay only, (2) three-unit generator controls, (3) heavy-duty, three-unit controls, and (4) heavy-duty, four-unit controls.

Be sure *battery polarity* agrees with the specified polarity. Use a well-charged battery when checking the generator controls.

See that closing voltage of *cut-out relay* is at the correct value. Check with voltmeter and ammeter.

The *voltage regulator* unit must be at the correct operating temperature before testing or adjusting. A headphone may be used to check its action. Clean contact points if necessary. The cover must be in place when testing.

When checking or adjusting the *current regulator*, the voltage regulator must be prevented from operating.

Many thousands of new units are installed needlessly when by *cleaning points and adjusting*, the old unit can be restored.

Questions

1. What are the three parts of the generating system that may need attention?
2. Name three possible defects in the wiring.
3. Why is it important that circuit resistance be kept within the allowable limits?
4. What is used on many of the late model cars in place of the ammeter?
5. Name six troubles that may affect the generator.
6. What precaution should be taken when generators are lubricated?
7. What corrective measure should be taken in the case of a worn commutator?
8. What determines the maximum permissible output of a generator?
9. Where is the greatest trouble point from high resistance in the regulator ground circuit?
10. What is the effect of high resistance in the charging circuit?
11. What does a fully charged battery and low charging rate indicate?
12. What does a fully charged battery and high charging rate indicate?
13. What does a low battery and high charging rate indicate?
14. Name three possible reasons for a low battery and low charging rate.
15. What would cause burned cut-out relay contact points?
16. How is the generator polarized on a generator with field grounded in the regulator?
17. How is the generator polarized on a generator with field internally grounded?
18. What might prevent a generator from putting out current?
19. What can a test light be used to indicate?
20. On a generator with field grounded internally, if the test light lights when one prod is touched to the insulated brush and the other to the generator frame, what does this indicate?
21. What would you do to increase generator output voltage?
22. How would you detect a shorted armature?
23. How would you check an armature for grounds?
24. In a generator with field externally grounded, what would be the result if there was an internal ground in the field circuit?
25. What might be the result if the battery temperature were excessive?
26. How would you tell whether "no current output" is due to the generator or the regulator?
27. What are the three units in the usual DC generator control?
28. What is the purpose of the cut-out relay?
29. How does battery condition affect the generator charging rate?
30. How does the voltage limiter control generator output voltage?

SECTION VI

The Ignition System

CHAPTER TWENTY

The Ignition System— Coil and Condenser

In previous chapters the basic theories and principles pertaining to electricity, magnetism, Ohm's Law, induction, circuits, storage batteries, engine operation and mechanical parts and engine troubles have been covered. The next two sections will be concerned with the "anatomy" and "diseases" of the ignition and fuel systems, which will occupy a substantial proportion of the automotive diagnostician's attention in his daily work.

The medical student must study the anatomy of the human body and learn about the correct functioning of the muscles, organs, bones, arteries, veins and glands in order to diagnose and treat the patient. The knowledge of structure, composition, arrangement and correct action makes it comparatively easy to arrive at the cause of wrong action and to prescribe the remedy.

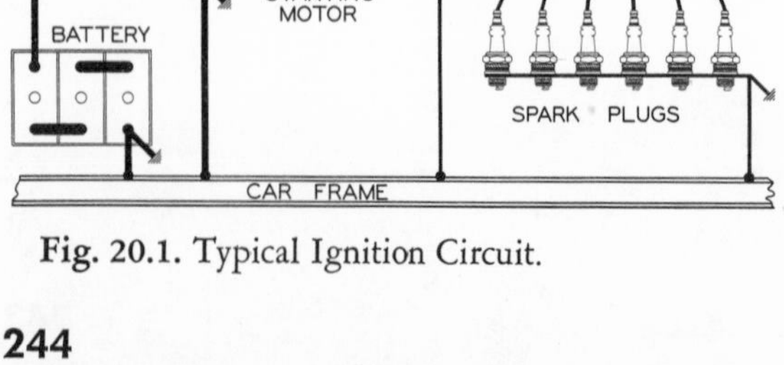

In the same way diagnosis of automotive troubles requires a thorough knowledge of the construction, arrangement, functioning and relationships of the parts which make up each of the power plant systems. Knowing the structure of the various units and their correct operation, the diagnostician, with the help of his instruments, can make the necessary tests and determine the cause of wrong action. It then is a relatively simple matter to prescribe the corrective procedure.

General Description

The ignition system consists of the ignition switch, ignition coil, distributor, spark plugs, low-tension wiring, high-tension wiring and battery. The battery is sometimes considered as a unit by itself as it also serves the lighting, charging and starting systems, but it may properly be considered as part of the ignition primary circuit. This system can be divided into two separate circuits: the low-tension or primary circuit and the high-tension or secondary circuit. The ignition switch, primary winding of the ignition coil, distributor breaker points, condenser, battery, and the primary wiring make up the *low-tension primary circuit*. The

Fig. 20.1. Typical Ignition Circuit.

frame and/or engine block must be used as a conductor to complete the primary current path from the battery, through the units and wiring in the circuit, and back to the battery. Fig. 20.1 shows a typical ignition circuit.

The *secondary or high-tension circuit* includes the secondary coil winding, distributor cap and rotor, spark plugs, high-tension wiring and grounded portion of the circuit.

All parts of the system must be capable of operating at high speeds in order to provide ignition throughout the entire speed range of the engine. If any one part of the primary or secondary systems should fail to function, the entire ignition system will fail and the engine will not operate.

When the system is operating, primary current (at battery or generator voltage) flows through the ignition switch to the coil primary winding, then to ground through the distributor contact points. When the contact points or breaker points open, the current tends to continue flowing across the gap. The condenser, which is connected across the contacts or in parallel with them, momentarily absorbs this current. By so doing, it hastens the collapse of the magnetic field produced by the current in the coil primary winding.

As described in the chapter on induction, the rapidly collapsing magnetic field induces a very high voltage in the secondary winding which is carried by the high-tension wire to the center

terminal of the distributor cap. The spark produced by the high-tension current ignites the fuel in the particular cylinder to which it is directed. This process is repeated for every power stroke of the engine. At high engine speed, the ignition system may be required to produce a spark 500 or more times per second. Operating with maximum efficiency at high speeds requires precise functioning of all the parts of the ignition system. Fig. 20.2 gives a comparison of battery ignition and a water ram to illustrate the working of the ignition system.

Ignition Wires

Two types of ignition wires are used to connect the various parts of the ignition system. The *primary wiring* is usually a larger conductor than the *secondary wiring* and is covered with an insulation and protective sheath to protect it from oil and abrasion. The terminals are preferably soldered and the circuit is designed to have minimum resistance combined with sufficient mechanical strength. The primary circuit will normally carry 2 to 6 amperes at 6 or 12 volts.

The high-tension wiring can have smaller metallic conductors, but must have its insulation designed to withstand a much higher voltage without serious leakage. It must also withstand vibration, heat, abrasion, and oil. The high voltage carried by these wires combined with atmospheric and oil conditions frequently causes the insulation to become brittle and crack or break. Minute cracks in the insulation permit water and dust to enter; this establishes an electrical path which partially grounds the high-tension voltage and reduces the ability of the current to cause a satisfactory spark at the spark plug.

Resistor Cables — Suppression

About 1960 there was general adoption of the so-called TVRS (Television-Radio Suppression) secondary cable. Its purpose is to reduce interference with radio and television reception caused by the emission of high-frequency waves

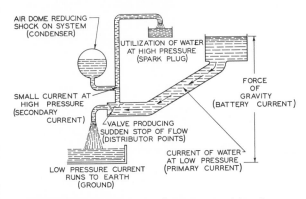

Fig. 20.2. Comparison of Battery Ignition System and Water Ram.

from automobile ignition systems. This cable uses linen strands, impregnated with graphite, as the conducting medium instead of copper. Its resistance of approximately 4000 ohms per foot of length introduces the desired suppression to avoid the unwanted radio and television interference.

Since the TVRS cable is more fragile than the metal core cable, it must be handled more carefully. When removing a cable end from the distributor cap or spark plugs, apply a steady pull to the rubber sleeves rather than to the cable itself and never jerk. Rough treatment will cause a break in the linen strand resulting in a spark gap inside the insulation. This will gradually get larger and make an open conductor, or will pull the conductor away from the terminal, with the same result.

In 1963 a new suppression cable was introduced making use of graphite impregnated glass fiber instead of linen strands. The newer cable has greater mechanical strength and will probably replace the linen core cables on new cars.

The resistance of 4000 ohms per foot does not decrease the effectiveness of the ignition because there is no current flowing prior to the occurrence of a spark. As soon as the spark has occurred there will be a few milliamperes of current flowing for a very brief period, but since the spark has already ignited the fuel-air

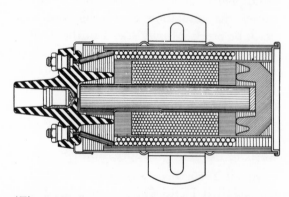

Fig. 20.3. Cross section through ignition coil. The small circles surrounding the core represent the high-tension winding. The larger circles represent the primary winding.

mixture in the cylinder the added resistance has no effect. Suppression also apparently reduces spark plug erosion at the electrodes and makes the plugs last longer. There is more than sufficient energy available for good ignition. The system can tolerate resistance in the secondary circuit up to 20,000 ohms with no undesirable effects. Suppression can also be obtained by using resistor spark plugs which have a resistance of 10,000 ohms each. Resistor cable and resistor spark plugs must not be used together as this would be too much resistance.

Ignition Coil

The function of the ignition coil is purely electrical. Its job is to transform the low voltage supplied by the battery into the high voltage necessary to jump the spark gap. A cross section of a typical coil is shown in Fig. 20.3.

The voltage output will vary considerably depending upon engine speeds and loads. The sparking current delivered by the coil must jump the gap between the electrodes on the spark plugs. The resistance between the spark plug electrodes will vary with the cylinder pressure at the time the spark occurs. When the engine is idling, the vacuum in the cylinder will be somewhere between 12 inches and 20 or 21 inches of mercury, and there will be a very small amount of explosive mixture. This means that the resistance against the spark jump will be low, and probably 4,000 to 6,000 volts will be sufficient to cause the spark. On the other hand, when the throttle is wide open under heavy load, the compression will be high caused by more molecules of air and fuel mixture between the spark plug electrodes. The additional resistance may increase the voltage requirements to as much as 20,000 volts.

Each unit in the ignition system must have sufficient capacity range to handle the necessary ignition current which will range from 4,000 to about 20,000 volts. This helps to explain why engines will sometimes run satisfactorily at idle or light loads, yet will not run satisfactorily under heavy loads. If any of the units in the ignition system are not in condition to efficiently handle the higher voltage, the sparking current will not get to the plugs with sufficient force or regularity to permit the engine to fire properly.

An ignition coil has two windings on a single soft iron core, one on the *primary winding*, consisting of comparatively few turns of heavy wire, and the other the *secondary winding*, composed of many turns of very fine wire. The primary winding is usually wound around the outside of the secondary winding. A soft iron shell encloses both windings and serves to complete the magnetic circuit. Fig. 20.4 illustrates the connections inside the coil.

When the distributor contacts or breaker points are closed, a primary current flows from the battery to the coil primary, to the distributor contacts, to ground. The current flowing in the primary winding produces a magnetic field in the coil core and case. When the distributor contacts or breaker points open, the current stops flowing. The resulting collapse of the magnetic field causes the lines of force to cut the coils of the windings. This induces a voltage in the secondary that is sufficient to make it spark at the spark plug electrodes.

Coil Types

The particular types of terminals, external design, and internal connections of coils will vary, depending upon the application for which the coil is intended. Ignition coils are connected so that the high-tension current will

have a negative polarity, regardless of battery polarity. With a voltage of 4,000 to 20,000 volts, either side of a 6-volt or 12-volt system can act as a ground. Two coil types are shown in Figs. 20.5 and 20.6.

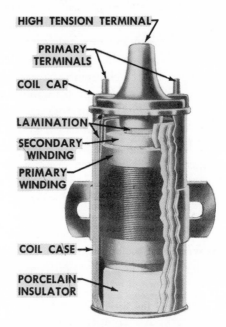

Fig. 20.5. Cut-away view of typical ignition coil, showing its principal components. (DR)

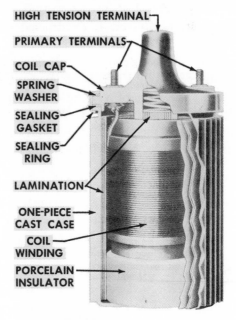

Fig. 20.6. Cut-away of heavy duty, hermetically sealed coil showing its parts. (DR)

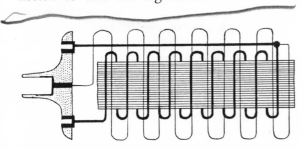

Fig. 20.4. Diagram of internal coil showing coil windings and connections.

Most spark coil applications use a snap type of high-tension terminal. In some instances a soldered connecting terminal on the cable is used while others may use a pin connection that punctures the insulation to contact the wire near the end. A marine-type coil may have the primary and secondary terminals sealed with gaskets and sleeve nuts to exclude moisture.

Reversal of coil polarity when connecting or replacing a coil or changing the polarity of the battery will affect the performance of the engine and may affect the performance of the car radio. Where the coil number is known, the correct polarity can be determined by referring to coil specifications. However, all coils do not carry a catalog number, in which case it is advisable to test the polarity of the coil either on the car or before a new coil is installed.

The coil must be so designed that it will operate with extreme rapidity. For example, a six-cylinder engine running 3,000 rpm requires 150 sparks per second. The distributor breaker points are closed for approximately .005 second for each spark. An eight-cylinder engine running 4,000 rpm requires 267 sparks per second. After 100 miles of travel, the ignition system will have produced about one million sparks.

A typical 6-volt coil is constructed of approximately 21,000 turns of No. 38 copper wire wound on a soft iron core. Laminated flat iron pieces or round iron wires may make up the core. The primary winding consists of approximately 240 turns of No. 20 copper wire, wound around the secondary winding. A soft iron shell encloses both windings and becomes part of the magnetic circuit.

A cork washer is placed over one end of the core to hold it securely in place when subjected to severe magnetic stresses. A porcelain insulator is at the bottom of the coil and a bakelite insulator with external connections molded in place is at the top. The insulation between the winding layers, between the primary and secondary windings, and between the outer soft iron shell and the primary winding is carefully selected and tested.

Before the windings are assembled in the outside case, a special insulating compound is poured into the bottom of the case. Once the windings are installed, more compound is poured into the top of the case so that in the center there is room for expansion and contraction of all parts with temperature changes. Some ignition coils have oil-filled, hermetically sealed cases. After all parts are assembled, the outer case is soldered in order to seal the entire unit against moisture.

Inside moisture is probably the principal factor that determines coil life. Ignition coils are subjected to rain, snow, road splash and occasional high-pressure steam-cleaning devices. In addition, some moisture may get inside the coil from condensation and the normal breathing of the coil caused by temperature changes.

Operating and Checking the Coil

If the coil secondary circuit should be opened, as when a spark plug cable is disconnected and not grounded, the voltage may reach 30,000 volts which greatly increases the electrical strain on the coil. If this condition persists for more than a few minutes, coil failure may result from the excessively high electrical pressure piercing the coil insulation.

A simple method of testing coil polarity on the car makes use of the voltmeter. Connect the *positive* lead to a good ground on the engine. Touch the negative lead to the spark plug terminal of No. 1 cylinder; this puts the voltmeter across the coil high-tension winding. Run the engine at idle speed and if the voltmeter indicates up-scale the coil has negative polarity. A similar test can be made on a bench with a battery, putting a resistor of 15,000 to 17,000 ohms in the tower of the coil. Connect the negative lead from the voltmeter to the resistor and the positive lead to the low-tension terminal on the coil which is normally connected to the distributor. Connect one lead from the battery to the battery side of the coil and momentarily touch the other lead from the battery to the distributor side of the coil, observing the same battery polarity that the coil would receive if in a car. If the voltmeter reads up-scale, the polarity of the coil is negative.

Another easy check of coil polarity can be done with an ordinary lead pencil. With the engine at idle speed, insert the pencil point in the gap between the end of the ignition cable (or an extension of it) and the spark plug terminal. If the flare appears on the plug side of the pencil point, the polarity is correct, negative.

An inspection should be made for loose primary or secondary terminals, broken or punctured high-tension tower, and corroded high-tension terminal inside of the high-tension tower. When coils have been operated with the high-tension cable not properly pushed into the brass insert, an arc is drawn from the end of the cable to the top of the brass insert. This arc burns the insulation from around the top of the insert, sometimes in a complete ring around the inside of the hole. This condition is often hard to find, especially if not specifically checked. The high-tension terminal can be cleaned with sandpaper or a stiff wire brush if it is not too badly corroded.

Current Draw

The current draw of ignition coils decreases as engine speed increases, due to the shorter time the distributor contacts are closed. A general idea of the relative current draw can be obtained from the following figures: 4.4 amperes at 400 rpm; 2.0 amperes at 4,000 rpm. In actual car operation, an engine speed of 4,000 rpm is seldom reached, so that the normal current draw will be higher than 2.0 amperes. On 12-volt systems, the current draw will be about the same.

The figures given for ampere draw on igni-tion coils are laboratory figures measured with very sensitive instruments. When similar meas-urements are made with the ammeters usually found in service departments, the indicated cur-rent draw will be considerably less than these figures. This is due to the instrument lag which keeps it from following the current change fast enough to indicate the true draw. For a type CE Auto-Lite coil at 7 volts connected to a distributor with a six-lobe cam, the ammeter will indicate approximately 2.0 amperes at 400 rpm, and .5 ampere at 4,000 rpm.

Temperature is another important factor to consider when dealing with ignition coils. Some coils are mounted in a cool place and others are mounted directly on the engine where they are subjected to high temperature. With in-creasing temperature, the resistance of the coil winding is increased which reduces the current draw of the primary winding. This reduced current results in a lower output of the second-ary winding. An excessively high temperature might also impair the coil insulation by re-ducing its resistance and weakening it mechani-cally.

For military use in crossing streams, ignition systems have been developed which will function efficiently completely submerged in water. All contacts and ignition joints are sealed to make them water-tight.

The Condenser

The ignition coil in a circuit with a battery and only a switch to open and close the circuit would be of very little value. If the switch were closed, current would flow through the primary, and during the fraction of a second when the magnetic field is being built up there would be a surge of moderately high voltage in the second-ary. If the switch were opened, the field would collapse and there would again be a moderate surge of high-tension current in the second-ary. Neither of these current surges would be of sufficient voltage to cause a spark to jump across the spark plug electrodes.

Therefore, to produce high-tension current with sufficient electrical pressure to jump the spark gap under all conditions of engine opera-tion, other units are needed in the ignition sys-tem. The condenser* is one of these important

---

*Electrical terminology for a condenser is the *capacitor*.

units, even though it has a comparatively insignificant size and has no moving parts. The construction of a condenser is shown in Fig. 20.7.

As a general description, the condenser is made up of two plates or thin metallic sheets which are electrically insulated from each other. The plates in an automotive ignition condenser are two long narrow strips of lead or aluminum foil and are insulated from each other with special condenser paper. The plates and insulation are rolled into a cylinder.

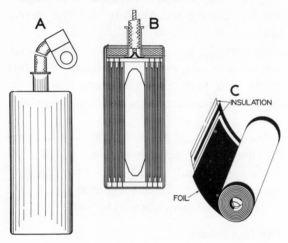

Fig. 20.7. Condenser details as shown by Autolite — (A) exterior, (B) cross section through condenser, (C) metal foil and insulation rolled ready for insertion in metal case.

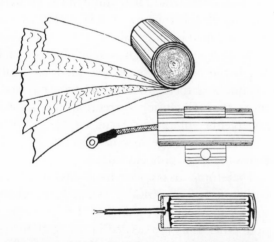

Fig. 20.8. Condenser details as shown by Allen — (top) metal foil and insulation partially rolled, (middle) exterior, (bottom) section diagram showing foil connections.

More specifically, two layers of very thin insulating paper are used because there might be minute holes in either piece of paper. Of course, there is a very remote possibility that holes in both pieces of paper would register in the same spot to permit leakage. The paper insulation is $\frac{1}{8}''$ narrower than the metal foil. The foil and paper are started on a wood core and are wound very tightly in such a manner that alternate layers of foil project beyond the paper insulation at either end. After the condenser is wound, the projecting metal at each end is crushed together; one end is then connected to the condenser case to form a ground, and the other end is connected to the lead which comes through the top of the case. Thus, a good contact to the plate is made, yet the two plates are thoroughly insulated from each other. Refer to Fig. 20.8 for condenser details.

After the condensers are completed, they are tested with 660 volts AC and are checked for capacity. They are then placed in heavy steel containers under high vacuum and temperature. An insulating wax is drawn by vacuum into all the crevices inside the condenser, forming an effective and durable insulation. This results in long life in service.

A condenser should never be condemned solely because the distributor contacts are burned or oxidized. Oil vapor or grease from the cam or high current may be the cause of such a condition.

Condenser Function

The function of a condenser is to prevent excessive arcing at the contact points and also to cause very rapid collapse of the primary magnetic field in the coil. Without a condenser, there would be destructive arcing at the breaker points and the coil would not function with sufficient rapidity to develop the high-tension spark needed for jumping the spark plug gap and igniting the fuel-air charge.

It will be recalled from the chapter on induction that the *rate of change* of magnetic flux is important in building up a high induced voltage. The higher the rate of flux change, the higher the induced voltage.

The condenser is connected across the contact breaker points or in parallel with them. When the points begin to open, the primary current is flowing and tries to continue flowing. Without a condenser the current would continue to flow in the form of an arc jumping from point to point. However, a condenser in the circuit momentarily provides a place for the current to flow. The current charges the condenser instead of jumping across the gap between the rapidly separating breaker points. Fig. 20.9 shows a condenser in place in the ignition system.

The instant the points separate, even as small an amount as a millionth of an inch, the current is diverted into and charges the condenser, immediately stopping the flow of current in the primary winding. This causes an extremely fast collapse of the primary magnetic field so that the magnetic lines of force rapidly cut the large number of turns in the secondary winding of the coil. This produces the high voltage surge of current which is necessary to jump the gap in the spark plug in the engine cylinder. Fig. 20.10 shows the collapse of a coil magnetic field with and without a condenser.

As the magnetic lines of force cut the turns of wire in the secondary winding, they also cut the smaller number of turns in the primary winding, inducing a counter emf as high as 250 volts temporarily. But in the meantime the spark has occurred at the spark plug so that the induced high voltage in the primary winding has no effect on the spark. As soon as the breaker points close in the distributor, the condenser is discharged and is ready for the next spark cycle.

It was formerly thought that the condenser charged up as the points opened then suddenly discharged back into the primary winding to cause the quick collapse in the magnetic field that induced the high secondary voltage. Careful investigation and tests have shown, however, that the condenser is still charging at the instant the spark occurs at the spark plug gap so that each ignition spark has already occurred before the condenser discharges. Therefore, the discharge of the condenser has no effect on the spark itself. Its sole function as far as ignition is concerned is to absorb and hold the current

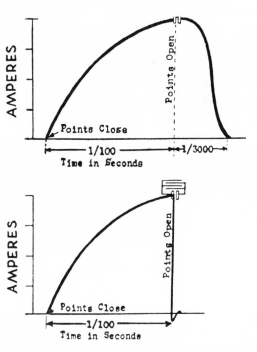

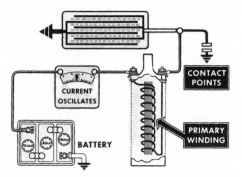

Fig. 20.9. Action of the condenser in the ignition system. Notice that a path to ground is provided for current that would otherwise cause sparking at points.

Fig. 20.10. The saturation and collapse of a coil magnetic field without condenser (above) and with condenser (below). Notice that the total time is only 1/3000 second less with the condenser in the circuit, but this makes the difference between a good spark and no spark.

that would otherwise cause arcing and delay the collapse of the primary magnetic field.

As a matter of fact, during the first few millionths of a second after the breaker points separate, there is a small amount of arcing across the points as the condenser is not capable of absorbing the total amount of current. However, the condenser is sufficiently effective, as proved by its use, to give long life to breaker points and satisfactory action in building up the high-tension current surge required for the ignition spark.

The capacity of the condenser must be large enough to prevent arcing and burning of the contacts and small enough to reduce the transfer of material from one contact or breaker point to the other. The exact capacity required for any particular application depends upon the design of the entire ignition system and also upon the operating conditions encountered. Most original equipment condensers are designed for use over a broad speed range of the engine in order to give satisfactory performance for all operating conditions.

It is important that the condenser be firmly mounted and make a good ground contact. Also, the connection terminal from the condenser pigtail must be tight.

Condensers in most ignition systems are mounted inside the distributor housing. The exact location of the condenser is not important as long as it is close to the breaker points and has a good ground connection and a good insulated lead connection without resistance.

Ignition System Ballast Resistor

With the general adoption of the 12-volt electrical system on passenger automobiles, a series resistor was introduced into the primary ignition circuit. This resistor performs an important function in starting an engine.

Those familiar with storage batteries know that when a heavy current is drawn from the battery, the battery voltage drops. While the cranking motor is operating, it will normally drop to around 5 volts on a 6-volt, well-charged battery in good condition, or to 10 volts on a 12-volt battery.

The series resistor has sufficient resistance to lower the primary voltage about 3 volts, so a coil designed to operate on about 9 volts is used. To offset the normal voltage drop during starting motor operation, on Delco-Remy and Ford equipment, an extra circuit is closed which bypasses the resistor. Thus, full coil voltage of 9 to 10 volts is available for starting in spite of the voltage drop due to the starting load. When the cranking circuit is broken, the bypass circuit is also broken and the ballast resistor is again in the ignition circuit reducing the effective voltage to 9 to 11 volts on 12-volt systems. On Auto-Lite and Chrysler equipment, a resistor with a high temperature coefficient is used so that it offers little resistance when cold, but when heated it drops the primary voltage about 3 volts. This accomplishes about the same effect, with no bypass circuit.

Another reason for the ballast resistor is that at higher speeds the current in amperes drops off somewhat. With less current flowing through the ballast resistor, there will be less voltage drop (in accordance with Ohm's Law), so that the effective voltage on the ignition system will increase. This will give more watts of energy for ignition and cause improved ignition performance. (Remember watts of power is volts x amperes.)

On many of the later model cars the ballast resistor is inserted in the wiring harness of the car's electrical system and is difficult to locate. Its presence can be checked with a voltmeter connected from the battery side of the ignition coil to ground. The ignition circuit voltage on a running engine will be around 9 to 10 volts with a ballast resistor instead of the 12 to 14.5 volts without such a resistor.

Another vital part of the ignition system, the distributor, is discussed in the following chapter.

Summary

The *ignition system* consists of ignition switch, ignition coil, distributor, spark plugs, low-tension or primary wiring, high-tension or secondary wiring and battery.

All parts must be capable of operating at *high speed*.

During operation, *primary current* at battery or generator voltage flows through the ignition switch to the coil primary and to ground through the distributor contact points. When the points open, the current tends to continue to flow across the spark plug gaps. The *condenser* absorbs this current.

The *collapsing magnetic field* induces the high secondary current.

Primary and secondary ignition wires are used to connect parts of the ignition system.

The function of the *ignition coil* is to transform low-voltage current from the battery to a sufficiently high voltage to jump the spark plug gaps. The resistance at the spark plugs varies with the cylinder compression pressure. The voltage at the plugs generally runs from 4,000 to 20,000 volts.

The ignition coil has *two windings* on a soft iron core — primary winding and secondary winding. When the distributor contact points are closed, primary current flows from the battery through the points and produces a magnetic field. When the points open, the magnetic field collapses and as the lines of magnetic force cut the many turns of the secondary winding, a high-voltage secondary current is induced.

Coil types are standard duty and heavy duty. The coil must be able to operate with extreme rapidity.

If a *coil operates on an open circuit* it may fail due to punctured insulation. *Coil polarity* should be negative at the spark plug terminals. Inspect coil condition for loose terminals or corroded high-tension terminals in the high-tension coil towers.

Current draw of the ignition coil decreases with increased engine speeds. Temperature is an important factor in coil performance, as resistance increases with temperature.

The ignition coil without a *condenser* in the contact point circuit would not function. The condenser is composed of sheets of metal foil between sheets of insulating paper, which are rolled up, inserted in a metal case and sealed. It is tested at 660 volts AC.

The *function of the condenser* is to prevent excessive arcing at the contact points and to cause a rapid collapse of the coil magnetic field.

An *ignition ballast resistor* is installed in most 12-volt systems to permit use of a coil with lower voltage than battery voltage. This also gives improved ignition performance at high engine speed.

Questions

1. What are the parts of the ignition system?
2. What does the frame and/or engine block do?
3. Name four parts of the secondary system.
4. Trace the path of the primary current through the ignition system.
5. What induces the high-voltage secondary ignition current?
6. What are two types of wires used in the ignition circuit?
7. What device may be used to illustrate the action of the ignition system?
8. What is the purpose of suppression in the ignition system?
9. How is suppression most commonly accomplished?
10. What specifically is the function of the ignition coil?
11. What affects the voltage required to jump the spark plug gaps?
12. What is the usual voltage range in the high-tension circuit?
13. What are the two windings in the ignition coil?
14. What happens when the distributor contact points open?
15. Name two coil types.

16. How may coil polarity be reversed?
17. What is the correct polarity at the insulated spark plug terminals?
18. What happens in the ignition system if a spark plug circuit is open?
19. How can coil polarity be tested?
20. What effect does temperature have on coil resistance?
21. How is the condenser constructed?
22. At what voltage are condensers tested?
23. What is the function of a condenser in an ignition circuit?
24. How is the capacity of a condenser determined for an ignition system?
25. Why is a ballast resistor inserted in most 12-volt ignition systems?

CHAPTER TWENTY-ONE

The Distributor – Electronic Ignition System

Function of the Distributor

The distributor is the only unit in the ignition system that has mechanical motion, and it performs three functions. First, it opens and closes the low-tension circuit between the ignition coil and ground so that the primary winding is supplied with intermittent surges of current. Remember that each surge of current builds up a magnetic field in the coil. When the circuit is opened, the magnetic field quickly collapses and causes the coil to produce a high-voltage surge in the secondary circuit.

The second function of the distributor is to accurately time these surges with regard to the engine requirements, based upon speed and load. This is accomplished by the centrifugal and vacuum advance mechanisms. A development in distributor design is the control of both load and speed timing by means of vacuum only, as exemplified on some of the Ford car models. This will be discussed in detail in the following chapter.

The third duty of the distributor is to direct each high voltage surge through the distributor cap, rotor, and high-tension wiring to the spark plug in the cylinder which has its pistons and valves in firing position.

To perform these jobs, two separate circuits are necessary in the distributor. One of these is the *primary circuit* which includes the distributor contact points or breaker points, and the condenser. The other is the *secondary high-tension circuit* which includes the distributor

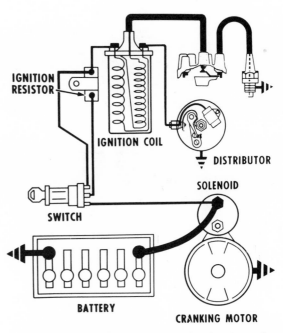

Fig. 21.1. Typical ignition circuit showing where the current is picked up at the cranking motor relay. Notice the circuit for bypassing the ballast resistor while the cranking motor is energized. A separate contact in the ignition switch closes the bypass on some cars; on others it is energized from the starter switch.

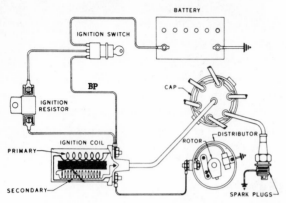

Fig. 21.2. Diagram of ignition circuit showing both the low-tension and high-tension portions of the distributor. *BP* is the ignition bypass for starting.

cap and rotor. Figs. 21.1 and 21.2 are diagrams of the ignition circuit.

The primary circuit is opened and closed by means of the contact points (breaker lever and contact support) and the breaker cam. The cam is rotated, through the centrifugal advance mechanism, by the distributor shaft. The shaft is driven by gearing within the engine from the camshaft on four-cycle engines. The distributor shaft and breaker cam are rotated at half engine speed and the breaker cam has the same number of lobes (on most engines) as there are cylinders in the engine. In a few cases there are

Fig. 21.3. Distributor with both automatic and vacuum advance. The breaker plate is pivoted on the center bearing, moved by the vacuum advance. (AL)

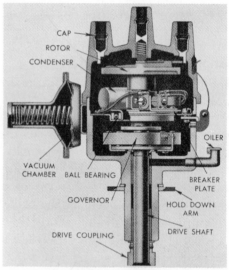

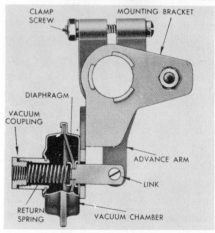

Fig. 21.4. (Above) Sectional view of distributor, showing governor, breaker plates, and rotor. (Below) Vacuum advance arrangement when the whole distributor is rotated.

two sets of breaker points and only one-half as many lobes as there are cylinders. However, this design is not used on the late model American cars.

Each breaker cam lobe passes under the breaker arm rubbing block to open the contact points so that a high-voltage surge is produced in the ignition system. Thus for every breaker cam revolution, one spark will be produced for each engine cylinder. Since each cylinder fires every second revolution in a four-cycle engine, each cylinder will fire once for every two crankshaft revolutions or every single distributor shaft revolution, turning at half of crankshaft speed.

The breaker points, the contact points, or the contacts, as they are variously called, constitute a rapid make-and-break switch which allows short surges of low-tension current to flow to the primary winding in the coil. Fig. 21.3 shows distributor details. Fig. 21.4 shows a cross section of a distributor.

With a wide open throttle, an engine may require as many as 16,000 to 20,000 sparks per minute. Therefore, the breaker arm must have sufficient rigidity and stiffness to keep the contact point it carries making good contact at extremely high speed; at the same time, it must be light enough to move as rapidly as necessary without breakage or distortion. Fig. 21.5 graphically shows the ignition system parts that operate in each spark cycle.

Automatic Spark Advance Mechanism

When the engine is idling, the spark is timed to occur in the cylinder just before the piston reaches top dead center. With higher engine speeds, however, there is a shorter interval available from the initial timing position for the mixture to ignite, burn and release its power to the cylinder piston. Consequently, in order to realize the maximum amount of power from the explosive charge at higher engine speeds, it is necessary for the ignition system to deliver the voltage surge to the cylinder earlier in the cycle to allow the required time for combustion to take place. This is accomplished by the centrifugal advance mechanism assembled on the distributor shaft. Fig. 21.6 illustrates the centrifugal advance mechanism.

The combustion process takes an appreciable amount of time, regardless of engine speed. At higher speeds the spark to begin combustion must be started earlier (in crankshaft travel) in order to supply power at the most efficient point.

The centrifugal advance mechanism consists of two weights which move outward against spring tension as engine speed increases. This motion is transmitted to the breaker cam so

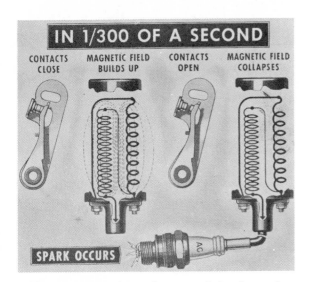

Fig. 21.5. In 1/300 of a second, breaker points close, magnetic field builds up, points open, and magnetic field collapses.

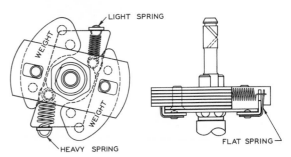

Fig. 21.6. Arrangement of mechanical or automatic advance springs and weights. Notice that this distributor uses one light and one heavy spring.

that it is moved (rotated) to an advanced position with respect to the distributor drive shaft. Moving the breaker cam in the direction of rotation of the distributor drive shaft will cause the spark to advance, and moving it in the opposite direction will cause the spark to be retarded. Fig. 21.7 shows one spark cycle.

As engine speed is increased, the weight continues to move outward, up to the maximum advance allowed, and advances the breaker cam. The distributor drive shaft is linked to the engine crankshaft through the distributor drive gears. Consequently the breaker cam advances with respect to the position of the engine crankshaft and the piston. It is, of course, necessary that the spark occur with the valves closed and with the piston in the position which has been found to give the most efficient results.

This means that at higher speeds the breaker cam opens and closes the distributor contact points earlier in the cycle, as the piston is moving upward on the compression stroke. The high-voltage surge is produced and delivered to each spark plug earlier in the cycle so the spark occurs in ample time to allow the charge to ignite, burn, and give up its power to the piston.

The amount of advance required varies for each model of engine. In order to determine just how much advance any given engine should have, the engine is operated at various speeds and with wide open throttle. The centrifugal advance is varied at each speed until the amount of advance which gives the maximum power is found. The cam contour, weights, and springs are then selected to give the required advance. Fig. 21.8 illustrates the need for ignition advance as speed increases, while Fig. 21.9 shows valve lap.

Vacuum Advance Mechanism

Under part throttle operation there is high vacuum in the intake manifold, but the limited throttle opening only permits a relatively small amount of fuel-air mixture to be drawn into the cylinders. This small amount of gaseous mixture will have lower compression pressure (compared to wide open operation) when the piston is at the top of the compression stroke. With this reduced compression, additional spark advance over the advance provided by the centrifugal advance mechanism will increase fuel economy. In other words,

AS ENGINE SPEED INCREASES
SPARK MUST BE TIMED EARLIER

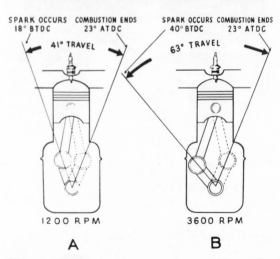

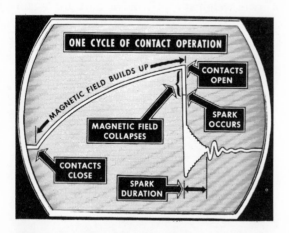

Fig. 21.7. One cycle of breaker point operation: contacts close, contacts open, magnetic field collapses, spark occurs. Note the spark duration.

Fig. 21.8. The ignition must be started sooner at higher speeds in order to be completed at the required 23° ATDC.

with lower compression, the mixture will not burn quite so rapidly, and in order to realize the maximum power, the ignition must take place earlier in the cycle. Slower burning requires that more time be allowed for the combustion process to take place. Fig. 21.10 illustrates the vacuum advance mechanism.

To provide this spark advance, based on intake manifold vacuum conditions, most automotive applications use a vacuum advance mechanism in addition to the automatic advance. The vacuum advance mechanism has a spring-loaded diaphragm connected by linkage to the distributor. The spring-loaded side of the diaphragm is air-tight, and it is connected by a vacuum passage to an opening in the carburetor. This opening is on the atmospheric side of the throttle when the throttle is in the idling position. Therefore when the engine is idling there is no vacuum advance. As soon as the throttle is opened it swings past the opening of the vacuum passage. This permits the intake manifold vacuum to draw air from the air-tight chamber in the vacuum advance mechanism so that the diaphragm is moved against

the springs. This motion is transmitted by the linkage to the distributor which causes the breaker points and rubbing block to be rotated slightly against the direction of the distributor shaft rotation, advancing the time of the spark occurrence. The amount of rotation of the breaker points is governed by the amount of vacuum in the intake manifold up to the limit imposed by the design of the vacuum advance mechanism. Therefore, the extent of spark advance is based on the amount of vacuum in the intake manifold, changing in proportion to the effective compression in the cylinder and permitting greater efficiency in engine operation.

The vacuum advance mechanism rotates the breaker plate through an angle of 10°-20°. The breaker plate, which carries the breaker arm and breaker points, is mounted on a ball bearing or a bushing at the center of the plate so it can rotate with respect to the remainder of the distributor. Moving the breaker base plate, or the distributor itself, in a direction *against* the distributor shaft rotation, has the same spark-advancing effect as moving the breaker cam in the direction of shaft rotation.

Need for Spark Advance

The correct time to ignite the fuel in a cylinder is determined by the time the combustion

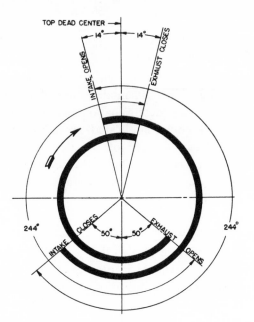

Fig. 21.9. Valve timing diagram. This shows a valve lap of 28° during which both intake and exhaust valves are open.

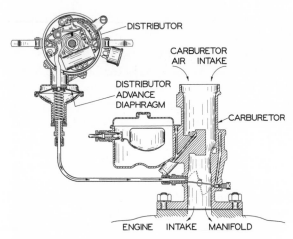

Fig. 21.10. Distributor, showing breaker plate assembly and connection to carburetor for vacuum advance. Notice that the throttle blocks off the vacuum outlet when closed.

should be completed in relation to the position of the piston in the cylinder. However, the linear position of the piston in the cylinder is not too easy to determine accurately. Also, the movement of the piston in the cylinder is relatively slower as the crank approaches top or bottom dead center. For these reasons, it is more satisfactory to use the angular position of the crankpin to indicate timing rather than the linear position of the piston itself.

The time at which combustion should be *completed* is very definite and is usually between 10° and 20° *past* top dead center, depending upon the design and type of a particular engine. There is an appreciable time required for fuel to complete its burning after it is ignited — approximately .003 second in a 3-inch diameter cylinder with a 8:1 compression ratio. Therefore, combustion must be started early enough to allow the time necessary to burn the fuel completely. This allowance is known as *spark advance* and is usually given in *degrees of crankpin travel*.

If automobile engines were operated with a constant load at a constant speed, the timing of the spark would be very simple. But when a car is in operation on the road, there is a constant variation in load and speed conditions, including idling with constant speed; high speed under load, such as going up hills; and heavy load under various conditions, such as pushing another car, towing a trailer, or deceleration. In addition to the factors of speed and load, there are other important considerations such as engine temperature, cylinder bore, compression ratio, character of fuel, fuel mixture, and octane or knock rating of the fuel.

All of these conditions have their effect on the engine operation and require various spark advances to meet the conditions most efficiently. The effect of these conditions is given in Table 6.

There are other factors which affect engine timing such as shape of the combustion chamber, location of the spark plug in the cylinder,

Table 6
SPARK ADVANCE CONDITIONS

Engine Condition	Combustion	Spark Advance Required
Engine Load		
Less Load	Slower	More
More Load	Faster	Less
Engine Speed		
Low Speed, Low Load	Slower	More
Low Speed, Full Load	Faster	Less
High Speed, Full Load	Slower	More
Engine Temperature		
Cold Engine	Slower	More
Hot Engine	Faster	Less
Cylinder Bore		
Large Bore	Slower	More
Smaller Bore	Faster	Less
Compression Ratio		
Low Ratio	Slower	More
High Ratio	Faster	Less
Fuel Character		
Less Volatile	Slower	More
More Volatile	Faster	Less
Air-Fuel Mixture		
Poor Mixture	Slower	More
Good Mixture	Faster	Less
Knock Rating of Fuel		
High Octane	Slower	More
Low Octane	Faster	Less

the efficiency of the cooling system, efficiency of the carburetor, and uniformity of mixture as distributed by the intake manifold. All of these make the determination of the ignition timing a highly complicated procedure which takes a large amount of research by engine designers to establish the advance which will produce best economy and performance under all operating conditions.

Operating Conditions

To appreciate fully the complete spark advance mechanism incorporated in distributors, it is very helpful to obtain a clear picture of the two fundamental conditions of engine operation in a car. One of these considerations is wide open throttle operation, such as top speed driving, rapid acceleration, or climbing hills with the accelerator pedal in wide open throttle position. Under this operating condition, power is of prime concern and economy is secondary. The other condition is sustained driving on a level road at a uniform rate of speed — 30, 40, or 50 miles per hour — with part throttle opening. This is referred to as "road load" operation and requires the best possible fuel economy in miles per gallon. Road load operation is more important to the average driver because he is interested in fuel economy. However, wide open throttle operation is also important as performance is a worthwhile consideration.

So we have the two extremes, (1) *wide open throttle*, with best power desired and (2) *road load operation*, with best economy desired. All other conditions of operation fall in between these two extremes. For example, a car may be accelerated at part throttle or climb a hill with the throttle not fully open.

Operating at road loads with the throttle only partly open, the engine cylinders take in only part of their possible full charge during each intake stroke. Therefore the compression pressures at road load are relatively low which means slow combustion. In other words, more time is required to complete combustion at road load. Regardless of engine speed, for best results it is still necessary to complete the combustion process at the required instant — around 10° after top dead center crankpin position. This position may vary somewhat from engine to engine, but for any given engine it is relatively fixed. Therefore, under a condition which causes fairly slow combustion, ignition must be started earlier by advancing the spark.

The spark advance charts are drawn showing results of the advance of the spark due to speed and also the advance due to changes in intake manifold vacuum. Superimposing one curve on the other will give the total advance for different conditions. Figs. 21.11, 21.12 and 21.13 are examples of distributor calibration curves.

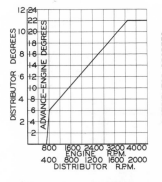 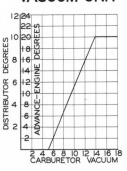

Fig. 21.11. Calibration curves for full range of both automatic (governor) advance and vacuum advance. (AL)

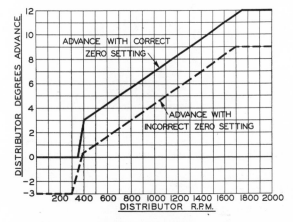

Fig. 21.12. A wrong zero setting of the distributor will carry the error through the full range of spark advance. (AL)

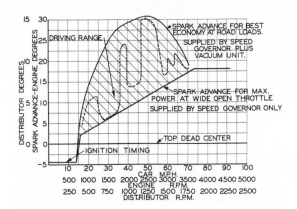

Fig. 21.13. Spark advance chart showing result of combined automatic and vacuum advance. Notice that advance angles are given in both distributor degrees and crankshaft degrees. (AL)

In any consideration of engine timing it must be remembered that the distributor shaft turns only one-half as fast as the crankshaft and therefore 1° of distributor shaft, breaker cam, and distributor rotor movement is equivalent to 2° of crankshaft travel.

Manifold vacuum is higher at road loads than at wide open throttle. Therefore it is logical to utilize manifold vacuum to operate the spark advance mechanism in such a manner as to make the addition of road load advance proportional to the manifold vacuum.

Letters are commonly used to indicate the reference point from which crank angles are measured such as ATDC (after top dead center), or BTDC (before top dead center). The extreme upper position of the crankpin is referred to either as *top center* or *top dead center* while the extreme lower position is referred to as *bottom center*, *lower center* or *bottom dead center*.

The spark advance in all the various cases between the two extremes of operation will be the result of the two advance devices, one governed by speed, the other by throttle position. Each control operates independently of the other and there will be many possible combinations of the two in actual road operation.

The amount of spark advance caused by either the centrifugal advance or the vacuum

Fig. 21.14. Procedure for removing the distributor cap on the external adjustment Delco distributor.

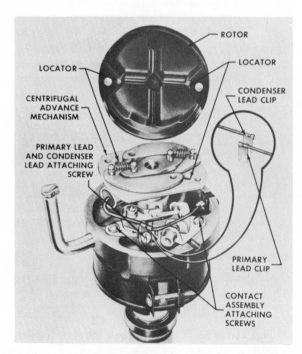

Fig. 21.15. External adjustment type distributor with cap and rotor removed.

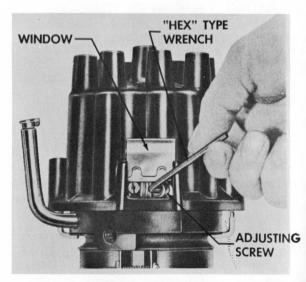

Fig. 21.16. Adjusting dwell angle on external adjustment type distributor.

advance has nothing to do with ignition timing. Wherever the spark is set at engine idle the full amount of centrifugal advance will take place from this point. This is also true of the vacuum advance. For example, if the timing is set 4° ahead of that specified, the whole range of operation (from idle to full power) will be advanced 4°. Therefore, it is very necessary that engine ignition timing be correctly set to begin with, so that there will be the most efficient operation of the engine as related to spark timing.

Time of Ignition

The time the spark occurs depends upon the angular position of the distributor compared to No. 1 crank position. Rotating the distributor body against the direction of the distributor shaft rotation will advance the spark, and moving it in the direction of distributor shaft rotation will retard the spark. When the ignition timing is set correctly the distributor should be locked in position. Some helpful distributor details are shown in Figs. 21.14, 21.15, 21.16, and 21.17.

In order to set or adjust the ignition timing, it is necessary to know the direction in which the distributor rotor turns. Looking from the top, some distributor shafts turn in a right-hand direction and some in a left-hand direction. To determine the direction of distributor shaft rotation quickly and easily, take hold of the rotor with the distributor cap removed and try to turn it, first in one direction and then the other. It will move 10° to 15° in the direction in which the rotor will turn. This is true because the advance governed by the centrifugal advance mechanism can be operated by turning the rotor slightly and the direction in which it turns will be the direction in which it would be advanced by the centrifugal advance mechanism. This does not apply to a Ford vacuum-controlled distributor. On some distributor cams, a small arrow is stamped on the top indicating the direction of rotation for which the distributor is designed. Refer to Fig. 21.18 for checking direction of distributor rotation.

Ignition timing is checked by means of a timing light. This is a stroboscopic light which flashes each time No. 1 spark plug fires. By watching the timing mark on the flywheel or dynamic balancer in the stroboscopic beam, the mark will appear to stand still so its position in relation to the pointer can be readily seen.

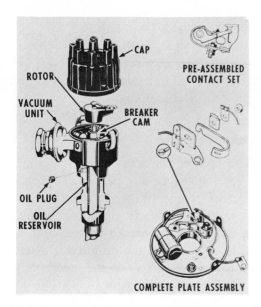

Fig. 21.17. Typical internal adjustment type distributor with automatic advance mechanism below the breaker plate.

Fig. 21.18. To determine the direction of rotation, turn the rotor both ways. The direction in which it moves and springs back is the direction in which it rotates.

This will indicate whether the spark occurs in accordance with factory specifications, too early, or too late. Fig. 21.19 shows a timing light in use.

Static Timing

Many of the European cars are statically timed; that is, timed when the engine is not running. A test light is used which is connected in such a way that it is turned on and off by means of the ignition breaker points.

The test light may be connected in either of two ways. (1) With the ignition current turned on, the light is connected from the distributor side of the coil to ground. When the contact points are closed, the ignition current has a

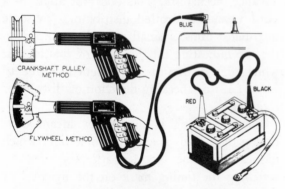

Fig. 21.19. Checking ignition timing by power timing light. It may be checked at the crankshaft pulley (or dynamic balancer), or through the inspection hole by observing the flywheel marks.

Fig. 21.20. Contact surfaces of breaker points which have been used will not appear smooth and bright, but if free from projections they may make better contact than with new points. (DR)

direct path through points to ground so the light does not light. As soon as the points separate the least bit (which in operation would cause the spark to occur), the light will glow. When the points close again the light will go out. (2) With ignition current turned off, a separate battery is connected in series with the test light. The primary lead from the coil to the distributor is disconnected at the coil. The separate battery and test light are connected from the opened coil connection to the terminal of the disconnected lead, putting the battery and test light in series with the contact points. When the points close the test light will glow. When the points separate slightly, which would normally cause the spark to occur, the test light will go out.

The distributor is turned a little at a time by "bumping" the engine with the cranking motor. When the test light glows with connection No. 1, or goes out with connection No. 2, the timing pointer on the engine should point directly to the timing mark on the fan pulley, dynamic balancer or flywheel, depending upon the timing mark location. If the timing is not correct, move the distributor in the direction necessary to make the light agree with the timing mark.

Remember that dwell must be correctly set before ignition is timed as there will be one degree of error in timing for every degree of error in the dwell setting.

Breaker Contacts

The breaker contacts or breaker points get the severest use of any part of the distributor and most frequently need attention. A good deal about the efficient operation of the ignition system can be learned from examining the distributor points with a magnifying glass after they have been in service for a few thousand miles. The color of normal points is a light gray, and used contact surfaces are generally bright, as seen in Fig. 21.20. If the contact surfaces are black, it is usually due to the presence of oil, dirt or some other foreign matter. Oil vapor or grease from the cam may be the cause. If the points are blue, the cause is usually excessive heating due to improper alignment or excessively high wattage in the primary circuit of the ignition coil. High resistance or an open condenser circuit may be caused by excessively high temperature or vibration. Different conditions of contact points are shown in Fig. 21.21.

When the points have seen several thousand miles of service, it is difficult, if not impossible, to measure the space between them accurately by means of a feeler gauge. Breaker contacts do not wear evenly and with each thousand miles of service the surfaces will deviate more. Refer to Fig. 21.22. If they are not in correct alignment, they will overlap each other with excessive wear where they come in contact and no wear at the sides where they do not come in contact.

Even if the points are in correct alignment, there will be uneven wear on the contact surfaces. Frequently there will be a transfer of metal from one point to the other resulting in a crater on one point and a projection on the other. Refer again to Fig. 21.21.

When the breaker points are new the stationary point will have a convex surface. Specifications for this point call for a 3-inch radius, which would be approximately .002″ when measured from the highest point to the edge of the contact point. This design is used so that the contact of the surfaces of the two points which break the current will be nearer to the center of the mass of the metal, to give better heat radiation. The movable contact point has a flat surface. If both contacts were flat it would be practically impossible to align them to avoid an arc at the two outer edges, as shown in Fig. 21.23.

Breaker contacts should never be filed. The breaker contacts are so hard that if they are filed, minute pieces of the file may be broken off and imbedded in the surface of the contact,

which would cause greater concentration of heat and welding of the metal to the breaker contact. When the breaker points begin to

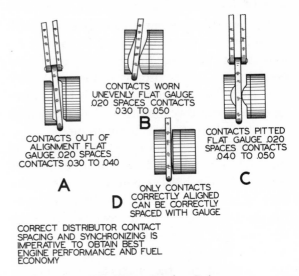

CORRECT DISTRIBUTOR CONTACT SPACING AND SYNCHRONIZING IS IMPERATIVE TO OBTAIN BEST ENGINE PERFORMANCE AND FUEL ECONOMY

Fig. 21.21. Distributor Breaker Points.

Fig. 21.22. Reason why a feeler gauge must not be used on rough contact points. Note that the gauge measures from high spot to high spot.

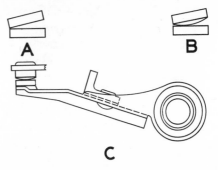

Fig. 21.23. (A) Flat breaker contact points would be very difficult to align perfectly parallel. (B) Actually, they are made with the stationary points slightly rounded. (C) They should be adjusted to make contact in the middle of the point surface for best life. (AL)

show considerable deviation from smooth surfaces they should be replaced.

Dwell Angle

Tune-up specifications usually give the dwell angle, dwell, or cam angle in degrees of distributor shaft rotation, though frequently the breaker point gap is also given, such as 0.018″ to 0.020″. The gap setting itself is not important. It is the dwell or cam angle, which is related to the gap, that is important.

The *cam angle*, also called *dwell angle*, is the angle through which the distributor shaft turns while the breaker points are closed. See Fig. 21.24. In other words, it is the rotation of the shaft from the time the points *close until they just open* to break the primary circuit. This angle is very important because it governs the time allowed for the magnetic field in the ignition coil to be built up preparatory to the points opening, breaking the circuit and initiating an ignition spark. The cam angle is measured by means of the dwell meter or cam angle meter (described in Chapter 11). Fig. 21.25 illustrates adjustment of breaker contacts.

Breaker arm spring tension is very important. If the tension is too great, the breaker arm will bounce and cause an interruption of the current in the coil and missing in the engine. If the spring tension is not sufficient, the rubbing block will not follow the cam, causing a variation in current flow period in the coil. Fig. 21.26 shows how spring tension may be measured. Several types of breaker arms are shown in Fig. 21.27.

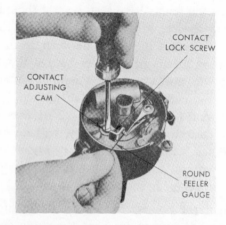

Fig. 21.25. Adjusting breaker contacts. To adjust, loosen the lock screw and turn the adjusting cam to get the correct gap; then tighten the lock screw and recheck. (AL)

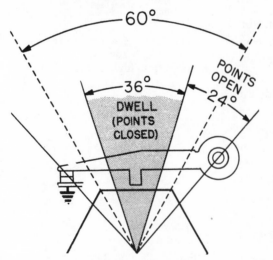

DOTTED LINES INDICATE THE 60° BETWEEN CAM LOBES ALLOTED TO THE FIRING OF EACH CYLINDER OF A 6 CYLINDER ENGINE

Fig. 21.24. Cam angle or dwell is the angle through which the distributor shaft turns while the breaker points are closed. When the points are closed, the rubbing block does not make contact with the cam.

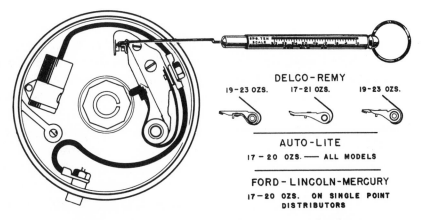

DELCO-REMY
19-23 OZS.   17-21 OZS.   19-23 OZS.

AUTO-LITE
17-20 OZS. — ALL MODELS

FORD-LINCOLN-MERCURY
17-20 OZS. ON SINGLE POINT DISTRIBUTORS

Fig. 21.26. Checking spring tension on breaker arm or contact lever. This should be within the specified limits to get satisfactory action.

Replacement Points

Most of the replacement breaker point sets are now supplied as an assembly consisting of: (1) stationary point support with terminal binding post for making electrical connection; (2) pivot for the movable point; and (3) movable point, breaker arm and rubbing block mounted on the pivot, with spring properly adjusted. It is advisable, however, to check the alignment of the two points and bend the stationary contact if necessary to make the points contact at the center. The assembly is mounted on the breaker plate and its position adjusted to give the correct dwell or cam angle. This is determined by the position of the rubbing block relative to the breaker cam.

Double-Contact Distributors

Some distributors have two sets of contacts which must be synchronized in accordance with the manufacturer's specifications. For example, a distributor with a four-lobe cam installed on an eight-cylinder engine will have two ignition coils, one connected to each breaker arm. One coil and one set of contacts will operate four of the eight cylinders, and the other coil and other set of breaker points will operate the other four cylinders. With an eight-cylinder engine there will be an explosion each 45° of

Fig. 21.27. Three types of Delco-Remy distributor breaker arms or levers. From left to right — rib; single channel; triple channel, heavy duty.

distributor shaft rotation. Therefore the contact for each cylinder must be adjusted so that it breaks exactly 45° from the next.

Some distributors are made with two breaker arms and eight lobes on the distributor cam (for eight-cylinder engines). In this case, one of the breaker arms will close ahead of the other, closing the primary ignition circuit; then the other one will close, but has no effect. At the end of the dwell period the first one to close will be the first one to open, but this will have no effect since the second set of points is still closed. When the second points open, the ignition circuit is broken to initiate the spark. The object of this arrangement is to give a somewhat longer dwell period without making the point gap too small.

Lead Wires

The connecting leads into and within the distributor must be securely fastened and must not interfere with the cap or rotor. This includes the lead for carrying the ignition current to the breaker arm, the leads from the breaker base to the ground, and also the condenser lead. All installations of leads — those connecting external terminals to the breaker cam and the ground leads inside the distributor — may be tested with a 110-volt circuit with a 10-watt lamp in series. An ohmmeter may also be used as explained later. When leads are tested for open circuits, a slight tension should be placed on them or they should be moved back and forth. This will disclose any broken wires inside the insulation, which might temporarily make contact during a static test. All leads inside the distributor should be bent away from contact with the housing or with moving parts of the distributor so that the insulation will not be worn through by vibration or rubbing.

The distributor is the only unit in the ignition system which has mechanical movement. Therefore both the mechanical operation and the electrical functioning of the distributor must be thoroughly understood.

Distributor High-Tension Circuit

We have considered the first two jobs of the distributor — making and breaking the ignition current, and timing the ignition current in accordance with engine speed and road conditions. The third job of the distributor is to direct the high-voltage surge to the spark plug. It is this third function which gives the distributor its name.

The distributor cap will have four, six, or eight contacts, depending upon the number of cylinders on the engine. For each contact there is a socket or tower for a wire which goes to one of the spark plugs. Wires from these contacts will go to the various spark plugs in the same order as the engine firing order, counting in the direction of rotation. For example, on a right-hand rotation distributor for a six-cylinder engine, starting with the outlet which goes to number 1 spark plug, the wires would go in the firing order of the engine, 1-5-3-6-2-4.

Any one of the contacts on the outside of the distributor cap (center contact usually comes from the coil) can be No. 1, depending on just how the shaft is meshed with the timing gear which drives the distributor shaft from the camshaft. It is desirable to maintain the manufacturer's location of No. 1. Wherever the distributor rotor happens to point when No. 1 cylinder is in firing position and timing is correct will be No. 1 spark plug connection. With No. 1 connection located and following the direction of distributor shaft rotation, the other wires can be connected to the distributor cap in the same order as the firing order.

The high-tension current surge initiated by the breaker points is brought to the center of the distributor cap where the rotor conducts it to the terminal leading to the proper spark plug. The end of the rotor does not actually contact the metal stud which leads to the spark plug wire; instead there is a gap from .010″ to .020″ across which the high-tension spark jumps and is then conducted to the spark plugs. This small gap has negligible resistance compared with that between the spark plug electrodes, since plugs are under engine compression at the time the spark occurs while in the distributor only atmospheric pressure is present. Remember there are always two spark gaps in the secondary circuit, one at each plug and one at the end of the rotor.

Rotors

Rotors are molded from a phenol-resin or similar material, depending upon the conditions to be met in service. The most common type of rotor is molded with a recess to fit over the end of the distributor shaft. One face of the end of the distributor shaft is usually flattened and fits against a flattened face in the recess of the rotor to drive the rotor without slipping. In addition to the molded rotor body, there is a segment of metal which carries the current to the adjacent cap terminal and a spring which contacts the center terminal of the cap. The spring and segment are attached to the molded rotor body by means of a rivet which is molded in place when the rotor is made. For heavy-duty service the segment is supplied with a tungsten tip on the outer end so it will better withstand the burning effect of the high-voltage surges as they jump between the rotor segment and the cap terminals. Fig. 21.28 shows some typical distributor rotors. The rotor conducts the high-tension current from the center contact to that contact leading to the plug which is to fire.

Electronic Ignition Systems

For many years there have been no changes other than minor improvements in the automotive ignition system. In 1956 there was a general change from 6 to 12 volts and adoption of the negative ground by those manufacturers who previously used positive ground battery systems. This gave somewhat better ignition results, especially at high speeds.

Beginning in 1963, however, some major changes began to be made in the ignition system, taking advantage of some of the possibilities of solid state semi-conductors, in the form of transistors and diodes. While there has been no general adoption of the new systems, transistor ignition systems are available from many automobile manufacturers.

Several well-known companies have designed and are manufacturing systems using transistors to interrupt the primary ignition current instead of conventional distributor breaker points. Five of these companies are Electric Auto-Lite Company, Delco-Remy Division of General Motors Corporation, Motorola, Ford and Tung-Sol.

Prestolite Transigniter

The Prestolite Division of the Electric Auto-Lite Company offers the Prestolite Transigniter system which makes use of the conventional distributor breaker points to establish and interrupt a triggering circuit. This in turn actuates a transistor to establish and interrupt the primary ignition circuit through the ignition coil. The

current that flows through the breaker points is only approximately 0.3 ampere, thus assuring the contact points of freedom from point burning, arcing, electrical erosion and deterioration, with correspondingly long life.

The parts making up the system in addition to the breaker points are (1) transistor circuit in its heat sink which also houses the internal circuitry, (2) special ignition coil, and (3) special ballast resistor. The element in this ballast resistor has low resistance when cold but much higher resistance when heated to normal running temperature. This allows full battery voltage when the system is cold, but drops the primary voltage to the coil by 2 to 3 volts at running temperature. Thus, the normal

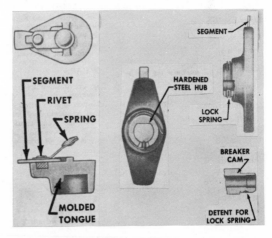

Fig. 21.28. Distributor rotors — (left) Standard duty, (right) heavy duty. These are small but very essential parts. (DR)

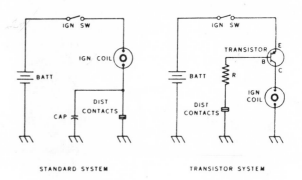

Fig. 21.29. Simple diagram showing the comparison between the standard or conventional ignition system and the transistorized system.

function of the ballast resistor is performed without the need for a bypass starting circuit. No condenser is required.

Fig. 21.29 compares the conventional ignition system with the transistor system in which a transistor is placed in series with the ignition

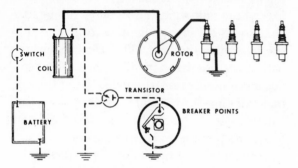

Fig. 21.30. Diagram of a contact controlled transistor system.

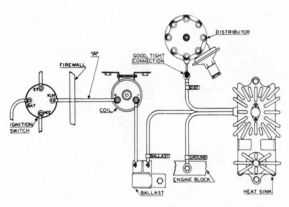

Fig. 21.31. Wiring layout for Prestolite Transigniter. At the right is the transistor heat sink and at lower center is the special ballast resistor which has low resistance when cold for starting, and higher resistance for running.

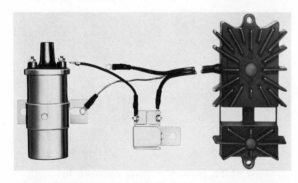

Fig. 21.32. Parts included in the Transigniter ignition system.

coil primary and is controlled by the distributor contacts or breaker points. Fig. 21.30 shows a pictorial diagram of a contact-controlled transistor system. When the contacts are closed, current can flow from the transistor emitter *(E)* through the base *(B)* rendering the transistor conductive. Therefore current will flow through the transistor from emitter to collector *(C)* and through the coil primary. When the contacts open, the transistor emitter-to-base current is broken, making the transistor nonconductive. Thus the coil primary current is broken, causing a high-voltage surge in the coil. Ignition timing is accomplished by the distributor cam and breaker points in the same manner as in the conventional system. The major difference between the two systems is the small amount of current handled by the breaker points, a reduction of approximately 90%.

The advantages of this system are (1) two to ten times longer point life, (2) higher secondary output since higher amperage can be used in the primary circuit, and (3) lowest cost for a transistor system, as the simple circuitry only requires one transistor. Rubbing block wear will still require adjustment of dwell occasionally, though this is a much simpler operation than changing the points. Fig. 21.31 is a diagram showing the Prestolite Transigniter system, while Fig. 21.32 shows the parts in the system.

Delcotronic Ignition System

In the development of the Delcotronic Ignition System, the objective was to produce a system that would provide long life and high reliability, and one that would require no periodic maintenance attention for the life of the vehicle. The result was a full transistor-ignition system which makes use of a timed voltage pulse from a pulse generator to operate a transistor amplifier, which in turn controls the ignition primary current flowing to the coil. The conventional breaker points and condenser have been eliminated. The components of the system include the distributor which houses the conventional secondary units and the pulse generator, the ignition coil, two external ignition resistors, and the amplifier which houses the transistors and internal circuitry.

A circuit diagram is shown in Fig. 21.33. Three transistors, three capacitors, a diode and the associated resistors are housed in the amplifier box. *TR3* is the output transistor, *TR2* is the driver, and *TR1* is the trigger transistor. The function of *TR3* is primarily to control the current through the ignition coil. The remainder of the circuitry is used to control *TR3*. In order for the system to operate properly it must do two things: (1) turn off the coil current at the proper time, as initiated by the pulse generator and *TR1*, and (2) turn the current back on again at the proper time, which is the function of capacitor C and resistor R_4. Fig. 21.34 shows the basic pulse generator controlled transistorized system. Fig. 21.35 illustrates this system installed on a car.

A Zener diode is included in the circuit to protect against any voltage pulse that would exceed the voltage rating of the output transistor. If it were not for the Zener diode the system would have to be designed so that the primary induced voltage would not exceed 120 volts under the most abnormal operating conditions, and this would mean that under normal conditions the output transistor would only be operating at two-thirds its rating. With the Zener the system can operate closer to the rating of the *TR3* transistor.

An important advantage of the transistor ignition systems is that there is little reduction of available voltage at high speed. A limitation of the Transigniter system is that ample voltage is available at speeds below which there is no objectionable point bounce. With the Delcotronic system, there are no points, so this limitation does not apply. Engines have been operated at up to 9000 rpm with perfect functioning of the ignition system. Fig. 21.36 shows the Delco-Remy pulse generator distributor.

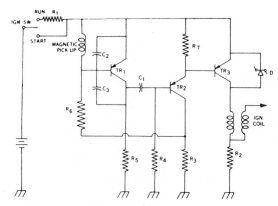

Fig. 21.33. Wiring layout for the Delcotron (Delco-Remy) transistorized ignition system with a magnetic pulse distributor. Notice that there are two resistors.

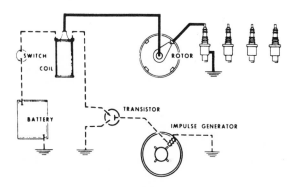

Fig. 21.34. Magnetically Controlled Circuit.

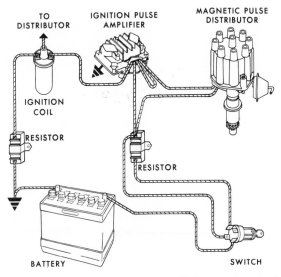

Fig. 21.35. Generator-controlled transistorized pulse-generator system in use.

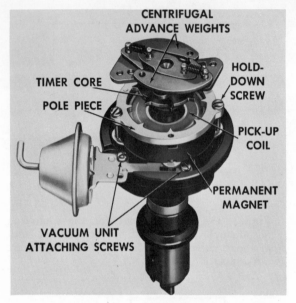

Fig. 21.36. The magnetic pulse distributor. When the points on the rotor align with the points on the pole piece, magnetic flux is at a maximum. As the rotor turns and the points get out of alignment, the flux weakens. This causes a weak electrical current to be induced which triggers the transistors and causes an ignition spark to be sent to the right spark plug. Notice that the centrifugal or automatic advance weights are above the rotor, pick-up coil and pole piece.

The manner in which the triggering pulse is introduced into the pickup coil is illustrated in Fig. 21.37. When the distributor shaft is in a position such that the teeth on the rotating pole-piece are lined up with those on the stationary pole-piece, a flux path is established as shown on the left. This is the minimum gap position. As the shaft is rotated to a point where the teeth on the rotating pole-piece are halfway between those on the stationary pole-piece, a maximum air gap condition is established and the magnetic flux field collapses as shown on the right. Thus as the distributor shaft rotates, the magnetic field is made to build up and collapse alternately, thereby inducing a transistor triggering voltage into the pickup coil. The result is a series of current impulses with rapid collapse which cause the necessary ignition sparks to occur at each spark plug, channeled by the distributor rotor in the same way the conventional distributor acts.

Motorola Transistor Ignition System

The pulse generator in the Motorola system has a rotor with relatively long teeth, the

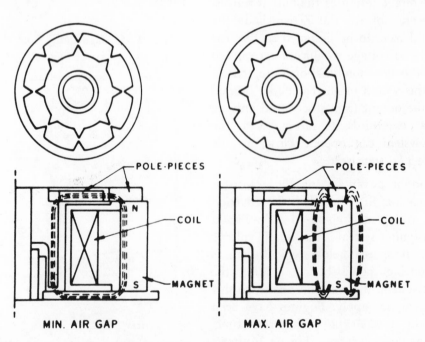

Fig. 21.37. Diagram showing how the rotor and pole piece are (1) in alignment with minimum air gap and (2) out of alignment with maximum air gap.

same in number as the engine cylinders. The pulse pickup consists of two magnet cores located radially relative to the rotor, with a small coil wound on each core. The two cores are spaced the same as two teeth on the rotor. Thus when two teeth are aligned with the two magnet cores, there is maximum buildup of magnetic flux. As soon as the rotor teeth turn out of alignment with the two cores, the magnetic field collapses, causing an electrical pulse to be generated. This pulse is amplified and used to trigger the breaking and re-establishing of the primary ignition current flow. The action is similar to that of the Delcotronic described above. Fig. 21.38 shows the Motorola pulse generator distributor and Fig. 21.39 shows the components of the system.

Ford Transistor Ignition System

The Ford System is much like the Prestolite, making use of the conventional distributor breaker points to interrupt the small current which triggers the transistor. The transistor actually makes and breaks the primary ignition current. Fig. 21.40 shows the components of the Ford System.

Capacitor Discharge System

In addition to the two types of transistor ignition systems discussed (the breaker-point-triggered transistor system and the pulse-generator system) there is a third system, the *capacitor discharge system*. It generally uses the conventional breaker points to trigger the transistors, but means are provided to charge

Fig. 21.38. Motorola Magnetic Pulse Distributor. The rotor alternately is in alignment and out of alignment with two magnets and their coils, generating pulse currents for each ignition spark and thereby triggering the transistorized circuit.

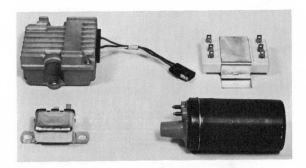

Fig. 21.40. Transistorized ignition system as supplied by Ford Motor Company. For 1963 this was optional on certain truck models.

Fig. 21.39. The parts composing the Motorola transistorized ignition system with pulse generating distributor.

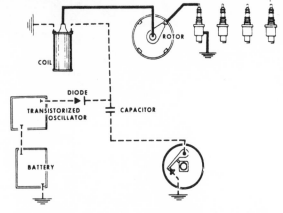

Fig. 21.41. The capacitor discharge ignition system in which the conventional distributor triggers the transistorized circuit to send ignition sparks to the spark plugs by discharging a capacitor or condenser.

a capacitor. In most systems, the capacitor, in turn, is discharged to the primary side of the ignition coil. Refer to Fig. 21.41.

The capacitor discharge system offers unusual ability to fire partially fouled plugs. The outstanding feature of this system is the extremely rapid voltage rise at the spark plugs, which takes place in one to two millionths of a second (1-2 microseconds). Compared with 80 to 130 microseconds for the conventional systems (without transistors) and from 100 to as high as 210 microseconds for the contact-controlled and magnetically-controlled systems, this is an extremely rapid operation.

The speed with which voltage rises at the spark plug electrodes has a direct effect on the system's ability to fire partially fouled spark plugs. In considering the effect of voltage-rise time, remember that a spark cannot jump an electrode gap until the voltage climbs to the breakdown value of the gap. When conductive

deposits on the spark plug insulator nose form a low resistance "shunt path" to ground, the ignition system high-tension voltage literally bleeds away. When the shunt path or electrical resistance is low enough, the voltage never reaches sufficient value for sparking, and the plug misfires. With the capacitive discharge system, more deposits can be tolerated on the plugs before fouling and misfire occur.

In addition to the fifty or more manufacturers of transistorized ignition systems, there are several producers of capacitor ignition systems. Two of these are Motion, Inc., a division of Tung Sol Electric, Inc., and Delta Products, Inc., Grand Junction, Colorado.

Motion Capacitor Discharge System

The capacitor discharge system offered by Motion, Inc., is more expensive than the transistorized systems but has some advantages. It takes less current than either the conventional

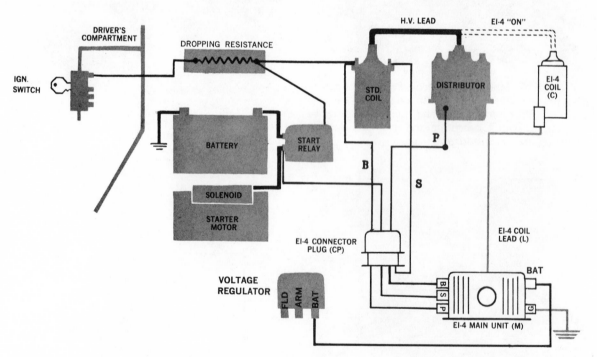

Fig. 21.42. Wiring layout for capacitor discharge transistorized ignition system. By reversing the connector plug (CP) and changing the conductor that runs from the distributor to the coil, from the capacitor discharge coil to the conventional coil (which remains in place), the ignition returns to conventional operation. This is convenient for testing with a dwell meter, tachometer, and oscilloscope, and is also helpful in cases of possible failure of the transistorized system. (Motion, Inc.)

or transistorized systems; it will fire the plugs even with a partially discharged battery; it has less deterioration on the spark plugs, giving longer plug life; and the extremely rapid spark buildup gives some improvement in engine performance. The wiring layout and parts that compose this system are shown in Figs. 21.42 and 21.43.

Fig. 21.44 helps to explain how this system operates. During the first engine revolution when starting, the circuit begins to function when the breaker points open. At this time, current flows through the primary of the transformer T_2, momentarily building up a magnetic field in the transformer core. When the breaker points close, current flow through the primary is stopped, the magnetic field collapses and induces a high voltage in the transformer secondary. This voltage is transferred through rectifier V_1 to capacitor C_1 where it is stored until the breaker points open again. When the breaker points open the second time, the current flowing through the primary of T_2 builds the magnetic field in the transformer coil and also produces a voltage on the secondary. Part of this secondary voltage is applied to the grid of Thyratron V_2 causing it to conduct. The energy previously stored in capacitor C_1 is then discharged into the spark plugs through the special coil T_4.

The primary circuit of the capacitor discharge system uses a transistor to carry and switch the heavy current flowing from the battery or generator through the main transformer so that the breaker points carry only a small control current of approximately one ampere. This small current results in elimination of pitting and possible bluing of breaker point contact surfaces so that electrically they will operate indefinitely without replacement. It is possible that the rubbing block will wear gradually, changing the dwell, which should be checked and adjusted once or twice a year.

Delta Capacitor Discharge System

The Delta System, called the Thunderbolt Mark 10, Energy Transfer Ignition System, is unique in its ease of installation as well as its outstanding performance. It makes use of the conventional ignition coil, the conventional distributor (for triggering only), the standard condenser, and the conventional original equipment ballast resistor. All that is added is the housing, approximately 3″ x 3″ x 6″, and two dual conductors, as shown in Fig. 21.45.

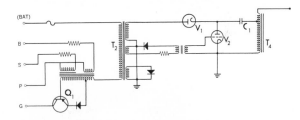

Fig. 21.44. Circuit diagram of the Motion, Inc. capacitor discharge ignition system.

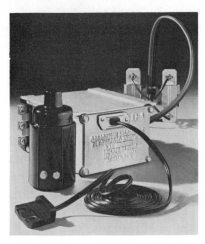

Fig. 21.43. Parts composing the capacitor discharge ignition system. (Motion, Inc.)

Fig. 21.45. Thunderbolt Energy Transfer Ignition System housing is 6″ x 3″ x 3″ and makes use of the capacitor discharge principle, aided by several transistors, diodes, capacitors, and a transformer.

To install the Thunderbolt it is only necessary to fasten the housing in place with three self-tapping sheet metal screws and to make the connections to the coil terminals. The two dual conductors each terminate in a two-panel junction block. The panels, each about ½″ square, are insulated from each other.

To make the connections, disconnect the ignition switch wire from the coil. Connect the junction block at the end of the green-white dual conductor to the terminal on the battery side of the coil, and connect the wire removed from this terminal to the binding post on the junction block. Disconnect the distributor wire from the coil, and connect the junction block with the red-white dual conductor to the coil; then connect the distributor wire to the binding post. This completes the installation, which can be done in 15 minutes or less. Fig. 21.46 shows the Thunderbolt installed on an automobile.

In the schematic diagram, Fig. 21.47, Section *A* is an oscillator converter circuit which steps up the primary voltage to approximately 400 volts and rectifies it. Section *B* contains the silicon-controlled rectifier control circuit. *C-2* is an energy storage capacitor which is discharged through *SCR-1* to turn the *SCR* on and fire the coil.

Fig. 21.46. Thunderbolt capacitor discharge ignition system mounted on the front wheel house panel in a late model Mercury. The installation consists of anchoring the housing with three self-tapping sheet metal screws and making four simple connections.

Section *C* contains the point cathode circuitry used to switch on *C-2* through silicon transistor *Q-3* at the proper firing interval. It is also used to invert the point signal to cause *SCR-1* to turn on only when the breaker points open. Section *D* contains the capacitor *C-1* which stores the energy until the proper moment of firing. When the points open, the ground is removed from the distributor terminal, allowing battery voltage, which has been flowing to ground, to raise the base voltage of transistor *Q-3* to battery voltage, causing *Q-3* to conduct. The energy stored in capacitor *C-2* and the current through resistor *R-5* now discharge through *Q-3* to ground. Since the silicon-controlled rectifier has an extremely low resistance when fired, capacitor *C-1* discharges through *SCR-1* and the coil. This supplies an applied voltage peak of 400 volts across the coil which builds up very high voltage secondary sparking current in about two millionths of a second (two-micro seconds). This is less than one-fiftieth the time required in the conventional or transistor electronic systems.

The indications at this time are that the capacitor discharge ignition system will be favored over the other systems, as its good features, especially the extremely rapid secondary voltage rise time, become recognized. Because of the number of expensive components in the capacitor discharge system, its cost is higher than the transistor electronic types, but the actual, rather than the theoretical results, justify the higher acquisition expense.

Summary

The *distributor* is the only unit in the ignition system that has mechanical motion. Each breaker cam lobe passes under the breaker arm rubbing block to open the contact points to initiate the spark. The points constitute a fast-acting make-and-break switch.

A *wide open throttle* may require 16,000 to 20,000 sparks per minute.

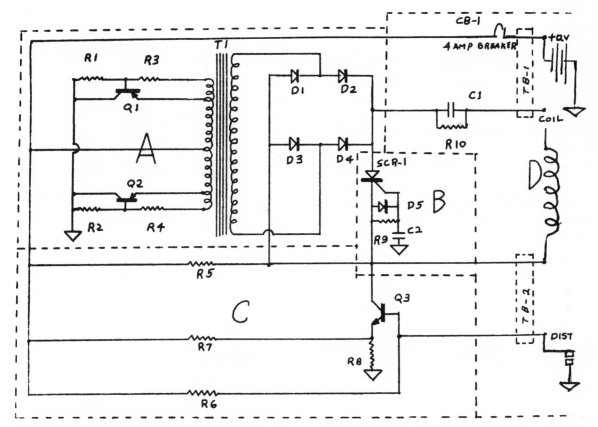

Fig. 21.47. Schematic of the Thunderbolt ignition system, showing the different circuits, components, sections of the system and their relation to each other. SCR-1 is a silicon controlled rectifier. Capacitor C-1 supplies the energy to generate the ignition sparks by discharging through the ignition coil at the correct time in each firing cycle.

At *high engine speed* there is a shorter interval available from the initial timing position for the fuel-air mixture to ignite and burn. Therefore the ignition timing must be advanced to allow the required period for combustion to take place.

The *centrifugal advance mechanism* consists of two weights which move outward against spring tension as the engine speed increases and cause the breaker cam to rotate slightly on its shaft, resulting in spark advance.

Under *part throttle* there is a high vacuum in the intake manifold but a relatively small amount of fuel-air mixture is drawn into the cylinders. Therefore there is low compression. At lower pressures, the fuel mixture burns more slowly and so needs more time for combustion. Ignition timing must be advanced by the *vacuum advance mechanism*.

The *correct time to ignite* the fuel-air mixture in a cylinder is determined by the time when the combustion should be completed in relation to the position of the piston in the cylinder. The angular position of the crankpin is used to designate timing position.

Operating conditions range from wide open throttle with best power to road-load operation with best economy desired. Operating at road loads with throttle partly open, the engine cylinders take in only part of their possible full charge during each intake stroke. Therefore the compression pressure at road load is relatively low and that means slow combustion. Advanced ignition timing is required.

The *initial spark timing* should be correct as otherwise all the spark advance curves will have the same error.

Time of ignition depends upon the angular position of the distributor compared to No. 1 crank position. Rotating the distributor body against the direction of rotation of distributor shaft will advance the spark. It is necessary to know the direction of distributor shaft rotation when advancing or retarding ignition timing. The timing is checked with the *timing light*.

Static timing is frequently done on European cars. It is done by using a test light with the engine not running.

Breaker contacts generally need the most attention. The normal color should be light gray. Oil vapor will cause point failure. New breaker points have one contact with a slightly convex surface and the other flat.

Dwell or cam angle is the angle through which the distributor shaft rotates while the contact points are closed. It is important because during this period the coil becomes saturated magnetically.

Replacement of points is usually the installation of an assembly on recent cars.

A common cause of *point failure* is presence of oil or lubricating compound on the contact surfaces. Only an approved lubricant should be used on the distributor cam.

Lead wires inside the distributor must have tight terminals and connections. They may be tested with 110-volt test light or an ohmmeter.

In the *distributor high-tension circuit*, wires to spark plugs are connected to the distributor cap in the same order as the engine firing order. There are always two spark gaps in this circuit, (1) one at end of distributor rotor and (2) one at each spark plug as it is being fired.

Rotors are molded from a resin, phenol or similar material. The rotor conducts the high-tension current from the center distributor contact to the correct spark plug cable contact.

Electronic ignition systems have been offered since 1963 by many manufacturers.

Most of the systems use the *conventional distributor* to interrupt the triggering circuit while a transistor makes and breaks the ignition primary circuit.

The *Delcotronic* system uses a pulse generator in place of the breaker points to trigger the transistors.

Motorola uses a pulse generator to trigger the transistor circuit.

A *capacitor discharge system* uses conventional breaker points to trigger the system but also uses transistors, transformer and capacitor. The discharge of the capacitor supplies the ignition spark. The voltage-rise time of this system is very much less than with either the conventional system or the transistorized system.

Questions

1. What are the three duties performed by the distributor?
2. How fast does the distributor rotate in relation to engine rotation?
3. Why is the automatic spark advance required?
4. How does the automatic mechanism cause the ignition timing to advance?
5. Why is the vacuum advance device required?
6. How does the vacuum advance device operate?
7. What do the letters ATDC and BTDC mean?
8. What is meant by *initial spark advance*?
9. How can you tell the direction of distributor shaft rotation?
10. What is meant by *static timing*?
11. How is ignition timing usually checked?
12. What part of the distributor gets the hardest use?
13. What is the usual result of oil around the breaker points?
14. How should the breaker point gap be measured?
15. What is meant by dwell angle?

16. Why should breaker arm spring tension be checked?

17. How is breaker arm spring tension measured?

18. What is the usual result of incorrect condenser capacity?

19. What are the two kinds of double contact distributors?

20. What two lead wires inside the distributor are possible causes of trouble?

21. What is the important job for the distributor to do in the high-tension circuit?

22. Where is the high-tension conductor from the coil connected to the distributor?

23. How does the transistorized ignition system differ from the conventional system?

24. What are the two types of transistorized ignition systems?

25. What are three parts of a transistor?

26. Name the main advantages of the transistorized system which makes use of breaker points.

27. What is the general principle of the capacitor discharge ignition system?

28. Name four companies that offer transistorized ignition systems?

29. Why is a condenser not needed in the transistorized ignition system?

30. How do the Delco-Remy and Motorola transistorized ignition systems work without breaker points to interrupt the primary circuit?

CHAPTER TWENTY-TWO

Full-Vacuum-Control Distributor —Spark Plugs

The need for advancing ignition timing in accordance with certain conditions of operation was described in Chapter 21. It is necessary to advance the spark with increases in engine speed. In conventional distributors, centrifugally-operated weights are used to rotate the distributor breaker cam in the same direction as distributor shaft rotation. This produces the spark advance timing as a function of the engine speed. The amount of the

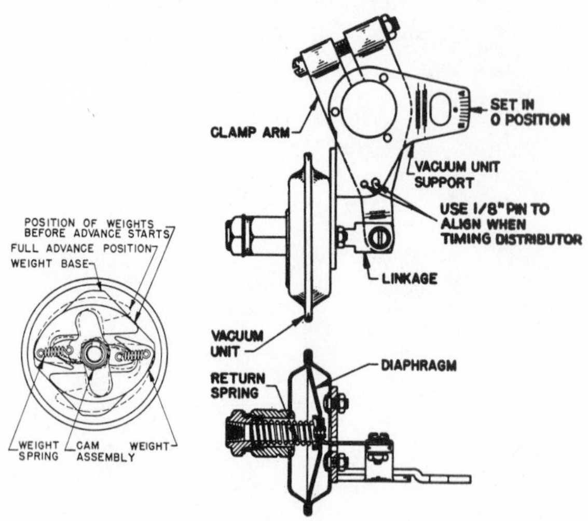

Fig. 22.1. The total spark advance on conventional ignition systems for any condition of load and speed is determined by two advance mechanisms acting together, the automatic advance (left) and the vacuum advance (right).

spark advance is controlled by the tension of the springs reacting against the movement of centrifugal weights. The weights operate a cam which in turn moves the breaker cam on the distributor shaft. The weights, springs, and cams are so adjusted and designed that they correctly meet the requirements of *ignition advance* in proportion to engine speed.

Additional spark advance control is necessary when the engine is operating under *partial power* or partial throttle operation. Achieving this control requires an additional mechanism. Since intake manifold vacuum varies inversely with throttle opening, a vacuum-actuated diaphragm linked to a movable breaker plate will move the contact points about the breaker cam in a direction opposite to the distributor shaft rotation. This will also produce spark advance. The vacuum connection in the carburetor is so located that the diaphragm will not be actuated when the engine is idling; however, it will be actuated when the throttle has opened slightly to give the engine more power and speed than it would have in the idling position. This gives a variation in spark advance which is proportional to engine load.

Thus the conventional system includes two means of producing spark timing advance, which may operate independently or have a cumulative effect. The centrifugal governor satisfies the requirements of advance in proportion to engine speed, and the manifold vacuum system satisfies the further advance requirements of partial load operation. Refer to Fig. 22.1.

Full-Vacuum Ignition Control

In 1948 the Ford Motor Company introduced the full-vacuum-control distributor. This was used on all the Ford-built automobiles for several years. The V-8 engines were then again equipped with the conventional type of automatic and vacuum advance, though most of the Ford six-cylinder engines used in both passenger cars and trucks still make use of the full-vacuum-control type, as shown in Fig. 22.2.

Since this method of ignition advance is one of the accepted standards in our present ignition systems, it should be understood. Engines on which it is used will not have any value given for automatic advance; therefore if the tune-up specifications mention vacuum advance only, this will indicate the presence of the full-vacuum-control distributor.

The full-vacuum system of spark advance control eliminates centrifugal weights and only indirectly employs manifold vacuum. The elimination of the governor weights considerably simplifies the distributor design. The spark advance is obtained by moving the base plate which carries the breaker points. This is controlled by a single diaphragm which is vacuum actuated. The vacuum is set up in the carburetor through the use of specially drilled openings and passages which are interconnected in the carburetor body. Two holes are very accurately and precisely located in the carburetor and are connected to a constricting opening so that the resultant differential vacuum is a measure of both engine speed and load condition. The size, shape, and location of the openings in the carburetor produce this result. The carburetor must be engineered for the specific type of engine on which it is to be used and it is not interchangeable with those

carburetors which do not have the openings and passages drilled in them. Refer to Fig. 22.3.

The distributor is practically the same as the conventional distributor except that the housing is more shallow, entirely omitting the compartment below the breaker point plate in which the centrifugal weights are located. The breaker cam is solidly fixed to the distributor shaft and cannot vary in position from the driven end of the shaft, in contrast to the conventional distributor.

Having the cam tightly fixed to the distributor shaft eliminates the wear which takes place in the conventional type. It also eliminates the possibility of torsional vibration appearing at the driven end of the distributor shaft, which is often amplified at the breaker

Fig. 22.2. A vacuum-controlled distributor as used on Ford six-cylinder engines.

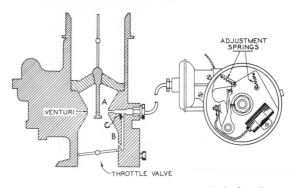

Fig. 22.3. The full-vacuum-controlled distributor gives the desired total spark advance based on modified vacuum only. It is transmitted from a carburetor with special passages and restrictions at *A*, *B*, and *C*.

cam due to the linkage through the breaker springs, weights, cams and bearings.

This distributor does not rotate but is locked firmly in place. The breaker plate is mounted on a separate bearing so it can rotate through a suitable angle about the cam. The breaker plate assembly includes the breaker contacts and the condenser. Springs modify the movement of the breaker plate from the initial timing position. There is one light spring and one heavy spring, or in some cases two heavy springs. One end of each spring is attached to the breaker plate; the other end is attached to an adjustable post, which permits changing the tension on the spring slightly. The springs are very carefully selected as to strength and length to permit a reasonable latitude in adjusting the spark advance to meet engine requirements. Refer to Fig. 22.4.

The breaker plate is rotated by the distributor vacuum diaphragm which is connected to the plates by a rod linkage. The diaphragm is vented to atmosphere on the distributor breaker plate side and is actuated by the distributor differential carburetor vacuum on its closed side.

Mechanical Design

The mechanical design of the distributor is well worked out. Sturdy bearings are provided for both the distributor shaft and the breaker plate. A long, sintered-metal bearing is used at the upper end of the distributor shaft and serves the dual purpose of guiding the distributor shaft and carrying the breaker plate assembly. This upper bearing is closely concentric so that the breaker plate is centered very accurately. Lubrication for the bearings is provided from an oiler located in the base of the distributor assembly which furnishes lubrication for both distributor shaft and breaker plates. The upper end of the bearing provides a thrust face for the distributor cam and shaft. The bearing is impregnated with SAE 40 lubricating oil. Care should be taken not to over-lubricate

the bearing as this will cause bleeding of oil which may get to the breaker points and damage them. There is a similar but smaller bearing at the bottom of the distributor base and a thrust collar pinned to the shaft to limit end play.

Vacuum Source at Carburetor

Since the spark advance control for this ignition system depends entirely on vacuum; the net or differential vacuum which is transmitted to the distributor must accurately reflect engine operating conditions. This means that the design of the vacuum outlet or pickup at the carburetor must be accurately coordinated with the distributor design in order to meet the spark advance requirements of the particular engine on which it is to be installed, under all conditions of speed and load.

A sectional drawing of the typical carburetor, Fig. 22.5, shows the positioning of the special distributor vacuum passages. There is one opening at the throat of the main carburetor venturi. The air passing through the venturi is proportional to engine speed since the engine acts as a pump on the intake stroke, and the faster it goes the more air there will be passing through the carburetor. The vacuum at the throat of the venturi will be proportional to the amount of air flowing through the throat. Therefore, the vacuum at the venturi throat will be proportional to engine speed. If only the vacuum conducted through this opening were used, the vacuum transmitted to the distributor diaphragm would move it in accordance with engine speed, which would produce a spark advance corresponding to engine speed advance requirements. By modifying the distributor plate movement with the proper spring loading, the full power spark advance requirement of the engine could be met. This would give a spark advance at full power comparable to that obtained through the use of centrifugal spark advance weights only, but would not satisfy the road load or partial throttle requirements.

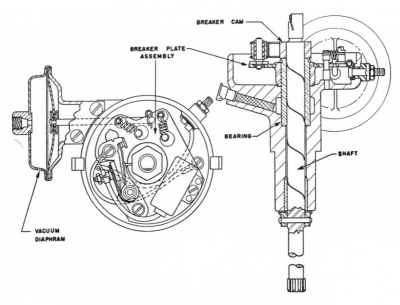

Fig. 22.4. The distributor has a breaker plate with center bearing, and movement is modified by two springs with adjustable tension. There is no automatic advance.

To modify this vacuum from the venturi throat to produce spark-advance results comparable to the combined advance of both the conventional centrifugal advance and vacuum advance, there is a second opening in the throttle body slightly above the closed throttle valve position. This location is similar to the point from which the vacuum is picked up for the conventional vacuum spark advance control. It is slightly above the throttle valve so that no vacuum is picked up when the throttle is in a closed or idling position. The spark advance is then at full retard due to the action of the breaker plate springs. The manifold vacuum opening, located just above the throttle valve in its closed position, is interconnected to the venturi opening through a vertical passageway marked C in the diagram, Fig. 22.5. A restriction is placed in the upper portion of the vertical passageway between the two openings. Being cross-connected, the vacuum of the two orifices are affected by each other under various speeds and load conditions of the engine.

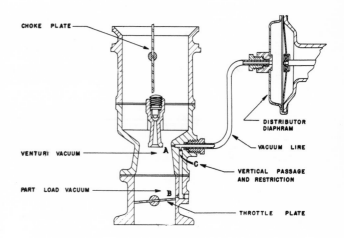

Fig. 22.5. Details of the special vacuum passages in the carburetor. Note the restrictions at A, B, and C, and also how B is affected by the throttle position.

During wide open throttle operation, the manifold vacuum is less than that developed in the venturi. Airflow occurs from B, the lower orifice, through the vertical restriction at C and out the upper orifice at the throat of the venturi at *A*. See Figs. 22.6 and 22.7. The restrictions at *A*, *B* and *C* determine the amount of bleeding one orifice will produce on the other and the these hole sizes must be very carefully figured. The relative sizes of these three openings will also affect the differential or resultant vacuum which is transmitted to the distributor. Unless the sizes are accurately determined, the resulting spark advance will not conform to engine requirements. A great amount of testing and research is required to properly design

the opening for any given engine. The total vacuum for maximum spark advance will not exceed 4″ Hg. (four inches of mercury).

Under part throttle operation, especially at the lower speed ranges, the manifold vacuum is considerably greater than that developed at the venturi orifice, and air will flow into the venturi orifice down the vertical passageway and out at the lower orifice. This means that the upper orifice is "bleeding" the higher vacuum, *i.e.,* allowing air to help break the vacuum. The amount of bleeding is governed

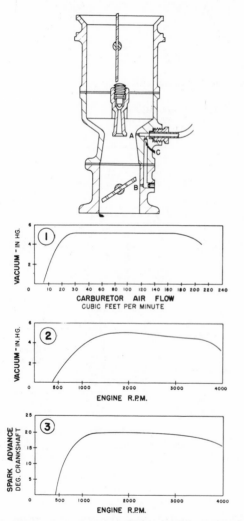

Fig. 22.6. The curves above show the relation between (1) vacuum and airflow, (2) vacuum and rpm, and (3) spark advance and rpm — when the throttle is partially opened.

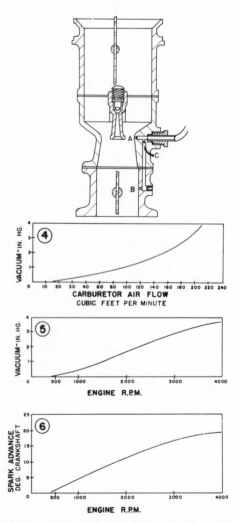

Fig. 22.7. The same relationships as in Fig. 22.6 are shown here, except that the throttle is now wide open. Notice the difference between each set of graphs.

by the size of the restrictions. If the venturi throat orifice and the restriction in the vertical passage are large as compared to the lower orifice, the carburetor distributor vacuum produced is low. For a given spring adjustment under wide open throttle condition, the resulting part throttle spark advance would be lower than that produced if the relative restrictions were reversed. Thus a very delicate system of balance exists which will only follow engine spark advance requirements if the orifices and their locations are precisely accurate. Based on the information obtained from research and testing it has been possible to design these orifices so that a vacuum results which will follow engine spark advance requirements very closely. With the desired vacuum produced, the distributor plate can be properly moved to meet engine requirements and give correct spark advance, at different conditions of speed and load.

Spark Plugs

The majority of servicemen know little about the technical points involved in the operation or failure of spark plugs. Most of their knowledge is concentrated on the following facts: (A) spark plugs should be changed every 10,000 miles (this idea was largely sold to the public by the major spark plug manufacturers), (B) correctly gapped, clean spark plugs in good condition are necessary to make an engine run at its best, and (C) poor engine acceleration and missing may in many cases be corrected by changing the spark plugs.

Spark plugs in use today are basically the same as those used twenty-five years ago. However the separable plugs which could be taken apart for cleaning have given way to the one-piece plugs.

Spark Plug Design

The spark plug is a comparatively simple product. It is made up of the shell, which is a metal body with threads on one end; the insulator; the sealing gasket; the center electrode

or center wire; the side electrode, side wire, ground wire, or ground electrode; and the connection terminal. Fig. 22.8 shows a cross section of a typical spark plug.

The *ceramic insulator* affects plug quality more than any of the other items of construction. An insulator ingredient, aluminum oxide, has greatly increased insulator durability by (1) improving its resistance to thermal shock, (2) giving better and more uniform electrical resistance throughout the operating range of the plug, (3) providing better heat conducting characteristics, and (4) giving greater mechanical strength. The spark plug parts are shown in Fig. 22.9.

The *side wires or grounded electrodes* are welded to the shell. The *center electrode* is

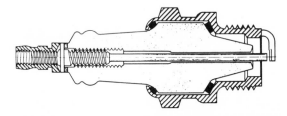

Fig. 22.8. Cross section of a spark plug showing its construction. The ceramic insulator is extremely important for good performance and long spark plug life. High-grade insulators will have a high proportion of aluminum oxide. (AL)

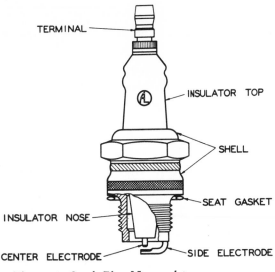

Fig. 22.9. Spark Plug Nomenclature.

cemented into the ceramic insulator in such a way that provision is made for expansion due to heat and at the same time for a good heat path so that the heat picked up by the center wire can be transmitted into the ceramic insulator.

The first spark plugs were made with a $\frac{1}{2}''$ tapered pipe thread which fitted into a correspondingly tapped hole in the cylinder block. The tapered threads made the necessary gas-tight joints in the same way that pipe and pipe fitting go together to make a tight joint. This type was superseded by the $\frac{7}{8}''$ - 18 thread, which was a straight thread without taper making use of a shoulder on the plug and a soft copper gasket to make the necessary gas-tight seal. The $\frac{7}{8}''$ plug was rather large and cumbersome, so the 18 mm plug (slightly over $\frac{5}{8}''$) was introduced. Between 1936 and 1938 most of the cars changed from the 18 mm plug to the 14 mm, with a thread which slightly over $\frac{1}{2}''$ in diameter. This is the size now used in all of American cars except Fords. For a short time Packard, Chevrolet and Cadillac used 10 mm plugs with a thread approximately $\frac{3}{8}''$ diameter. The small-size plugs did not give as good results as the 14 mm and were soon discontinued. Ford-built cars adopted the 18 mm with tapered shoulder and no gasket beginning with the 1955 models. All the current spark plugs have straight threads and depend on either a gasket or tapered seat for a gas-tight seal. Refer to Fig. 22.10 for gasket details.

The spark plug has a very difficult function in engine operation. Between 4,000 and 20,000 volts of electrical pressure is trying to get from the center electrode to ground. When the spark plug is operating as it should, this pressure will cause a spark to jump from the center electrode to the ground electrode or side wire. This will continue until a path which can be followed more easily becomes available. The spark plug insulator is the only barrier between the center electrode and the ground. Such things as moisture on the surface of the ceramic insulator, a crack in the insulator or a conducting layer of carbon on that part of the insulator exposed to the combustion gases, will supply an easier path than across the electrodes and the plug will then misfire.

The ceramic insulator must not only withstand the electrical stress, but it must also conduct heat away from the plug. Since as many as two thousand explosions take place per minute in the cylinder, poor heat conduction might allow the temperature to become high enough to cause pre-ignition in the cylinder. At the time of the explosion in the cylinder, the plug must also withstand gaseous pressure up to 500 pounds per square inch. The flame temperature of the explosion may reach a point as high as 4000° F. If the heat which the tip of the porcelain picks up is conducted away too rapidly, the temperature at this point will fall low enough that carbon will be deposited on it. This may offer a path for the high-tension current, and cause the plug to misfire.

The exact mechanism of how a spark occurs is not known; however, it is assumed that the high-tension current first ionizes the gas which

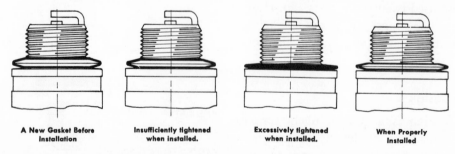

A New Gasket Before Installation   **Insufficiently tightened when installed.**   **Excessively tightened when installed.**   **When Properly Installed**

Fig. 22.10. Use a new spark plug gasket every time you install a new or cleaned spark plug to insure better performance and longer life.

is between the electrodes. This is equivalent to saying the current prepares the gas for the passage of the spark which then breaks through the high resistance of the gases and ignites the surrounding combustible mixture. The voltage required for a spark will vary with the size and condition of the spark gap and with the compression pressure. The higher the compression pressure at the time of the explosion, the higher the voltage will have to be to break through it, because there will be more molecules of the fuel-air mixture, which has a high insulating value. Also the voltage required to jump the gap will be approximately proportional to the length of the gap so that the larger the gap, the higher the required voltage. It is for this reason that spark plugs should be regapped approximately every five thousand miles, as the gap gradually increases due to the electrical erosion of the electrodes. Oxide or lead from the fuel deposited on the surfaces of the center electrode or side wire will also increase the voltage required to jump the gap.

Heat Range

It is important that spark plug heat ranges and their applications be thoroughly understood so that correct applications are made in the field. The term *heat range* refers particularly to the ability of the plug to conduct heat away from the inner tip of the ceramic insulator. A plug which conducts the heat away rapidly will have a lower ceramic insulator temperature and is referred to as a *"cold" plug*, while one which conducts the heat away more slowly will have a higher temperature at the ceramic tip and will be referred to as a *"hot" plug*. A plug is rated hot or cold by the length of the heat path from the tip of the porcelain to the sealing gasket at the lower shoulder of the insulator where the heat passes through the gasket into the sealed shell of the plug. Figs. 22.11 and 22.12 show the difference in varying heat ranges. From the sealed shell, the heat is transferred through the threads, the

shoulder and sealing gasket, to the cylinder block.

The heat range of spark plugs is indicated by their number. The lower numbers indicate colder plugs and the higher numbers, hotter plugs. The particular plug recommended for any given engine will depend upon the engine type and the location of the plugs in the engine.

The coolest location in a cylinder is directly over the intake valve because the cool, fresh gases entering the cylinder sweep over the plugs. The hottest location is directly over the exhaust valve where the hot gases pass over the plug. A plug located between the two valves would operate at a temperature somewhere between the two extremes.

Each plug is numbered in such a way that the number will indicate its place in the heat scale. Some of the numbers include a letter and some use numerical digits only. Since the numbering systems of the important plug makers do not exactly correspond, conversion charts are supplied by most of the manufacturers so that equivalent plugs can be selected.

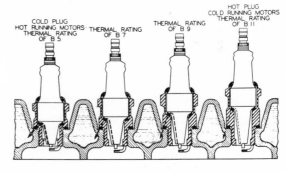

Fig. 22.11. "Heat Range" of Plugs.

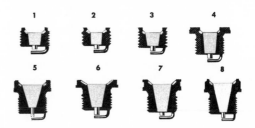

Fig. 22.12. "Heat Range" steps in AC Spark Plug designs. Notice that the principal difference is the length of the insulator inside the shell.

After a car has been in service for several years and has high mileage, the engine will have deteriorated and its characteristics have changed somewhat. If original equipment plugs should be installed, they might become fouled after a short time from a low operating temperature. In this case hotter plugs should be used.

There also is a difference in the service in which a car may be used. Slow speeds, door-to-door service, short trips, or slow or heavy traffic, usually produce lower operating temperatures and require hotter plugs. The same car, if largely driven on long trips at high speeds, would require a colder plug because the operating temperatures would be higher.

The use of butane gas as an engine fuel is increasing. This gas burns with a very hot, clean flame and engines using it as a fuel should have a colder spark plug. Propane is a similar fuel used practically interchangeably with butane, and the same caution as to the spark plug type applies.

Insulator Color

There is only one sure and practical test to determine the plug that should be used. This is to examine the firing tips of insulators on plugs that have been run at other than idling speeds for at least a few hours, under normal operating conditions. The color of the spark plug insulator will indicate whether the plug is too hot, too cold or correct for the engine under its normal conditions of operation.

If the proper plug is being used, the insulator will be a light tan, and it will be clean. If the plug is too cold, the insulator will be black; if the plug is too hot, the insulator will have a white ashy appearance and the electrodes will seem to be burned. After long periods of use there may be a build-up of oxide or lead deposits from the fuel on the ground electrode which reduces the plug effectiveness.

In cases where the color of the ceramic indicates that the correct heat range has been used, and the plug has served a normal period, an equivalent plug should be used for replacement. If the color is dark or black, one or two numbers hotter should be used; if the appearance indicates too hot a plug has been used, replace with plugs one or two numbers colder.

Plug Installation

The installation of plugs is generally considered a very simple operation, and there is certainly nothing difficult about it. However, certain precautions should be observed to get the best results and to eliminate possible causes of trouble. Before removing a spark plug from an engine, use an air jet to blow away gravel, sand, or other foreign matter which might have collected in the pockets in which the plugs are set. Otherwise dirt might get into the cylinders and cause scoring of cylinder walls or pistons.

In removing or installing spark plugs, the correct tool to use is a deep socket. Driving the socket with a ratchet handle will save time. In some cases where the rear plug is not easily accessible, it may be necessary to use a socket extension and a universal joint. A $13/16''$ deep socket will take care of practically all plugs in current use, including the 14 mm and 18 mm sizes. Deep sockets with the $3/8''$ drive and rubber inserts will be found to be most convenient, and ample force can be applied to the $3/8''$ drive ratchet to tighten the plugs properly. Make it a habit whenever spark plugs are removed to observe the color of the porcelain insulator. This will tell whether the same heat range plug should be installed or whether a hotter or colder one will work better.

The heat picked up by the spark plugs must go through the gasket and surface of the block in order to get into the metal of the block and be properly dissipated. Therefore, it is essential that the surface of the block against which the gasket presses be clean and that the pressure of the shoulder of the spark plug against the gasket be sufficient to insure adequate flow of heat. Plugs should be tightened until the gasket is fairly well flattened. Apply 20 pound feet of torque to 14 mm plugs; for the 18 mm plugs with tapered seat used on Ford products use 15 to 20 pound feet of torque. The effect of length of heat path is illustrated in Fig. 22.13.

If a torque wrench is not available, draw the 14 mm plugs down until they are snug against the gasket and then give them a quarter turn. With 18 mm plugs, draw them down snug and then give them one-eighth turn. If 18 mm plugs are difficult to loosen, use a $\frac{1}{2}''$ drive nut spinner.

Before putting in any new plugs, first check the spark plug gap and adjust it (if necessary) to that specified by the car maker. The only way that the spark plug gap can be accurately checked is with a round wire gauge; do not try to use a flat feeler gauge as errors will be introduced. If it is necessary to reset the gap, bend the side electrode. Tools for this purpose are available and are frequently given away by the spark plug suppliers.

A very handy and useful tool which makes the adjustment of spark plug electrodes much quicker is a screwdriver which has one point ground off at a 45° angle with the hypotenuse of the triangle running from one corner of the screwdriver tip. To close the gap merely tap on the grounded electrode with the blade of the screwdriver. To open the gap, use the point on the end as a pry to force the electrode away from the shell. It is recommended that a new gasket be used every time a plug, whether new or used, is put in place.

The proper tightening of spark plugs is the most important item of their installation as 50% of the troubles caused by overheated spark plugs are due to the plugs being too loose in the cylinder heads. It is obvious that if a spark plug is not tightened sufficiently to properly compress the sealing gasket, there will not be adequate contact between the plug shell and the cylinder head. This will retard the flow of heat from the spark plug to the water jacket and may result in overheating the spark plug. It could further result in preignition, burning of the insulator and electrode, and possible leakage, with poor engine performance.

The installation of plugs in aluminum heads requires particular care as there is danger of stripping the soft thread in the cylinder head. Do not use graphite or any other lubricating compound on the thread as lubricant will retard the heat transfer by separating the metal of the threads. It will also make the plugs go in too easily which will result in too much torque being applied so that the threads may be stripped in the cylinder heads.

As far as possible, spark plugs should be installed in cast iron cylinder heads when the engine is at normal operating temperature.

Spark Plug Types

The *most common spark plug* is the 14 mm plug with a single side wire or grounded electrode. Most of the grounded electrodes are made of a flat wire though in some cases round wire is used. On a few plugs, the electrode is made of wire round on one side and flat on the side that is bent towards the center electrode or insulated electrode. The end of the side wire is usually carried well past the edge of the center electrode. This gets greater

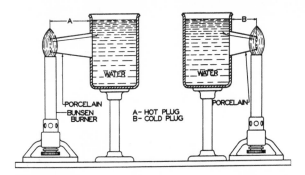

Fig. 22.13. It can readily be seen that less heat will be transferred to the water through the longer porcelain at *A* than through the shorter one at *B*. Therefore the tip at *A* will be hotter, corresponding to a hotter spark plug.

ionization effect from the lower edge at the end of the side wire, thus helping the plug burn clean.

A deviation from standard spark plug construction is exemplified in the *resistor spark plug*. This plug appears to be the same as the conventional plug and is made like it except for the introduction of a 10,000-ohm resistor in the plug in series with the insulated center electrode. Fig. 22.14 compares the two types. The built-in resistor makes a wider gap setting practical. According to the plug manufacturer, its use could result in improved gasoline economy because it permits burning of leaner mixtures and reduces misfiring. It also causes a smoother engine idle because its wider spark gap helps eliminate occasional missing. Electrode life is considerably increased. Because of the damping effect of the resistor on the oscillatory spark, there is less interference with radio, radar, and television reception. Resistor plugs provide suppression in the ignition system. Fig. 22.15 shows a resistor type spark plug.

In the construction of the resistor plugs, a four-piece center electrode is used. A bottom center section reaches up from the spark gap to approximately the middle of the shoulder section of the insulator. Next is the 10,000-ohm resistor unit which is a small cylinder fitting in the recess in the porcelain insulator. Above that is a spiral spring which contacts the upper section of the center electrode. This section also carries the tip at the upper end of the plug to which the cable is connected.

Resistor spark plugs sometimes fail by disintegration of the resistor which is in series with the center electrode. When this is the case the spark plug opens the secondary circuit to the cylinder in which it is located and the cylinder misses. Plugs in missing cylinders should be tested with an ohmmeter and if they show 15,000 ohms or more they should be discarded.

The so-called *"power tip" spark plugs* have a long ground electrode and ceramic insulator tip, and they project into the cylinder much further than the conventional plug. The idea

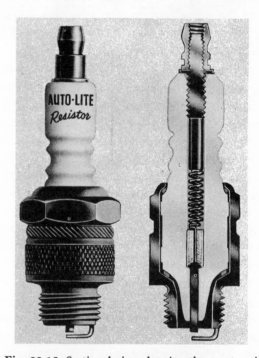

Fig. 22.15. Sectional view showing the construction of a typical resistor type spark plug. The small black cylinder just under the upper terminal is the resistor. Normal resistance will be about 10,000 ohms; any plug that tests more than 15,000 ohms should be discarded.

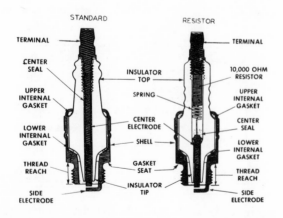

Fig. 22.14. Details of the standard spark plug and the resistor type. In the latter type, note the resistor which sometimes disintegrates causing the plug to misfire.

is that at low speeds the tip will get hot enough to burn off deposits that might form, while at high speeds the incoming sweep of the relatively cool unburned gases will keep the plugs cool enough for satisfactory operation under severe conditions. These plugs are designed for late model, overhead valve engines. Fig. 22.16 shows 14 mm and 18 mm plugs.

Spark Plug Polarity

It is very important that the polarity of the insulated electrodes be negative. In some cases, where the battery is put in backwards or the connections to the ignition coil have been reversed, the polarity may have become reversed, making the polarity of the high-tension circuit positive instead of negative. This requires 50% greater sparking voltage and often causes erratic engine performance. In all cases of ignition difficulty this should be checked.

To test the polarity, connect a voltmeter with *negative* lead in contact with the insulated terminal of the spark plug and the *positive* lead grounded. With the engine running, the meter should have small reading upscale.

Word of Caution

Years of widespread advertising have convinced the motoring public that spark plugs should be good for 10,000 miles. The earlier engines could use theirs for this amount and, in many cases, more. With the higher compression engines in general use at this time, however, mileage is no guide to spark plug life.

As a general guide, spark plugs should be used only as long as the engine is firing properly. As soon as it starts to miss, the plugs should be checked. The missing could come from other causes, but spark plugs are often guilty. There have been many cases where the plugs have not lasted more than a few thousand miles before missing started. Even though the plugs look just as good as new and even test out as "good," they often will not fire satisfactorily in an engine. Their replacement alone will stop the missing.

Summary

Control of *ignition timing* in proportion to engine speed is provided by centrifugally operated weights. Additional control in proportion to throttle opening is supplied by the vacuum advance.

Intake manifold vacuum varies inversely in proportion to throttle opening. Thus two independent means are employed to cause ignition timing advance to be most suitable for conditions of speed and load.

In 1948 Ford Motor Company introduced the *full-vacuum-control distributor* which was used on all Ford-built engines for several years. At this time it is used on most of the Ford six-cylinder engines. No automatic or mechanical advance is used in these distributors.

The *ignition advance* is obtained through moving the breaker plate by means of the vacuum advance device. The vacuum is the resultant of vacuum from the carburetor through specially drilled orifices and passages; it is proportional to both engine speed and load.

The *full-vacuum-control distributor* is similar to the conventional distributor except for the absence of the automatic advance device.

Fig. 22.16. Power tip spark plugs designed for high-compression engines. (Left) Autolite 14 mm. (Right) Champion, 18 mm. for use in Ford-built engines. The tapered seat makes a gas-tight joint without using a gasket. The 14 mm. is made with a flat seat for the gasket.

The distributor cam is tightly fixed to the distributor shaft. The movement of the breaker plate is restricted by two carefully calibrated springs, usually one heavy and one light.

Mechanical design of the full-vacuum-distributor is well worked out, with ample bearings. Do not over-lubricate as excessive oil can cause breaker point failure.

The *vacuum source at carburetor* must be accurately coordinated with distributor design to meet the ignition advance requirements.

The general motoring public has been sold on the idea that *spark plugs* should be changed every 10,000 miles. They also know that missing engines and poor performance can often be improved by changing plugs.

The *spark plug* is relatively simple, composed of a shell, ceramic insulator, gaskets and electrodes. The side wire or ground electrode is welded to the shell. The most common plug size is 14 mm thread, except on Ford-built engines which use 18 mm thread size. Most of the body hexes take 13/16″ wrench.

In *spark plug operation*, electricity at 4,000 to 20,000 volts pressure is trying to get from the center electrode to ground. Normally this causes a spark to jump across the electrodes.

The *spark plug insulator* is the only barrier between the center electrode and ground. A crack in the ceramic material or a conductive coating will cause the plug to misfire.

The *flame temperature* in the cylinders may get up to 4000°F. Higher compression pressure requires higher voltage to cause the spark to jump the gap.

Heat range refers to the relative ability of spark plugs to conduct heat away. Heat range depends on the length of the heat path from the insulator tip to the sealing gasket at the insulator shoulder, in contact with the cylinder block casting. In some cases different kinds of automobile use will require hotter or colder plugs. For butane-fuel engines, a colder plug must be used.

Insulator color indicates whether the plug is too hot or too cold. A clean light tan color shows correct heat range.

The *heat path* of the plug is through the gasket and block surface to get into the metal of the block and be dissipated into the engine coolant. Plugs should be properly tightened.

Before installing plugs, check spark gap with a round wire gauge, and adjust to specified size. Proper tightening of plugs is important.

Conventional spark plugs, 14 mm and 18 mm, and resistor types are used. For two-cycle outboard engines, the ground electrode only reaches the middle of the center insulated electrode.

Power-tip plugs have extended ground and center electrodes and ceramic insulator.

Spark plug polarity is very important. The insulated electrod must have negative polarity, regardless of primary circuit polarity or battery ground.

Questions

1. How is ignition advance in proportion to engine speed conventionally provided?
2. How is ignition advance in proportion to throttle opening conventionally provided?
3. Where is the full-vacuum-control distributor used?
4. How is the full-vacuum-control distributor different from the conventional type?
5. Is the distributor cam tight or allowed to rotate on the distributor shaft (vacuum type)?
6. How may action of the distributor be adjusted (vacuum type)?
7. How is the breaker plate moved to cause ignition spark advance?
8. Where is the source of the vacuum that operates the ignition advance?
9. Name the parts of the conventional spark plug.
10. How is the side wire or ground electrode attached to the shell?

11. What two sizes of spark plugs are now standard?
12. What two methods of sealing the plug in place in the engine are used?
13. What is meant by spark plug *heat range*?
14. What are two important functions of the ceramic spark plug core?
15. What kind of a plug would you recommend for a car that is habitually driven at high speeds on long trips?
16. How can you tell if plugs are of the correct heat range?
17. How do power tip plugs differ from conventional plugs?
18. What is the effect of using resistor spark plugs?
19. How do resistor plugs differ from conventional plugs?
20. What polarity should the insulated spark plug electrodes have?

CHAPTER TWENTY-THREE

Ignition System— Maintenance and Troubles

When the ignition system is not functioning satisfactorily, the usual trouble-shooting procedure is to eliminate a unit at a time until the cause of the trouble is located. After the difficulty is found, it is a simple matter to remedy the problem. If the diagnostician knows *what can happen* to the various members of the ignition system, it will make it easier for him to localize failure or causes of inefficiency.

It is often desirable to make a quick test to see if the ignition system will deliver a spark to the high-tension wire running from the center of the coil to the distributor. With the ignition turned on, pull the end of the wire out of the distributor cap and hold it about $3/16''$ from a good ground, such as the motor block. Then open and close the breaker points by hand. If a good spark is obtained each time the points are opened, it shows that the system is good, at least to the distributor cap and rotor. If no spark is obtained, then the ignition system must be checked to locate the cause of the trouble; it could·be in the breaker points, among other possible spots.

Ignition Wiring

The first place to look for trouble is in the wiring of the ignition system.

Using a dry, greaseless cloth clean all primary and secondary wiring between the coil, distributor, spark plugs and ignition switch. Remove the high-tension wires one at a time from the distributor cap and spark plugs. Check the terminals for looseness and corrosion. Inspect the wires closely for breaks and cracked insulation where they enter the conduit or clamp. Inspect for an oil-soaked condition and for a damaged surface on the insulation. Any of these insulation conditions may cause a partial or complete ground and result in a weak spark or no spark. Refer to Fig. 23.1 for further visual checks. Fig. 23.2 shows rotor checks.

To be sure that current is getting up to the battery side of the coil, use a test light with one side grounded. With the ignition turned on, touch the test light prod to the coil terminal. The light will light if current is getting to this point. To test the coil primary for continuity, touch the test light prod to the distributor side of the coil and open and close the breaker points by hand. The light should light when the points are open and remain unlit when the points are closed. If the lamp does not light, either the coil primary is open or the points are not making contact with each

INSPECT DISTRIBUTOR CAP FOR:

1. Coating of oil and dust.
2. Cracks and badly burned electrodes.
3. Positioning lug broken away.
4. Sticky or worn carbon brush.
5. Corroded spark plug wire contact socket.
6. Clogged vent hole where distributor cap has one.

Fig. 23.1.

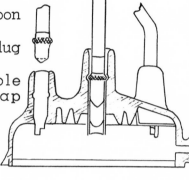

INSPECT HI-TENSION CABLES FOR:

1. -Cracks.
2. -Wear.
3. -Faulty insulation.
4. -Hardness and brittleness.
5. -Heavy coating of grease, oil and dust.

Inspect spark plug wire sockets for corrosion dirt, heavy coating of grease or oil.

other. A voltmeter also can be used.

For further checks, disconnect the primary wire from the distributor or distributor side of the coil, and connect an ammeter between the wire and the terminal. Turn on the ignition and have no other load on the battery. If necessary turn the engine slightly to close the distributor contact points. The ammeter should show a reading within the limits for that type of coil. If the ammeter reading is not correct, thoroughly inspect the primary wiring for loose terminals and breaks or grounds. Check from the battery to the starting switch, ignition switch, coil and the distributor. Check the voltage drop over each part of the circuit as out-

lined in Table 7. If the meter reading is higher than the maximum specified, repair or replace the defective wire or unit. Fig. 23.3 shows the basic trouble spots in an ignition circuit.

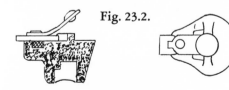

Fig. 23.2.

INSPECT ROTOR FOR:

1. —Corrosion.
2. —Cracks and broken positioning lug.
3. —Burned or pitted contact.
4. —Broken or bent contact spring.

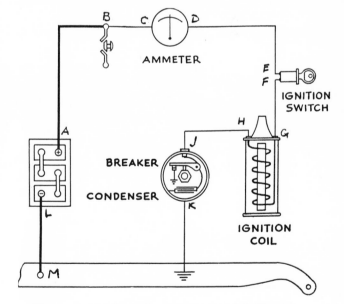

Fig. 23.3. The lettered connections on this diagram indicate spots that should be checked when trouble develops in the ignition system. Loose or corroded contacts are sometimes difficult to locate.

Where misfiring is experienced, one cause may be in the secondary spark plug cables. These cables to the spark plugs may have copper conductors or may be the high resistance TVRS type. The latter has a linen core impregnated with graphite and has a resistance of approximately 4000 ohms per foot of length (described in Chapter 20). The TVRS type is more fragile than the copper core type; and unless the TVRS cable is handled carefully when either end is disconnected, the linen core may be broken or the terminals loosened from the conductor core. In either case, the high-tension current may be interrupted.

To test the cables, an ohmmeter should be used. If the resistance is more than 16,000 ohms, the cable should be replaced. The conductor from the center of the ignition coil to the center of the distributor cap is also often made of the TVRS cable. If all the plugs appear to be missing, this cable could be responsible. In some cases, copper core wires have been substituted for the TVRS linen core conductors although this is not recommended. When this has happened, at least the coil-to-distributor conductor should be of the high resistance type in order to provide the minimum suppression needed to avoid radio and television interference.

Fig. 23.4 shows connections for checking with voltmeter.

Ballast Resistor

Most of the 12-volt ignition systems use a ballast resistor in the primary circuit and have a special circuit to bypass the ballast resistor while the cranking motor is working. Under some conditions the bypass circuit is not broken when the cranking motor circuit is broken, and this allows full battery voltage to flow in the primary ignition system, at all times. When this is the case, the primary system voltage will be higher than normal and will shorten the life of the distributor breaker points considerably. With the ballast resistor in the circuit, the breaker points closed, the engine not running, and the ignition current supplied by the battery, the voltage should be 9 to 10 volts. (See Chapter 20.)

If the wiring has been checked and is found to be satisfactory, then the next step is to check the ignition coil.

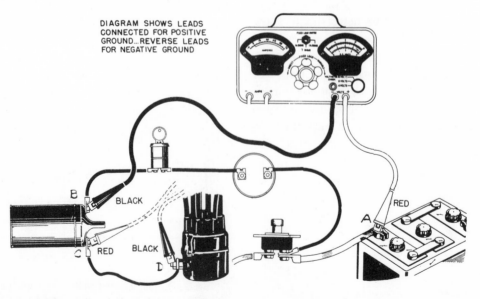

Fig. 23.4. Using the voltmeter to check voltage drop in the coil from the insulated battery terminal through the battery cable, ammeter, switch, and connections.

Table 7
Voltage Drops in Ignition Circuit

Circuit Unit Test	Allowable Voltage Drop
Battery ground terminal to distributor base	(0)
Battery ground terminal to car frame	(0)
Distributor base to car frame	(0)
Battery terminal to coil primary terminal (ign. sw. side) (through ign. switch)	(.25 volt max.)
Battery terminal to starting switch terminal	(0)
Starting switch terminal to ignition switch terminal	(.05 volt max.)
Ignition switch terminal to coil primary terminal (ign. sw. side) (6-volt systems)	(.1 volt max.)
Distributor base to coil primary terminal (distr. side) (through breaker points)	(.1 volt max.)
Coil primary terminal to distributor primary terminal	(.05 volt max.)
Distributor primary terminal to distributor base (through breaker points)	(.05 volt max.)

Ignition Coil

If the coil is not working it will be because (1) the primary winding is open, (2) the primary winding is grounded, (3) the secondary is open, shorted, grounded or its insulation is defective. In some cases, as previously mentioned, the high-tension terminal on the wire going to the tower of the coil is not pushed down all the way in the recess and the spark jumps inside the tower. This burns a ring in the metal sleeve of the coil tower above the top of the metal contact and causes the metal to corrode. This may result in a weak spark and should be kept in mind as a possible cause of trouble.

It is not practical to repair coils and therefore it is only necessary to know what may happen to the coil and how to determine if it is functioning properly. If it is definitely proven that the coil is defective, the only remedy is to replace it.

Ignition coils do not normally require any service except to keep all terminals clean and tight, and to keep the coil reasonably clean. Unless the coil is hermetically sealed, it should not be subjected to steam cleaning or other similar cleaning methods which may cause

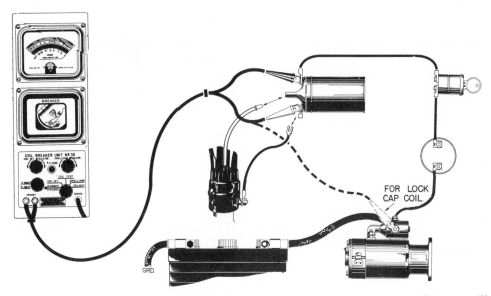

Fig. 23.5. Connections used for checking the ignition coil with the coil tester. This test will indicate defective coils which should be replaced.

moisture to enter. Rubber nipples on the high-voltage terminals are valuable in preventing leakage of current across exposed surfaces.

If the coil is suspected of being the cause of poor ignition performance, it may be tested with a coil tester either on or off of the car, as shown in Fig. 23.5. Where a coil tester is not available, temporarily replace the coil with one known to be good. Then if the engine apparently runs normally, the old coil is defective and should be replaced.

The testing of the coil and checking it for performance was described in Chapter 20. A quick check to see if the coil is worth further testing can be made with a lamp and test points. Refer to Fig. 23.6.

To be sure that current is getting to the coil, turn on the ignition, put the test light clamp on a good ground, and touch the prod to the

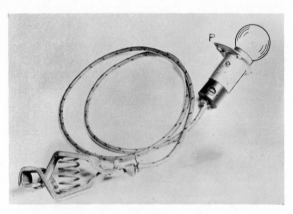

Fig. 23.6. A test light used to check such things as "hot" wires or current in the terminals. With the clip grounded, the lamp will light if the prod *(P)* touches a live contact.

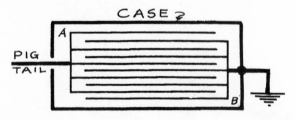

Fig. 23.7. Construction of a condenser. One side is connected to the case which is grounded, and the other side to the pigtail. Side *A* must be completely insulated from side *B*.

battery side of the coil. The lamp should light.

To test for an open primary coil, touch the prod to the distributor side of the coil (clamp grounded). The points should be in good condition. With the points open, the lamp will light if the primary winding is good; or, with the engine being turned over by the starter, the light will go on and off as the points open and close.

To check the secondary circuit, remove the wire from the center tower of the distributor and attach the clip of the test light to the end terminal. Touch the prod to either coil terminal, which puts the secondary winding in series with the lamp. The lamp will not light, but tiny sparks will be noted as the test prod is rubbed against the coil terminal, with good contact inside of the coil tower.

Most ignition coils can be tested for an internally grounded winding by placing one test point on a clean part of the metal container and touching the other point to the primary or high-tension terminals respectively. If the lamp lights or tiny sparks appear at the points of contact the windings are grounded and the coil should not be used.

It should be remembered that the primary circuit winding runs from one terminal of the coil to the other and this winding should be insulated from any of the external parts of the coil.

The Condenser

Several different things can cause a condenser to become inoperative: (1) it may be shorted or grounded internally, (2) there may be a break or "open" in its internal circuit, or (3) the insulation may be defective so that it will not hold a charge. Condensers cannot be repaired, so if defective in any way they must be replaced.

The condenser must be well grounded since one of the plates is connected to the case; the insulated lead must have a good tight connection. Fig. 23.7 is a condenser schematic.

For diagnostic purposes, a careful test of the condenser should be made with precision instruments. This test will give the microhms (resistance), the microfarads (capacity), and the megohms (insulation).

As a preliminary test, block the breaker points open with a small piece of dry cardboard or fiber between the rubbing block and cam. Place one test point on the distributor primary terminal and the other on the distributor base. If the lamp lights, the condenser is shorted and must be replaced. This test is made by running a test lead with a lamp in series from the hot side of the battery to the distributor primary contact, and grounding a lead. Refer to Fig. 23.8.

Inspect the condenser for broken lead or pigtail, frayed insulation, loose or corroded terminals.

Distributor

The distributor performs both electrical and mechanical functions and therefore will be subject to both kinds of trouble. In general, distributors will function with a high degree of accuracy for many thousands of miles. Proper servicing and care will promote freedom from trouble.

Mechanical Troubles

The mechanism of the distributor includes distributor shaft, automatic advance weights and springs, breaker cam, breaker contact arm with its rubbing block, stationary point, vacuum advance chamber and linkage, and movable breaker plate. Possible trouble spots in the distributor are shown in Fig. 23.9.

Use over a period of time will cause normal wear on the moving parts such as the distributor shaft bearing and the breaker cam on the distributor shaft. Looseness of the shaft in the bearing and wear on the breaker cam can cause varying cam angles and irregular operation of the breaker cam. The remedy is to rebush the distributor.

To check the wear of the distributor shaft in its bearing, mount a dial indicator on the base with its plunger resting against the shaft just above the cam. Apply a 5-pound pull to the shaft in line with the plunger of the dial indicator and read the instrument. If the side play exceeds .005″ the distributor should be overhauled and the bearing replaced.

A quick check on the automatic advance mechanism operation can be made. Turn the

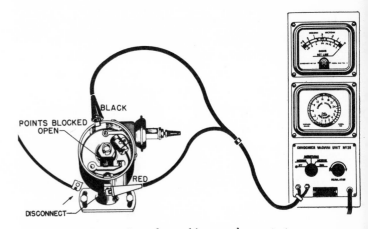

Fig. 23.8. Connections for making condenser test, with the breaker points blocked open at the rubbing block. The condenser is checked for continuity of current flow into the insulated side, for insulation between the two sides, and for capacity.

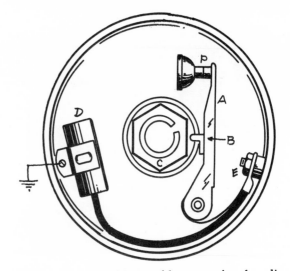

Fig. 23.9. Possible trouble spots in the distributor. *(A)* Breaker arm *(B)* rubbing block *(C)* cam *(D)* condenser *(E)* internal connection *(P)* breaker or contact points.

cam by moving the rotor in the direction of distributor rotation as far as it will go and releasing it. The cam should return to its original position with no drag or restriction. If the governor action is sluggish, the distributor should be overhauled. The automatic advance may be checked for free action as described in Fig. 23.10.

The mechanical operation of the vacuum advance can be checked in a similar manner. Move the breaker plate against the direction of distributor shaft rotation and release. The plate should return to its original position without drag or hesitation. If the action is not free, the vacuum advance mechanism should be checked. The breaker plate is supported by (1) center bushing or (2) center ball bearing.

Trouble in the distributor may result from either under-lubrication or over-lubrication. The moving parts of the distributor must have lubrication, but the several methods should be thoroughly understood and instructions should be carefully followed. On some distributors there is a spring-covered lubricating oil fitting which should get 5 to 8 drops of engine oil every time the car is lubricated. Other distributors use a grease cup. Certain distributors have

built-in shaft lubrication by means of oil impregnated bearings. In this case the shaft bushing is of a special porous material which extends from the upper to the lower part of the housing, spanning an oil reservoir. During initial assembly of the distributor this reservoir is filled with oil, the oil plug is installed and sealed with a sealing compound. During operation of the distributor the oil seeps through the bearing to provide lubrication. This arrangement makes frequent oiling unnecessary, the factory recommendation calling for a lubrication check every 50,000 miles. The newer distributors include a flexible coupling of synthetic rubber between the driving member at the extreme lower end of the coupling and the driven member. The flexible cushion absorbs the torsional vibration from the engine which might otherwise cause wear of the centrifugal advance mechanism in the distributor.

A trace of an approved type of cam and ball bearing lubricant should be placed on the breaker cam every 1,000 miles, except in distributors having cam lubricators which require attention only every 10,000 miles. If the lubricator felt becomes hard and stiff, add three to four drops of light engine oil (10W) to the center hole of the lubricator.

Great care should be used to avoid excessive lubrication. If too much oil is used, the excess is apt to get on the contact points, causing them to burn as shown in Fig. 23.11.

Breaker Arm and Rubbing Block

The rubbing block on the breaker arm is made of vulcanized fiber or a similar material and will wear down gradually. As it wears, the contact gap will get smaller, but this is often offset to some degree by wear and electrical erosion on the contact points. However, if the wear on the rubbing block is faster than on the points, the gap will change in size when the points are fully opened. The important point to keep in mind is that not only will the breaker gap be made smaller, but the ignition timing will also change.

Fig. 23.10. Checking automatic advance for freeness of operation by turning the breaker cam in direction of rotation. There should be no binding, and it should spring back when released.

Assuming that the rubbing block wears down somewhat more than the points, the breaker cam will have to turn through a greater angle before a cam lobe will contact the rubbing block and separate the contact points. In other words, the spark will occur later in the cycle and to compensate for this, retiming is needed from time to time. A change of 1° of dwell causes 1° change in ignition timing.

Breaker Contact Points and Breaker Cam

The correct action of the distributor can be affected by irregularities between cam lobes caused by wear, improper breaker arm spring tension, incorrect alignment of rubbing blocks and cams, or incorrect alignment of the contacts. Irregularity in the cam lobes can only be corrected by replacing the defective cam with a new one. An inspection of contact points should include areas mentioned in Fig. 23.12.

Breaker arm spring tension is extremely important. If the tension is too great, the breaker arm will bounce and cause interruption of the coil current and missing in the engine. If the spring tension is not sufficient, the rubbing block will not follow the cam, causing a variation in dwell or cam angle. The spring tension is measured by a special spring balance designed for this purpose.

One of the most prevalent causes of contact point failure is the presence of oil or lubricating compound on the contact surfaces. This is usually due to over-lubrication of the wick at the top of the cam for lubricating the shaft, or too much grease on the rubbing block which follows the breaker arm. Sometimes by capillary attraction, it reaches the contact surfaces. Refer again to Fig. 23.11.

If this condition is caught in time, the contacts can be cleaned with carbon tetrachloride on lintless tape drawn through the contact points. The residue left on the contact surfaces can be wiped off by drawing a clean dry piece of lintless tape between the contacts.

If the contacts show a crater or depression on one contact and a high spot of metal on the other contact, the cause is an electrolytic action which transfers metal from one contact to the other. Sometimes this is the result of unusual operation of the car. A slow-speed driver in city traffic or door-to-door delivery vehicles would be one extreme and high-speed, long-distance driving would be the other. This also may be caused by an unbalanced ignition system. This condition can sometimes be improved by a slight change in the condenser capacity. If the crater is on the positive contact, the condenser has too much capacity; and if the crater

INSPECT IGNITION CONTACT POINTS FOR:
1.—Misalignment.
2.—Coating of grease or oil.
3.—Pits in contact surfaces.
4.—Dirty or corroded contacts.
5.—Burned contact surfaces.

Fig. 23.11. Observing a streak of oil under the breaker points, as shown by the arrow. When points fail prematurely, suspect excess of oil which causes them to burn.

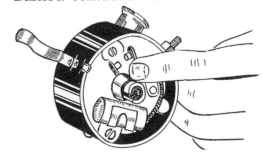

Fig. 23.12.

is on the negative contact, the condenser has too little capacity. A condenser can be selected from stock with a slightly higher or lower capacity as indicated by the condition of the contact.

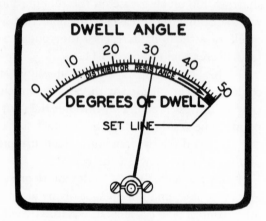

Fig. 23.13. Dial of cam angle or dwell angle meter. Dwell should be constant throughout speed range of engine. If not, the distributor must be carefully checked to detect the cause.

Fig. 23.14. Adjusting the breaker point gap. On the later model cars, it is adjusted by loosening the lock screw, turning the eccentric screw to get the correct setting, and tightening the lock screw. (Above) a six-cylinder distributor. (Below) an eight-cylinder distributor: *(1)* lock screw, *(2)* eccentric screw, *(A)* gap.

Under normal operating conditions distributor contact points will provide many thousands of miles of service. Points which have undergone several thousand miles of operation will have a rough surface, but this should not be understood to mean that they are worn out. If the surfaces, even though rough, match so that a large contact area is maintained, the points will continue to provide satisfactory service until most of the tungsten is worn off.

Burning and Pitting of Contact Points

Burned or pitted points will soon become unsatisfactory for further operation. Not only must they be replaced, but the ignition system and engine must be checked to determine the cause of the trouble, so that it can be eliminated. Unless the condition causing the point burning or pitting is corrected, the new points will soon be in the same condition.

Contact point burning will result from high voltage, the presence of oil or other foreign materials, a defective condenser, or improper point adjustment. High voltage, which causes an excessively high current flow through the contact points, can result from an improperly adjusted or inoperative voltage regulator.

Oil or crankcase vapors which work up into the distributor and deposit on the point surfaces will cause them to burn rapidly. This is easy to detect since the oil produces a smudgy line under the contact points. This line will be somewhat parallel to the line of the breaker arm. Clogged engine breather pipes permit crankcase pressure which will force oil or oil vapors up into the distributor. Overoiling the distributor will also produce this condition.

If the contact point opening is too small (that is, with too large a cam angle), the points will be closed an excessive part of the operating time. The average current flow through the points may be so high that they will burn rapidly. Refer to Figs. 23.13 and 23.14 for methods of checking and adjusting point gap.

Some dwell meters can be used to check contact point resistance, as shown in Fig. 23.15.

High series resistance in the condenser will prevent normal condenser action so that the contact points will burn quickly. This resistance may be caused by loose condenser mountings or connections, or by poor connections inside the condenser. A special condenser tester is required to detect excessive resistance. Other checks to which the condenser should be submitted include breakdown, low insulation resistance, and capacity.

Pitting of the contact points results from an out-of-balance condition in the ignition system, which causes a transfer of tungsten from one point to the other, so that a tip is built up on one point while a pit forms in the other. The direction of tungsten transfer can be used as a basis of analysis. For instance, if the material transfers from the negative to the positive point one or more of these corrections may be made: increase condenser capacity; shorten condenser lead; separate distributor-to-coil low- and high-tension leads; move these leads closer to ground (*i.e.*, engine block, frame, or panel).

If the material transfers from the positive to the negative point, reduce condenser capacity, lengthen the condenser leads, move the distributor-to-coil leads closer together, or move these leads away from ground.

Understanding the causes of excessive wear or deterioration of contact points is important. If the cause is not corrected, even though new points are installed, the same thing will happen again.

Contact Point Installation

When contact points are installed the breaker arm should be free on the hinge pin, the contacts properly aligned with the outside diameters registering perfectly, and contact made approximately in the center of the contact surfaces. This is done by bending the stationary contact. Never bend the breaker arm between the rubbing block and the contact.

The rubbing block which bears against the cam is burnished when it is manufactured. It should never be filed or sandpapered as this destroys the hard polished surface and will cause excessive wear.

Some distributors have two sets of contacts and these must be synchronized in accordance with specifications in the service manual. As an example, for a distributor with a four-lobe cam installed on an eight-cylinder engine, two ignition coils are used, one connected to each set of contacts. One coil and one set of contacts operate four of the eight cylinders, and the other coil and set of contacts operate the other four cylinders. If the 360° in one complete revolution of the distributor is divided by eight cylinders, the quotient will be 45° for each cylinder; therefore the contacts for each cylinder must be adjusted so they break exactly 45° apart. Synchronizing the points on this

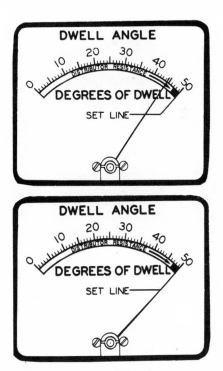

Fig. 23.15. Some makes of dwell meters can be used to check distributor contact point resistance. The reading in the "black band" indicates low resistance, which generally means satisfactory points unless an inspection shows a need for replacement.

type of distributor must be done on a precision machine. A well known tester is shown in Fig. 23.16.

Some distributors have two breaker arms, but with eight lobes on the breaker cam. One of these breaker arms is used to make the contact and the other is used to break it. That is, one distributor arm is so located that it will open slightly ahead of the other. The one that opens last will break the circuit, and then the one that opens first will close first, completing the circuit. The other arm when it closes has no effect on current flow. This arrangement makes possible a slightly bigger cam angle than would otherwise be obtained.

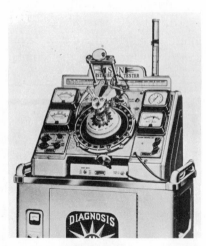

Fig. 23.16. A distributorscope or distributor tester will show definitely and quickly the condition of a distributor, as well as the performance of the automatic and vacuum spark advance devices. The distributor is removed from the engine and put on the instrument for testing.

When trouble is experienced in the ignition system it can be detected most exactly with the distributorscope or distributor tester. The distributor must be removed from the car and operated in the tester under conditions equivalent to operation in the automobile. The operation of the automatic advance mechanism as well as the vacuum advance mechanism (the two timing control devices) can be checked separately. The cam angle or dwell angle can be checked by a meter which is part of the tester equipment.

Some general quick ignition checks are explained in Fig. 23.17.

Spark Plug Troubles

Spark plugs, as other units in the ignition system, are subject to failure. It is important that the cause of failure be determined and corrected to avoid repetition of the trouble.

A large percentage of the troubles due to overheated spark plugs is caused by plugs being too loose in the cylinder head. Spark plugs pick up a considerable amount of heat as they are used in a running engine. As long as this heat can be dissipated by good contact to the cylinder block or head casting, they will maintain a normal operating temperature. However, if there is resistance in the heat path, or heat flow is restricted due to poor contact, the plugs will become overheated. This will eventually damage them and will cause unsatisfactory engine operation due to pre-ignition.

Spark plug electrodes will wear over a period of use. Also, most present-day fuels have a

QUICK IGNITION CHECKS

I. ENGINE WILL NOT RUN		II. ENGINE RUNS, BUT NOT SATISFACTORILY
A. Spark Occurs Primary and Secondary Okay	B. No Spark	If due to Ignition:
	1. Ammeter Fluctuates	A. Overheating
Check:	A. Primary Okay	1. Out of Time
1. Plugs	B. Check Secondary	B. Detonation
2. Timing	2. No Reading	1. Fuel
3. Valves	A. Primary open	2. Out of Time
4. Carburetion	B. Points not closing	3. Plugs
5. Other Engine Components	3. Steady Reading	4. Distributor
	A. Primary Grounded	C. Missing--Hard starting
	B. Points not opening	Complete engine Tune-Up

Fig. 23.17.

tendency to form a brown oxide deposit on the insulator firing tip and, to a certain extent, on the grounded electrodes. Refer to Fig. 23.18. Therefore it is advisable to clean the plugs occasionally with a suitable spark plug cleaner, as shown in Fig. 23.19. Fig. 23.20 illustrates plugs that have been properly and improperly cleaned.

It is also necessary to resize the gaps to that specified by the car manufacturer. For passenger cars the plugs should be regapped at intervals of from 4000 to 5000 miles of operation. Heavy-duty service, such as in certain types of commercial vehicles, may make it necessary to clean and regap the plugs at more frequent intervals. Spark plugs should be replaced when the electrodes are worn to an extent where it is impossible to readjust them to the recommended gaps and still maintain a reasonably square alignment between the electrodes. Fig. 23.21 shows how to measure spark plug gap.

Fig. 23.18. (Left) A dirty top insulator such as this can cause poor ignition performance. Insulators must be kept clean. (Right) Lead fouling, causing a heavy, hard, glazed coating on the insulator, will make an engine miss at high speeds or under heavy loads.

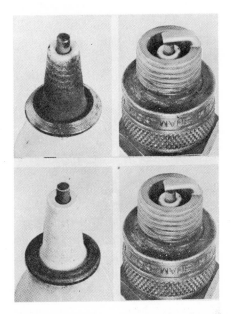

Fig. 23.20. (Upper) Improperly cleaned plug. (Lower) Correctly cleaned plug. It is necessary to completely remove carbon and glaze from the insulator to get satisfactory results.

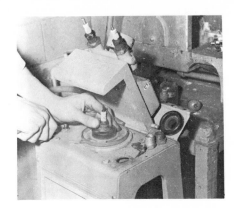

Fig. 23.19. A good spark plug cleaner will do a thorough job of removing all carbon and glaze from the insulator.

Fig. 23.21. Always use a wire gauge to correctly measure spark plug gap on worn plugs, never a flat one.

Spark plug troubles are generally caused by: (1) wrong application, *i.e.*, using a plug that is too hot or too cold, (2) improper installation, which may lead to damage to the plug, (3) normal wear due to long periods of use, and (4) trouble in the engine, the ignition system, or the fuel system.

A knowledge of what to look for and the meaning of the indications as shown by the plugs will make it easy to diagnose the trouble and determine whether the failure is due to the spark plugs or the conditions of operation. In the following paragraphs the most common causes of spark plug failure, indications, and remedies will be given.

Broken Insulator Top

A cracked or shattered insulator top is caused by careless handling of the plug or improper installation. See Fig. 23.22. Accidental striking of the plug with a wrench or using a socket wrench that fits loosely will damage the porcelain. Spark plugs should always be installed with a properly fitting deep socket, and it is also recommended that a 3/8″ drive with a ratchet handle be used. The latter will get inside the places where there is not much room

Fig. 23.22. Broken lower insulator. When the center wire is worn pointed and the ground electrode is like new, the plug has been operating too hot, causing split insulator lips. This also could be caused by improper tightening.

to manipulate the wrench and at the same time will give sufficient torque to draw the plug up properly. The most desirable method of installing spark plugs is to use the torque wrench, drawing 14 mm plugs in cast iron heads up to 20 pounds feet. If the engine has an aluminum head, reduce the torque to 15 pound feet.

Split Insulator Nose

If the insulator firing tip shows a clean split after a short period of operation, the cause is almost always due to bending or straining the center electrode while resetting the gap. A plug damaged in this way must be replaced.

Side Electrode Excessively Worn

The insulator firing tip may be a light gray color and possibly show indications of swelling and even blistering. This will be caused by a plug that is too hot, *i.e.*, has too high a heat range. A colder plug should be used. On some makes of plugs the side electrode and sometimes the center electrode will show excessive wear while the insulator tip shows no signs of undue heat. When this is the case, the excessively worn electrode may be due to the use of a high output coil, resulting in an excessive amount of current passing through the spark plugs. If a coil on the car is other than the original equipment or equivalent replacement, it might be well to change it to the one specified by the manufacturer of the car. Refer to Fig. 23.23.

Plugs Badly Burned

An insulator firing tip may be swollen, blistered, fused or broken, and both the center electrode and the side electrode may be excessively worn. These are definite signs of overheating and disintegration. In this case the plug is too hot for the engine or it may have been improperly installed. Examine the plug gasket to see if it is clean and fully compressed. The presence of wrench marks on the hex or top of the shell would indicate the use of improper wrenches. The remedy is to use a colder plug and follow the recommended procedure for installation.

There are several other reasons for badly burned plugs. One reason is an excessively overheated exhaust valve causing pre-ignition and abnormal temperatures in the combustion chamber. This may be due to insufficient tappet clearance, valve sticking in the guide, warped valves or those not seating properly, lean mixture or retarded spark. The remedy in this case is reconditioning the engine, if necessary, or replacement of the exhaust valves. If the valve is defective, a compression check will indicate this very quickly. Proper adjustment of the tappet clearance, if this is not correct, will also help.

Excessive spark advance resulting in heavy detonation and overheating of the spark plugs to the point of pre-ignition can also cause badly burned plugs. This would be the fault of engine conditions, and can be corrected by timing the engine in accordance with the manufacturer's specifications. Whenever this condition is observed it is advisable to check the spark timing and, if necessary, recondition the spark advance mechanism in the distributor.

Carbon in the combustion chamber forming incandescent spots might also lead to pre-ignition and burned plugs. When this condition exists, the carbon should be removed, and the fuel used and the functioning of the carburetor should be investigated. Refer to Fig. 23.24.

Badly burned spark plugs may also be caused by inadequate cooling of the plug due to: insufficient water in the cooling system of the engine, clogged up radiator, improperly operating fan or water pump, sticking thermostat, or obstructions in the water jacket. In winter, a lack of anti-freeze might cause the water in the engine block to freeze, resulting in an overheated engine and burned plugs. In these cases where the cooling system is not functioning properly, it is necessary to clean it or put on a new radiator, thoroughly clean the water jacket and so on, to remedy the condition.

Blow-By

Blow-by between the plug body and the insulator top is usually made evident by the presence of gray-black streaks on the insulator top just above the shell. In most cases, plugs which show signs of blow-by are also badly burned. This may be due to abnormally high temperatures, careless handling, or the use of improper wrenches resulting in damage to the plug. Occasionally a defective plug may get through the manufacturer's inspection department. Where blow-by is observed, the tip of the plug and the electrode should also be carefully examined, as probably the condition which causes the blow-by will also cause these

Fig. 23.23. (Left) Rapid gap wear at low mileage is caused by too hot plugs. Check for correct heat range, improper installation, faulty fuel mixture. (Right) Gas fouling will cause soft, fluffy, dry, black carbon deposits. Check the carburetor operation.

Fig. 23.24. (Left) Excessive amounts of oil getting into the cylinders will foul the plugs with wet, black deposits, preventing their firing. (Right) Oil in the cylinders in smaller amounts will bake onto the insulator as a hard carbon deposit, causing the plugs to miss.

parts to show evidence of excessive over-heating. The remedy in cases like this will be to replace the plug and properly install it, using the correct tools.

Oxidized Conducting Deposits

After prolonged operation at high speeds or under heavy load, the plugs will frequently have a coating on the insulator firing tip. This may in time interfere with the proper performance of spark plugs. In some cases the oxide will form a glaze over the end of the porcelain; this glaze has a good insulating value when cold but will conduct electricity if it is hot. Therefore, plugs which test out when cold on a plug testing machine still may fail when in service under heavy loads. When this condition exists the plugs should be cleaned, and if they then function satisfactorily they can be used for another four or five thousand miles ordinarily. If the engine performance still is not satisfactory, the plugs should be removed and new ones installed.

Carbon Deposits

The presence of a black coating on the insulator firing tip or of carbon accumulation between the insulator nose and shell indicates the plug is partially or completely fouled. Cleaning the plug will provide a temporary remedy. However, to maintain consistently good performance the trouble should be cured at its source. The cause of the carbon deposits is the use of either a plug that is too cold or a fuel mixture that is too rich. In some cases the engine is pumping oil due to worn cylinder bores, defective piston rings, or the use of an oil that is too thin for the type of driving.

A hotter plug will frequently remedy the condition. If the trouble persists when using plugs as hot as can be used successfully in the engine, then the engine must be reconditioned to overcome the oil pumping condition. It is a good idea to check to see that the air cleaner is not clogged; if the normal amount of air cannot come through the cleaner, an additional vacuum will occur in the cylinders that may result in an excessive amount of oil being drawn up into the combustion chambers. This condition also will help to foul the plugs.

It is frequently difficult to determine from the appearance of the plugs whether the trouble is due to an over-rich mixture, too cold plugs, or oil pumping. In such cases a compression check should be made on all cylinders of the engine. If the compression is uniformly good, an over-rich mixture or too cold a plug may be the cause. Otherwise, oil pumping is the source of the carbon deposits. In some cases the insulator firing tip presents a clean appearance, but carbon accumulations are formed on the inside of the shell. This indicates that the engine is either pumping oil or operating on an over-rich mixture, but the plug is sufficiently hot to burn the carbon deposits off the insulator firing *tip*.

In some cases the insulator tip is covered with a soft layer of carbon or soot. This may be the result of operating the engine for a long period at idle or very light load, and does not necessarily indicate a bad engine condition. Opening the throttle for a few minutes usually burns off the soot thus restoring the plug to its original condition.

Additional Troubles

Frequently the vehicle owner complains about poor performance of his spark plugs while the condition of the plugs does not indicate any trouble. In such cases even though the plugs may be blamed, they are often not at fault. The most common of these complaints are: (1) pinging, (2) poor idling, and (3) missing or sluggish performance. Excessive spark advance or the use of a fuel having a knock rating too low for the engine may cause pinging due to detonation. In most cases this type of pinging occurs while accelerating or climbing a hill at low speed, and frequently will disappear at speeds over 25 to 40 miles per hour. Spark plugs are not at all responsible for this condition.

Missing and sluggish performance may be due to a multitude of causes; the most important ones are: improperly adjusted spark plug gaps, improper adjustment or poor condition of distributor breaker points, poor connections or defective parts any place in the ignition system, retarded spark, lean mixture, and improperly seated or sticking valves.

When missing occurs on low speed acceleration it is often due to a defective accelerator pump in the carburetor. High speed missing is frequently caused by improper operation of the carburetor power jet. These will be discussed in Chapter 24, *Fuel System.* Any of the engine failures mentioned earlier under "Spark Plug Troubles" may cause pre-ignition at high speed, resulting in reduced top speed, sluggishness and irregular firing. This may or may not be accompanied by pinging, depending upon the engine characteristics.

Satisfactory idling can seldom be obtained unless the engine is in first-class condition. Proper seating of the valves is one of the most important factors in satisfactory idling. It is also necessary that each unit of the ignition system be in excellent condition to insure a good spark under low speed operation. There is only a small amount of gas in the cylinder when the engine is idling, and this amount will not be ignited quite as readily as a richer and larger quantity of the air-fuel mixture in the cylinder. When installing a new set of spark plugs it is sometimes necessary to readjust the idling speed and the idling mixture of the carburetor.

The information given under "Spark Plug Troubles" is not intended and cannot cover all of the engine troubles for which spark plugs may receive the blame. The only sure way to be positive that the engine is in first-class condition, resulting in the opportunity for good spark plug performance, is to make a complete analysis of the engine using the standard diagnostic procedure.

From the discussion in this section it can be seen that spark plugs deserve a considerable amount of attention. When their condition is questionable, they are often replaced without inspection and correction of the operating conditions which caused the plug failure. If the primary object is to sell spark plugs, this is a good way to make the additional sale. However, if the object is to make the customer's car run in the best possible manner and to keep the cost of his servicing as low as possible, the plugs should be inspected, analyzed, cleaned and gapped if they are reusable. When replacement is necessary, the cause of the trouble should be determined to prevent further occurrence.

High-grade spark plugs are supposed to give a minimum of 10,000 miles and may give thousands of miles of service over this amount, but do not count on it. Plugs often have to be replaced after only a few thousand miles. Cheap plugs, bought on the basis of price alone, may fail at any time after the first five miles of operation.

Resistor Plug Troubles

Resistor spark plugs have a 10,000-ohm resistor in series with the terminal and insulated electrode. Under some conditions this resistor will disintegrate into powder. When this happens, a third spark gap is introduced into the high-tension ignition circuit which is usually large enough to open the circuit and cause the plug to misfire.

When a plug of the resistor type appears to be misfiring, it should be tested with an ohmmeter. If it shows a resistance of over 15,000 ohms it should be replaced. Resistor plugs usually have a gap about 0.004" larger than the standard type.

Summary

A knowledge of *common problems* of the ignition system will make it easier to localize failure or causes of inefficiency.

The first place to look for trouble is in the *wiring of the ignition system.* Be sure current is getting to the battery side of the coil. A test light is a good way to check this although a voltmeter may be used.

An *ammeter* in the ignition circuit will show current flow. A *voltmeter* will give the voltage drop in the circuit.

The *secondary cables* may be either copper conductors or the higher resistance TVRS type. Use an ohmmeter to test the cables for circuit continuity.

A *ballast resistor* is in most of the 12-volt ignition circuits and may have a bypass circuit that is closed while the cranking motor is in operation.

The *ignition coil* may not be working because of (1) open primary winding, (2) grounded primary, (3) open, shorted or grounded secondary winding. In some cases one or more of the *coil tower contacts* may be burned or corroded. A coil cannot be repaired but must be replaced if defective. The primary may be checked for continuity with a test light. Replace all coils that do not work satisfactorily.

The *distributor* performs both electrical and mechanical functions. Proper servicing and care will promote freedom from trouble.

Mechanical troubles may appear in bearings, automatic advance, breaker contact arm, or vacuum advance. The automatic advance and vacuum advance can be checked for mechanical action by moving by hand. A trace of approved lubricant should be applied to the distributor cam.

The *breaker arm and rubbing block* may wear and change the point gap and dwell. A 1° change in dwell will cause a 1° change in ignition timing.

The *breaker plate* rotates on a center bearing. It carries the stationary breaker point and breaker arm on its pivot. A ground pigtail from plate to distributor housing gives definite ground for the ignition system. There must be good connections from the condenser and primary lead from coil to breaker points.

In checking the *breaker contact points and breaker cam,* breaker arm spring tension is important. Points must be properly aligned.

One common cause of *point failure* is over-lubrication or use of the wrong kind of lubricant. Transfer of metal between points or pitted points is due to wrong condenser capacity. Burned or pitted points must be replaced. Be sure when new points are installed that the breaker arm works freely and points are accurately aligned. The best way to test a distributor is on a distributor tester.

Spark plug troubles and failure may be due to loose plugs, wrong heat range, wrong adjustment, carbon build-up, broken insulator, burned plugs, or leakage. When plugs fail, check the cause to avoid its repetition.

Resistor plugs are used in some 12-volt systems. In some cases the resistor will disintegrate and cause misfiring. In this case, check the plug with an ohmmeter. Resistance should not exceed 15,000 ohms.

Questions

1. What is a quick test of the high-tension circuit?
2. Where is the first place to look for trouble in the ignition system?
3. How can you check to see if current is getting to the battery side of the coil?
4. What are the two kinds of conductors that are used from distributor to plugs?
5. What instrument is recommended for testing the secondary cables?
6. What is the effect of the ballast resistor in the ignition system?
7. How would you check the bypass circuit?
8. Name four possible distributor cap defects.
9. Name three possible coil defects.
10. If an ignition coil is suspected of being defective what would you do?
11. How would you test a coil primary winding for open circuit?
12. Name three possible condenser defects.

13. Name five important parts of the distributor.
14. How can you make a quick check of the automatic advance device?
15. How can you make a quick check of the vacuum advance device?
16. Name three possible defects of the distributor.
17. What effect, if any, will too much lubricant have on the breaker points?
18. What effect, if any, will a change of 2° in cam angle or dwell have on ignition timing?
19. What are the effects of too much and too little breaker arm spring tension?
20. What important adjustment must be accurately made when new distributor points are installed?
21. Where there are two sets of breaker arms and points with an eight lobe cam, what are the functions of each breaker arm?
22. What is the best way to check and adjust a distributor?
23. What is meant by spark plug *heat range?*
24. Name three causes of plug trouble.
25. How can you tell if a plug is of the right heat range after being used a while?
26. What is the effect when plugs are not properly tightened in place?
27. Describe the appearance of a burned or overheated plug.
28. What would be the effect of a cracked ceramic insulator?
29. What would be the effect of a conductive coating on the insulator tip?
30. What sometimes happens to resistor plugs?

SECTION VII

Fuel
System
and
Carburetion

CHAPTER TWENTY-FOUR

Fuel System

There are three main engine requirements, as emphasized in Fig. 24.1: (1) compression, (2) ignition, and (3) carburetion. Carburetion is probably the least understood; yet it is extremely important since an engine cannot possibly perform the way it should unless the fuel system is functioning efficiently.

The fuel system consists of the fuel pump, air cleaner, carburetor, automatic choke, manifold heat valve or heat riser valve, fuel tank and connecting tubing. The intake manifold, which is actually part of the engine, is part of the induction system and indirectly may be considered part of the fuel system. The fuel gauge may also be included in the fuel system, but this will be covered in the chapter on dash instruments. Fig. 24.2 shows the fuel system as an

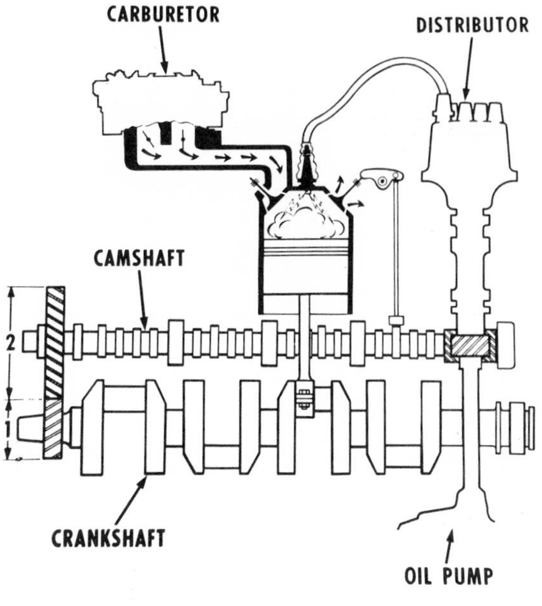

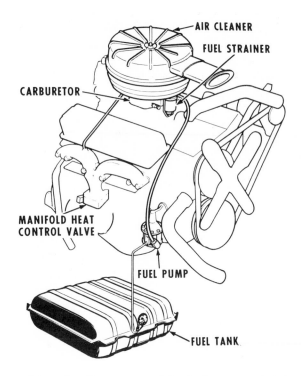

Fig. 24.1. Relation of the carburetor to the other two engine requirements, compression and ignition.

Fig. 24.2. Components of the fuel system and their relation to each other.

assembly. The air cleaner and heat control valve will be considered in Chapter 26.

Continuing the general plan that has been followed in preceding chapters the following discussion will be centered around the "anatomy" of the fuel system, analyzing each of the various components in its normal operating condition. Thus the diagnostician will be familiar with the design and construction of each unit so that he can quickly recognize trouble and prescribe its remedy.

Fuel Pumps

Both mechanical and electrical fuel pumps are used for automotive fuel systems. The mechanical pump is most commonly used, but the electrical pump should be familiar to the diagnostician since in some cases he may need to recommend its installation, or he may be required to service cars that are equipped with it.

The purpose of the fuel pump is to draw fuel from the fuel tank and elevate it under pressure to the carburetor. An ample amount of fuel must be supplied to the carburetor, under all conditions of engine speed and load, to enable the engine to deliver the required power.

Single Mechanical Fuel Pumps

This refers to the pump which handles nothing but fuel as distinguished from the combination fuel and vacuum pump.

The single pump consists of a die-cast housing which contains or supports a gasoline strainer, a specially treated fabric diaphragm, a pull rod, springs, inlet and discharge valves and an actuating arm.

The action of the pump is simple. The actuating arm is moved by rotation of a cam on the engine camshaft. This causes the diaphragm to be pulled downward, drawing in liquid fuel from the fuel tank because the discharge valve is closed and the inlet valve is open. Fig. 24.3 shows the working parts of a fuel pump.

Between power suction strokes the pressure spring exerts pressure on the diaphragm, which in turn builds up liquid pressure from 2.5 to 5 pounds per square inch, depending upon the particular pump model. The liquid fuel under pressure flows through connecting tubing to the carburetor float chamber at a rate which closely follows engine fuel requirements. The carburetor float needle valve restricts the fuel flow to the amount needed to maintain the desired fuel level in the float chamber.

It should be remembered that fuel pump pressure is governed entirely by the pressure spring and cannot exceed this pressure except under a few abnormal conditions which will be discussed later. The power stroke is always the suction stroke, drawing fuel into the pump while the fuel discharge results from spring pressure on the diaphragm. The load on the

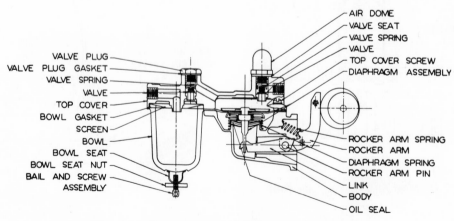

Fig. 24.3. Common type of fuel pump in general use.

fuel pump is determined by figuring the static head (vertical distance from the level in the fuel tank to the level in the carburetor float chamber) plus the fluid friction caused by the fuel flowing through the tubing from the tank to the carburetor.

The proportion of the total lift that is done on the suction stroke and on the discharge stroke will depend upon the location of the fuel pump on the various engine models and upon the fuel level in the tank. The latter will vary approximately 6 inches, from full to empty. A widely used fuel pump is shown in Fig. 24.4. A disassembled fuel pump is shown in Fig. 24.5, and a Carter pump is shown in Fig. 24.6.

A fuel pump is operating correctly when its pressure is within the specifications and the capacity is equal to the engine fuel requirements at all loads and speeds. The pressure and capacity are checked by two tests while the pump is mounted on the engine. These tests are known as *static pressure* and *capacity bleed*. Pressure which is within the specified minimum and maximum indicates that the working parts

of the pump are in good condition. (For the particular method of making these tests refer to Chapter 26.)

The fuel delivery of the fuel pump is measured by the time required to discharge ¾ pint to 1 pint. The amount of delivery is adequate when this volume is discharged: in one minute for engines under 225 cubic inches displacement; in 45 seconds for engines of 225 to 400 cubic inches; in 30 seconds for engines over 400 cubic inches displacement.

Combination Fuel and Vacuum Pump

The fuel section of a combination pump operates as a single fuel pump does. The vacuum section of the pump acts as a booster to the intake manifold vacuum to provide for uniform operation of the windshield wiper even though the throttle may be open enough to cause a drop in the normal intake manifold

Fig. 24.5. Fuel pump with top removed, showing diaphragm, sediment bowl seat, and inlet and discharge holes.

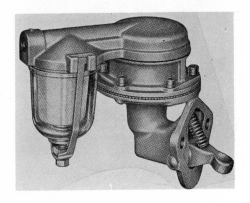

Fig. 24.6. Carter mechanical fuel pump.

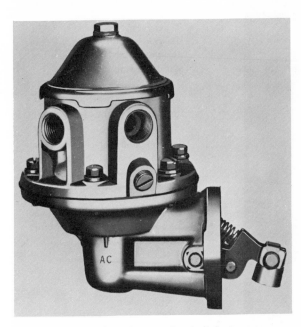

Fig. 24.4. Single-action mechanical fuel pump.

vacuum. A single fuel pump and a combination pump are shown in Fig. 24.7.

Both sections of the combination pump are actuated by a single rocker arm. Details of construction of the various series numbers and makes differ, but functionally all are the same.

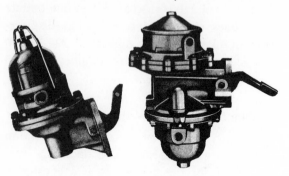

Fig. 24.7. (Left) AC single-action fuel pump. (Right) AC double-action combination fuel pump and vacuum pump.

In the operation of the vacuum section, power is applied to the rocker arm by an eccentric cam on the camshaft. Rocker arm movement to the link and rod pushes the diaphragm into the air chamber against a spring pressure of from 80 to 150 pounds. Pressure, created by the diaphragm movement, expels air through the outlet port into the intake manifold. The return stroke releases the compressed diaphragm spring, creating a vacuum and drawing air through the inlet valve from the windshield wiper. This maintains a vacuum on the windshield wiper so that it operates at practically a constant speed regardless of throttle opening. Refer to Fig. 24.8.

Some cars are equipped with electric windshield wipers making the combination pump unnecessary to obtain uniform wiper action.

HOW THE VACUUM SECTION OPERATES

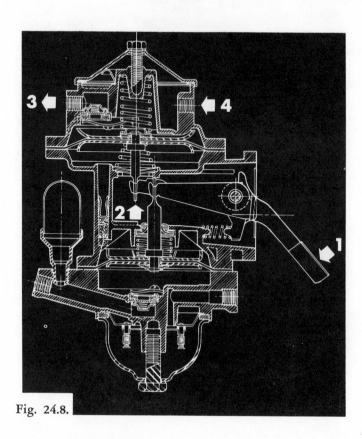

Fig. 24.8.

1 Power is applied to the rocker arm by an eccentric on the camshaft.

2 Rocker arm movement through the link and rod pushes the diaphragm up into the air chamber against spring pressure.

3 Pressure created by the diaphragm movement expels air through outlet port to manifold

4 The return stroke starting at the high point of cam releases the compressed diaphragm spring, creating a vacuum which draws air through the inlet valve from the windshield wiper. The diaphragm operates only when engine vacuum is insufficient for wiper action.

Electric Fuel Pumps

There are four electric fuel pumps available: the Autopulse, the Bendix, the Stewart-Warner and the Carter. All can be supplied to operate on either 6 or 12 volts.

The Autopulse (Fig. 24.9) operates by means of a magnet which pulls an armature through its metal core. The armature in turn moves one end of a metal bellows, drawing in liquid fuel through a built-in strainer. As the armature moves it breaks the magnetic circuit, and a spring on the end of the bellows applies pressure to the gasoline causing it to flow to the carburetor float chamber in proportion to fuel requirements. The stroke is only 3/64″, but the number of strokes is sufficient to apply the engine's fuel requirements up to about 6 gallons per hour.

The Stewart-Warner electric fuel pump works on the same general principle, but the magnet armature moves a pump diaphragm instead of a metal bellows. The capacity of a single pump is 15 gallons per hour. Multiple units can be used when more fuel is needed. See Fig. 24.10.

The Bendix electric fuel pump (Fig. 24.11, Left) is more compact than either of the others mentioned. The energized magnet actuates a hollow plunger. The stroke of the plunger is controlled by both a set of interrupter points in the electrical circuit and a calibrated plunger spring. The interrupter system is sealed in helium gas, and consequently field service is impractical. If any of the electrical components become inoperative the complete pump should be replaced.

The Carter electric pusher pump (Fig. 24.11, Right) is a motor-driven centrifugal pump without valves. It is located inside and at the bottom of the fuel tank. Fuel flows through the pump providing cooling and lubrication.

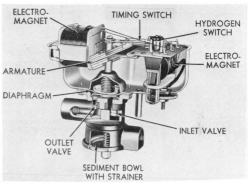

Fig. 24.10. Stewart-Warner electric fuel pump.

Fig. 24.9. Autopulse electric fuel pump.

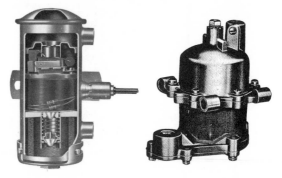

Fig. 24.11. (Left) Bendix electric fuel pump. (Right) Carter electric pusher fuel pump for mounting inside the fuel tank.

HOW THE CIRCUITS WORK

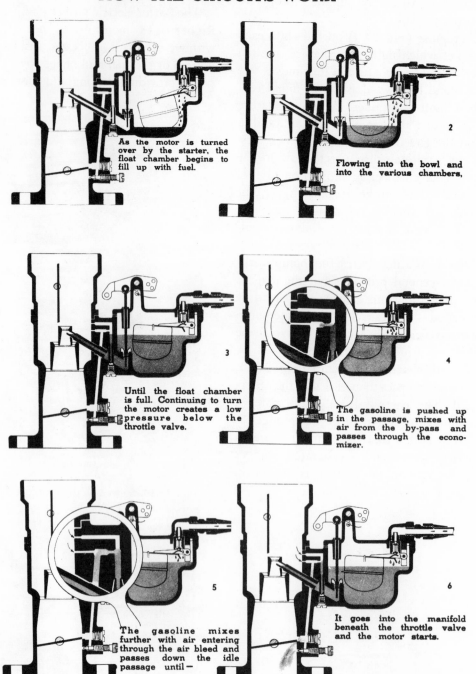

As the motor is turned over by the starter, the float chamber begins to fill up with fuel.

Flowing into the bowl and into the various chambers,

2

Until the float chamber is full. Continuing to turn the motor creates a low pressure below the throttle valve.

3

The gasoline is pushed up in the passage, mixes with air from the by-pass and passes through the economizer.

4

The gasoline mixes further with air entering through the air bleed and passes down the idle passage until—

5

It goes into the manifold beneath the throttle valve and the motor starts.

6

Fig. 24.12. Functions of the carburetor. (CC)

HOW THE CIRCUITS WORK

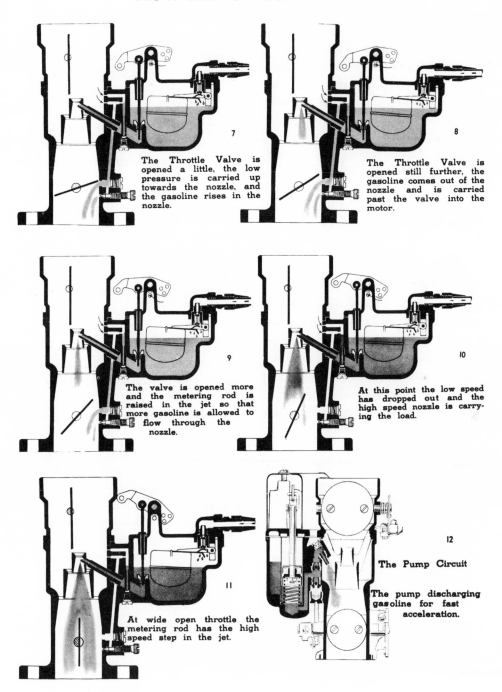

7

The Throttle Valve is opened a little, the low pressure is carried up towards the nozzle, and the gasoline rises in the nozzle.

8

The Throttle Valve is opened still further, the gasoline comes out of the nozzle and is carried past the valve into the motor.

9

The valve is opened more and the metering rod is raised in the jet so that more gasoline is allowed to flow through the nozzle.

10

At this point the low speed has dropped out and the high speed nozzle is carrying the load.

11

At wide open throttle the metering rod has the high speed step in the jet.

12

The Pump Circuit

The pump discharging gasoline for fast acceleration.

Fig. 24.13. Continuation of carburetor functions. (CC)

To install this pump it is necessary to cut a hole in the top of the tank and then insert a plate to close the hole. While the installation of this pump is not as easy as the other electric fuel pumps, it has some definite advantages. The fuel is always under pressure from the tank to the carburetor, eliminating vapor lock. As there are no valves between pump and carburetor, the fuel drains back into the tank when the engine is stopped, eliminating pressure build-up and possible difficulty in starting a hot engine. Fuel for starting is immediately supplied to the carburetor, and delivery of fuel is steady and non-pulsating. The motor armature is balanced both statically and dynamically assuring quiet operation and long life. The pump is protected from road hazards and is easily removed for servicing.

Electric Fuel Pump Advantages

The advantage of the electric fuel pump is that it is connected to the ignition switch and starts to pump as soon as the ignition is turned on. This immediately fills up the carburetor float chamber and assures a fuel supply without having to turn the engine over with the starter. This is important, especially to those who allow their engines to stand unused for days or possibly weeks.

The diagnostician should keep this in mind for cars which are driven intermittently as well as for those where dependability is a factor. Electric fuel pumps can be installed in parallel with the mechanical fuel pump. In this case the mechanical fuel pump will operate as usual when the engine is running but the electric fuel pump will fill the float chamber as stated and will supply fuel if the mechanical fuel pump fails for any reason.

The electric fuel pump, having breaker points, must have the correct polarity for the car in which it is to be installed. The positive or negative ground must have a pump with the corresponding polarity. If this caution is not observed, the life of the interrupter points will be shortened in the same way that breaker points on the voltage regulator are affected by the wrong polarity.

Tank and Fuel Lines

The tank and fuel lines are part of the fuel system, but their functions are so obvious it is unnecessary to elaborate on them.

On a number of cars a flexible length of tubing called *flex line*, 6″ to 10″ long, is introduced on the suction side of the fuel pump to minimize the danger of breakage from the motion of the engine on its rubber mounts.

The Carburetor

The carburetor is generally considered the most important component of the fuel system but naturally it cannot function unless the other units are in good condition.

The purpose of the carburetor is to furnish a combustible fuel-air mixture that is suitable, as to amount and proportions, to engine requirements under all conditions of speed and load.

If automobile engines could run at constant speed and uniform load, the carburetor could be a simple mixing valve. But engines are required to operate at a wide range of speeds, from a slow idle to maximum road speed. The loads vary from idle engine operation at no load, to full power output as when accelerating, climbing hills, or pulling trailers. It is the requirement of meeting these wide variations of speed and load that makes modern carburetors somewhat complicated. They are further complicated by the need for working satisfactorily with automatic transmissions.

There are five makers who supply the various passenger car builders with carburetors. In addition to these, several other makers supply carburetors for trucks and off-the-road requirements. Some builders use one, two or even three different makes of carburetors in the same model year. In some cases one model will have one carburetor and another model of the same make will have another carburetor. In each case however, the carburetor is engineered specifically for the car that uses it.

The makers of carburetors for passenger cars are (1) Carter Carburetor Co., (2) Rochester Carburetor Division of General Motors, (3) Holley, (4) Ford, and (5) Stromberg (Bendix Aviation Corp.). Each of these types of carburetors is described at the end of this chapter so its general characteristics will be recognized. However, detailed specifications must necessarily be omitted because of the large number of specific models, the mass of servicing details, and the many changes made as new car models are introduced.

Modern automotive carburetors have six systems or circuits, which are: (1) choke, (2) low-speed system or idle system, (3) part throttle power system or high-speed system, (4) power enrichment system, (5) accelerating pump system, and (6) float system. Each system provides the proper fuel-air mixture for an operational need. Different carburetor manufacturers may present these systems or circuits in different arrangements, but they are all present in one way or another on all the American carburetors. Refer to Figs. 24.12 and 24.13 "How the circuits work."

The Choke

The choke on all the different makes of carburetors is about the same. The manual choke is operated by a control from the dash while the automatic choke device is usually operated by a bimetallic spring which is very sensitive to temperature.

The function of the choke is to supply a very rich combustible gas mixture for starting which it does by shutting off nearly all of the air supply. Gasoline is not a single chemical combination of hydrogen and carbon. Rather, it is a mixture of a number of hydrocarbons of different volatilities, covering a range of boiling points from about 98°F. to nearly 300°F. In a hot engine all the constituents will readily evaporate and burn on the power stroke, but with a cold engine only those with low boiling points will ignite. Therefore it is essential to have much more gasoline in the intake manifold for cold starting than for normal engine operation when warm. After the engine has started and has warmed up partially, all the gasoline constituents will burn.

The heavy, higher-boiling-point hydrocarbons that collect in the manifold will dilute the oil on the cylinder walls if the choke is used excessively. Therefore, it is important that the engine be warmed up as quickly as possible or practicable, to minimize the effects of cold starting.

Where the manual choke is used, it should be entirely closed until the engine starts to fire and then partially opened and allowed to run in this position for a mile or two. As soon as the engine has warmed up, the choke can be opened all the way. On engines equipped with the automatic choke this is taken care of by the automatic choke valve operating device. Refer to Fig. 24.14.

Low-Speed System

The low-speed system or circuit is much the same on all American passenger car carburetors. To illustrate typical construction, the Carter Carburetor will be described.

The idle or low-speed system completely controls the supply of gasoline to the engine during idle and light load, low speeds up to approximately 20 mph, and it partially controls the supply of fuel for light load speeds between 20 and 30 mph.

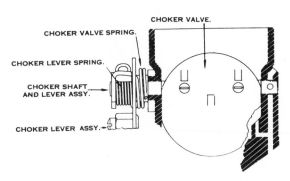

Fig. 24.14. Detail of carburetor choke. (CC)

The idle or low-speed circuit, Fig. 24.15, consists of the low-speed jet (E), bypass (F), economizer air bleed (G), port opening (H), idle adjusting screw (I), throttle valve (J), and carburetor bore (K).

During idling and low-speed operation of the engine, gasoline flows from the float bowl through the idle speed jet to the point where it is combined with a stream of air coming in through the bypass. The combining of the stream of air with the stream of gasoline tends to atomize or break up the gasoline into a vapor.

This mixture of air and gasoline continues on through the economizer until it begins to pass the point where it is further combined with a stream of air coming into the lower air bleed (G). This further breaks the gasoline particles into a fine vapor. The gasoline and air mixture that flows downward in the passage from the lower air bleed is still richer than an idle mixture needs to be, but when it mixes with the air which has just passed the throttle valve it forms a combustible mixture of the right proportions for idle speed. Another low-speed circuit is shown in Fig. 24.16.

The idle port (H) is made in a variety of round or slotted shapes so that as the throttle valve is opened it will not only allow more air to come in past it but will also uncover more of the idle port. This latter feature will allow a greater quantity of the gasoline and air mixture to enter the carburetor throat from the idle mixture passage.

The idle position of the throttle is such that, at an idle speed of 6 mph, it leaves enough of the slotted port as reserve to cover the range in speed between idle and the time when the high-speed system begins to cut in.

The idle adjusting screw (I) varies the quality of the idle mixture.

During the idle period and at no-load speeds up to 20 mph, all the gasoline flowing from the float bowl flows through the small metering hole in the low-speed jet. This hole is held to a manufacturing tolerance of .00025″ and is a very important factor in controlling the flow of gasoline into the engine during these speeds. It should never be cleaned out in any way other than by the use of compressed air; small wires

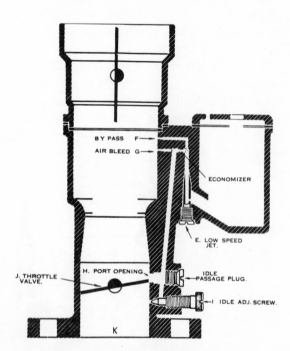

Fig. 24.15. Low speed circuit. (CC)

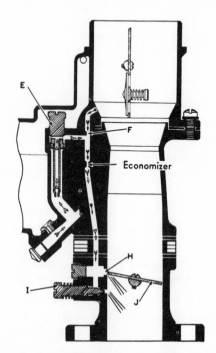

Fig. 24.16. Low-speed circuit, Carter B-B carburetor.

and drills tend to increase the size of the hole and thereby change the calibration of the carburetor. Naturally it would take only a very small particle of dirt to restrict the passage of gasoline through this hole and totally destroy the idle of the engine.

The outside of the barrel of a new low-speed jet for the Carter carburetor is straight from the base to the tip, but as it is installed in a carburetor the tip of the barrel contacts the tapered seat in the body of the carburetor between one and two complete turns of the jet before it is fully seated. As the jet is screwed into place, a gasoline-tight fit is made between the tip of the jet and the body of the carburetor by the rolling and tapering action of the tapered seat. The idle engine speed is adjusted by the throttle stop screw.

Part-Throttle Power System

This system is also called the high-speed circuit. On the Holley, Stromberg, Rochester and Carter B-B carburetors the part-throttle power systems are similar. On the Carter carburetor a different method is used which will be discussed when this carburetor is fully described. The high-speed circuit is shown in Fig. 24.17.

An essential part of the part-throttle power system is the venturi, without which the present carburetor design could not work. An understanding of the precise function and operation of the venturi will help to clarify carburetor action when the part throttle power system takes over from the low-speed or idle system.

The venturi consists of a portion of the carburetor main air passage with a restriction having a diameter about 70% of the main air tube. This gives a throat opening of approximately 50% of the tube cross-section area. Therefore the air flowing through the restricted portion or "throat" will have approximately twice the velocity of the air which flows through the full-size portion of the air passage.

The total air pressure of the air flowing through the carburetor is made up of static air pressure plus velocity air pressure, and this total air pressure will be a constant amount for any combination of throttle opening and engine speed. When the air flowing through the venturi gets to the throat, its velocity, as stated, will be doubled which means that its velocity pressure will be double. This will make the static pressure decrease proportionately, since the total pressure does not change unless the throttle opening or engine speed is changed. Decreased static pressure will cause a partial vacuum or "suction."

The main fuel discharge nozzle is located at the point of greatest vacuum (in or near the throat of the venturi), so that the vacuum will cause the liquid fuel to flow out of the end of the discharge nozzle into the air stream at approximately the point of highest velocity.

On a number of modern carburetors a double or triple venturi is used to give greater suction. With a double arrangement, the smaller venturi discharges into the next one, and in

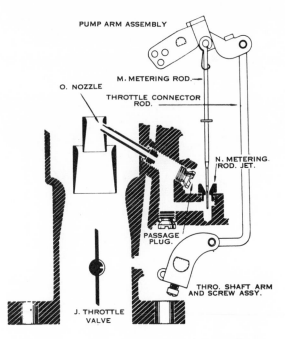

Fig. 24.17. High-speed circuit, Carter carburetor. Note the metering pin which is a distinctive feature of this carburetor.

the case of a triple venturi the second discharges into the throat of the third or main venturi. The inlet end of the venturi is a gently rounded cone to guide the incoming air into the throat with a minimum of air friction. The discharge end is a long, tapering, hollow cone.

As the throttle is opened wide enough for a level road speed of a little more than 20 mph, the velocity of the air flowing down through the carburetor throat creates a pressure at the discharge nozzle which is slightly less than atmospheric pressure, or a "partial vacuum."

The gasoline in the float bowl is acted upon by atmospheric pressure, so the difference in pressure between the two points causes gasoline to flow from the bowl, through the metering jet, and out the discharge nozzle to the throat of the carburetor.

As the speed increases from 20 mph, the high-speed system continues to cut in more and more, and the idle or low-speed system to cut out; until at approximately 30 mph, the high-speed system is carrying the entire load and the idle system is doing nothing. It requires more vacuum to operate the low-speed system than it does the high-speed system; therefore, the low-speed system ceases to operate at around 30 mph, because the vacuum in the bore of the carburetor has decreased until it is no

longer strong enough to draw gasoline from the low-speed system.

The reason the part-power throttle system or high-speed circuit does not operate at speeds under 20 mph is that the high vacuum which causes the low-speed circuit to operate exists *only below the throttle valve* in the carburetor. Therefore the high-speed discharge nozzle is not subjected to any appreciable vacuum until the volume of airflow through the venturi throat is great enough to build up a partial vacuum, causing this circuit to operate.

The operation of an engine under different loads and speeds demands different mixtures. The ideal mixture, in which the gasoline and air unite completely, is 14.88 pounds of air to 1 pound of gasoline. The car will run on a leaner ratio than this, but at about a mixture of 16:1, the power-per-stroke is lost so rapidly that gasoline consumption per mile is increased rather than decreased. The idling mixture is considerably richer than the ideal mixture, and the mixture for maximum power is also richer, about 12.5:1. The mixture for part load conditions can be as lean as 16:1. Depending on the make and model of car, the part load condition exists at a speed on level roads from about 25 mph to 60 mph.

Power Enrichment System

The power enrichment system is sometimes called the *economizer* and is incorporated in all American passenger car carburetors. Fig. 24.18 shows this system in a Holley carburetor.

When high power output is required, the carburetor delivers a richer mixture than that required for normal cruising when no great load is placed on the engine. The function of the power enrichment or economizer is to supply the added fuel for high power operation.

This system is actuated by (1) throttle opening, (2) vacuum piston, (3) vacuum diaphragm, or (4) metering pin. The first three mentioned operate a needle valve which permits additional gasoline to flow into the passage leading to the main discharge nozzle.

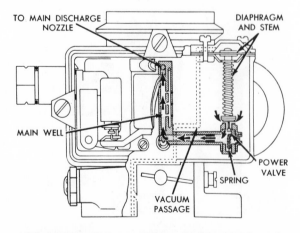

Fig. 24.18. Power enrichment system used on the Holley carburetor. The vacuum-controlled diaphragm operates the power valve against spring pressure.

Thus more fuel than that which would normally flow past the main metering jet is carried into the air stream at the throat of the venturi. The metering pin, in effect, accomplishes the same result by enlarging the cross-section area of the main metering jet. The vacuum piston and vacuum discharge diaphragm work in the same way except that, as the name would imply, the vacuum piston is a plunger which operates the economizer valve, while the diaphragm is affected by the vacuum to actuate the economizer valve. Fig. 24.19 illustrates a Rochester carburetor with power enrichment system at the points K, L, and J.

Manifold vacuum inversely follows the power demand placed on the engine, being highest at light loads with a small throttle opening and lowest with wide throttle opening when there is the greatest load put on the engine. This is due to the fact that as the load on the engine increases, the throttle valve must be opened wider to maintain any given speed.

Manifold vacuum is reduced because the opened throttle offers less restriction to the air flow entering the intake manifold.

Manifold vacuum at the bottom of the carburetor, below the throttle valve, is transmitted through a vacuum passage to the top of the economizer diaphragm or the vacuum piston in the vacuum chamber. The vacuum carried to the vacuum chamber at idle and normal cruising speed is strong enough to hold the economizer valve closed, compressing the spring which otherwise would open the valve.

The Stromberg, Rochester and Carter B-B use vacuum pistons while the Holley and Ford carburetors use a vacuum diaphragm. On the Carter, the smallest step on the metering pin performs the same function, following the amount of throttle opening. Fig. 24.20 shows the metering pin used in Carter carburetors.

When high power demand places a greater demand on the engine and reduces manifold

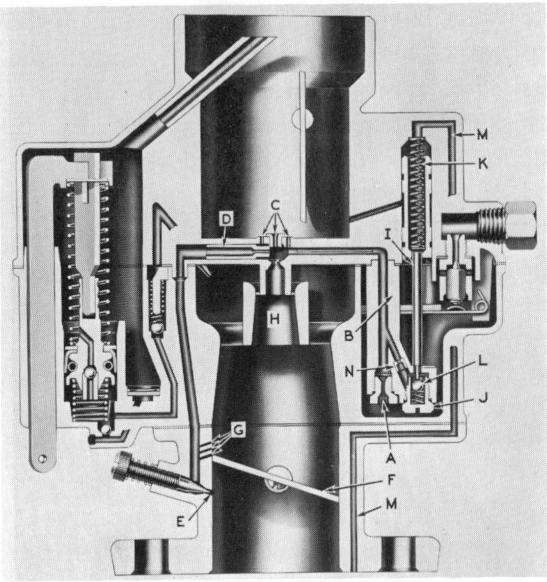

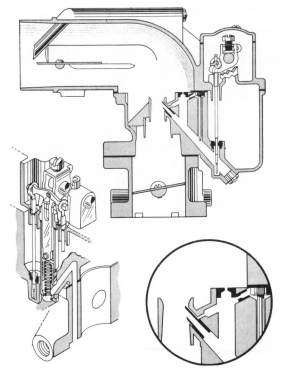

Fig. 24.19. Rochester model B carburetor. *(A)* Main metering jet; *(B)* main well support assembly; *(C)* calibrated air bleeds; *(D)* idle tube; *(E)* idle needle adjusting hole; *(F)* throttle; *(G)* idle holes; *(H)* main discharge nozzle; *(J)* power valve; *(M)* manifold vacuum passage to operate power system; *(N)* power jet.

Fig. 24.20. High-speed circuit, Carter WGD carburetor. Vacumeter system of controlling the metering rods uses a vacuum cylinder.

vacuum beyond a predetermined point (frequently about 5 inches of mercury), the economizer spring expands. This overcomes the reduced vacuum above the diaphragm or the vacuum piston, forcing the valve stem to open the economizer valve. Fuel from the float chamber flows into the valve and passes through a

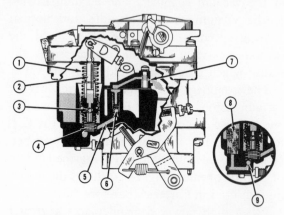

Fig. 24.21. Accelerating pump system used on the Rochester carburetor. Note the lever on the throttle valve shaft which actuates the accelerating pump plunger.

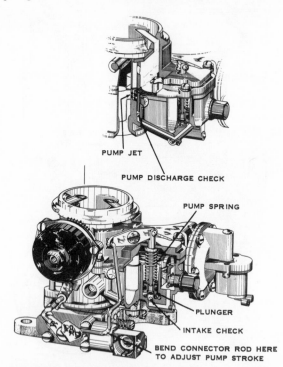

PUMP JET

PUMP DISCHARGE CHECK

PUMP SPRING

PLUNGER

INTAKE CHECK

BEND CONNECTOR ROD HERE TO ADJUST PUMP STROKE

Fig. 24.22. The accelerating pump system on the Carter BBD carburetor showing the actuating linkage.

passage to the main well where it is added to the fuel flow in the main metering system, enriching the mixture for full power.

In some models of carburetors the economizer valve is actuated by the piston rod in the accelerating pump. When the throttle valve reaches a predetermined position the accelerating pump piston will have gone far enough down in the pump cylinder to touch the end of the economizer valve, opening it and permitting the required enrichment of the mixture to carry the high power load.

Accelerating Pump System

The idle system provides a good fuel mixture for speeds from 16 to 20 mph. Then the part-throttle power system (or high-speed circuit) starts to take over. However, during the transition there is a flat spot when the idle system decreases its fuel to the engine and the part throttle system starts to cut in. Although the air flow through the carburetor responds almost immediately to any increase in throttle opening, there is a brief interval before the fuel in the narrow passages can gain speed to maintain the desired balance of fuel and air. The accelerating pump system operates during this interval, supplying fuel until the other systems can provide the proper mixture.

In late model Holley and Ford carburetors the accelerating pump uses a diaphragm; others use a leather-topped piston, which operates in a cylinder. As the throttle is closed the plunger moves upward drawing gasoline out of the float chamber through a screen and through a check valve into a pump cylinder. An air pocket remains between the fuel and the plunger. Fig. 24.21 shows the accelerating pump system on a 2G Rochester carburetor.

The slightest opening of the throttle moves the plunger down, compressing the air and causing the immediate discharge of fuel past the outlet in the check valve and through a jet which discharges fuel into the main venturi. When the throttle is fully open the discharge is continued for a few seconds by the air compressed between the plunger and the fuel. Fig. 24.22 shows the Carter BBD pump system.

Float System

The float circuit, float system, or as it is sometimes referred to, the gasoline-level system, is important because it controls the gasoline level in the carburetor bowl or float chamber and also in the main discharge nozzle. A gasoline level which is too low or too high will cause trouble in the low- and high-speed circuits, and will be difficult to identify. The float circuit in the carburetor consists of the needle valve, the needle valve seat, needle valve seat gasket, float and level assembly, float bowl, float bowl cover, bowl cover gasket, and vent. The float system is shown in Fig. 24.23.

The float bowl acts as a reservoir to hold a supply of gasoline throughout the entire range of load and speed of the engine. The level of gasoline in the bowl is controlled by the action of the float. When the level rises, the float rises to close the needle valve; and when the level falls, the float falls, permitting the needle valve to open. Thus the level of the fuel in the float chamber is maintained within very close limits. The float closes the needle valve against fuel pump pressure and only permits gasoline to flow from the pump in proportion to the engine requirements for fuel. Fig. 24.24 shows the Rochester 2G float system.

Needle Valve with Resilient Tip

Flooding of carburetors is a fairly common trouble and is generally caused by a particle of dirt, rust, scale or other foreign matter sticking to the float needle valve or its seat. This prevents the needle valve from seating properly and causes it to leak under pressure from the fuel pump, raising the fuel level in the float chamber so high the air-fuel mixture is upset and often will leak out the top of the carburetor.

To correct this trouble, it has been necessary in the past to remove and replace the float needle valve and its seat. In the past few years the needle valve with a resilient tip has been introduced which practically eliminates the flooding problem.

The resilient tip, made of a fluor elastomer, has excellent petroleum, synthetic lubricant, fuel and chemical resistance through a temperature range from —10°F. to 500°F. It makes a tight joint between the needle valve and seat by enfolding foreign matter.

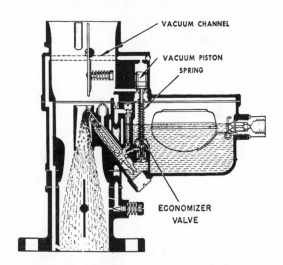

Fig. 24.23. Typical float system, showing how the float needle valve controls the inlet of liquid fuel to maintain the desired fuel level in the float chamber. In this Stromberg carburetor is also shown a vacuum-operated fuel enrichment or economizer valve.

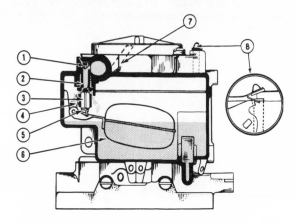

Fig. 24.24. Arrangement of the float system on a typical Rochester carburetor. Note that the float needle valve is vertical in this unit.

Fig. 24.25. (Left) Needle valve with a resilient tip and triangular cross section. (Right) One design of needle seat as furnished by Carter carburetor.

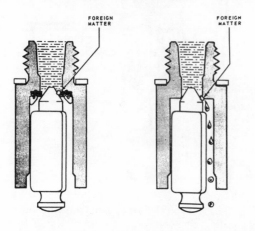

Fig. 24.26. (Left) The resilient needle valve seat of a Carter carburetor enfolds foreign matter and keeps the joint tight. (Right) In a metal seat, a particle of foreign matter may lodge between the needle tip and seat causing the valve to leak.

Fig. 24.27. (Left) Needle valve with a resilient tip and square cross section. (Right) Needle seat furnished by Rochester.

Carter Carburetor Division of ACF Industries originated the resilient needle tip, although now it is also furnished by the Rochester Division of General Motors Corporation, Vernay Laboratories, and some others. Carter furnishes triangular-section needle valves as shown in Fig. 24.25, which illustrates a needle and its seat. This company also supplies a solid needle and a resilient seat as shown in Fig. 24.26. The type of tips furnished by Rochester is square in cross section and is shown in Fig. 24.27.

Any solid needle valve on a reasonably late automobile can be replaced by one with a resilient tip, and many Carter needle seats can be replaced with the resilient seat type. Either one effectively corrects carburetor flooding trouble due to leaking needle and seat combinations.

Anti-Percolating Valve

While the car is being driven, the engine compartment is kept cool by the large volume of air passing through it and by the heat absorbed through the atomization of the fuel.

When the car and engine have stopped, the cooling system is not able to carry off the heat stored up in the engine parts and it is radiated into the air under the hood. The carburetor absorbs some of this heat, so that in hot weather or after a long, hard drive the fuel in the high-speed passage may boil. When this happens the vapor bubbles rise and those which are trapped in the passage of the main nozzle push gasoline ahead of them, out of the nozzle and into the venturi.

As the bubbles continue to the main nozzle, the gasoline collects in the manifold until the float chamber is empty. This flooded manifold condition makes it difficult to restart the engine until it has stood long enough for the gasoline to evaporate.

To prevent this action, which is known as *percolation*, an anti-percolating valve is used in most of the Carter carburetors. Other carburetors have either an anti-percolating valve or a vent arranged in such a way that percolating will be avoided. The valve opens a vent which connects directly to the bottom of the main nozzle and carries off any vapor bubbles which may form so that gasoline is not forced out of the nozzle. The valve is opened by the throttle linkage when the throttle closes to the idle position, and it closes with the slightest opening of the throttle.

Slow Closing Throttle

On some cars it is desired that the throttle should close slowly on deceleration. This is particularly important on cars using automatic transmissions as the engine is liable to stall if the throttle closes suddenly.

Slow closing is accomplished by having the equivalent of a dash pot in the carburetor. In this dash pot is a plunger with a ball check in it, seated in a cylinder at the bottom of the float bowl. The upper end of the plunger is connected through linkage with the throttle shaft and thus controls the closing of the throttle when sudden deceleration occurs. Fig. 24.28 shows the anti-stall dash pot used on Ford and Holley carburetors.

Fast Idle Operation

During the warm-up period, it is desirable to run the engine slightly faster to keep it from

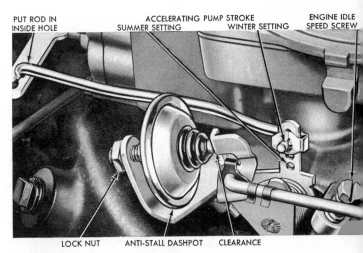

Fig. 24.28. Anti-stall dashpot as used on Ford and Holley carburetors. It prevents the throttle from closing too rapidly, possibly causing the engine to stall. In some other carburetors, a plunger and cylinder are used for the same purpose.

stalling. A fast idle cam, located between the idle speed adjusting screw and its stop, holds the throttle open enough to give the necessary higher engine speed.

When the engine has warmed up sufficiently so that it will run at regular idle speed without stalling, the operation of the choke moves the fast idle cam out from between the idle adjusting screw and its stop.

For the manually operated choke, the fast idle cam is moved when the choke button is pushed in all the way. On the automatic choke this is accomplished by the thermostatic spring which opens the choke butterfly valve.

The Carter Carburetor

The Carter carburetor is manufactured in the largest carburetor factory in the world. Produced in single-barrel, two-barrel and four-barrel types, it includes the six systems or circuits previously discussed, but is distinctive in its use of a metering pin, shown in Fig. 24.29.

The metering pin is a pin held in a vertical position and connected at its upper end to the throttle level linkage. Its lower end, which has two or three different diameters, projects

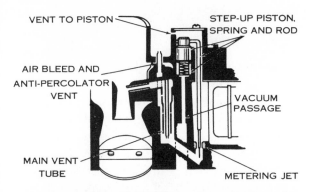

Fig. 24.29. Metering pin used on Carter carburetors. The pin is controlled by either throttle action or a vacuum cylinder, depending upon the model. When it is raised, the smaller pin section has the effect of increasing the opening of the main fuel jet to allow increased fuel flow.

through the main metering jet. When the throttle is closed, the largest diameter occupies space in the cross section of the metering portion of the main jet. When the throttle is partially open the largest diameter (of two) or intermediate section (of three) is in the metering portion of the main jet. For almost wide open throttle position, the smallest diameter takes its position in the metering jet, thus enlarging the jet's cross section and giving the same effect as the power enrichment system on other carburetors. This replaces the throttle actuated or vacuum actuated power enrichment or economizer valve. The float arrangement is shown in Fig. 24.30.

The other basic features follow other conventional American carburetor practice.

A large number of different models specially engineered to fit particular car models incorporate the different items needed to provide the special features desired by car manufacturers. A number of the Carter models make use of a double or triple venturi.

Carter was the first company to introduce the resilient neoprene-tipped float needle valve to eliminate leakage of fuel at this point. The soft end of the needle valve will close tightly even though particles of rust, carbon, mud or other foreign matter may be on the needle or seat.

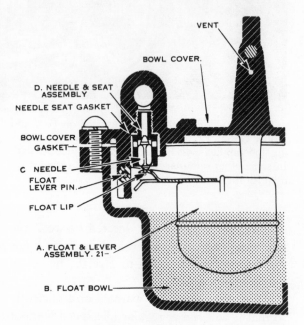

Fig. 24.30. Float and needle valve arrangement on the Carter carburetor. The float maintains a constant level of fuel in the float bowl. This should be in accordance with the manufacturer's specifications.

The Carter B-B Series

This carburetor differs from the Carter in that it does not have a metering pin. This design has a single venturi, and a vacuum piston is used for controlling the power enrichment system. This is furnished in single barrel and double barrel units. The design of the double barrel unit is shown in Fig. 24.31.

Holley Carburetors

Carburetors made by Holley Carburetor Company were used almost exclusively on Ford-built automobiles for a number of years. Now, however, Ford is building many of the carburetors used on these cars. Holley and Ford are used interchangeably on a number of models.

Holley carburetors are furnished in single-, double-, and four-barrel units. Some of the single-barrel units have glass float chambers.

The power enrichment system is fully automatic being operated by a vacuum type diaphragm power valve which supplies added fuel

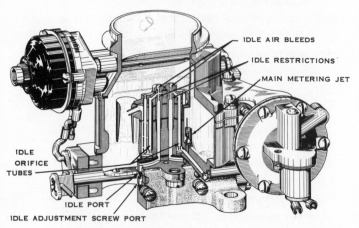

Fig. 24.31. Carter B-B two-barrel carburetor showing idle or low-speed system. The high-speed discharge nozzle is in position to discharge into the left venturi.

to both main metering systems when the load on the engine demands high power output. Versions of this carburetor model used for Ford six cylinder engines contain passages for vacuum pickup for the full vacuum control distributor. Refer to Fig. 24.32 for two-barrel carburetor.

An interesting feature of the Holley carburetor is the fuel nozzle bar which also carries the idle tube and the aspirating or breathing nozzle. The central portion of the nozzle bar forms the main discharge nozzle. In this construction it is possible to locate the discharge nozzle in the center of the air stream without the need of attaching brackets or bosses which interfere with air flow into the venturi. A single venturi is used in each barrel.

The Ford Carburetors

The Ford carburetor is furnished in single-barrel, two-barrel, and four-barrel models. The single barrel is used on six-cylinder engines. In common with the other makes of carburetors, the Ford-built units have the conventional six circuits. The choke may be either manual or automatic, although with automatic transmissions the choke is generally automatic.

The single-barrel carburetor consists of an upper-body and lower-body assembly. The upper assembly contains the major metering components: the main or part throttle system, idle system, power valve, and fuel inlet system.

The lower body assembly contains the fuel bowl, accelerating pump assembly, idle mixture

Fig. 24.32. External view of the Holley two-barrel carburetor. Notice how compact it is.

adjusting screw and distributor vacuum fitting (for full-vacuum-controlled distributors used on Ford six-cylinder engines). On all Ford carburetors, an inner venturi is used combined with the part-throttle fuel discharge nozzle.

The Ford dual carburetor has two main assemblies: the air horn and the main body. The air horn assembly, which serves as the main body cover, contains the choke plate and the vents for the fuel bowl. The throttle plate, accelerating pump assembly, power valve assembly, and fuel bowl are in the main body. The automatic choke housing is attached to the main body. Figs. 24.33 and 24.34 show the Ford dual carburetor.

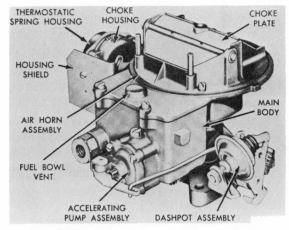

Fig. 24.33. Ford dual carburetor. Note the dashpot assembly for the slow closing throttle.

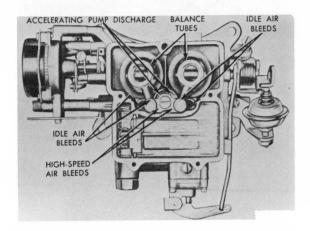

Fig. 24.34. Top view of the Ford dual carburetor showing the double venturi and other parts.

For high performance installations on V-8 engines, three dual carburetors are furnished, coupled together so that for low and moderate speed requirements only the middle unit is in action. As a certain throttle opening is reached, the other two units are cut in to supply the fuel requirements for extreme power and acceleration.

The Rochester Carburetor

Rochester carburetors are made by the Rochester Carburetor Division of General Motors Corporation and are widely used on the automobiles made by this company. Single-, dual-, and four-barrel units are supplied, and installations of three two-barrel units are supplied when specified for use on V-8 engines.

These carburetors are of a side-bowl design. The carburetor float bowl is located at the side of the main bores of the carburetor. All of the fuel metering is centrally located in a compact design, so that each system will give instantaneous response for maximum efficiency and performance. This places the main well tubes, idle tubes, mixture passages, air bleeds and pump jets in a removable assembly, easily

taken out for cleaning and inspection purposes. Fig. 24.35 shows the Model 2GC, a two-barrel unit used on Chevrolet V-8 engines.

The idle and main well tubes are permanently installed in the cluster body by means of a precision pressed fit. The main nozzles and idle tubes are suspended in the fuel in the main wells of the float bowl; this insulates them from engine heat, thus helping to prevent heat expansion and percolation spillover during hot idle and short stops with a hot engine.

The main metering jets are fixed, so that no wear can take place at the metering orifice. Metering calibration is accomplished through a system of calibrated air bleeds which give the correct fuel-air mixtures throughout all operational ranges. A vacuum-operated power system is used for extra power when needed. In this way power mixtures are regulated by drop in engine manifold vacuum, regardless of the degree of throttle opening. This is shown in Fig. 24.36.

Stromberg Carburetors

Stromberg carburetors are made in single-barrel, double-barrel, and the four-barrel design.

The construction follows general American carburetor design. Most of the models make

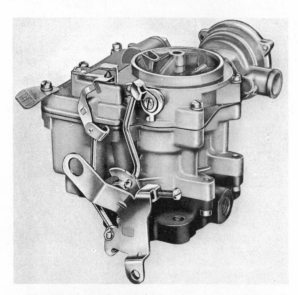

Fig. 24.35. Rochester dual carburetor, model 2GC, used on many of the General Motors Corporation V-8 engines.

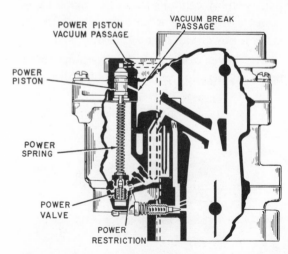

Fig. 24.36. Power enrichment system on a typical Rochester carburetor, 2GC.

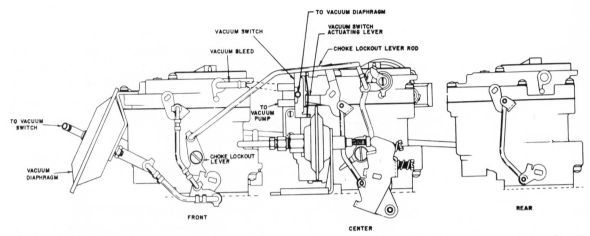

Fig. 24.37. Triple two-barrel carburetor installation. The middle unit is the primary and the two end units are the secondary carburetors.

use of a double venturi. The power enrichment or economizer system is controlled either by a vacuum piston or by movement of the accelerating pump piston which on some models opens the economizer valve.

The various special features desired by some car builders are supplied on Stromberg carburetors where specified.

Triple Two-Barrel Carburetor Installation

In this installation three two-barrel carburetors are mounted in tandem. Rochester carburetors are shown in Fig. 24.37.

The center carburetor of the three, called the primary carburetor, contains the six conventional systems. The front and rear units, called the secondary carburetors, contain only the float, accelerating pump, and main metering (part-throttle or high-speed) systems.

The primary carburetor is the only one used during idle, warm-up, or part-throttle operation. At this time the two secondary carburetors are kept out of operation by closing-springs externally attached to the throttle shafts.

The throttle valves and accelerator pumps on the secondary carburetors are operated by a vacuum diaphragm which is controlled by a vacuum switch mounted on the center carburetor. The throttle shafts on the outside carburetors are connected by common rods so they

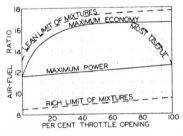

MAXIMUM POWER {SUPPLY EXCESS FUEL FOR BEST UTILIZATION OF AIR IN ENGINE.

MAXIMUM ECONOMY {SUPPLY EXCESS AIR FOR BEST UTILIZATION OF FUEL IN ENGINE.

Fig. 24.38. Range of air-fuel mixtures, showing proportions for maximum power and maximum economy. The rich limit of mixtures is also shown. (AL)

will both operate simultaneously, controlled by the vacuum diaphragm.

During idle and part-throttle ranges, the center carburetor alone feeds fuel. When the outside carburetors are to be used, a vacuum switch on the center carburetor is operated by a tang on the acelerator pump lever. The vacuum switch is connected directly to the vacuum booster pump on the engine. The switch also has a vacuum line which runs to the vacuum diaphragm. This in turn is connected by linkage to the throttle lever on the front carburetor.

On normal acceleration the center carburetor feeds air and fuel until the throttle valves are opened approximately 60 degrees. At this time the vacuum switch opens and applies vacuum to the diaphragm. This opens the throttle valves on the front and rear carburetors simultaneously, feeding fuel from both the accelerating and main metering systems.

This arrangement permits the greatest fuel economy at low and moderate speeds yet has fuel capacity to give the maximum in the way of performance.

Summary

Three main *engine requirements* are (1) compression, (2) ignition and (3) carburetion.

Carburetion is probably the least understood, yet is extremely important, for an engine cannot possibly perform the way it should unless the fuel system is functioning efficiently.

The *fuel system* consists of the fuel pump, air cleaner, carburetor, automatic choke, manifold heat valve or heat riser valve, fuel tank and connecting tubing.

Two general types of *fuel pumps* are used for automotive fuel systems: (1) mechanical and (2) electric. The purpose of the fuel pump is to draw fuel from the fuel tank and elevate it under pressure to the carburetor.

Single mechanical fuel pumps handle nothing but fuel as distinguished from the combination fuel and vacuum pump.

Fuel pump pressure is governed entirely by spring pressure and cannot exceed this pressure except under a few abnormal conditions. The power stroke is always the suction stroke while discharge results from spring pressure on the pump diaphragm. Fuel pump delivery is measured by the time it takes to deliver 3/4 pint to 1 pint. Depending upon the size of the engine, this should be accomplished in 30-60 seconds.

The *combination fuel and vacuum pump* is a fuel pump and vacuum pump in combination. The vacuum pump boosts the intake manifold vacuum to give more uniform operation of the windshield wiper.

Four *electrical fuel pumps* are available: the Autopulse, Bendix, Stewart-Warner and Carter. All can be supplied to operate on either 6 or 12 volts.

The *Carter electric pusher pump* is designed to be mounted at the bottom of the fuel tank and pushes the fuel under pressure up to the carburetor.

The *carburetor* is generally considered to be the most important unit in the fuel system but naturally cannot function unless the other units in the system are in good condition.

The *purpose of the carburetor* is to furnish a combustible or explosive mixture of gasoline and air that is suitable as to amount and proportions to engine requirements under all conditions of speed and load.

Carburetors have *six systems,* sections, or circuits which are necessary to meet engine requirements for fuel. They are (1) choke, (2) idle system, (3) part-throttle power system, (4) power enrichment system or economizer, (5) accelerating pump system, and (6) float system.

The *five makers* of passenger car carburetors are Carter, Rochester, Holley, Ford, and Stromberg. Figs. 24.12 and 24.13 show how the circuits work.

The *choke* supplies a very rich combustible gas mixture for starting, which it does by shutting off most of the air supply.

The *low-speed or idle system* controls the supply of gasoline to the engine during idle and light load speeds, up to approximately 20 mph.

The *part-throttle power system* or high-speed circuit supplies fuel by means of vacuum created in the venturi. The discharge nozzle allows liquid fuel to flow into the air stream that goes through the venturi.

The *part-throttle system* does not work at speeds under 20 mph because there is not sufficient air flow through the venturi at slower speeds and not enough vacuum to cause the fuel to flow out the discharge nozzle.

The *power enrichment system,* also called the economizer, supplies a richer fuel-air mixture when the engine is operating at high speed or under heavy load. On the Carter Carburetor the metering pin performs this function. On most of the other carburetors a vacuum piston actuates the power enrichment fuel valve.

The *accelerating pump system* provides additional fuel during the transition from low-speed system to part-throttle power system and on rapid acceleration.

An *anti-percolating valve* is used to prevent percolation of gasoline from the float chamber, caused by heat from the engine when it has been stopped after a period of operation.

A *slow closing* of the throttle is accomplished by a cylinder or diaphragm dash pot to prevent stalling of the engine when the throttle is suddenly released.

Fast idle operation is obtained by the fast idle cam on the throttle which holds the throttle open slightly until the operation of the automatic choke releases it when the engine has warmed up somewhat.

The *Carter carburetor* is distinctive in its use of a metering pin to obtain power enrichment. A full line is available.

The *Carter B-B series* differs from the Carter in that it does not make use of a metering pin as is used in the regular Carter carburetors. It is made in single- and dual-barrel models.

Holley carburetors were used exclusively by Ford for a number of years. Now they are used along with Ford-built carburetors. They are supplied in single-, dual- and four-barrel models.

Ford carburetors are furnished in single-, two-barrel and four-barrel models. They have the conventional six systems or circuits.

Rochester carburetors are widely used on automobiles made by General Motors Corporation. They are furnished in single-, dual- and four-barrel models.

Stromberg carburetors are used on some of the Chrysler-built automobiles.

In a *triple two-barrel carburetor installation,* three two-barrel carburetors are mounted in tandem. The middle unit is used for idle and low-speed operation. Two end carburetors cut in when the throttle is open about 60°. Their use is actuated by means of a vacuum-operated valve.

Questions

1. What are three main engine requirements?
2. Name six parts of the fuel system.
3. What are two types of fuel pump?
4. What is the specific purpose of the fuel pump?
5. What generates the liquid pressure on the fuel in the fuel pump?
6. How do you tell when a fuel pump is operating dependably?
7. What is the purpose of a combination fuel and vacuum pump?
8. How and where does the Carter electric pusher pump work?
9. What is the purpose of the carburetor?
10. Name four makers who supply passenger car carburetors.
11. Name the six systems or circuits included in American passenger car carburetors.
12. What is the function of the choke?
13. Through what speed range does the low-speed circuit supply engine requirements?
14. What actuates the fuel flow in the low-speed system?
15. What are two adjustments on the low-speed system?
16. What is the essential component of the part-throttle system?
17. What is the principle of operation of the venturi?
18. Where is the fuel discharged in the part-throttle circuit?
19. What is the function of the power enrichment system?

20. How does the enrichment system work on Carter carburetors?
21. How does the power enrichment system work on the other carburetors?
22. When is intake manifold vacuum greatest: at low engine speed? at high engine speed?
23. What actuates the accelerating pump plunger?
24. What is the function of the accelerating pump system?
25. What is the function of the float system?
26. What is the purpose of the anti-percolating valve?
27. Why is a slow-closing throttle provided on some carburetors?
28. What does the fast idle do, and why is it included on the carburetors?
29. With three two-barrel carburetors, which is the primary carburetor?
30. When do the secondary units become operative?

CHAPTER TWENTY-FIVE

Four-Barrel Carburetors —Automatic Choke

Since 1952 four-barrel carburetors have been used on V-8 engines where high performance is desired. The four-barrel carburetor consists essentially of two dual carburetors. The two carburetors are referred to as *primary side* and *secondary side.*

Four-barrel units are supplied by Rochester, Carter, Holley, and Ford. Those made by Rochester, Ford and Holley are similar with only a few design differences. Carter four-barrel carburetors differ in the use of metering rods, a standard Carter feature, in the two primary barrels only. In the secondary barrels there is only the float system and the high-speed system. There are no secondary idle systems, accelerating pump or power valve.

The *primary side* completely controls the metering of fuel to the engine throughout the idle and part-throttle range.

The *secondary side* supplements the fuel from the primary side throughout the power or wide open throttle range.

Rochester 4GC Carburetor

The Rochester four-barrel carburetor makes use of the six basic systems or circuits of carburetion, which are idle, part-throttle, accelerator, choke, power and float. The following

descriptions will trace and describe the operation of each of the carburetor systems in the Rochester unit. Refer to Fig. 25.1.

At small throttle opening, the vacuum created at the main discharge nozzle is not great enough to cause fuel to flow from the nozzle because the volume of air going through the venturi is not sufficient. Therefore, additional systems have been produced to provide the proper mixture ratios required throughout the idling range.

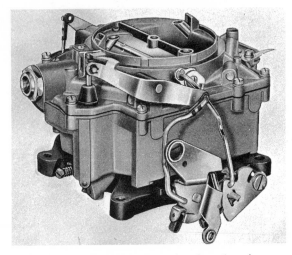

Fig. 25.1. Rochester 4GC four-barrel carburetor used on General Motors Corporation large V-8 engines.

Keep in mind in following through the operation of this carburetor that it is the equivalent of two two-barrel carburetors having one complete two-barrel carburetor for the lower speed range and another complete one for extra power or top speed range. See arrangement as shown in Fig. 25.2.

Idle System

A fixed idle system regulates the fuel provided from the secondary side of the carburetor. This system provides about half of the required fuel for normal idle mixtures. As shown in Fig. 25.3, the secondary idle fuel is drawn from the float bowl through the main metering jet (1), into the fuel well in the bottom of the float bowl. It then passes through the calibrated restriction in the end of each idle tube (2). The fuel is next drawn up through the idle tube, is bled at the idle bleed (3), through the calibrated restriction (4), and is again bled by the calibrated bleed (5). The mixture is then drawn through a channel in the float bowl around the secondary throttle body bore, is further bled by the lower idle air bleed (6), and is discharged from the throttle idle orifice (7).

As the throttle is opened, the vacuum or suction on the idle discharge hole (7), decreases very rapidly. These discharge holes, therefore, stop bleeding fuel in the off-idle range.

In addition, an adjustable idle system is provided on the primary or pump side of the carburetor. This system supplies the balance of fuel required for normal curb idle as well as that required for operation in the off-idle range. Refer again to Fig. 25.3. The primary idle fuel is drawn from the float bowl through the main metering jet (8) to the fuel well in the bottom of the float bowl. It passes through the calibrated idle tube restriction (9), and idle tubes. Air joins this fuel in the calibrated bleed (10). This mixture then passes through the calibrated

Fig. 25.2. Rochester 4GC carburetor. (Above) Assembly of throttle body to bowl. (Below) Location of main metering jets on the primary side.

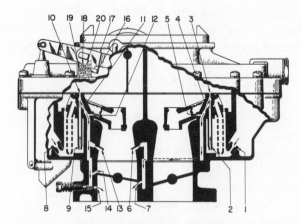

Fig. 25.3. Cross section of Rochester 4GC showing *idle system.* (1) Main metering jet; (2) idle tube; (3) idle air bleed; (4) idle restriction; (5) idle air bleed; (6) lower idle air bleeds; (7) idle discharge hole; (8) main metering jet; (9) idle tube; (10) idle air bleed; (11) idle restriction; (12) idle air bleed; (13) lower idle air bleeds; (14-15) idle discharge hole; (16) idle vent contact lever; (17) throttle pump lever; (18) idle vent valve; (19) vent valve spring; (20) vent valve retainer.

restriction (11), and is bled further at the secondary idle bleed (12).

The mixture passes through the float bowl idle channel, is further bled at the lower idle air bleed (13), and secondary idle hole (14), and is discharged from the throttle body idle needle hole (15). As the throttle valves are opened the bleed effect of the secondary idle hole gradually diminishes. When these holes become exposed to manifold vacuum they become fuel discharge holes to meet the increased demand of the engine.

To minimize the effects of hot weather or rough idling, the carburetor incorporates an external vent when the throttle valves are in a closed position. This external idle vent consists of an actuating lever (16) attached to the pump shaft and lever assembly (17), idle vent valve guide (18), idle vent valve string (19), and idle vent valve (20). When the throttle valves are closed, the actuating lever contacts the spring-loaded vent valve and holds it open. This permits vapors from the float bowl to vent themselves to the atmosphere. As the throttle valves are opened the idle vent valve spring closes the vent valve thus eliminating atmospheric vent and returning the carburetor to an internal balance.

Part-Throttle System

As the throttle valves are opened to a greater degree and more air is drawn through the carburetor, it is necessary to provide means other than the idle system for supplying additional fuel to meet the engine requirements. The part-throttle system is shown in Fig. 25.4.

The primary or pump side of the carburetor meets this increased demand for fuel in the following manner. At a point of sufficient throttle opening, the manifold vacuum or suction multiplies several times in the primary venturi (1) and secondary venturi (2) and is transmitted to the tip of the main well tube or main discharge nozzle (3). This suction draws fuel from the float bowl through the calibrated main metering jet (4), and into the air-bled main well tube (5). After passing through the main well tube (5), air joins the mixture at the main well bleed (6). The mixture then passes from the tip of the nozzle through the mixture passage (7), to the secondary venturi (2), and on into the intake manifold. As the throttle opening is progressively increased and more fuel is drawn through the main well tube, the fuel level in the main well drops. As this drops, the calibrated holes in the main well tubes are no longer covered with fuel. They become air bleeds, thus mixing progressively more air in the fuel passing through the main well tube. Although the nozzle suction is increased by increasing the throttle opening, the fuel mixture to the engine remains constant throughout the part-throttle range.

Since the part-throttle mixture tends to become excessively lean as the throttle opening increases, lower idle air bleed (8), which now becomes part-throttle fuel nozzle, has been placed in the main air flow channel below the primary venturi (1). These nozzles being exposed to manifold vacuum during part-throttle

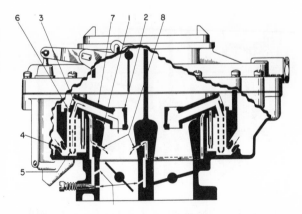

Fig. 25.4. Cross section of Rochester 4GC showing *part-throttle system*. (1) Main venturi; (2) main discharge nozzle outlet; (3) main discharge nozzle tube; (4) main metering jet; (5) main well tube; (6) main well bleed; (7) main discharge nozzle tube; (8) lower idle tube air bleeds; (9) idle discharge holes.

operation draw fuel through both the primary and secondary idle systems as described previously. It will be noted that these nozzles act as air bleeds during the operation of the idle system. Now that they are acting as discharge nozzles, the idle discharge holes in the throttle body (9), are back-bleeding air and mixing it with the fuel passing through these part-throttle nozzles.

The throttle valves on the secondary or fuel inlet side of the carburetor do not open until the car is traveling at approximately 90 mph, unless high power is required for rapid acceleration, hill climbing, and so on. They must then open fully during the remaining few degrees of primary throttle travel. The secondary side, therefore, supplies fuel to the primary side in

the idle, part-throttle and power ranges and to the intake manifold through the secondary side in the power range only. The part-throttle or intermediate range is controlled completely by the primary side of the carburetor. Parts of the 4GC are shown in Fig. 25.5.

Power System

To achieve the proper mixture required when more power is desirable or sustained high-speed driving is to be maintained, the model 4GC Rochester carburetor employs the use of a vacuum-operated power piston (1) in the air horn, and a power valve (2) in the float bowl. The power system is located on the primary or pump side of the carburetor. This is illustrated in Fig. 25.6.

The power piston vacuum channel (3) is exposed to manifold vacuum beneath the throttle valves. The vacuum in this channel varies directly with the manifold vacuum. In the idling and part-throttle ranges, the manifold vacuum is normally quite high. This vacuum is sufficient to hold the power piston (1), in its extreme "up" position. However, as the throttle valves are progressively opened, manifold

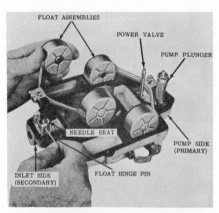

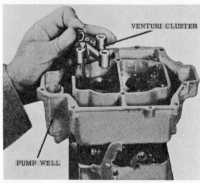

Fig. 25.5. (Above) Removing float assembly. (Below) Removing venturi cluster from Rochester 4GC carburetor.

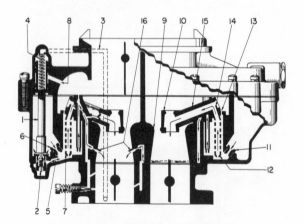

Fig. 25.6. Cross section of Rochester 4GC showing *power system*. (1) Plunger rod; (2) power valve; (3) vacuum channels; (4) power piston spring; (5) power restriction; (6) main metering jet; (7) main well tube; (8) relief passage; (9) main venturi; (10) main fuel discharge; (11) main metering jet; (12) main well tube; (13) main well bleed; (14) main discharge nozzle; (15) main discharge nozzle tube.

vacuum drops. If this vacuum drops below approximately 7″ of mercury, the calibrated spring (4) beneath the power piston forces the piston down. This situation occurs at very high driving speeds (approximately 90 mph) or on rapid acceleration.

When the piston drops down, it unseats the spring loaded power valve (2). This permits additional fuel to flow from the float bowl through the calibrated power restriction (5), and into the main well. This additional fuel supplements that already flowing through the main metering jet (6) and the main well tube (7) (on the primary side), thus making the mixture being delivered to the manifold considerably richer than normal part-throttle mixture. This power mixture continues to be supplied as long as the manifold vacuum remains below approximately 7″ of mercury. When the manifold vacuum again increases sufficiently, the force of the power piston spring (4) is overcome and the piston is drawn up, thus returning the carburetor to the economical part-throttle mixture.

Note that the power piston cavity in the carburetor air horn is connected to the main air flow passage by a vacuum break hole (8). Its purpose is to prevent the transfer of vacuum acting on the piston from acting also on the top of the fuel in the float bowl. Any leakage of air past the upper rings of the piston will be compensated for by this vacuum break hole and will not affect carburetor calibration.

It is also in this range that the secondary side of the carburetor provides additional air and fuel to the engine for increased power. For high-speed operation beyond the part-throttle range, the throttle linkage engages the secondary throttle valves and opens them completely the remaining few degrees of primary throttle travel.

Manifold vacuum or suction acting on the secondary side of the carburetor is multiplied at the primary (9) and secondary (10) venturi, and draws fuel from the float bowl through the calibrated main metering jet (11) in the main well. This fuel passes through the main well (12), and is bled in a manner similar to that discussed previously in the operation of the primary main air well bleed. This mixture is bled further at the main well bleed (13), and is drawn to the tips of the main well tubes (14). It then passes through the mixture passage (15), into the secondary venturi (10), and is discharged into the intake manifold.

The lower idle air bleed (16) also supplies fuel throughout the power range in a manner similar to that discussed under "Part-Throttle System."

Accelerating Pump System

When the throttle is opened suddenly, the air flow and manifold vacuum change almost instantly while the heavier fuel tends to lag behind, causing a momentary leanness. The accelerator pump provides the additional fuel necessary for smooth operation on rapid acceleration. Refer to Fig. 25.7.

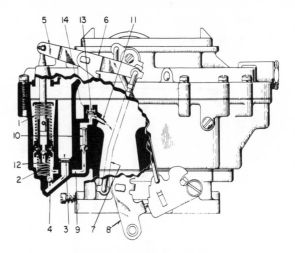

Fig. 25.7. 4GC Rochester carburetor *acceleration pump system*. (1) Pump spring; (2) pump return spring; (3) pump inlet screen; (4) pump inlet ball check; (5) pump lever; (6) throttle pump lever; (7) pump rod; (8) throttle lever; (9) pump discharge passage; (10) pump discharge needle check; (11) pump discharge nozzle; (12) plunger vent valve; (13) pump vent valve; (14) pump vent valve seat.

Since the throttle valves on the secondary or fuel inlet side of the carburetor remain fully closed throughout part-throttle operation, it is only necessary to have one accelerator pump, that being located on the primary or pump side of the carburetor.

A double-spring top plunger is used. This provides a smooth sustained charge of fuel for acceleration. The pump plunger head has been vented to minimize the effect of fuel percolation on the fuel bowl pump well. There is, therefore, always a charge of solid fuel beneath the plunger head for rapid acceleration.

Float System

To aid in maintaining the correct fuel level under all conditions of operation, two sets of twin floats are employed. Refer to Fig. 25.8.

Both sides of the carburetor incorporate individual float systems for maintaining the proper fuel level in each float bowl. All fuel enters the carburetor on the secondary or fuel inlet side.

As the fuel level on the secondary side drops, the twin floats also drop thus moving the inlet needle from its seat. Pressure from the

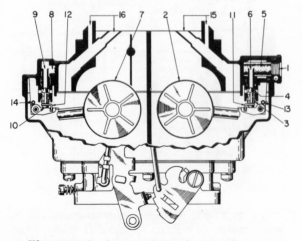

Fig. 25.8. Rochester 4GC carburetor *float system.* (1) Fuel inlet; (2) float; (3) needle valve; (4) needle valve seat; (5) fuel inlet screen; (6) fuel passage; (7) float; (8-9) fuel passages; (10) needle valve; (11-12) needle valve retainer; (13) balance spring; (14) internal vents.

fuel pump forces fuel through the filter screen into the inlet passage and the float bowl. As the fuel level rises the floats rise and once again close off the inlet needle.

As fuel is drawn from the float bowl on the primary or pump side of the carburetor, the float action is identical to that on the secondary side. Refer again to Fig. 25.8. When the twin floats drop (7), pressure from the fuel pump forces fuel through the fuel inlet (1), and filter screen (5). This fuel passes through a channel cored in the air horn and enters the inlet passage on the primary side at (8). It passes through the needle seat channel (9), past the now open inlet valve (10), and into the float bowl. As on the secondary side, when the fuel level rises the floats rise and once again close off the inlet needle.

Both sides of the carburetor are individually and internally vented by channels (15 and 16). These vents transmit pressure from beneath the air cleaner to the fuel in the float bowl. The amount of fuel metered by the carburetor is dependent upon the pressure in the float bowl causing fuel to flow. By locating the vent below the air cleaner or internally, the carburetor automatically compensates for air cleaner restriction as the same pressure causing air to flow will also be causing fuel to flow.

A cored passage in the float bowl, slightly above the normal fuel level, links the primary and secondary float bowl together. In this way any abnormal rise in level on one side will be absorbed by the other and should not seriously disrupt the operation of the engine.

Choke System

A fully automatic choke is employed to insure proper starting and driving during cold weather operation. Choking of the carburetor is necessary only on the primary or pump side due to the fact that the secondary throttle valves are locked in a closed position whenever the choke valve is even partially closed. See Fig. 25.9.

This choke system makes use of a vacuum piston and a thermostatic coil. Automatic chokes will be described in a later section.

Carter WCFB Four-Barrel Carburetor

This carburetor is basically two dual carburetors contained in one assembly. The primary side consists of two barrels and contains the typical Carter metering rod, accelerating pump and choke. The other section is called the secondary side. The five conventional systems or circuits used in Carter carburetors are also used in this unit. The Carter carburetor, using

a metering pin, needs no full-power circuit, as the metering pin provides the additional fuel which is provided by the economizer or power circuit on other carburetors.

The Float Circuit

There are two float bowls, the primary and the secondary, which are separated by a partition. Each float chamber contains two floats, which together control one needle valve. With the floats properly set in accordance with factory specifications, an adequate supply of fuel in the bowls for all operating conditions will be assured.

The two bowls are vented inside the air horn. The bowl vents are calibrated to provide proper air pressure above the fuel at all times. A connecting passage along the outside of the body affects the balance of the fuel levels and air pressures between the two bowls. The float circuit is shown in Fig. 25.10.

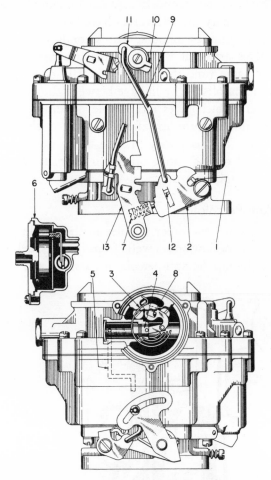

Fig. 25.9. Rochester 4GC carburetor *choke system.* (1) Fast idle cam; (2) cam lever; (3) thermostatic spring (automatic choke); (4) back of spring housing; (5) vent; (6) thermostatic spring housing; (7) throttle stop screw; (8) end of choke valve; (9) choke valve rod; (10-11) choke valve lever; (12) valve rod retainer; (13) throttle lever.

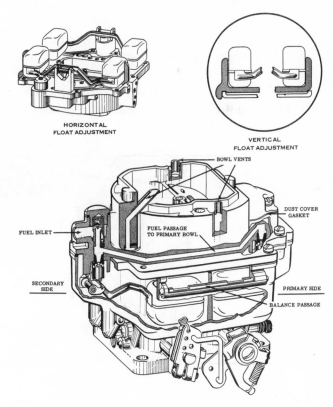

Fig. 25.10. Carter WCFB carburetor, showing the float circuit.

Low-Speed Circuit

Fuel for idle and early part-throttle operation is metered through the low-speed circuit, as shown in Fig. 25.11.

Gasoline enters the idle well through the metering rod jet on the primary side of the carburetor and through the main metering jet on the secondary side.

The low-speed jet measures the amount of fuel for idle and early part-throttle operation. The air bypass passages, economizer, and idle air bleed are carefully calibrated and serve to break up the liquid fuel and mix it with air as it moves through the passages to the idle port and idle adjustment screw port. Turning each idle adjustment screw toward its seat reduces the quantity of fuel mixture supplied by the idle circuit. There are no idle adjustment screws on the secondary side of the carburetor.

The idle ports are slot-shaped. As the throttle valves are opened, more of the idle ports are uncovered, allowing a greater quantity of fuel-air mixture to enter the carburetor bores. The secondary throttle valves remain seated at idle.

The vapor-vent ball check operated by the arm on the countershaft provides a vent for fuel vapors to escape from the carburetor bowl to the outside both at idle and when the engine is not in operation.

High-Speed Circuit

Fuel for part-throttle and full-throttle operation is supplied to the high-speed circuit as shown in Fig. 25.12.

On the primary side, the position of the metering rods in the metering rod jets controls the amount of fuel. Their position is controlled mechanically by movement of the throttle and by manifold vacuum applied to the vacuum piston and on the vacuometer link.

Fuel for the high-speed system of the secondary side is metered at the main metering jets where no metering rods are used. Throttle valves in the secondary side remain closed until the primary throttle valves have been opened a predetermined amount. The secondary throttle valves arrive at wide-open throttle position at the same time the primary throttle does. This is accomplished by linkage between the throttle levers which gives more rapid opening of the secondary throttles after they once start to move. The secondary throttle valves are locked closed during choke operation to insure faster cold-engine starting.

Anti-Percolator

To prevent vapor bubbles in the nozzle passages and low-speed wells from forcing fuel out of the nozzle, anti-percolator passages and cali-

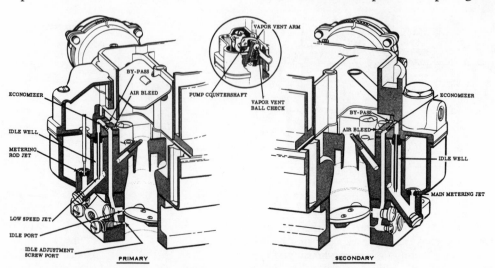

Fig. 25.11. Carter WCFB carburetor, showing the low-speed circuit.

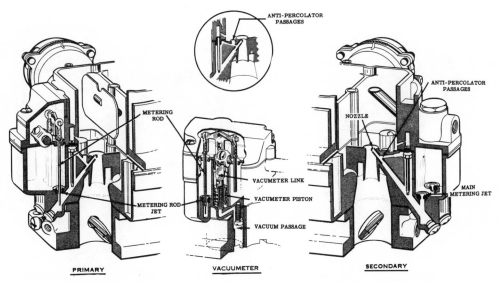

Fig. 25.12. Carter WCFB carburetor, showing the high-speed circuit.

brated plugs or bushings are used. Their purpose is to vent the vapors and relieve the pressure before it is sufficient to push the fuel out of the nozzle and into the intake manifold.

Pump Circuit

The accelerating pump circuit is found only in the primary side of the carburetor. It provides the measured amount of fuel necessary to insure smooth engine operation for acceleration and speeds below approximately 30 mph. Pump action in the four-barrel carburetor is the same as in other Carter single- and double-barrel carburetors. Refer to Fig. 25.13.

At speeds above 30 mph, pump discharge is no longer necessary to insure acceleration. Therefore, when the throttle valves are open a predetermined amount the pump plunger bottoms in the pump cylinder eliminating further pump discharge.

Choke Circuit

The choke circuit, shown in Fig. 25.14, is controlled by the climatic control or automatic choke similar to that used on other Carter carburetors. A piston and thermostatic spring operate as controls; these will be described in more detail in the section on the automatic

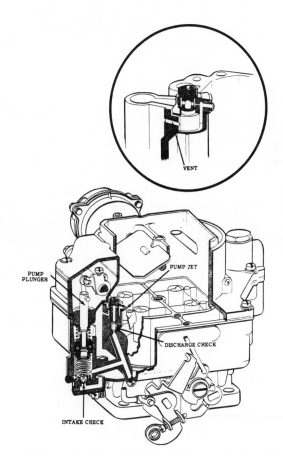

Fig. 25.13. Carter WCFB carburetor, showing the pump circuit.

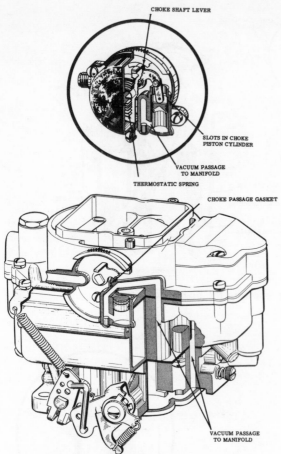

Fig. 25.14. Carter WCFB carburetor, showing the choke circuit.

choke. Only the primary barrels are equipped with choke plates.

Ford Four-Barrel Carburetor

The Ford four-barrel carburetor has two main assemblies, the air horn and the main body. The air horn assembly, which serves as the main body cover, contains the choke plates, the vents for the fuel bowls and the secondary throttle-control vacuum tube. Fig. 25.15 shows a ¾ front view; Fig. 25.16 shows a bottom view.

The primary and secondary throttle plates, the accelerating pump assembly, the power valve assembly, the secondary operating diaphragm assembly, and the fuel bowls are in the main body. The automatic choke housing is attached to the main body.

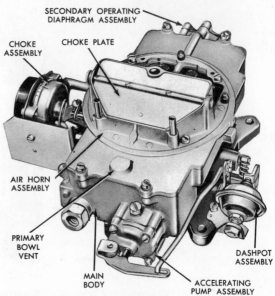

Fig. 25.15. Ford four-barrel carburetor, ¾ front view, showing the choke plate, slow closing throttle dashpot, and accelerating pump assembly.

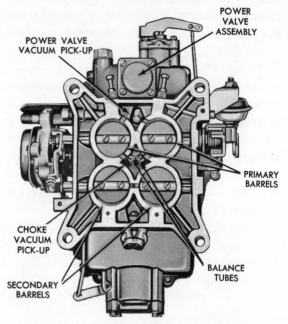

Fig. 25.16. Ford four-barrel carburetor, bottom view. The power valve assembly and arrangement of the four barrels can be clearly seen.

The two primary (front) barrels each contain a main and booster venturi, main fuel discharge, accelerating pump discharge, idle fuel discharge and a primary throttle plate. The two secondary (rear) barrels each have a main booster venturi, idle fuel discharge, secondary main fuel discharge and a vacuum-operated throttle plate.

A separate fuel bowl is provided for the primary and secondary stage. The fuel first enters the primary bowl through the fuel inlet. A drilled passage through the right side of the main body connects the fuel bowls. There is a separate float and needle valve for each float chamber to control the fuel level.

The power fuel system is controlled by manifold vacuum. This vacuum acts on a diaphragm which controls the power fuel valve. The diaphragm holds the valve closed at idle speed or normal load conditions. When the vacuum drops with opened throttle, a spring in the valve housing opens the valve, allowing extra fuel to be discharged into the air stream flowing through the venturi.

As the primary throttle plates are opened, primary venturi vacuum increases to operate the secondary throttles. When this vacuum reaches a predetermined amount, it starts to act on the secondary-stage operating diaphragm which in turn starts to open the secondary throttle plates.

Holley Four-Barrel Carburetor

The Holley four-barrel carburetor is a two-stage unit. It can be considered as two dual carburetors, one supplying a suitable fuel-air mixture throughout the entire range of engine operation (primary stage) and the other functioning only when a greater quantity of fuel-air mixture is required (secondary stage). Fig. 25.17 shows a ¾ front view of the Holley Carburetor. Fig. 25.18 shows a bottom view.

The primary stage (front section) contains a fuel bowl, metering block and an accelerating pump assembly. The primary barrels each contain a primary and booster venturi, main fuel discharge nozzle, throttle plate and idle fuel passage. The choke plate, mounted in the air horn above the primary barrels, is automatically controlled.

The secondary stage (rear section) of the carburetor contains a fuel bowl, metering body, and a secondary throttle-operating diaphragm assembly. The secondary barrels each contain a primary and secondary booster venturi, idle fuel passages, main secondary fuel discharge nozzle and throttle plate.

There are four primary stage fuel systems and two secondary stage fuel systems. A fuel inlet system for both primary and secondary stages

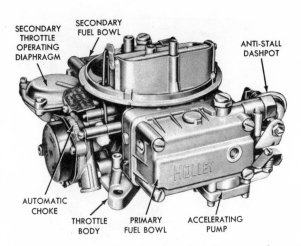

Fig. 25.17. Holley four-barrel carburetor, front view, showing the automatic choke, secondary throttle operating diaphragm, accelerating pump and anti-stall dashpot.

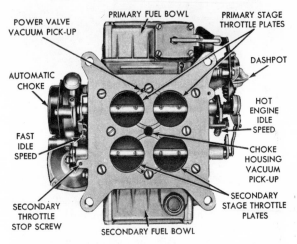

Fig. 25.18. Holley four-barrel carburetor, bottom view, with important parts indicated.

provides the various fuel metering systems with a constant supply of fuel. In addition, an automatic choke system provides a means of temporarily enriching the fuel mixture to aid in starting a cold engine.

Fuel-air mixture is supplied from both the primary and secondary stages during operation of the idle system. During part-throttle operation of the engine, the fuel-air mixture is supplied from the primary part-throttle system. The power system works with manifold vacuum in the same way as in the Ford four-barrel carburetor.

The secondary throttles are controlled by primary venturi vacuum, similar to the Ford carburetor.

Automatic Choke

The discussion of the choke circuit in Chapter 24 pointed out the reasons a choke is needed for starting the engine. A majority of the cars now use automatic chokes for this purpose, so that the operator is not required to regulate this necessary part of engine starting.

The automatic choke performs three duties: (1) closes the choke valve entirely on cold engines before the starter turns over the engine, (2) opens the choke valve part way as soon as the engine starts firing, and (3) opens the choke valve completely when the engine reaches a good running temperature.

The detailed arrangement of the automatic choke devices varies somewhat in the five makes of carburetors, but all of them use vacuum to open the choke part way when the engine starts firing.

An integral part of the carburetor, the automatic choke consists primarily of two major assemblies: (1) the thermostatic coil spring and housing assembly and (2) the assembly, consisting of piston housing, choke shaft, lever, screen, and piston. Refer to Fig. 25.19.

The operation of the automatic choke is governed by intake manifold vacuum, exhaust manifold temperature, and velocity of air stream through the air horn. When the engine fires on initial starting, the vacuum created in the manifold pulls the piston down, exerting tension on the thermostatic spring and opening the choke valve far enough for initial running. Hot air is drawn from the "stove" on the exhaust manifold through the connecting pipe

Fig. 25.19. The climatic control (automatic choke) used by Carter has the choke valve closed when the engine is cold. As soon as the engine fires, the intake manifold vacuum operates the vacuum cylinder C, partially opening the choke. As the engine warms up, the thermostatic spring S fully opens the choke.

Fig. 25.20. Automatic choke adjustment used on Holley and Ford carburetors. To increase the spring tension, loosen the three screws and turn the thermostatic spring counterclockwise.

and screen to the automatic choke housing and around the piston to the carburetor and intake manifold. The adjustment is shown in Fig. 25.20.

As the heat increases around the thermostatic spring, the spring loses its tension allowing the choke to open gradually. After it reaches its full open position, it will remain open of its own weight. Sudden acceleration during warm-up period results in a decrease in manifold vacuum which would allow the coil to pull the choke valve to full choke position. During this time the increased air velocity strikes the off-center pivoted choke valve and tends to push the choke valve open thus preventing a *loading condition*. When the engine is stopped, the thermostatic spring cools off, and revolves the choke valve to the closed position. Fig. 25.21 shows the Holley automatic choke system.

Summary

Since 1952 *four-barrel carburetors* have been used on V-8 engines where high performance is desired.

The *primary side* completely controls the metering of fuel to the engine throughout the idle and part-throttle range.

The *secondary side* supplements the fuel from the primary side throughout the power or wide open throttle range.

The *Rochester 4GC carburetor* has the idle system, part-throttle system, power system, accelerating pump system, float, and choke system in the two primary barrels. The primary and secondary sides of the carburetor each have their own float system.

The *Carter WCFB four-barrel carburetor* also makes use of separate float systems for the primary and secondary sides. Typical of the Carter design, metering rods replace the usual power enrichment system.

An *anti-percolator valve* is included to prevent fuel being forced out of the nozzle by vapor bubbles in the nozzle passages and low speed wells.

The *Ford four-barrel carburetor* is similar in general design to the Rochester, with separate float systems for primary and secondary sides of the carburetor.

The *Holley four-barrel carburetor* also follows conventional carburetor design. The secondary throttles are controlled by primary venturi vacuum, in a manner similar to the Ford carburetor.

An *automatic choke* performs three duties: (1) closes the choke valve entirely before the starter turns over the engine, (2) opens the choke valve part way as soon as the engine starts firing, and (3) opens the choke valve all the way when the engine has reached a good running temperature. The automatic choke is provided with a vacuum cylinder with a connection to the intake manifold. When the engine starts to operate, it builds up a vacuum in the manifold, opening the choke slightly by the action of the piston. The choke opens wide when the engine heats up, by means of a thermostatic spring.

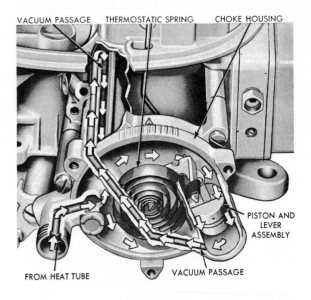

Fig. 25.21. Cut-away view of the Holley automatic choke system. The vacuum passage and heat tube are indicated. At lower right is the piston that partially opens the choke plate as the engine is started.

Questions

1. What companies supply four-barrel carburetors?
2. What does the primary side of the four-barrel carburetor control?
3. What does the secondary side control?
4. What is the purpose of the secondary side?
5. Where does the idle fuel supply come from on the Rochester four-barrel carburetor?
6. What causes the secondary throttle plates to open on the Rochester Four-Barrel?
7. What actuates the power system on the Rochester Four-Barrel?
8. What is the purpose of the accelerating pump system?
9. How many floats are there in four-barrel carburetors?
10. How many systems or circuits are used on Carter four-barrel carburetors?
11. What is the distinctive feature of Carter carburetors?
12. How many idle adjustment screws are used on Carter four-barrel units?
13. What controls the position of the metering rods on Carter four-barrel carburetors?
14. What is the purpose of the anti-percolating valve?
15. How are the secondary throttles opened on Ford four-barrel carburetors?
16. How is the power fuel system controlled on Ford units?
17. Where does the idle fuel supply come from on Holley four-barrel carburetors?
18. How are the secondary throttles controlled on the Holley?
19. What are the two major assemblies of the automatic choke?
20. What is the purpose of the choke system?
21. What causes the automatic choke initial opening when the engine starts?
22. What causes the automatic choke to open fully as the engine warms up to operating temperature?
23. What does the automatic choke do when the engine stops and is allowed to cool to atmospheric temperature?
24. What prevents closing of the choke valve when vacuum drops on sudden acceleration of a cold engine?
25. How should the automatic choke be adjusted?

CHAPTER TWENTY-SIX

The Fuel System—
Maintenance
and Troubles

Air Cleaners

The early air cleaners consisted, in many cases, of a housing containing oil-moistened steel wool with suitable air passages to silence the air flow. This type was followed by the oil-bath air cleaner which did a much better job. In the oil-bath air cleaner, the air flow is directed downward and across a pool of engine oil so that any air-borne dust is thrown out of the air stream due to its reversal of direction. Passages are so arranged that the cleaner also acts as a silencer. Refer to Fig. 26.1. A high oil level in the oil-bath air cleaner will restrict the flow of

air and will cut down engine performance, especially at high speed.

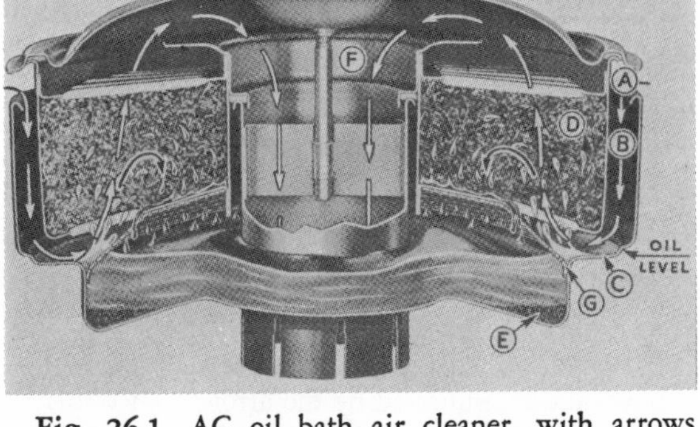

About 1956 the current type of corrugated paper air cleaners was adopted, largely because the trend to lower hood lines allowed less vertical space for the cleaner. The new type did not have to be directly over the carburetor, but could be offset at an angle, and also could be made considerably thinner than the oil-bath type. See Fig. 26.2. The treated, corrugated

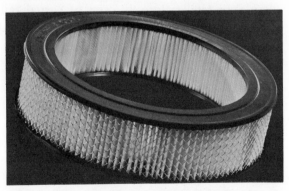

Fig. 26.2. Typical replacement cartridge for air cleaner. In some cases, if the accumulated dust and foreign matter is dry, it can be shaken off, but generally it is best to put in a new one. An obstructed cleaner will restrict the air for combustion and will affect engine performance.

Fig. 26.1. AC oil bath air cleaner, with arrows showing the path taken by the air. Be sure that the oil is at the correct depth.

paper cleaner is very effective but it requires occasional inspection and replacement, especially in dusty sections of the country, as the pores in the paper filtering medium may become clogged and restrict the flow of air to the carburetor.

In cases of unsatisfactory engine operation where the engine acts as if it is not breathing normally, check the air cleaner and replace it if necessary. With dirty air cleaners, where the accumulated dust is dry, a considerable proportion can be shaken off by removing the cleaner element and brushing and bumping it against a flat surface. However, the usual procedure is to put in a new one.

Beginning with the 1963 models, some of the cars, notably some Ford models, run the crankcase blowby into the air cleaner in connection with the crankcase ventilating system. This eliminates some smog production, but may shorten the useful life of the air cleaner considerably by clogging it with varnish and oily material from the crankcase.

Fuel Pump

Fuel pumps require no maintenance or service as long as they are performing satisfactorily. However, the entire fuel system should be inspected periodically, as shown in Fig. 26.3.

Fuel pump trouble may show up as either partial or total failure. In cases of partial failure, the action will be defective due to a tiny leak in the pump diaphragm, a slightly warped check valve, a dirty strainer, loosened screws around the pump housing or worn pump linkage.

Total failure will be due to a ruptured diaphragm, broken pump spring or excessively worn or broken linkage. In cases of either partial or total failure, the pump should be tested and if not up to specifications, should be repaired or replaced.

Fuel pumps should be tested in different ways. If a pressure gauge is connected in the line on the discharge side and shows from $1\frac{1}{2}$ to $5\frac{1}{2}$ pounds pressure, depending upon the specification for the car being checked, the pump will usually be satisfactory. A second test is to see that the carburetor float chamber is full; then disconnect the discharge side of the pump and start the engine again. Catch the discharged fuel in a container and measure the amount. For engines up to 225 cubic-inch displacement, the discharge should be from $\frac{3}{4}$ pint to one pint, in one minute. For larger engines, from

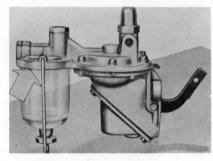

Fig. 26.4. Fuel pumps may leak at the sediment bowl gasket, indicated by the arrows. Since this is on the suction side, leaks will prevent gas from going to the pump. Whenever the bowl is cleaned, a new gasket should be used.

Fig. 26.3. Periodically the whole fuel system should be checked for leaks at joints, cracked tubing, leaks at the fuel pump, leaks at the carburetor, and flooding of the float bowl.

225 up to 400 cubic inches, the volume mentioned should be discharged in 45 seconds.

If there is any doubt about the pump, remove it so that it can be tested for both suction and pressure with a combination pressure and vacuum gauge. Connect the gauge first to the suction side and work the lever by hand. A vacuum of from 6 to 8 inches should be indicated on the gauge and held for approximately 30 seconds when the valves in the pump are dry. Then connect the gauge on the pressure side; the pressure should be from 1½ to 5½ pounds, in accordance with the specifications, and should also hold for 15 to 30 seconds.

If the gas flow is restricted or there is no flow, check the following:

1. Look for a leaking sediment bowl gasket, Fig. 26.4. This is on the suction side and if the gasket is not tight, it will permit air to leak in and break the suction on the suction side of the pump. To be sure about this, it is advisable to put in a new bowl gasket.

2. Remove and clean or replace the strainer or filter.

3. Check for loose fuel line connections all the way back to the tank. Trace all connections. Here again, loose connections may admit air which will break the suction and prevent fuel from being drawn out of the tank.

4. Disconnect the suction line at the fuel pump. Using an air line, blow compressed air through the line from the fuel pump to the tank to remove any foreign matter from the line. Also disconnect the line from the fuel pump to the carburetor and blow air through it.

5. Be sure all pump cover screws and external covers over pump valves are tight. In some cases, there is a drain valve in the strainer compartment. If this is loose, it will keep the pump from operating.

6. Check flexible lines where these are used on the suction side. If there is a small leak or break, it will permit air to get in on the suction side of the pump line, destroying the pump's ability to draw fuel from the fuel tank.

Be sure that there is fuel in the fuel tank and that the vent is open to atmosphere as a restricted tank vent will prevent fuel from flowing to the pump.

Remember that a pump which has been operating satisfactorily cannot build up excessive pressure. The fuel discharge pressure depends entirely upon the strength of the spring which forces the diaphragm up after being drawn down on the suction by mechanical action of the lever and cam.

Fuel pumps are comparatively inexpensive, and therefore, considering the labor involved, there will be just about the same expense involved to replace the fuel pump as to try and repair it. If the type of fuel pump required is not available, or if labor conditions make it profitable to do so, it is a simple matter to rebuild the pump, putting in a new diaphragm, new pins and levers, and where necessary, new valves and a new gasket at the bowl.

Vacuum Pump Troubles

If the windshield wiper does not maintain its uniform speed with open throttle, the vacuum pump is not performing as it should. Check the tubing line to the wiper. If the trouble is not in the line, it will be in the vacuum pump.

Noisy vacuum pump operation usually indicates either a worn or improperly installed oil seal or a worn vacuum tube link and rocker arm.

In some cases high gasoline pressure and noise may be caused by the fuel pump striking the vacuum pump diaphragm.

If the vacuum pump diaphragm is punctured or ruptured, oil will be drawn from the crankcase causing high oil consumption and possibly ignition irregularity due to fouled spark plugs. Refer to Fig. 26.5. With a small hole, the trouble first encountered may be an occasional miss on the two cylinders adjacent to the spot

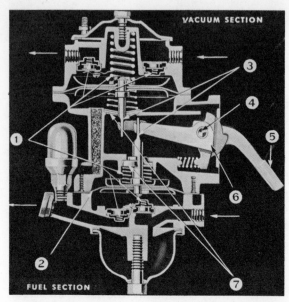

Fig. 26.5. AC combination fuel and vacuum pump. If the diaphragm on the vacuum pump leaks, it will draw oil out of the oil pan. This may give the impression that the engine is burning an excessive amount of oil. The diaphragm or pump should be replaced.

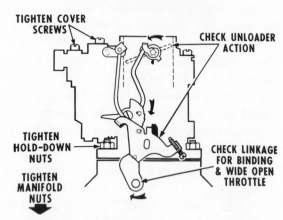

Fig. 26.6. Several mechanical checks should be made on the carburetor when diagnosis and tune-up work are done.

where the vacuum line taps the manifold. A large hole will cause missing at low speeds with the throttle closed, due to the amount of air leaking into the manifold. This condition can be checked (1) by observing the action of the wiper, (2) with a vacuum gauge, or (3) by disconnecting the line on the manifold side of the vacuum pump and inspecting for oil.

The combination fuel and vacuum pump is more complicated and more difficult to disassemble and reassemble than a plain fuel pump. Therefore, consideration should be given as to whether it is less expensive to repair or replace the pump.

Detailed instructions for disassembling and reassembling the different models of either the single pump or the combination pump can be obtained from the makers of this equipment.

Carburetors

As discussed previously, the function of the carburetor is to supply a suitable explosive mixture of fuel and air so that the engine can operate properly under all conditions of speed and load.

As long as there is an adequate supply of fuel, all fuel passages are clean, and the various parts of the carburetor are working as they should, the engine, as affected by the fuel system, will operate satisfactorily. However, if any of the carburetor components function improperly, the engine will either run poorly, use excessive fuel, or not run at all. Fig. 26.6 shows points to watch.

Occasionally, the throttle lever will loosen on the throttle shaft. When this happens, proper adjustment of idle speed will be impossible. The throttle lever must be repaired or the carburetor replaced. There is a correction for this condition which can be obtained at most parts houses.

The float needle valve is always a possible source of trouble. If it or the float should stick in a closed or partly closed position, the flow of fuel will be restricted. The float bowl will flood if the float needle does not close properly against the pressure of the fuel from the fuel pump, if it is worn excessively, or if the float leaks and loses its buoyancy. This usually will cause hard engine starting, frequent engine stoppage, and very poor or intermittent operation of the engine at low speeds. Worn needle valves are shown in Fig. 26.7.

Usually this trouble can be remedied by removing both the float needle valve and its seat and conditioning the valve so that it will work freely. With the valve in position in the seat and both removed from the carburetor, it is a good idea to give a light, sharp tap on the end of the needle valve so that it will go against the seat, thereby removing any foreign matter or slight irregularities. If the needle is worn, it is necessary to replace both needle and seat; check to see that the valve works freely against the seat before inserting them in the carburetor. Always check the float to be sure it works freely and easily from lowest to highest position and that it has its normal buoyancy.

Leaking float needle valves are usually caused by deposits of foreign matter on the needle seat. However, neoprene-tipped needles are now available which will prevent leaks even though the seat may have dirt or metal particles on it. Fig. 26.8 illustrates how the needle seat may be damaged.

Float adjustment is important so that it will maintain fuel level in the float chamber at the specified point within the allowable tolerance. High float level will reduce the distance from the level of the fuel to the level of the main discharge nozzle and will result in an over-rich mixture, causing high fuel consumption and below normal engine performance. Low float level will cause an opposite condition, resulting in a lean mixture. Engine performance may be affected, and a sufficiently lean mixture may result in burned valves.

The correct float level is reestablished by bending the float arm in accordance with the manufacturer's specification; this is one of the important adjustments that should be made any

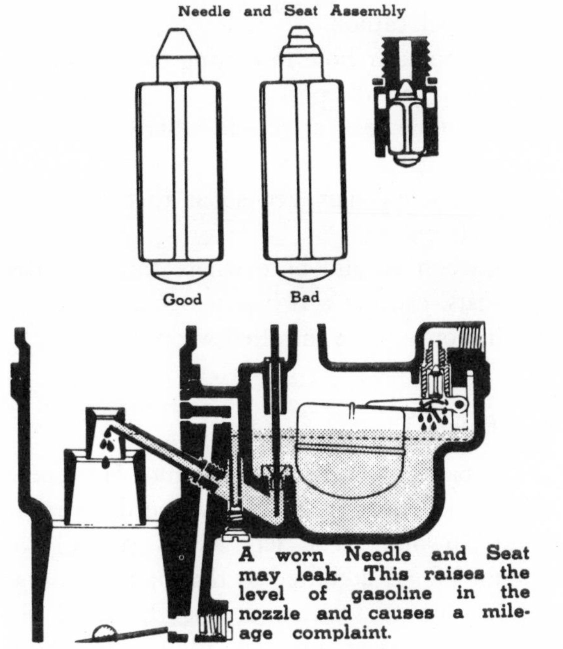

Fig. 26.7. Carburetors with high mileage will frequently have worn needle valves which will leak. Wear also may cause a high fuel level which will waste fuel.

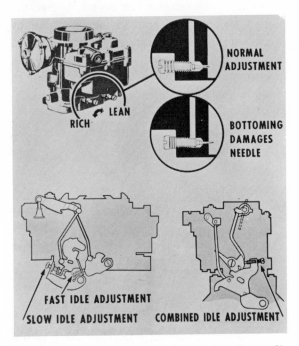

Fig. 26.8. (Upper) Common way that the needle valve seat in the idle system can be damaged. (Lower) Location of fast idle and slow idle adjustments.

time work is done on the carburetor. The setting is usually given as the distance from either the cover to the float or from the metal edge of the float bowl to the top of the float depending upon the particular carburetor model and design. Fig. 26.9 illustrates checking the float level.

Low-Speed System or Idle System

This system includes a number of passages and small openings for both fuel and air. It also includes the idle mixture adjusting screw. If a portion or portions of the system become obstructed or worn, the delicate balance which must exist will be destroyed.

There are two adjustments to be made on the low-speed system, with the engine operating; (1) idle speed, and (2) idle mixture. The idle speed should be set at 450 to 500 rpm except where automatic transmissions are used. In the latter case, set the speed in accordance with the car builder's specifications. Refer again to Fig. 26.8 for idle adjustments.

Normally, the engine can be set to give the highest vacuum and best engine operation by means of the idle mixture adjusting screw. Nevertheless, occasionally abuse, loose parts, or errors in assembly may make it impossible to obtain a good adjustment.

Possible Causes of Lean Idle
1. Restricted metering hole in low-speed jet. Replace.

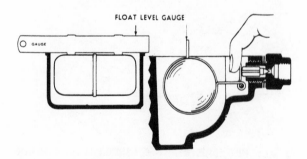

Fig. 26.9. Checking float position on Carter B-B carburetor with gauge. Whenever carburetors are worked on, the float position should be in accordance with maker's specifications.

2. Oversize air bypass or bleed-in hole in casting oversize.
3. Restricted economizer hole in casting.
4. Restrictions in casting passage from low-speed jet to port hole and idle screw.
5. Port opening too small.
6. Port hole restricted.
7. Hole restricted in casting where idle screw seats.
8. Thread in casting carbonized not letting idle adjustment screw regulate the amount of air needed to adjust carburetor.
9. Air leak at flange gasket.
10. Idle screw burned.
11. Port plug loose or not seated in casting.
12. Loose lever on throttle shaft making it hard to get correct idle adjustment.

Possible Causes of Rich Idle
1. Unsoldered head on low-speed jet.
2. Worn or too large metering hole in low-speed jet.
3. Upper end of low-speed jet not seated in casting.
4. Air bleed or bypass hole in casting restricted with carbon.
5. Economizer hole in casting too large.
6. Damaged idle port.
7. Gasoline leak at nozzle where it seats in casting.
8. Idle screw damaged so as to prevent adjustment.
9. Carbon around bore where throttle valve seats, causing a rich port opening.
10. Throttle valve installed wrong.

Part-Power Throttle System

The part-power throttle system or high-speed circuit takes over from the low-speed system at about 20 mph. The jets which control the amount of gas admitted to the main discharge nozzle, due to vacuum at the throat of the venturi, are fixed and not adjustable. Therefore, on a carburetor where this system quits working as it should, there are several possible causes which might make the fuel-air mixture too lean or too rich. Fig. 26.10 illustrates the power system.

Causes for Lean Condition

1. Low fuel pump pressure.
2. Restrictions in gas line connection to needle seat which does not allow sufficient gasoline to enter the bowl for high-speed driving.
3. Low float level.
4. Opening in needle seat too small due to restrictions or to wrong needle and seat.
5. Restrictions outside vent bore.
6. Air horn assembly loose on casting.
7. Worn throttle shaft.
8. Porous intake manifold.
9. Excessively worn intake valve stem guides.

Causes for Rich Condition:

1. High fuel pump pressure.
2. High float level.
3. Warped or bent bowl cover allowing an air leak at the gasket.
4. Choke valve hinge stuck in air horn, causing carburetor to be partly choked.
5. Dirty air cleaner.
6. Choke not operating properly.
7. Clogged air bleed in air bleed nozzle.

There is always the possibility, when a carburetor has been serviced or rebuilt that the wrong parts were used, parts were incorrectly installed, or the carburetor may have been improperly assembled. In diagnosing carburetor troubles, it is always wise to find out from the owner if the carburetor is the one which has been on the car for some time or if it is a replacement unit.

In general, if a carburetor has been used long enough to build up deposits which need cleaning, it is advisable to thoroughly "boil it out" and also install new jets, new gaskets, float needle valve and seat, new pump leather, and possibly a new economizer valve. If the carburetor uses fabric or neoprene diaphragms for the economizer or accelerating pump, it is advisable to check the condition of these and possibly replace them also.

Accelerating Pump

The accelerating pump is operated by the movement of the throttle lever, either directly or through linkage. On a number of carburetor models, the pump operating link may be placed in two or three positions, to discharge more or less gasoline with each pump stroke. The greater amount is for cold weather operation and the smaller amount for warm weather operation. Naturally, using the longer pump stroke for summer operation will cut fuel economy. A typical accelerating pump is shown in Fig. 26.11.

Being made of leather, the plunger cup will eventually need replacing.

Poor accelerating pump performance will cause too lean a mixture on acceleration, never too rich. The causes of lean mixture are:

1. Weak plunger spring. Replace.
2. Worn, cracked, damaged, or dried-out plunger leather, or weak pump spring. Replace.
3. Leather loose, not installed tightly on plunger.

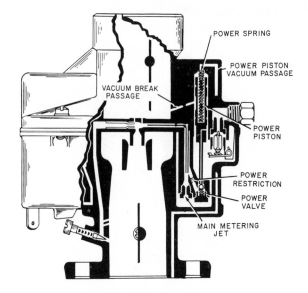

Fig. 26.10. Power system on model B Rochester carburetor. Note the vacuum piston (upper right) which operates the power valve. The latter opens when full power for acceleration, hill climbing, or top speed is wanted. If it is inoperative, the engine performance will be affected.

4. Wrong plunger assembly.

5. Intake or discharge check valves not seated properly in casting.

6. Leaking or sticking discharge or intake valve. Replace.

7. Passages in casting or pump restricted.

8. Pump jet restricted or not seated properly in casting.

9. Pump disc check sticking or leaking. Replace.

10. Pump not adjusted properly.

11. Worn linkage from throttle to accelerating pump. Replace. When throttle is moved open from closed position, the pump jet should start to discharge instantly. Therefore, there should be little play in these parts.

Carburetor Passages

The modern carburetor contains a number of passages, openings, recesses and compartments. Under some conditions of operation, long periods of non-use and/or with some gasolines, there may be deposits in the nature of gums, varnishes, scale or powder. These deposits may clog or restrict passages and/or jets. Therefore, it becomes necessary to "boil out" the carburetor body. For this operation it is necessary to remove all the jets, floats, pump and leather, fiber or cork parts and gaskets.

The cleaning is done by one of the solvents prepared for this purpose. It may be used either hot or cold, depending upon the directions supplied by the maker. This treatment will ordinarily thoroughly clean out all small passages, corners, and crevices, and make the carburetor body as good as new, barring mechanical wear due to years of use. It will take anywhere from half an hour to several hours for the solvent to do its job thoroughly. After the cleaning is completed, check to see that all of the solvent is out of the carburetor, particularly the small passages drilled or cored in its body. Fig. 26.12 shows some of the carburetor passages.

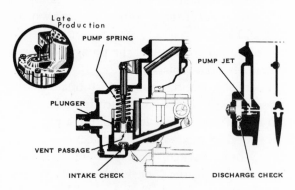

Fig. 26.11. Accelerating pump circuit on Carter BBC carburetor. The accelerating pump supplies fuel to give a smooth transition from idle to high speed system operation. It is actuated by the throttle movement.

Automatic Choke Adjustments and Troubles

Since the Carter automatic choke is widely used, the troubles that may affect its operation will be discussed. Problems with the other automatic chokes will be largely similar to those of the Carter.

On most automatic choke models, there is a screen in the hot air line to prevent dirt and

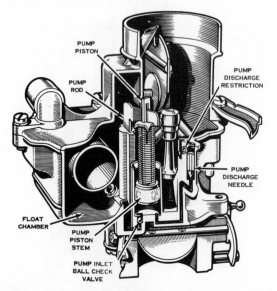

Fig. 26.12. Holley carburetors, used on Ford and Mercury cars, is simple to work on. The main parts, except for the diaphragm power valve, are shown here.

soot from entering the thermostatic spring housing. If this screen is clogged, it will restrict the flow of warm air from the manifold and will cause the choke to open too slowly, resulting in poor gasoline economy. A clogged screen must be washed thoroughly with gasoline and blown out with compressed air. It should be cleaned every 500 miles and replaced if damaged. See Fig. 26.13.

Except for cleaning the screen and checking the moving parts to see that they are operating freely, the adjustment of the unit itself should seldom be required as the choke is properly calibrated when originally installed on the car.

If the initial and part-throttle running mixture is too lean or too rich, the thermostat housing should be revolved as indicated on the housing face. Under normal conditions, it will seldom be necessary to enrich or lean out the choke from the standard factory setting, and if done, it should only be one or two graduations.

To clean the screen on units having the vertical choke pistons, simply remove the choke housing and take out the screen. If the piston has a circular stroke the carburetor will have to be removed before the screen can be.

Always check the vacuum piston for free movement. If it is not working freely, the choke valve will not open the valve part way when the engine fires and the engine will die.

To properly adjust the operating lever on the shaft, block the throttle approximately one-fourth of the way open. Remove the air cleaner from the carburetor so the position of the choke valve can be observed. Move the automatic choke lever until the hole in the brass shaft lines up with the slot in the bearing. Insert a rod, approximately 1/8″ in diameter, through the hole in the shaft. Push it all the way down to the manifold so that it engages in the base of the automatic choke. Loosen the clamp screw on the automatic choke lever and push the lever upward until the carburetor choke valve is tightly closed. Hold the lever in this position and tighten the clamp screw in it.

Then remove the adjusting tool, replace the air cleaner and check to be sure that the position of the air cleaner clamp does not make the choke valve bind. Check with the carburetor throttle partly open to see that all the mechanism operates freely. The hairpin-shaped thermostat in the base of the choke is not a spring, but is the operating thermostat which opens the choke as the engine warms up. It should not be bent or handled in any way. The Ford automatic choke is shown in Fig. 26.14.

Fig. 26.13. The climate control (automatic choke) must have all parts working freely. The heater, clogged at times from exhaust manifold carbon, must be cleaned.

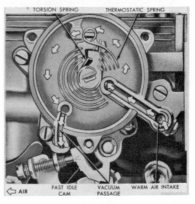

Fig. 26.14. Automatic choke used on Ford carburetor, with cover removed to show thermostatic spring. The arrows show the direction of air flow.

A leak at the choke suction-tube rubber gasket will decrease the action of the manifold vacuum on the choke piston. This will allow the choke to remain partially closed during low-speed operation as the engine warms up, and will result in poor gasoline economy at low speed. A leaking gasket must be replaced.

A leaking choke heater tube or connection should either be replaced or tightened, for an air leak at this point will prevent the control from functioning properly.

If the choke cover cork gaskets are shrunk or broken they will allow cold air to enter the cover, thereby slowing the opening action of the choke. New gaskets should be installed.

The choke linkage may be sticking, bent or improperly adjusted. All of these troubles will give the same result as a sticking choke valve and should be corrected so that the choke valve will be free to fall of its own weight.

A choke valve which is sticking may be caused by a bent shaft, an improperly installed choke valve or a warped air horn, which may be caused by clamping the air horn too tightly. Hard starting will result if the choke valve sticks open. If the valve sticks closed or partly closed it may result in hard starting and will probably cause poor gasoline economy as well as affecting all engine performance. Sticking parts should be freed and damaged parts should be replaced.

Under some conditions the choke piston may stick, or grit may get in it to slow it down so that the valve will not open properly when the engine starts; this will cause overchoking. If the piston and cylinder cannot be readily cleaned or if they are excessively worn, they should both be replaced. The thermostatic coil should never be removed from the cover. If damaged, the entire cover must be replaced.

Other Factors Affecting Performance and Economy

The carburetor flange may be loose on the manifold. If either nut on the manifold flange studs is loose as much as one-half turn, a sufficient amount of air will enter the intake manifold below the throttle to upset the idle and all engine performance. If a tight fit cannot be obtained by tightening the nut, a new gasket should be put in place. Be sure the old gasket is completely removed.

The throttle linkage may be improperly adjusted. If the linkage is adjusted so that the accelerator pedal will strike the floorboard before the throttle valve is wide open it will result in a low top speed.

The gasoline line may possibly be restricted. This will probably result in an apparent vapor lock action or it may cause a definite cut-off in the supply of gasoline. It can generally be corrected by blowing out the line with compressed air, but in some cases the line may have to be replaced.

The exhaust line may possibly be restricted. Quite often a tail pipe is found to be partially plugged by dirt or some other foreign substance. This is generally caused by backing into a dirt bank at the side of the road. Also, sometimes the engine exhaust pipe might be bent, crushed or obstructed by backing into a curb or wall. Such a restriction in the exhaust system will affect all engine performance.

The intake manifold may possibly be restricted with gum from gasoline or carbon build-up. A deposit of gasoline gum in the intake manifold will restrict the flow of air and gasoline to the engine, affecting all engine performance with a definite loss in power. In some cases the manifold can be cleaned by using acetone or a half-and-half mixture of benzol and denatured alcohol. A porous intake manifold is always a possibility. Test for this by brushing with gasoline and checking with a combustion analyzer. Occasionally it may be necessary to replace the manifold.

Manifold Heat Control

The manifold heat control should always be checked as it may be improperly adjusted, the thermostatic spring may have been disconnected during a tappet adjustment and then not properly installed, or the shaft that operates the damper may stick due to carbon building up around it. This valve is shown in Fig. 26.15.

In cases where the heat control shaft sticks, which is quite frequent, the valve must be freed so it will work easily. Sometimes this can be done by merely working the valve lever back and forth; but if this is not effective, a suitable solvent must be used. In the event that it cannot be made to work freely, the valve should be replaced.

If the heat control is so adjusted that it holds too much heat in the intake manifold, the engine will ping upon acceleration even though the ignition is timed properly. The engine also will have an apparent flat spot because of over-expansion of the fuel and air in the intake manifold.

If this control valve is adjusted to open too early, insufficient heat is retained in the intake manifold which will result in slow warm-up causing poor gasoline economy on short trips. If the thermostatic spring happens to become disengaged or is broken, the entire heat control system is destroyed, causing a decided loss in engine performance and gasoline economy.

Vacuum Spark Advance

The vacuum spark advance connection which goes to the intake manifold may leak at times. This will allow air to enter the carburetor throat in excess of that considered in the calibration of the carburetor and may result in poor gasoline economy through part-throttle intermediate speeds because of incorrect operation of the vacuum spark advance.

The diaphragm which operates the spark advance linkage may rupture or develop a leak. In this case the advance mechanism will not operate correctly and engine performance will not be satisfactory. Also, it is possible for gasoline vapors to get into the distributor and explode,

blowing off the distributor cap and possibly causing damage to the distributor.

Whenever work is done on the distributor, the spark advance linkage should be worked by hand to give assurance that it is working freely, and this should be checked in case of trouble in the ignition system.

Windshield Wiper Hose

The windshield wiper hose and its connections may leak. This condition will result in leanness in some cylinders and poor gasoline economy at all speeds. Generally it is necessary to replace the hose to stop the leak. This hose, being rubber, will dry out in time and may possibly crack or become loose, either at the connection to the operating valve or that to the windshield wiper motor. An electric windshield wiper unit does not present this possibility.

Muffler

A partially clogged or plugged muffler will cause sluggish engine operation. This may be due to carbon deposits or a combination of carbon deposits and rust. It can be detected by means of the vacuum gauge.

Fig. 26.15. Heat control valve or heat riser valve removed from the exhaust manifold. The thermostatic spring closes the valve against the load of the weight when cold and allows the weight to open the valve as the spring warms up. When closed, the valve diverts hot exhaust gases around the intake manifold "stove" to warm the incoming air-fuel mixture, but when open, it allows these gases to go directly into the exhaust pipe. Be sure that this often neglected part is in good operating condition.

Most commonly, holes will appear in the muffler shell due to rusting and corrosion. This is made evident by loud exhaust noises, and it is dangerous because of the possibility of carbon monoxide getting up into the body of the car.

Some of the points mentioned in the foregoing are not strictly part of the fuel system; but as they may affect its operation, they should be given consideration.

In the three chapters on the fuel system, the endeavor has been to point out the basic principles, functions and devices used in fuel pumps and carburetors. Detailed servicing instructions and specifications have been omitted since this information, where required, is available in shop and service manuals.

Summary

About 1956 the current type of *corrugated paper air cleaners* was adopted. In cases of unsatisfactory engine operation where the engine acts as if it is not breathing normally, check the air cleaner and replace it if necessary.

Fuel pump trouble may show up as (1) partial failure or (2) total failure. Total failure may be due to a ruptured diaphragm, broken pump spring, excessively worn or broken linkage.

Fuel pumps should be tested by checking fuel pressure and also fuel delivery, which should be from ¾ pint to one pint per minute.

If *fuel flow is restricted,* check for (1) leaking sediment bowl gasket, (2) dirty fuel strainer, (3) loose fuel line connections, (4) clogged fuel line, (5) loose fuel pump cover screws, (6) leaking flexible fuel line, (7) closed fuel tank vent.

A *properly operating fuel pump* cannot build up excessive fuel pressure. It may be just as economical to replace a defective fuel pump as to repair it.

Vacuum pump trouble may come from an improperly installed oil seal or a ruptured diaphragm. A leaking diaphragm will cause oil loss from the engine. The combination fuel and vacuum pump is more difficult to repair than a simple fuel pump, and is usually best replaced if defective.

The *function of the carburetor* is to furnish a suitable explosive mixture of gasoline and air so that the engine may operate properly under all conditions of speed and load.

The *carburetor float needle valve* is always a possible source of trouble. Adjustment of the fuel level in the float chamber is important and is corrected by bending the float arm.

The *low-speed system* has two adjustments, (1) idle speed, (2) idle mixture.

There are 12 *possible causes of lean idle.*

There are 10 *possible causes of rich idle.*

The *part-throttle system* takes over where the low-speed system becomes inadequate, at about 20 mph.

There are seven causes for *lean condition.*

There are seven conditions that will cause an overly *rich air-fuel mixture.*

The *accelerating pump* is operated by movement of the throttle through suitable linkage.

There are eleven causes of *lean mixture in acceleration.*

The *automatic choke* may cause trouble due to (1) clogged hot air screen, (2) inoperative vacuum piston, (3) wrong thermostatic spring tension, (4) leaking hot air tube, (5) shrunk or broken cork cover gaskets, (6) stuck choke linkage.

Other factors affecting performance and economy are: carburetor flange loose on intake manifold, throttle linkage improperly adjusted, gasoline line restricted, exhaust pipe possibly restricted, intake manifold restricted due to carbon or other material deposits.

The *manifold heat control* should always be checked to see that it works freely and is not stuck.

The *vacuum spark advance* may have a leaking diaphragm which will upset the fuel-air mixture and may cause an explosion in the distributor.

The *windshield wiper hose* and its connections are possible trouble causes if leaks occur.

A *muffler partially clogged* by carbon deposits will cause sluggish engine operation.

A *leaking muffler* will allow noisy operation of the engine and may be a hazard due to possible carbon monoxide leakage into the closed car body.

Questions

1. What are the two types of air cleaner that may be encountered in cars?
2. How should each be serviced?
3. Name three possible causes of partial fuel pump failure.
4. What is the usual cause of total fuel pump failure?
5. Name three fuel pump tests that should be made when fuel pump trouble is suspected.
6. If gasoline flow is restricted, what would you look for?
7. Upon what does fuel pump pressure depend?
8. What trouble may be caused by a leaking diaphragm on the vacuum pump?
9. What is the function of the carburetor?
10. What is the most frequent cause of carburetor trouble?
11. What type of float needle valve will correct most carburetor flooding?
12. What is the effect of low fuel level in the float chamber?
13. How is the correct level established?
14. What two adjustments are made in the idle system?
15. Name four possible causes of lean idle fuel mixture.
16. Name three possible causes of rich idle mixture.
17. At what speed does the part-throttle system start to operate?
18. Name three possible part-throttle conditions that will cause a lean mixture.
19. Name three possible part-throttle conditions that will cause rich mixture.
20. What actuates the accelerating pump?
21. Name four possible causes of lean mixture on acceleration.
22. What three parts of the automatic choke should be checked and possibly serviced?
23. How is the automatic choke adjusted?
24. What is a common trouble with the manifold heat control?
25. What two items should be checked in the vacuum spark advance device?
26. What could result from a leaking spark advance diaphragm?
27. How could a leaking windshield wiper hose affect the fuel system?
28. What danger could result from a leaking muffler?
29. What could result from a porous intake manifold?
30. What trouble may result from running crankcase blow-by to the air cleaner?

SECTION VIII

Other Circuits of the Automobile

CHAPTER TWENTY-SEVEN

The Starting Circuit— Maintenance and Troubles

The starting circuit consists of the cranking motor, starting switch, and the cables and wires. This system has the important duty of putting the engine into motion so that it can operate under its own power. This involves four operations which are: (1) engaging the starting motor pinion with the flywheel gear, (2) completing the starting motor electrical circuit, (3) breaking the circuit, and (4) disengaging the starting motor pinion from the engine flywheel gear. The exact sequence in which these operations occur will vary somewhat depending upon the driving device and switch arrangement used.

The Starting Motor

The starting or cranking motor and the device for energizing and for engaging and disengaging the drive pinion with the engine flywheel gear are built and installed as one assembly. However, for the purpose of analyzing and studying their operation, they will be considered as separate units. The electrical control system has several variations, and there are two types of starter drives.

The function of the electrical starting motor is to crank the engine, eliminating hand cranking. As such, it converts electrical energy into mechanical energy.

Operation

The operation of the starting motor depends upon magnetic attraction and repulsion. When electric current passes through the armature conductors, a magnetic field is generated around them. At the same time, current applied to the field coils causes magnetic lines of force to pass from the north pole to the south pole, through the armature laminations. The armature core serves to complete the magnetic circuit from field pole to field pole.

The magnetic field around the armature conductors, being of the same polarity as the lines of magnetic force in the motor field, causes the conductors to be powerfully repelled. This repulsion produces an armature rotation, as shown in Fig. 27.1. As soon as each armature

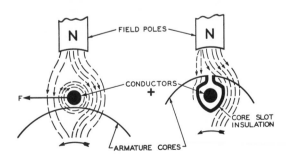

Fig. 27.1. Magnetic force revolving an armature. The magnetic field around each armature conductor tries to get out of the field magnetic circuit. (AL)

coil has rotated out of the magnetic field set up by the field windings and has approached the field magnet of the opposite polarity, the specific arrangement of the motor brushes and commutator reverses the flow of current in the coil. This reverses the magnetic field of the armature and it will continue to contribute its force to the cranking motor power output.

Design

The current-carrying conductors in the armature of a starting motor are very heavy, being designed to carry a large amperage. The magnetic forces thus created are powerful enough to enable the starting motor to crank the engine with comparative ease.

Starting motors have four or six poles, according to their rated capacity. Some four-pole motors have the field winding on only two of the poles, while the other two poles are just used to complete the magnetic circuit. The field circuit is often connected in series with the armature so that all of the armature current passes through the field circuit; making a *series* motor. The starting motor field winding is usually connected in series-parallel in order to increase the current-carrying capacity of the field coils and reduce the resistance of the motor as a unit. Refer to Fig. 27.2 for schematic diagrams of two- and four-pole cranking motors.

Other starting motors have field windings on all four poles to furnish more power. Where still larger starting motors are required, six poles are used, all of which would be fitted with field windings. Fig. 27.3 illustrates the magnetic circuit of a four-pole motor.

With series-parallel connections on starting motors with two field coils, it is important that the current be equally divided between the two series combinations. In order to accomplish this, the resistance of each field coil must be exactly the same. In making the series connections, the resistance of the starting cables must also be equal in both series combinations so that the current will be equally divided. The

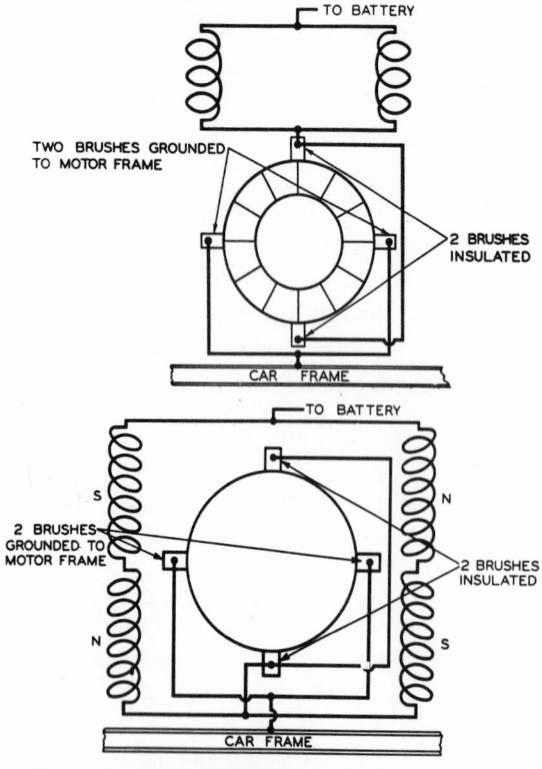

Fig. 27.2. (Above) Two-pole starting motor. (Below) Four-pole starting motor. Notice the equalizing connections on each pair of brushes. (AL)

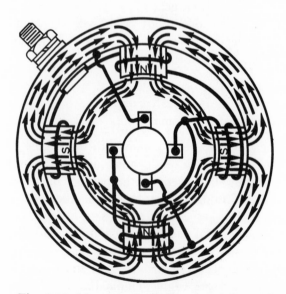

Fig. 27.3. Magnetic circuit in a four-pole starting motor. Notice the four complete magnetic circuits going through the pole shoes into the armature.

two insulated brushes with the same polarity on opposite sides of the commutator are connected by an equalizing conductor.

Starting motors turn out a surprising amount of power for their size, developing from 1 to 2 horsepower depending upon the size of the engine and the conditions existing when the engine is cranked. Allowing 50% overall efficiency, the current required to produce the necessary driving torque is 125 to 200 amperes for summer starting and from 200 to 300 amperes for winter starting. To carry such heavy current, the cable between the battery and starting motor at the starting switch must have ample current-carrying capacity. The exact size is dependent upon the length of the cables necessary to connect the battery, starting switch and motor.

Starting motor windings, commutator and brushes must be larger than those for generators because the starting current will be from 10 to 15 times as great as that produced by the ordinary passenger generator and 5 to 10 times maximum alternator output.

Starting motor commutator and brushes must have low resistance at points of contact. The brushes are approximately 96% copper which makes the brush seating or fitting process more difficult than would be the case if carbon brushes were used. However, carbon brushes would have too much resistance and could not carry the tremendous current required without undue heating. Commutators must be manufactured to be within .003″ concentricity with the armature shaft bearing surfaces.

While in many cases it is not done, it is recommended that starting motor commutators be undercut 1/64″, after which the motor should be assembled and run free at approximately 2000 rpm. The burrs from the undercutting will seat the brushes better and more quickly than the customary sandpaper method. After the brushes are seated to get 90% of contact surface, the commutators should be sanded with 00 sandpaper to remove the burrs and any roughness due to undercutting. By limiting the depth of undercutting to 1/64″, the grooves will be shallow and will not have a tendency to fill up with metal particles which might cause a short circuit. Undercutting should always be .002″ wider than the thickness of the mica between the commutator surfaces.

Correct brush spring tension is quite important for the proper operation of starting motors. When there is any doubt about the brush spring tension, it should be tested with a spring scale. Place a thin piece of paper between the brush and the commutator. When a slight pull by hand will move the paper, it indicates exactly when to read the scale.

Bearings on starting motors are generally a plain powdered sleeve type. They are made of bronze, bronze graphite or powdered bronze. Bearing clearance should be from .001″ to .006″ at the drive end, and from .001″ to .005″ at the commutator end. Where the absorbent, powdered bronze bearings are used, it is not necessary to furnish any external lubricant as the bearing itself contains all that is necessary to keep friction and wear down to a minimum.

On some motors, the pole pieces have one tip longer than the other in order to shift the magnetic neutral point. It is important that pole pieces always be correctly installed in accordance with the service manual specifications.

End play on the armature shaft should be measured after the armature and frame are assembled and should not exceed 1/16″ maximum.

It must be remembered that the cranking motor is a special-duty motor designed to produce a high horsepower for its size, and to do this a high current is taken through the unit. It is not designed to be used for more than approximately 30 seconds at any one time. Longer periods of continuous operation may result in its failure or damage to it. A cranking

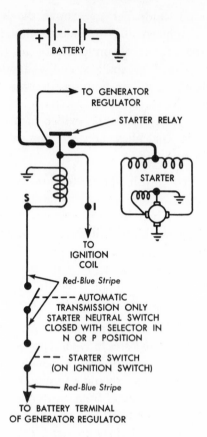

Fig. 27.4. Cranking motor circuit as used on Ford cars. The lead marked "to Ignition Coil" bypasses the ballast resistor while the starting motor is in operation.

motor circuit is shown in Fig. 27.4. Fig. 27.5 shows a disassembled cranking motor.

The Cranking Motor Drives

The cranking motor armature must revolve at a fairly high speed to produce a strong cranking effort. To accomplish this, the cranking motor is equipped with a small drive pinion which meshes with teeth on the engine flywheel so that a gear reduction of 16:1 or even higher is attained. The actual gear ratio will vary in different applications. A ratio of 16:1 means that the armature of the motor revolves 16 times for every revolution of the engine flywheel. This permits the cranking motor to develop a comparatively high armature speed and considerable power, while cranking the engine at a relatively low speed.

After the engine starts, the speed immediately increases and it may soon reach 3000 rpm. If, as frequently happens, car operators "step on" the accelerator pedal, engine speeds may even run much higher. With a 16:1 gear ratio, if the cranking motor drive pinion should remain meshed with the flywheel, the cranking motor armature would spin at 48,000 rpm or higher. This excessive speed would quickly

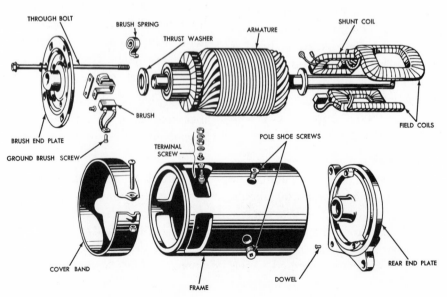

Fig. 27.5. Cranking motor used on Ford cars.

ruin the armature. To prevent this, the various devices which mesh the drive pinion with the engine flywheel for cranking have provision for releasing the starter gear from the engine flywheel after the engine has started. Two of these devices are: (1) the Bendix Drive, (2) the overrunning clutch drive.

Bendix Drive

The Bendix Drive, Fig. 27.6, provides an automatic means of engaging the drive pinion with the engine flywheel ring gear to crank the engine, and for disengaging it after the engine starts.

The drive pinion is mounted on a threaded hollow shaft which has spiral threads that match internal threads in the drive pinion. This threaded sleeve is loosely fitted on the cranking motor armature shaft. One end of the sleeve is bolted to the drive spring. The other end of the drive spring is keyed and bolted to the armature shaft of the drive head.

When the cranking motor is not operating, the pinion is disengaged from the engine flywheel ring gear. As soon as the cranking motor switch is closed, the cranking motor armature begins to rotate, picking up speed very rapidly. The threaded drive sleeve increases its speed with the armature, since it is driven by the drive spring. However, the drive pinion, which is a loose fit on the sleeve, does not pick up speed quite as fast as the armature. Thus, the sleeve turns within the pinion, forcing it endwise along the shaft into mesh with the flywheel ring gear. This action is somewhat similar to turning a screw in a nut that is prevented from rotating so that the nut would move from one end to the other of the screw. Once the drive pinion reaches the pinion stop on the end of the sleeve, it can move out no further and must then rotate with the sleeve and the armature so that the engine flywheel is turned and the engine is cranked. The drive spring compresses slightly to absorb the shock of engagement. If there were no springs in the driving device, the shock of engaging the starting drive pinion with the engine flywheel gear would cause both gears to be short lived.

After the engine has started, the flywheel spins the drive pinion more rapidly than the armature is rotating with the result that the pinion is "backed out" of mesh from the flywheel gear (withdrawn by means of the spiral thread).

There are several types of Bendix Drives, namely the Standard Bendix Drive, and Barrel type, the Compression Spring type, and the Friction Clutch type. The "Folo-Thru" Drive is used on Ford cars. Refer to Fig. 27.7.

The "Folo-Thru" starter drive has several refinements which make it more dependable and trouble-free than the other types. One advantage is that it has a lock pin which keeps the pinion from rotating when it is in the extended position. Once the pin has dropped into place it will not disengage unless the starter is mounted on the engine and the engine speed reaches 310 to 390 rpm. It cannot be forced out of position by hand.

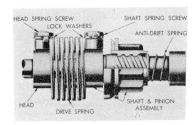

Fig. 27.6. Standard type Bendix drive. The head is keyed to the armature shaft, and torque is transmitted through the drive spring to the shaft and pinion assembly.

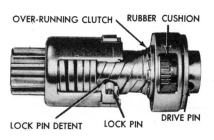

Fig. 27.7. Type of Bendix drive used on Ford's larger passenger cars and light trucks.

Some Bendix Drives have a small anti-drift spring between the drive pinion and the pinion stop which prevents the pinion from drifting into mesh when the engine is running. Others use a small frictional anti-drift pin and spring inside the pinion.

On some cranking motors, the drive pinion moves toward the cranking motor as it meshes, and therefore it is called "inboard" drive. On other motors it moves away from the motor and is called an "outboard" drive. A heavy-duty type is shown in Fig. 27.8.

Another type of Bendix Drive is the compression spring type. Instead of using a spiral spring attached respectively to the drive and to the armature shaft to absorb the shock of the engagement of the motor pinion and flywheel ring gear, it has a compression spring. As the gear is forced into mesh with the flywheel it bumps against this spring which cushions the shock.

A still further type of Bendix Drive is the friction clutch type. This is used for heavy-duty cranking motor work and employs a friction

clutch. It functions in much the same manner as the Standard Bendix Drive except that it uses a series of spring-loaded clutch plates which slip momentarily during the shock of engagement to relieve the shock and prevent it from being transmitted by the cranking motor. This slipping stops as soon as engagement is completed.

Overrunning Clutch Drive

The overrunning clutch type of cranking motor is designed to provide positive engagement and disengagement of the drive pinion and flywheel ring gear. It uses a shift lever to slide the clutch and drive pinion assembly along the armature shaft. The clutch transmits cranking torque from the cranking motor armature to the engine flywheel, but permits the drive pinion to overrun, or run faster than, the armature after the engine is started. This protects the motor armature from excessive speed during the brief interval that the drive pinion remains in mesh. Fig. 27.9 shows sections of an overrunning clutch starter drive.

The overrunning clutch consists of a shell and sleeve assembly which has internal splines to match those on the armature shaft. Both the shell and sleeve assembly and the armature shaft must turn together. A pinion and collar assembly fits loosely into the shell. The collar is in contact with four hardened steel rollers which are assembled into notches cut in the inner face of the shell. These notches taper inward slightly so that there is less room in the end away from the roller than in the end where the rollers are located in their normal position. These rollers are spring loaded.

The overrunning clutch might be described as a one-way drive which applies torque or turning effort to the pinion to drive the flywheel gear when engaged with it; but it will not drive the cranking motor if the engine's flywheel gear applies power to the pinion.

When the shift lever is operated, the clutch assembly is moved endwise along the armature

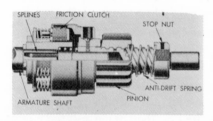

Fig. 27.8. Clutch-type Bendix drive incorporates a friction clutch which releases when overloads occur. This drive cannot be disassembled in the field. It is designed for heavy-duty operation. (AL)

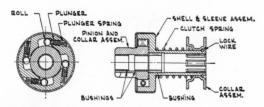

Fig. 27.9. Overrunning clutch starter drive, preventing flywheel from driving the motor when the engine starts. (DR)

shaft so that the pinion meshes with the flywheel ring gear. If the teeth, instead of engaging, should butt against one another the clutch spring compresses so that the pinion is spring loaded against the ring gear teeth. As soon as power is applied to the armature and it starts to rotate, the teeth on the pinion will spring into place, meshing with the flywheel ring gear. Fig. 27.10 shows a section of an overrunning clutch starting motor.

The same mechanism which shifts the clutch and pinion operates the switch that controls the current flow of the motor. This is discussed in the next section, "Starting Motor Controls."

Completion of the shift-lever movement closes the cranking motor switch so that the armature begins to rotate. This rotates the shell and sleeve assembly causing the rollers in the overrunning clutch to jam tightly in the smaller section of the shell notches. The rollers jam between the pinion collar and the shell so that the pinion is forced to rotate with the armature and crank the engine.

When the engine begins to operate, it attempts to drive the cranking motor armature (through the pinion) faster than the armature is rotating. This causes the pinion to rotate with respect to the shell so that it overruns the shell and the armature. The rollers are turned back slightly towards the larger section of the shell notches where they are freed and thus permit the pinion to overrun. This protects the armature for the short space of time that the car driver still has the starter switch closed, or until the automatic controls take over so that the shift lever is released, pulling the overruning clutch drive and pinion out of mesh with the engine flywheel gear. The shift lever movement also opens the cranking motor switch so that the armature quickly stops rotating. Operation of the shift lever is by electrical means. A disassembled motor is shown in Fig. 27.11.

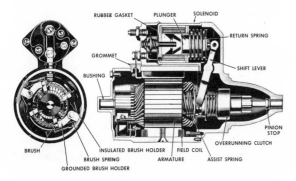

Fig. 27.10. Cranking motor with solenoid starting switch and overrunning clutch.

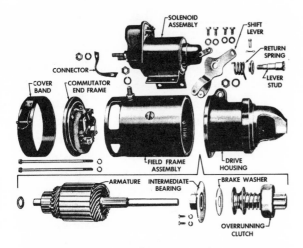

Fig. 27.11. Disassembled view of starting motor with solenoid operated switch and overrunning clutch. The solenoid shifts the drive pinion and then closes the switch. (DR)

Starting Motor Controls

On American passenger cars, both the Bendix and the overrunning clutch starter drives are controlled by electrical means.

The Bendix Drive causes the cranking motor pinion to engage and disengage the flywheel gear automatically as shown in Fig. 27.12. With control by electrical means, a switch operated by turning the ignition key actuates a magnetic

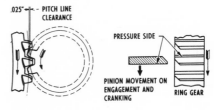

Fig. 27.12. The teeth of the drive pinion and flywheel ring gear mesh smoothly, without clashing, on the Bendix starting motor drive.

switch. After the magnetic switch coil is energized, the contact disc is drawn against the contact terminals and the battery current flows through the magnetic switch terminals to the cranking motor, thereby cranking the engine. The Bendix type of control is shown in Fig. 27.13.

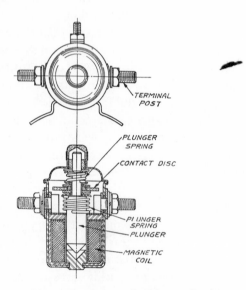

Fig. 27.13. Type of switch used with Bendix drive starting motors. The magnetic coil operates the plunger which in turn closes the starter circuit switch.

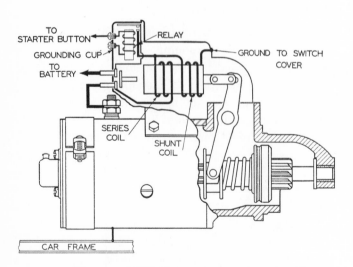

Fig. 27.14. Wiring connections for solenoid starting motor control with overrunning clutch. The small coil closes a switch, energizing the heavy solenoid coil which moves the gear shift lever and closes the starter circuit switch.

On the overrunning clutch there are two operations which must be performed to crank the engine, (1) engage the driving pinion with the flywheel gear, and (2) complete the starting motor circuit. The starting circuit switch is closed after the driving pinion meshes with the flywheel by the further movement of the shifting lever which moves the motor pinion axially. This is shown in Fig. 27.14.

The solenoid switch type of cranking motor is controlled by a switch on the dash. Its function is to shift the pinion into mesh and close the cranking motor contact. To accomplish this, a shift plunger linked to the shift lever is drawn into the solenoid when the solenoid windings are energized. There are two windings in the solenoid (1) a pull-in winding which is cut out as the cranking motor contact is closed and (2) a hold-in winding which holds the plunger in the solenoid as long as the cranking motor control circuit is not broken. The return spring of the shift lever opens the cranking motor circuit and disengages the pinion when the control circuit is opened.

Starting Circuit Maintenance and Troubles

In the event that trouble is experienced in the cranking motor operation, it may be necessary to check all of the various units in the control circuit to be sure that they are functioning normally. Failure of the cranking motor to operate at all might indicate an open circuit in the control wiring or possibly a defect in the cranking motor itself. Test the various units of the control circuit with a voltmeter to determine whether or not the battery voltage is being delivered to the unit in the proper manner.

Good maintenance practice will include inspection of cables and terminals for corrosion and looseness whenever the battery is checked and water added. If the terminals are corroded, wash them with a solution of baking soda and water and coat them with vaseline. Tighten all terminals which are loose on the battery posts. Inspect the cables to be sure they are not partially broken where they enter the terminals, and replace the cable if any breaks are found. Occasionally, trouble develops at the connection of the terminals to the cables. Where contact at this point is poor, points of high resistance may exist which may possibly heat excessively. Inspect for damaged or worn insulation on the battery-to-switch or switch-to-motor cables and replace the cable on which the insulation is not in good condition. Be sure that all terminal nuts and screws are tight.

On solenoid switches the control circuits should be inspected for broken wires, loose connections or terminals, and damaged insulation.

If there is some indication that the starting motor is not producing sufficient power, the starting circuit should be given a voltage-loss test to determine if the cables and switch are in good condition and have sufficient current-carrying capacity. This test should also be made whenever the starting motor has been overhauled and reinstalled. Connect a low reading voltmeter to both the battery and starting motor terminals, crank the engine in the normal manner, and read the voltmeter. Fig. 27.15 shows different voltmeter connections.

The voltage drop should be less than 0.20 volt per 100 amperes flowing in the circuit. The approximate current can be estimated from the specifications for the various types of starting motors. The cranking current will usually be slightly less than the stall torque current specified for $\frac{1}{3}$ the rated voltage, although this may vary depending upon the condition and temperature of the starting motor and engine. If the motor is cranking easily, or if the battery is low, the current will be somewhat less, while if the starting motor is laboring the current draw will be higher. If the voltage loss is more than 0.20 volt per 100 amperes, check the loss from the battery to the starting switch, the motor, and across the starting switch.

If either cable voltage loss is more than .10 volt per 100 amperes, inspect to find the cause. If no apparent defect can be found, the cable is too small and should be replaced by one of larger size. If the voltage drop across the switch is more than that specified in the switch maintenance instructions, the switch should be replaced.

Repeat the above procedure on the ground circuit by first connecting the voltmeter to the

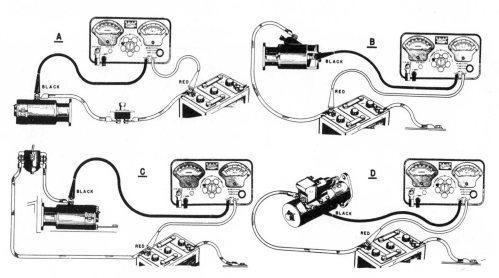

Fig. 27.15. Voltmeter connections for checking voltage drop in the insulated side of the starting circuit with various types of switches.

ground terminal and the starting motor frame. If this voltage loss is more than .15 volt per 100 amperes, check the voltage from the battery ground terminal to the engine block, and from the engine block to the starting motor frame. The first reading will be an indication of the condition of the battery ground strap, while the second reading will indicate whether the starting motor is properly grounded. A convenient test lamp for checking circuits is shown in Fig. 27.16.

Motor Maintenance

Due to the location and construction of starting motors, no maintenance operations are possible except for periodic lubrication, external cleaning, and checking for looseness of mounting. Because of this, starting motors are designed to require no service except for lubrication. In many instances, sufficient oil is incorporated in the construction of the motor to eliminate the necessity for this.

In order to obtain maximum efficiency, the starting motor circuits should be frequently inspected and cleaned and the motor checked for loose or cracked mountings. Where oilers are provided, from three to five drops of SAE No. 10 engine oil should be added at regular chassis lubrication periods.

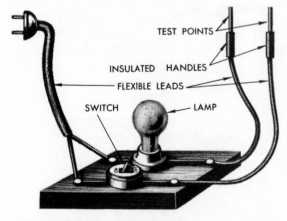

Fig. 27.16. A convenient test set can be made by connecting a lamp in series with one test lead. When the points touch wires or parts in electrical contact, the lamp will light.

The starting motor will normally perform without attention throughout the life of the engine. However, dirt, dust, water and frequent startings cause wear and deterioration and may make an overhaul necessary. If trouble should develop in the starting motor, a complete overhaul should be performed, since the additional trouble or expense involved is small compared to several partial jobs such as replacing brushes or cleaning the drive mechanism.

Do not remove the motor for an overhaul unless it is definitely known that it requires attention. Check the battery cables and starting switch first. If necessary, substitute a battery which is known to be fully charged and in good condition and then operate the motor, disconnecting the battery cables from the starting switch and holding the cable terminal firmly against the starting motor terminal. On some installations it may be necessary to remove the starting switch to expose the motor terminals. Motors with Bendix Drives should crank the engine at normal speed, while overrunning clutch motors should spin at a high rate without cranking the engine. If the motor acts as described, with the drive mechanism engaging and disengaging each time the starting motor is operated, do not remove the motor as the removal itself involves considerable labor which may be quite unnecessary.

To remove the starting motor from the engine, disconnect the leads. On the switches mounted on the motor, the battery lead should be covered with friction tape or a short piece of hose to prevent shorting in case it touches the frame or other grounded part of the car. Take out the mounting bolts and lift the motor from the engine.

Preliminary Tests for Starting Motor

Remove the motor cover band. Place the motor on a "V" block or partially opened vise and prepare for a no-load test by connecting the motor terminal and frame to a battery of rated voltage. If the motor operates without shorts or

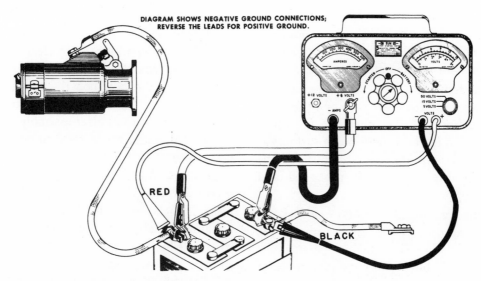

Fig. 27.17. To check the starting motor current draw, connect the ammeter and voltmeter as shown, where an ammeter with a built-in carbon pile resistor is used. If the current is higher than normal, trouble is indicated.

laboring, disconnect the leads from the motor terminal and insert an ammeter and shunt with a capacity of at least 500 amperes. Connect the voltmeter from the motor terminal to the frame. Hold a tachometer against the drive end of the armature shaft and read the "no load" speed, voltage, and amperage. Also, inspect the brush action while operating with no load. Compare the resulting figures with the test specifications.

The results of the test will indicate what should be expected when the motor is overhauled. If the motor runs at low speed with a low current draw, look for high resistance which might be caused by a dirty commutator, worn or faulty brushes and brush leads, or low brush spring tensions. Fig. 27.17 shows how to connect instruments to check starting motor current draw.

If the motor runs at low speed, draws a high current and is accompanied by arcing of the brushes, look for a faulty armature. If arcing is not excessive, look for worn bearings and shaft and for insufficient end play. Excessive arcing is caused by low brush spring tension, worn commutator, or a shorted or open armature. An open armature is readily detected because the

arcing always occurs at a certain point and only one spot on the commutator will be burned.

Excessive brush movement may be caused by low brush spring tension or, more commonly, by an out-of-round or worn commutator.

In some cases the motor becomes inoperative because of a dirty commutator. It frequently happens that the motor will regularly stop in the same position after a cranking operation. If there is only a slight amount of oil or grease on the commutator, it will cause arcing and solidifying of these substances, thus making an insulating layer under the brushes. In this case the starter will not operate when the current is turned on. This condition can be corrected by merely cleaning the commutator with No. 00 or 000 sandpaper.

Armature Inspection

The armature should be visually inspected for mechanical defects, such as worn or bent shaft, worn commutator, scored core laminations, and to see that all windings are properly in place in the core slots. Inspect for evidence of excessively high speed which would throw the windings outward at the ends and perhaps even cause them to leave the core slots.

Inspect to see that all windings are properly staked and soldered to the commutator. Resolder if necessary, being careful not to short between coils or commutator bars.

With a test prod, test the armature for grounds, touching the shaft with one prod and the commutator with the other. Do not touch the test prod to the bearing or brush surfaces as an arc would burn the smooth finish. If the lamp lights, the armature is grounded and should be replaced.

Clean the commutator with 00 or 000 sandpaper and remove all dirt from between the armature bars. Place the armature bearing surfaces on the "V" block and put a dial indicator against the commutator. Turn the armature slowly and read the total run-out. If this is over .003", turn the commutator down on a lathe. Mount the armature by the shaft bearing surfaces in the lathe and take light cuts until the commutator is completely cleaned. Remove all burrs with 00 to 000 sandpaper. This truing of the commutator should also be done if it is rough, burned, or if the mica extends above the surface of the copper. Recheck the run-out after turning the commutator.

The equipment manufacturers recommend that the commutator mica be undercut. This cut should be exactly centered on the mica and the tool used should be .002" wider than the mica. The undercut should be clean and square and should remove all mica to a depth of $1/64$" or .016". If the burrs on the copper are not large, they can be left on the commutator to help seat the brushes after assembly. However, be sure to remove the burrs with 00 sandpaper before completing the overhaul.

To check for shorts in the armature, place it on a growler and hold a thin steel strip or a piece of hack saw blade on the core. Rotate the armature slowly and if it is shorted the steel strip will become magnetized and vibrate. If a short is present, inspect the commutator risers and bars for copper chips or solder or for spots in contact that may be shorting between the bars. If the short cannot be found, the armature must be replaced.

Frame and Field Inspection

Clean the frame and field with a cloth dampened in cleaning solvent, but do not soak the insulation or brushes. Inspect for faulty insulation and stripped threads. With test prods, check for grounds by touching the terminal studs with one prod and an unpainted spot on the frame with the other. Be sure brushes or leads are not in contact with the frame. If a ground is present, remove the terminal stud nuts; and if the stud is removable, press it out of the frame. Then recheck the field coils for grounds with the test prod. If the terminal stud is soldered to the field coil or if the field coils are grounded, remove the pole shoe screws and take the coils out of the frame. It is a good practice to mark one end of the frame and also the shoe before disassembly so that each can be installed in its original position and direction. Replace any faulty or damaged parts, making sure all connections are tightly clinched and then soldered to make the required low-resistance connection. Pole shoe screws, being very tight, require special equipment for removal, as shown in Fig. 27.18.

Fig. 27.18. Special equipment necessary for removing pole shoes. (DR)

If the brushes are oil soaked or are worn to less than one-half of their original length, they should be replaced. To remove the brushes, unsolder and unclinch the leads from the field coil or connector. Insert the new brush lead to its full depth and insert the equalizer lead where used. Clinch, tighten and then solder to make a low-resistance connection. Do not use acid for soldering flux as it will damage the insulation and may corrode the metal.

Commutator-End Head Inspection

Clean the commutator-end head thoroughly, being careful not to soak the brushes in solvent. Inspect for a bent, cracked or distorted head, and replace if these conditions are present.

Place the armature in a padded vise and install the commutator-end head on the end of the armature shaft. Do not clamp the armature tightly as this distorts the laminated core. Feel the fit of the bearing on the shaft. If side play is excessive, the bearing or shaft is worn and should be replaced. Where the bearing is replaceable, press it into place with the correct arbor as the arbor determines the diameter of the bearing when in place. If the bearing is not replaceable, replace the complete head. It should be remembered that out-of-round bearings should not be reamed or honed on the inside. The only correct way to size this type of bearing is to press it in with an arbor of the desired size which will determine the inside diameter of the bore.

With the motor head mounted on the armature as above, check that the brushes are parallel to the commutator segments and that they move freely in the holders. If the alignment is not satisfactory, install a new arm (on the swinging type of brush holders) or replace the complete head or brush plates if the brush holders are of the box type. Measure the brush spring tension with a spring scale hooked under the brush screw or under the spring near the end, depending upon the type of construction. Pull the scale on a line parallel to the edge of the brush and make a reading just as the spring leaves the brush or just as the brush leaves the commutator, depending upon the brush type.

Adjust the tension by bending the brush spring at the point where it is clamped by the brush holder. Repeat this for all brushes. Be sure to remove the brushes from the holder before taking the head off of the armature as they may become chipped or cracked when snapping off of the commutator. On most box-type brush holders, the brush can be pulled out far enough so that the spring lever will push against the side of the brush and hold it at such an angle that it will not interfere with the removal or replacement of the armature. After the armature has been replaced, the brushes can be pushed back into their proper positions so that the correct spring tension will again be applied.

Brushes that are soldered to the field coils or connectors should be replaced as described previously under "Frame and Field Inspection."

General Note

The starting circuit system is comparatively free from trouble as long as a sufficient supply of current is available from a properly charged battery in good condition. However, its proper functioning is very necessary for satisfactory operation of a car, especially since hand cranks have become obsolete and the only other method of starting a car is by pushing it.

If the starter fails on a car equipped with an automatic transmission, the transmission must usually be in *low* when the car is being pushed to start it, in order to get up enough speed to overcome the slip in the fluid drive. Follow the manufacturer's instructions when pushing a car equipped with an automatic transmission.

The connections to determine battery voltage drop when the starting motor is operating are shown in Fig. 27.19. Fig. 27.20 shows the way a voltmeter is connected to check the entire car wiring system for electrical leaks.

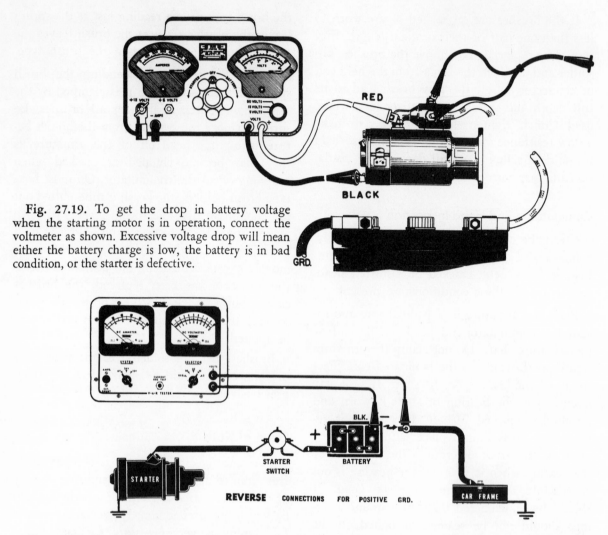

Fig. 27.19. To get the drop in battery voltage when the starting motor is in operation, connect the voltmeter as shown. Excessive voltage drop will mean either the battery charge is low, the battery is in bad condition, or the starter is defective.

Fig. 27.20. To check entire car wiring system for current leaks, remove the ground strap from the battery and connect the voltmeter as shown (8-10 volt position), with all switches, lights, and appliances off. If the voltmeter reading is obtained there is a current drain on the battery. A reading less than battery voltage indicates current leakage. A reading of battery voltage indicates that there is a short or that an appliance is on.

Summary

The *starting circuit* consists of the cranking motor, starting switch, cables and wires. It has the important duty of putting the engine in motion.

The *starting motor* and the *gear engaging device* are built as one unit. The operation of the motor depends on magnetic repulsion.

Starting motors have four or six poles, with field windings usually on only two magnetic poles. The motors are series-parallel connected.

Cranking motors turn out a surprising amount of power for their size. They require from 125 to 300 amperes, depending upon atmospheric temperature.

Starting motor *windings, commutator and brushes* must be much larger than corresponding generator parts. The starting motor brushes are approximately 96% copper. Commutators are held within .003″ concentricity with the armature shaft. It is recommended that cranking motor commutators be undercut.

Correct **brush spring tension** is important. Bearings are generally plain sleeve bearings. On some motors the pole pieces have one tip longer than the other. Armature end play should not exceed $1/16''$.

The *cranking motor* is designed to produce a high power output for a short time and therefore should not be operated for more than approximately 30 seconds at a time.

The *motor drive pinion* will usually have a ratio of about 1:16 with the flywheel ring gear. A device to engage and disengage the pinion from the ring gear is required. There are two methods (1) Bendix Drive, and (2) overrunning clutch.

The **Bendix Drive** provides an automatic means of engaging the drive pinion with the engine flywheel ring gear, cranking the engine and disengaging the drive pinion.

The *overrunning clutch* is designed to provide a positive means of engaging and disengaging the drive pinion and flywheel ring gear. An overrunning clutch permits the flywheel ring gear to turn faster than the drive pinion when the engine starts. Completion of the gear shifting movement closes the cranking motor electrical circuit.

Starting motor controls are of two types and each is controlled by electrical means.

If *starting circuit terminals* are corroded they should be washed with a solution of baking soda and water. Cables in bad condition should be replaced. In cases of insufficient motor power make a **voltage-loss test**. Loss should be less than 0.20 volt per 100 amperes. If either cable voltage loss is more than 0.10 volt per 100 amperes, determine the cause.

The *starting motor* will normally perform without attention throughout the life of the engine. However, dirt, water, and frequent starting cause wear and deterioration and may make an overhaul necessary. Do not remove the motor for overhaul unless it is definitely known that it requires attention.

As a *preliminary test*, if the motor runs at low speed and draws a high current, with arcing of the brushes, look for a faulty armature. In some cases the motor becomes inoperative due to a dirty commutator.

Armature inspection should be made to check for such mechanical defects as a bent shaft or worn commutator. Test armature for grounds, opens and shorts. Clean commutator.

In *frame and field inspection*, clean frame and field and inspect for faulty insulation. Check for grounds and opens. Replace worn brushes.

In a *commutator-end head inspection,* clean thoroughly, being careful not to get solvent on brushes. Check bearing looseness. Check brush tension.

The *starting system* is comparatively free from trouble as long as a sufficient supply of electric current is available from a properly charged battery in good condition. The only alternative if the starting system fails is to start the engine by pushing. On cars with automatic transmissions it is necessary to have the transmissions in low when pushing to start. Follow manufacturer's instructions.

Questions

1. Of what does the starting circuit consist?
2. What is its important duty?
3. What are the four operations involved in starting the engine?
4. What are the two important parts of the cranking unit?
5. Upon what does the operation of the starting motor depend?
6. How many magnet poles do starting motors usually have?
7. How are the field poles and armature connected?
8. How much horsepower does the average starting motor develop?
9. What kind of bearings do starting motors have?

10. What is the average motor pinion-to-ring gear ratio?

11. What is the purpose of the overrunning clutch?

12. What would happen if this clutch did not operate properly?

13. How does the Bendix Drive operate?

14. What type of electrical control is used with the Bendix Drive?

15. What type of electrical control is used with the overrunning clutch?

16. The electrical control unit performs two functions. What are they?

17. In case the cranking motor does not operate, what would you check first?

18. What part on the cranking motor is most likely to make the motor inoperative?

19. What is the allowable cable voltage loss per 100 amperes?

20. What is the allowable cable voltage loss on the ground circuit?

21. What would you use to check for opens or grounds in the armature and field circuit?

22. What are cranking motor brushes made of?

23. What defects might you find in an inoperative armature?

24. How would you clean the commutator?

25. How are field magnet shoes removed from the field frame?

26. When should starting motor brushes be replaced?

27. How would you check brush spring tension?

28. How is the current between the two insulated brushes equalized?

29. What automatic transmission speed is used when starting the engine by pushing the car?

30. How would you determine the battery voltage drop when the starting motor is operating?

CHAPTER TWENTY-EIGHT

Lighting and Horn Circuits —Turning Signals

Lighting and Accessory Circuit

The lighting and accessory circuit is generally taken for granted. This is natural because in general it gives little trouble. Occasionally, something does go wrong and like other troubles that may develop in other systems, it must be fixed.

It is important to keep one basic thought in mind when dealing with the lighting circuit — at every point in the insulated portion, electricity is trying to flow from one side of the circuit to the other and will take any path, desirable or undesirable, to do so. The desirable paths are to and through lamps, motors, coils, or resistances. The undesirable paths are through shorts or grounds. The service man's job is to keep the desirable paths open and under control, and to prevent or eliminate current paths that exist where they should not.

The lighting circuit includes the battery, the frame, all of the lights and accessories, the various switches that control their use, and the conductors carrying current to them. The battery has been considered in detail in Chapter 14.

The complete lighting system can be broken down into circuits, each having one or more lights or other appliances and switches and the required conductors. In each separate circuit

the lights or appliances are connected in parallel, and each switch is connected in series between the battery and the group of lamps or appliances it controls. In this connection, the lighting system actually can be considered to also include the radio, heater-motor, electric windshield wiper motor, and horn relays.

Usually only one switch is used to control an individual circuit. For example, in the parking light circuit, one switch controls several lamps which are connected in parallel. Sometimes one switch controls the connection to the battery while a selector switch determines which of two or more circuits will be energized. The headlights, with an upper and lower beam, are an example of this type of circuit. A variation of the series circuit is found in the panel lighting circuit where the main lighting switch controls the connection to the battery, while the panel light switch controls the brightness of the panel lights. In some cases, two switches are connected in parallel so that either switch may be used to turn on the lights. This is illustrated by the dome lamp which is controlled by the automatic door switch and the manual switch.

All the individual circuits in the lighting circuit can be traced from the battery, to the switch(es), where it may divide and go to the individual lamps or appliances. Each appliance must be grounded to the frame or have a ground wire returning to some grounded part. Keep in mind that the frame of the car is a conductor just as truly as the insulated wires act as conductors for the other side of the circuit. On two-wire systems the ground wire returns all the way to a battery terminal to complete the circuit instead of coming through the frame. The common sealed-beam headlight now in use has three terminals and uses three leads: one for the upper beam, one for the lower beam, and the other as a common ground lead to insure a perfect ground connection so there will be no difficulty in carrying the sizable current to a good ground. Fig. 28.1 is a sectional view of a sealed-beam light. Earlier headlights were grounded to a reflector and lamp housing and did not require a separate ground lead. This frequently caused trouble because of the absence of a good ground. A lighting circuit using a headlamp relay is shown in Fig. 28.2.

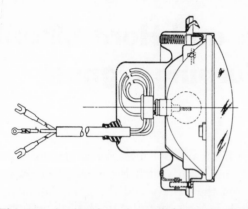

Fig. 28.1. Section through a sealed-beam headlamp. On this one, a separate inner bulb is used, although on the all-glass type, the lens and reflector act as the bulb. Of the three wires, one is ground, one is for near-bright, and one is for far-bright.

With four headlamps as most of the cars now have, the selector switch on the dash turns on two lamps for low beam. The lamps are embossed with number 2 for the outboard mounting and number 1 for the inboard mounting. The outboard lamps have two filaments and a three-blade terminal, while the inboard have a single filament.

For high beam, the bright beam of the number 2 lamps is turned on, plus the single beam of the number 1 lamps, putting all four lamps into use. The single filament lamps provide the high-intensity beam to reach ahead on the highway, while the other lamps illuminate the side of the road.

Lighting Circuit Troubles

Troubles in the lighting circuit are either *opens* where they should not be or contacts in the way of *shorts* or *grounds* where they should not be. The wiring in the lighting circuit should be periodically inspected for loose connections, chafed insulation, and corroded connections or terminals. Various junction blocks are localized spots where trouble can be suspected if there are open circuits. Inspect the switches, bulb sockets, lamp shells, reflectors and lenses for loose mountings and corrosion. Clean and tighten where necessary to make good contact and to eliminate the loss of effectiveness due to poor or dirty reflectors and lenses. Sometimes,

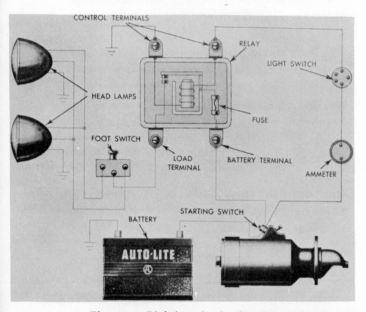

Fig. 28.2. Lighting circuit, showing application of light relay. Notice that the light switch only passes current through the magnet winding in the relay; it is the latter which closes the actual lamp circuit.

on old installations, it is advisable to solder a lead to the socket case and ground the lead at some protected spot on the frame or chassis in order to reduce the voltage loss in the ground connection.

Using a low-reading voltmeter, measure the voltage drop between the various lamp sockets or appliance connections and a clean unpainted ground on the chassis. Have each appliance turned on when making this test for high resistance ground connections. If any reading is obtained, thoroughly clean the socket and shell or connection to eliminate the resistance. Also, a ground lead may be installed, as previously mentioned.

To make a test that will reveal high resistance spots, connect the insulated battery terminal to a long voltmeter lead and install a test prod on the other lead. Turn on the various light circuits and touch the voltmeter prods to the insulated terminals at each lamp appliance. If the voltage loss is more than .6 volt, follow the circuit back to the switch and ammeter to locate the part of the circuit in which the loss occurs. If the voltage drop is due to a defective switch, it should be replaced. If the loss is at a connection or terminal, it should be cleaned, repaired and tightened; while if the voltage loss is in one of the leads, it should be replaced using a wire of larger size. Because of the low voltage (6 or 12 volts), relatively heavy current must be supplied to the appliances in order to get the number of watts to make them perform as they should. This requires conductors of ample carrying capacity, much heavier than the same amount of energy would require in a 110-volt circuit.

All terminals in the lighting circuit should be clinched and soldered, and insulating tape or loom should be used wherever the lead passes a place that may cause wear or cutting of the insulation.

The lighting circuit usually includes a fuse or overload relay connected between the battery and main lighting switch. This fuse or relay may be mounted on the switch, or in a holder connected in one of the lighting circuits. When overloads in the circuit occur, the fuse burns out and opens the circuit, or the relay opens. The thermal overload relay is a strip of bimetal on which a contact is mounted. When the charge is excessive, the bimetal becomes heated and bends, opening the contact and breaking the circuit. Usually cooling starts and the relay closes after a short period. If the overload is still present, the relay will again overheat and open the circuit. In some cases this heating and cooling take place so rapidly the relay will actually vibrate, making a buzzing sound.

If the fuse burns out or the thermal cut-out opens, it is very important to locate the cause of the excessive current. Turn off all electrical circuits. Check the wiring for evidence of shorts or grounds which will show up in the form of worn insulation or burned insulation. Often the odor of burned insulation will assist in locating the spot where the short occurs. Repair or replace the shorted lead.

After the defective leads have been repaired or if the fault cannot be found by a visual inspection, turn off all electrical loads and install a new fuse or wait until the thermal cut-out relay closes. If the fuse immediately burns out, look for the short between the fuse and the various switches. The short may also be in one of the other circuits which may be connected to the battery through the fuse. If the fuse does not burn out, turn on various circuits one at a time till the fuse again blows. The last circuit to be turned on will indicate the circuit in which the defect exists. Inspect this circuit carefully with the switch on to locate the cause. If the fuse does not burn out with all the circuits having been tested, then the short was temporary or intermittent and must be located by a very careful inspection. Shorts of this kind are very difficult to locate and require great care to find the defect. In case it cannot be located, the safest thing to do is run a new lead to replace the one in which the short is suspected.

Light Failures

Most lighting circuit failures are due to burned-out bulbs. When a lamp fails to light, check the bulbs by connecting them to a battery of the same voltage as that installed in the car or by installing the bulb in another socket which is known to be in good order. The next most probable cause of failure is a poor ground connection. This is readily checked by holding a jumper lead from the socket base to a clean ground on the frame or chassis. If the bulb has been found to be good and the jumper ground connection did not cause the bulb to light, inspect all the wiring in that lamp circuit, looking especially for breaks and open circuits. If the wiring appears in good condition, hold a jumper lead across the switch terminal; it is possible that the switch may be defective. If the lamp now lights, the switch requires repair or replacement. Most of the switches used in automotive wiring are not made to be readily repaired and therefore it is better to replace them with new ones.

To locate possible breaks in electrical conductors which are insulated, turn on the switch controlling the circuit. Then, using a test light with one end grounded and the other end having a needle for a prod, check the insulation every three inches where it is available and see if the test light lights. The break in the lead will be just the other side of the last point where the test lamp lighted. Use of a test light is shown in Fig. 28.3.

When replacing the lead in the lighting circuit, use wire of ample size to carry the load without excessive voltage loss, which would decrease the efficiency of the lights. The following table gives the recommended wire sizes for varying loads and lengths of circuits. This table is figured on the basis of an allowable drop of .6 volt between battery and lamp. Clinch and solder all connections and install grommets where abrasion is liable to occur. Bind the lead to the frame or other stationary part (except the engine) to prevent sagging, the vibration of which might wear the insulation.

Table 8
RECOMMENDED WIRE SIZES
FOR LIGHTING CIRCUITS
(For 6-Volt Systems; Safe for 12-volt)

Total Lamp Load	Length in Feet of Circuit From Batt. to Light					
	5	10	15	20	25	30
3 c.p.	16	16	16	16	16	16
5 c.p.	16	16	16	16	16	16
10 c.p.	16	16	16	16	16	16
15 c.p.	16	16	16	16	16	14
20 c.p.	16	16	16	14	14	12
25 c.p.	16	16	14	14	12	12
50 c.p.	16	14	12	10	10	8
75 c.p.	14	12	10	8	8	6

Circular mils:
#16 (1608) #14 (3829) #12 (6088)
#10 (9681) #8 (15392) #6 (29974)

To use this table, add the candlepower of the lamps on any one circuit, and measure the length of lead from battery to farthest lights. Find these figures on the table to determine correct wire size. Circular mils give comparative current-carrying capacity.

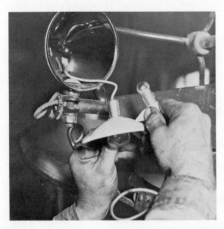

Fig. 28.3. Using a test light to check ground connection to lamp bulb to reflector on a farm tractor. With lights turned on and other end of tester grounded, the test lamp will light if the lamp base is making good contact with its socket and the reflector.

Light and Horn Relays

Relays are sometimes used in circuits requiring a rather heavy current, in order to reduce the voltage loss by shortening the path between the battery and appliance. For example, the relay can be placed in such a position that it will eliminate the length of wiring that would be required to go to a dash switch, thus reducing voltage losses in overcoming the resistance of the leads. Also, since the main switch will not be carrying all of the current load, the voltage loss due to possible burned switch contacts is eliminated.

While the relay is sometimes regarded as something mysterious, it is actually only an electrically-controlled switch, consisting of an electromagnet and a pair of contacts. One contact is stationary, while the other is mounted on a movable armature which is actuated by an electromagnet. Spring action holds the contacts apart when the electromagnet is not energized. Light relays differ from those designed for use in the horn circuit in that the winding of the electromagnet is designed for continuous duty and will not overheat when energized for long periods. The relay in the horn circuit is designed for short intermittent service and would overheat if used continuously.

Many of the relays used in the light circuits can also be used on other circuits such as heater or radio, where the capacity is sufficient. To increase the accessibility of the circuit, both ends of the relay winding are often brought out to a terminal. However, some relays have one end of the winding grounded and need only one control terminal. This also differs from the usual horn relay in that the horn relay winding is connected to the battery within the relay and the external circuit must be grounded to make it operate. Fig. 28.4 illustrates a horn relay circuit.

A relay in the headlight circuit, in addition to reducing voltage loss, increases the normal brilliance of the lights. For headlight circuits, a second terminal is grounded. However, for accessory circuits it is sometimes desirable to have a second control operation and the second terminal may be connected elsewhere.

Servicing of the relay is not required except to see that it is firmly mounted with the leads properly connected and tight. The fuse should be removed and inspected for corrosion and dirt; if it needs cleaning, also clean the inside of the holder and the lower fuse contact. This lower contact can be cleaned by using a strip of abrasive cloth, which has the dust removed with compressed air.

In case the relay should fail to close or open, or if the voltage loss in the relay becomes excessive, remove the relay cover and inspect for dirt and corrosion. File the contacts with a #6 American-Swiss equalling file to remove any burned or corroded spots and clean the contacts with linen tape and carbon tetrachloride.

To test a relay use a battery of the correct voltage. Connect a variable resistance or potentiometer, in series with the battery lead, to one of the control terminals on the relay and the other battery lead to the other control terminal. Connect a voltmeter across these terminals. To indicate when the relay is closed or open, connect an indicating light in series with the relay *L* terminal and ground, and connect the relay *B*

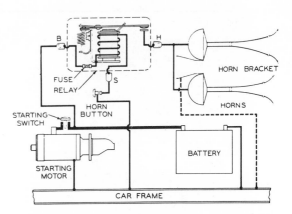

Fig. 28.4. Horn relay connections. Horn relays are made for short periods of operation and cannot be interchanged with light relays. The horn button is really a grounding switch, completing the relay coil circuit. (AL)

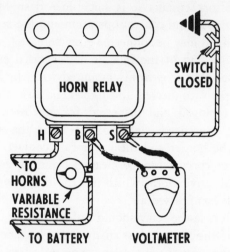

Fig. 28.5. Connections for testing closing voltage of horn relay. An ammeter with a built-in resistor is convenient for testing the relay as shown.

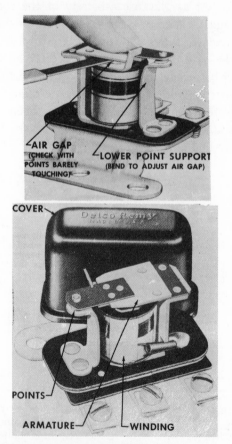

Fig. 28.6. Horn relay adjustments and main parts. (DR)

terminal to the battery. See Fig. 28.5. Slowly increase the voltage and note the voltage at which the contacts close as indicated by the lamp lighting. Increase the voltage to the rated value; then reduce the voltage, noting the voltmeter reading when the contacts open. Adjust the closing voltage by bending the lower spring hanger to change the armature tension. Adjust the opening voltage by raising or lowering the stationary contact to increase or decrease the contact gap. Keep the contacts in proper alignment and do not adjust the contact gap to less than the specified values. Refer to Fig. 28.6 for appearance and adjustments.

Keep the cover on the relay when making the opening and closing tests. After the adjustments are completed, install the gaskets and cover, clinching tightly to prevent moisture from entering.

Wiring Inspection

As the various parts of the electrical system are inspected, the wires connected to each unit should be checked for loose or corroded terminals, chafed or defective insulation, or breaks or partial breaks where the wires are clamped by the terminals. Insulation should be in good condition, especially on the high-tension systems as even very tiny cracks may allow oil or water to enter and cause a partial ground.

Bind the conduit or lead to the chassis at any point where vibration or sagging is likely to occur. When inspecting any electrical unit, pay special attention to the ground connection. On most units, this grounding is performed by the mounting screw. However, batteries and some headlights and horns are grounded by a wire. Make sure all mounting spaces used are clean and that mounting screws are equipped with lock washers.

Horn Circuit

The horn is a warning device, electrically operated, and actuated whenever the operator depresses the control button or ring. The circuit for operating the horn may be: (1) in series with the battery, to the horn control button, to ground, or (2) there may be a relay inserted between the battery and the horn. When there is a relay in the circuit, the horn button acts only as a grounding switch and carries just the relay control current. The spark formed when the contacts open and close is much less intense than it would be if all of the horn current were forced to flow through the button switch.

It must be remembered that the relay used in the horn circuit, similar to those used in the light circuit, is merely a magnetic switch which permits a relatively small current to control a much more intense current flow. Also, remember that the horn button is a grounding switch with the rest of the circuit under electrical pressure. This is the reason why a ground at any place in the circuit will cause the horn to blow, since it allows current to flow.

The horn consists of a diaphragm that is vibrated rapidly by an electromagnet. When the electromagnet is energized, it pulls on an armature that is attached to the diaphragm. The slight movement of the armature flexes the diaphragm and also opens a set of contacts. This opens the electromagnetic circuit and the steel diaphragm returns to its original position, thus closing the contact and repeating the cycle. This constant flexing and straightening of the diaphragm produces vibrations and resulting sound. Some horns have tubes or projectors to improve the quality of the horn tone and to direct its signal. Auto-Lite builds several different models of horns and all of them, whether with or without projectors, produce sound by the method described above. A current limit relay is often used as a circuit breaker as shown in Fig. 28.7.

Some horns have a resistance connected in series with the magnet winding. Others may have a condenser or resistor connected across the contact to decrease arcing at the contact points and prolong contact life.

Three basic horn circuits are commonly used. Two of these make use of the relays and the difference between them lies in the point where the power current is picked up. The third circuit does not include a relay and is used principally with a single horn having a low current draw. In this circuit the full current used by the horn goes through the horn button. A simple inspection will tell which type of circuit is used on any particular installation and whether or not a fuse is incorporated in the horn circuit.

Auto-Lite relays have either three or four terminals, depending upon the type. On the three-terminal type, the connecting points are marked *H* for the horn wire, *S* for the signal control or horn button, and *B* for the battery connection. On the four-terminal type there is an additional terminal marked *Ign* which is connected to the

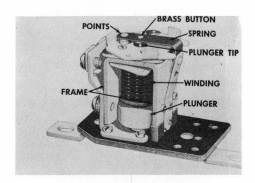

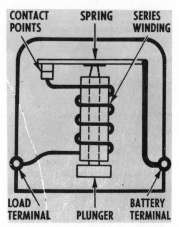

Fig. 28.7. Current limit relay, used as a circuit breaker to open the circuit when a predetermined load flows through the series coil (current coil). Below, the plunger is pulled upward lifting the spring and opening the contact points. (DR)

ignition switch so that the horn cannot be blown when the ignition switch is open. In the Delco-Remy relay there are three terminals marked *H* for the horn, *B* for battery and *S* for signal, in that order, reading from left to right. On the late model horn relays the terminals do not carry any markings but follow the same left-to-right order: *H - B - S*.

Horn Circuit Service

Inspect the wiring between the horns, the button or ring, the relay and the battery for loose connections, chafed insulation, corroded terminals and for partial breaks, especially where the wires enter a conduit or are clamped by a terminal. The power or battery wire to the horn or relay may be connected directly to the battery, but more often this connection is made at some other point such as the starting switch, ammeter, voltage regulator or ignition switch. For a complete check, inspect this circuit all the way back to the battery, including the battery ground.

If a fuse is incorporated in one of the wires or is mounted on the relay terminal, remove and inspect it, and clean the holder.

Trouble in the horn circuit is indicated by lack of operation of the horn, poor operation, or constant operation.

If the horn does not operate as it should when the button is depressed, check for opens in the horn button circuit by grounding the relay or horn terminal which is connected to the button. If the horn operates, it indicates proper operation of the horn and relay, and therefore the horn button and its leads should be carefully and thoroughly inspected.

In some cases there will be continuous operation of the horn, the reason for which is a ground in the horn button wiring. To check, disconnect the horn button wire from the horn or relay. If this stops the horn operation, inspect the wires or ground especially where it enters the steering column. If the horn does not stop when this wire is removed, disconnect the other

wires and inspect the horn and relays. When replacing wiring to the horn, use size #12 wire or larger as this carries a heavy current.

For best service, the horn should be inspected periodically. Wipe the dirt from its exterior and remove any debris from the projector or the tube portion. If the horn is rusted or corroded, it should be removed for an overhaul. If the horn mounting is cracked or loose, proper repairs should be made.

A horn should not be condemned unless the fuse and wiring have been previously checked, as most horn failures can be traced to a blown fuse or to faulty wiring.

To localize the trouble in the horn, connect a jumper lead from the battery to the horn terminal. A convenient place to make the connection is the starting switch battery terminal. Single-wire horns should operate with this wire in place. However, if they do not, ground the horn frame to the chassis to check the horn ground connections. If the horn now operates, the ground connection is at fault; the horn should be removed and the mounting surfaces cleaned to make a good ground when the horn is replaced. Two-wire horns will not operate with only the jumper lead in place, but require that a second wire be connected from the other horn terminal to a ground on the frame. If the horn(s) operate with these tests, the cause of the trouble will be found in the wiring, relay, or button. To test which side of the circuit is at fault, disconnect the test wires one at a time and operate the horn button.

If a horn is inoperative or does not have a clear steady tone, remove, clean and disassemble it. Inspect the diaphragm for cracks and distortions, and check the winding and connections for opens, faulty insulation and grounds. Check the resistor, if one is used, with an ohmmeter, or by the volt-ammeter method. Check the condenser for capacity, grounds and leaks with a condenser tester.

The contacts should be inspected carefully. Do not force them apart as this will tend to contract the springs and change the contact pressure. If the contacts are rough or burned, clean and polish with crocus cloth and carbon tetrachloride. If the contacts are excessively burned or are fused, they should be replaced. On some types, this requires the replacement of the complete dash assembly, while others can be replaced by installing new contact springs and contact screw assembly.

Assemble the horn, leaving the horn dome and dome bracket off until after the horn is adjusted. Be sure all gaskets are in place; then thoroughly tighten the flange screws and circuit breaker mounting screws. When a nut is used on the projector side of the diaphragm, be sure it is tight and has the proper size of lock washer in place. Solder all connections within the horn to make strong, low-resistance joints. Inspect to see that the circuit breaker contacts are in proper alignment and that the contact spring does not rub against the armature spring. A schematic wiring diagram of a horn is shown in Fig. 28.8.

Horn Adjustments

On horns which have an adjustable armature, measure the gap between the armature and field cup with two flat feeler gauges. Adjust the gap on all sides to the specified value by loosening the armature lock nut and turning the slotted armature stud. Round armatures do not have a slotted stud, but are adjusted by turning the armature to screw it in or out. It is sometimes necessary to tap the armature lock spring lightly with a screwdriver to free it before the armature can be turned. Tighten the lock-nut and check the gap. The correct gap size can be found from the specifications covering the horn number which is being adjusted.

Connect an ammeter and variable resistance in series with one horn terminal and a battery of the correct voltage, and connect the other horn terminal to the second battery terminal with a voltmeter across the horn terminal. If the horn has a single wire run the other terminal from the horn base. When tuning a pair of horns each horn should be connected and adjusted separately, then checked for tone by operating them as a pair.

Never stuff rags or other material in the projector to muffle the sound, as this changes the vibration frequency and will give a false current setting. Avoid clamping the flange in a vise as the pressure may cause a tension on the diaphragm and result in breakage. The type of mounting may affect the horn tone, and therefore for best results a special test fixture should be used.

To make the adjustment on Auto-Lite horns of the *H-A*, *H-D* and *H-K* types, back out the striker screw in the center of the horn back so that it is clear and does not touch the diaphragm assembly. Loosen the lock-nut on the circuit breaker screw, and adjust the screw and variable resistance to give the correct humming voltage current. Tighten the lock-nut and check the humming draw. Turn the striker screw in until it touches the diaphragm and adjust the screw and resistance to give the correct voltage and current. Tighten the lock-nut. Vary the voltage slightly above and below the adjustment figure to make sure the horn will operate under varying conditions. Also check the horn

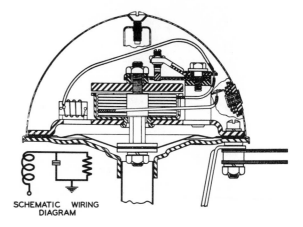

SCHEMATIC WIRING DIAGRAM

Fig. 28.8. Enlarged drawing of HH horn, showing arrangement of parts. Note the schematic wiring diagram at the lower left. (AL)

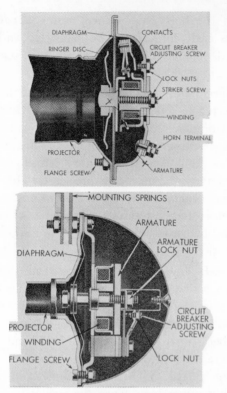

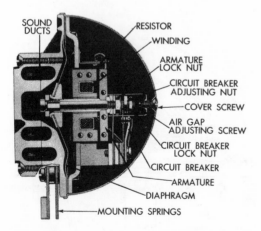

Fig. 28.9. Adjustments on Autolite horns HA, HD, and HK. (Left) Back out striker screw from diaphragm assembly. Connect voltmeter to horn terminal and adjust voltage as specified; adjust current and readjust striker screw. (Right) For HH, HJ, HL, HM, HO, HP, HT, and HW, adjust armature air gap by screwing round armature in or out. Current and voltage are adjusted by turning the contact screw.

Fig. 28.10. Adjustments on HB, HC, HF, and HG horns are made by loosening the circuit breaker lock-nut and turning the adjusting bolt. Current draw is adjusted by turning the large adjusting nut.

operation by opening and closing the circuit a few times. Refer to Fig. 28.9.

On Auto-Lite types *H-B*, *H-C*, *H-F* and *H-G*, loosen the small lock-nut on the contact adjustment. Adjust the variable resistance and the large brass nut to give the exact voltage and current setting; then tighten the lock-nut and re-check the setting. Vary the voltage slightly above and below the specified figures, and open and close the circuit a few times to check the horn operation. Install the dome bracket and dome. Then recheck the operation and tone. Refer to Fig. 28.10.

Horns not included in the above model numbers are adjusted by loosening the lock-nut and turning the circuit breaker contact screw. Hold the voltage at the specified value and turn the contact screw to get the correct current draw. Tighten the lock-nut and check the voltage and current. Install the dome.

The correct voltage and current draws for each model may be determined from tables available from the manufacturers.

Horn Relay Service

The horn relay is a possible trouble spot, along with the horn wiring and the horn itself. Therefore, it may be necessary to service the horn relay to get the horn circuit operating as it should.

Many horn relays have a fuse incorporated in the horn circuit to prevent damage when short circuits occur. The fuse is located in a holder mounted on the relay "battery" terminal. The fuse is removed for inspection and replacement by pressing in slightly and turning the top part of the holder. Inspect to see that the fuse is not blown, and that both the fuse and the holder are clean and bright. Sometimes the lower fuse holder contact becomes corroded and does not make contact. If the lower end of the fuse is corroded or dirty, clean it and also the spring contact with a small piece of very fine sandpaper.

When inspecting fuses, do not rely on visual inspection alone. Even if the fuse looks good, check it with a test light to be sure it will pass current. Sometimes one end of the fuse wire may come loose from the metal cap at the end of the fuse and it will not conduct current even though it looks satisfactory. An open in the circuit at this point is, many times, difficult to locate unless the fuse is checked.

To quickly check the relay operation, ground the control terminal which is usually marked *S* and is connected to the horn button. Relays which have four terminals receive their operating current through the ignition switch or some other control switch. If the relay does not close with the *S* terminal grounded, check the wiring as previously described. Finally, remove the horn and relay for a complete test unless inspection of the wiring and testing of the circuits make this appear to be in good condition.

Remove the relay cover and fuse. Inspect for burned or dirty contacts and damaged insulation. File the contacts with a #6 American-Swiss equalling file until they are clean and bright. Clean all dirt from the contacts with a strip of clean lintless tape and carbon tetrachloride. Thoroughly clean the fuse, fuse contacts and holder and inspect the fuse insulation. Make sure the armature operates easily and without interference and tighten the nut on the bottom of the magnet core.

To check the operation of the horn relays, connect a variable resistance in series between the battery and one of the relay control terminals in the same way the lighting circuit relay was connected for tests. Connect the other terminal to the second battery terminal. On some relays both ends of the winding are brought out to external terminals and the load circuit is completely separate from the control circuit. On other relays one end of the winding is connected to the battery terminal and the other is connected to the control switch terminal. An inspection will usually determine which terminals are connected to the winding. Connect the voltmeter to the relay control terminal. To indicate when the terminals are

open and closed, connect a test lamp in series with the battery and the relay load terminal. The lamp will light when the contact is closed and go out when the contact is open.

Increase the voltage slowly and note the voltage at which the contacts close. If the contact is mounted on a spring arm, increase the voltage until the armature seats against the yoke. Reduce the voltage and note the voltage at which the contacts open. Adjust the contact opening and closing voltage by changing the armature spring tension. Bend the lower spring hanger, or if no spring is used, bend the hinge ears, keeping the ears aligned. Be sure the cover gasket is in good condition and properly installed, then clinch the cover tightly in place. The correct voltages and current for the various relays are given in manufacturer's manuals.

Electric Windshield Wiper Circuit

The circuit which controls the electric windshield wipers will require the attention of the automotive electrician whenever it does not function as it should. Fig. 28.11 shows an Auto-Lite unit.

The circuit includes the source of current, the control switch, one or two fractional horsepower DC motors and the wiring connecting

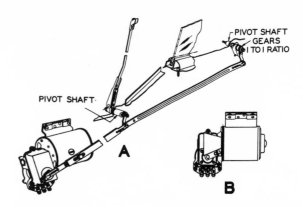

Fig. 28.11. Complete windshield wiper assembly. (A) Powerful shunt type motor in operating position. (B) Motor with gauge in place to measure the correct parking angle so the wiper blades will stop in the desired position. (AL)

these units. Usually a fuse or thermal circuit breaker is connected in the circuit to prevent damage to the motor when grounds or overloads occur. The load on the windshield wiper

motor may be quite variable, due to ice, snow or mud gathering on the windshield. A two-crank wiper motor is shown in Fig. 28.12.

The cautions pertaining to the wiring that have been given in the other circuits also apply to the windshield wiper circuit. Check for loose connections, chafed insulation, corroded terminals and partial breaks. Be sure the wires do not contact the motor cranks or linkage and that they are clear of the cowl ventilator lever. When inspecting the wiring, follow the battery circuit all the way back from the wiper motor to the wiper switch and ammeter to the battery. Check any fuses or overload relays that may be included. Be sure the motor is properly grounded.

The windshield wiper motor requires no periodic service except an occasional inspection to see that it is firmly mounted and operating correctly without excessive vibration or noise. This check should be made at both high and low speeds on motors designed for two-speed operation. If the motor operation is not satisfactory, it should be removed, disassembled, cleaned and lubricated according to the instructions pertaining to that particular type.

Two types of electric windshield wiper motors are in use. One, the *Dyneto*, is a series-wound, direct-current motor that transmits its

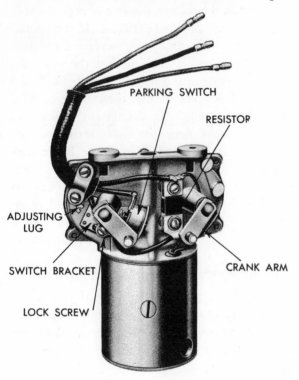

Fig. 28.12. Autolite windshield wiper motor which drives one or two crank arms through a worm gear on the armature shaft. A parking switch and special circuit provide for a fixed parking position.

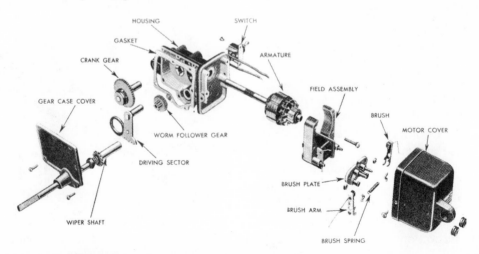

Fig. 28.13. Dyneto windshield wiper motor with a worm gear on the armature which drives a follower gear and in turn a crank gear. An eccentric on the crank gear moves the driving sector with a reciprocating motion; teeth on the sector rotate the wiper shaft back and forth.

power from a worm gear on the armature shaft through a series of gears to a crank arm. This crank cam moves a driving sector back and forth across a gear on the wiper shaft and gives a reciprocating action to the wiper. Refer to Fig. 28.13.

The other type uses a shunt wound motor with a worm gear on the armature shaft which drives one or two gears mounted on crankshafts. The cranks are linked to levers on the wiper pivot and move them back and forth to swing the wiper arm and blade.

Different circuits are used to provide for a fixed parking position, but all of them use a switch mounted on the motor which is actuated by a cam on one of the cranks. This switch is connected to the battery and keeps the motor in operation until the switch is opened by the cam. When the wiper is in operation this switch is bypassed and floats on the circuit. However, when the control switch is turned off, the motor continues to operate until the wiper arms reach the parking position, at which time the cam opens the parking switch and stops the motor.

Trouble apparently due to defective motor operation may be caused by worn or broken parts in the driving mechanism or the usual troubles experienced in the motor itself. Inspect the driving mechanism for excessive wear, worn or broken teeth or worn bearings. If the driving mechanism is in bad condition, it would probably be cheaper to replace the whole motor than to try to repair it. If the motor is responsible for the trouble, inspect its parts for wear, corrosion or other damage. If the commutator is dirty, it can be cleaned with No. 00 or 000 sandpaper. Worn or old oil-soaked brushes should be replaced. Check the feel of the armature shaft and the crank arm shaft and their bearings, and replace any worn parts.

Adjustments may be required from time to time to be sure the blades are parked in the correct position. This position is governed by the cam which operates the parking switch. If the motor should be disassembled, use great care in getting it back together in the same way it was taken apart so that the blades will be parked in the correct position when the motor stops. If both blades do not stop in the same position, relocate the arms on the pivot shaft. If this fails, it may be necessary to disassemble the motor and reassemble the crank arms in their correct relation. If the wiper will not stop, the fault may be a bad control switch or an inoperative switch. Check to make sure the cam strikes the switch button. If necessary, bend the cam slightly, being careful that it does not strike the side of the button. Check the parking position again. If the blades park slightly out of their correct position, adjustments can be made on many of the motors by loosening the lock screw, holding the parking switch bracket and rotating the switch slightly. Be sure to tighten the lock screw.

Turn Signal Circuit

All the new cars have turning signals incorporated in the lighting circuit, as shown in Fig. 28.14. The circuit uses double-filament lamps in the parking lights, and requires an extra conductor to each parking lamp from the signal control switch on the steering column. The extra filament is more powerful than the parking light filament and is the one that flashes. When the signal switch is moved into right or left turning position, the corresponding lamp is connected into the circuit which is controlled by the flasher. The schematic wiring diagram is shown in Fig. 28.15.

The rear signal makes use of the stop light filament in the tail light. When the switch lever is moved into right or left turning position, the corresponding stop light filament is taken out of the circuit controlled by the stop light switch on the brake system and connected into the circuit controlled by the flasher. The other stop light filament remains under the control of the stop light switch so that when brakes are applied and the signals indicate a

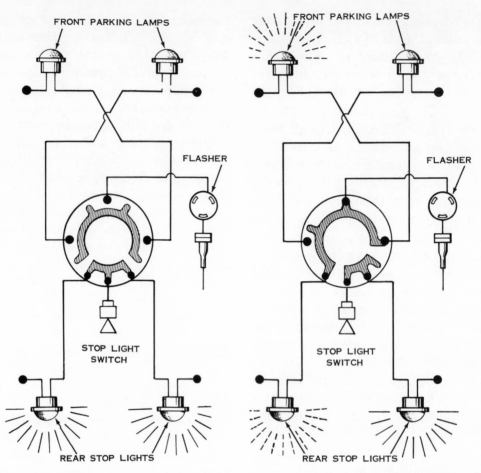

Fig. 28.14. The "Bell" circuit for directional signal switches uses existing stop lights for rear directional signal lights, without interfering with the normal operation of the stop lights. At right is a circuit with left lamps flashing for a left turn.

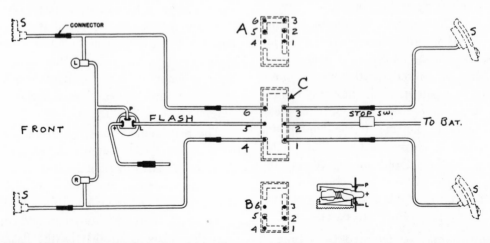

Fig. 28.15. Turning signal schematic wiring diagram. (A) For a right turn the contacts 1, 2, 3, 4, 5, and 6 are connected. This puts the front right parking lamp and the right stop light in the flasher circuit, taking the right stop light out of the control of the stop light switch. (B) The connections are shown here for a left turn. The dotted lines represent the connecting metal segments shown in Fig. 28.14.

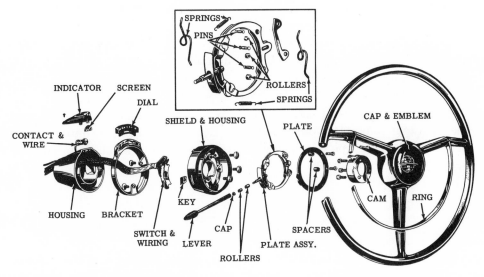

Fig. 28.16. Details of directional signal construction. Most of the signal switches have a self-cancelling device to return the switch to neutral position after a turn is made.

turn to be made, one rear lamp will glow steadily as a "Stop" signal while the other flashes. Fig. 28.16 shows the details of a turn-signal control.

Keeping in mind that the signal system operates by taking the lights on either side, respectively, out of their normal circuits, and throwing them into the flasher circuit, it will be relatively easy to run down any trouble developing in the signal system.

There are six wires attached to the signal control switch: two to the two front lamps, two to the two rear lamps, one to the flasher and current source and one to the wire which is connected to the "cold" side of the stop light switch. In addition there will be one or two wires leading to the indicating lamp(s) depending upon whether one or two lamps are used. These lamps show whether or not the system is operating.

The flasher and the indicating lamps may be located under the dash or, in some cases, incorporated into the switch body which is located on the steering column.

It is general practice to include a self-cancelling feature which turns off the signal as the steering wheel is rotated to guide the car around a corner. The self-cancelling feature works by means of a cam or striker which operates a trip on the switch and allows the switch lever to snap back to a center position.

If the self-cancelling device fails to work it may be because one of the parts is broken or bent. Also the lever may be stuck in one of the positions and the spring is not strong enough to snap it back to the center position.

The flasher is a separate unit and in case of its failure it can be detached and replaced.

In case one of the front signal lamps fails to operate, it is probably because of a burned-

Fig. 28.17. The stop light switch contains a flexible metal diaphragm which moves a small plunger and closes the contact points when brake fluid pressure is applied. (AL)

out filament. It should be remembered that the parking lamps, where turning signals are used, have double filaments so that the parking lamp may light while the front flasher may not. The bright filament tail lamp bulb is used in both the stop light signal and turning signal circuits. Therefore, if it works in one circuit and not in the other, the trouble is some place other than the bulb itself. Details of a typical stop light switch are shown in Fig. 28.17.

Summary

The *lighting and accessory circuits* are generally taken for granted, but now and then something goes wrong and must be fixed.

At every point in the insulated side of a circuit, electricity is trying to *flow to ground* and will take any available path, desirable or undesirable.

The *lighting and accessory circuits* include the battery, frame, lights, accessories, and various switches as well as the conductors carrying current to them. The lighting system can be broken down into separate circuits, each with its lights, accessories, appliances, switches and conductors.

All the *individual circuits* in the system can be traced from the battery to the switch(es) and to lights or appliances. Each light or appliance must be grounded, as the car frame is a conductor just as truly as the wires.

With *four headlamps* for high beam, as now generally used, the bright beam of number *2* lamps is turned on plus the single beam of number *1* lamps, making all four lamps in use. For low beam only the outboard lamps are turned on.

Lighting circuit troubles are either opens or shorts. Junction blocks are possible trouble spots. Inspect switches and connections. Measure circuit voltage drop with a voltmeter.

The lighting circuit usually includes *fuses or overload relays* to protect the circuits. If a fuse burns out, find out why, to avoid repetition of the trouble.

Light failures are generally due to burned-out bulbs. Check bulbs by connecting across the battery. It is possible a switch may be defective.

Light and horn relays are sometimes used in circuits requiring rather heavy current. A relay is an electrically-controlled switch. Light relays are designed for continuous duty whereas horn relays are designed for short intermittent duty. A relay in the headlight circuit will reduce the voltage loss that otherwise would occur in going through longer leads.

To *test a relay* use a battery of the correct voltage.

In *wiring inspection,* the wires to each unit should be checked for loose or corroded terminals, chafed or defective insulation. Where sagging and possible rubbing may occur, bind the conductors. Be sure there are good ground connections. The battery always has a heavy ground cable, and many headlights have ground leads.

The *horn* is a warning device and operates by grounding the horn circuit. The horn consists of a diaphragm that is vibrated by an electromagnet. To limit arcing at the horn vibrator contacts, the horn circuit has either a resistance or a condenser.

For *horn circuit service,* inspect the wiring between the horns, button or ring, relay and battery for loose connections, chafed insulation, corroded terminals and partial breaks where wires enter a conduit or are clamped by a terminal. Trouble in the horn circuit is indicated by either a lack of operation of the horn or poor operation. In cases of continuous horn operation, the reason is a ground in the horn button wiring. The horn switch is a grounding switch and any ground in the circuit can cause the horn to blow.

The *horn relay* is a possible trouble spot as well as the horn wiring and horn itself.

The *electric windshield wiper circuit* is another circuit that should be given some consideration in case the wiper does not function as it should. The circuit includes the source of current, control switch and one or two fractional horsepower DC motors. In case of trouble, check for loose connections, chafed insulation, corroded terminals, and partial breaks in conductors.

A *turn signal circuit* is shown in Fig. 28.14. An extra filament is supplied in the front parking light but the regular filament is used in the stop light. The system operates by taking the lights on either side, respectively, out of their normal circuits and throwing them into the flasher circuit. There are six wires attached to the signal control switch in addition to one or two wires for the dash indicator lights. The flasher is a separate unit and in case of failure may be removed and replaced by another unit. A self-cancelling device will turn off the turn signal after making a right-angle turn.

Questions

1. What is included in the lighting circuit?
2. What two kinds of lamps are used in the four-light headlamp arrangement?
3. Describe number *1* lamps; number *2* lamps.
4. What lighting circuit troubles may develop?
5. What is used to protect circuits against excessive current?
6. In case of failure of a protective device what precaution should be taken?
7. What is the most common cause of light failure?
8. How would you locate a break in an insulated conductor?
9. Why are relays often used?
10. What is a relay?
11. What is the difference between a lighting relay and a horn relay?
12. What happens when a horn circuit is grounded?
13. Of what does a horn unit consist?
14. How would you localize trouble in the horn circuit?
15. What operates an electric windshield wiper?
16. What controls the parking position?
17. How many wires go to the turn signal switch, excluding the dash indicator lights?
18. How many wires are needed for the dash indicator lights?
19. What is the basic principle of operation of the turn signal circuit?
20. Where are the front signals located?
21. Where are the rear signals located?
22. How is a defective flasher corrected?
23. In case one lamp fails to operate in the turn signal system what should be done?
24. What effect does the stop light switch have on the turn signals?
25. What would cause the self-cancelling device to fail to work?

CHAPTER TWENTY-NINE

Dash Instruments— Operation, Circuits, Servicing and Troubles

The dash instruments include the engine temperature gauge, the fuel gauge, the oil pressure gauge and the speedometer. In addition, some cars supply a dash ammeter, although it has largely been replaced by an indicating light which glows if the generator fails to charge. In some cases, the oil pressure gauge is also replaced by a signal light which will light if the oil pressure drops below a safe value. On some trucks, racing cars, and some of the foreign cars, a tachometer is added to indicate engine revolutions per minute.

Because some cars and trucks do include an ammeter in their dash instruments, a brief discussion of this instrument will be included in this chapter. The speedometer and tachometer are highly specialized instruments, and therefore will be touched upon only briefly.

Automotive type gauges give only approximate indications, as exact values are not needed for normal operating observations. Since the panel gauges are not accurate enough for making adjustments or tests, special test instruments should be connected into the circuit when these are made. In general, the temperature indicator and oil pressure gauge are more accurate than either the ammeter or the fuel gauge. However, automotive type ammeters do serve an important function by indicating the correct direction of current flow and whether current is flowing into or out of the battery.

Ammeter Service

In any cases where the ammeter does not operate, remove it from the panel, being careful not to ground the battery leads. Inspect the pointer and armature assembly. Make sure that it moves freely and has a slight amount of end play in the shaft. After adjusting the end play, apply a drop of air-drying varnish to the bearing to prevent its turning. Hold the ammeter in the same position as it would be mounted in the panel and check the zero position. If it is held in any other position the counterweight will act to throw the needle from its zero position. Hold the counterweight and apply a slight pressure to the pointer to bring the "at rest" position exactly to zero.

Connect the panel ammeter, a test ammeter, and a carbon pile rheostat in series with a battery. Adjust the current to various values by means of the carbon pile rheostat and compare the two ammeters. Reverse the connections to the panel ammeter and check the indications on

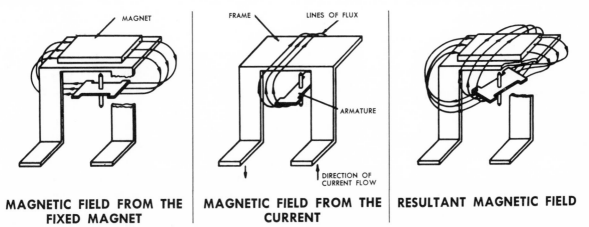

MAGNETIC FIELD FROM THE FIXED MAGNET | MAGNETIC FIELD FROM THE CURRENT | RESULTANT MAGNETIC FIELD

Fig. 29.1. When the full current to and from the battery goes through a dash ammeter, the magnetic field which causes the meter indication results from both the magnetic field from the fixed magnet and that from the current.

the discharge side. If the meter indicates the direction of current flow correctly and gives an approximately correct reading, it can be replaced in the panel. If the indication is not reasonably accurate, the ammeter should be replaced.

Inspect the ammeter for correct mounting, seeing that the gasket is in place and that there is no interference with the ammeter operation. Connect the leads to the meter making sure the terminals are tight. Turn on the lights or some other accessory and observe if the ammeter moves toward the *discharge* side. If it should show a charge under these conditions, the leads on either the ammeter terminals or on the battery have been interchanged. Check the battery ground polarity in accordance with the specifications for that particular installation. Such reverse ammeter readings may also be caused by reversing the permanent magnet when the meter was assembled. Fig. 29.1 shows the principle of dash ammeter operation. Fig. 29.2 shows the shunt type of ammeter.

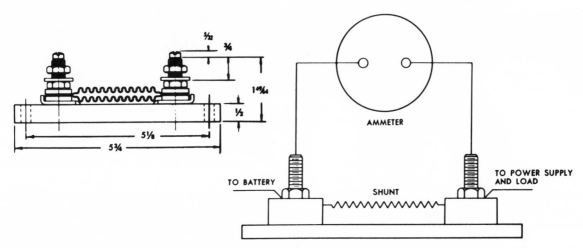

Fig. 29.2. Shunt-type ammeter, preferable for the heavy current put out by the late model generators and alternators. The current to and from the battery goes through a convenient, calibrated shunt, with leads going to the meter.

Oil Pressure Gauge

The oil pressure gauge indicates the pressure of the engine lubricating oil. There are two entirely different types of oil pressure gauges used, and either one of them may be encountered on cars that come in for service. The two types are the Bourdon tube and the electric oil gauge.

Bourdon Tube

For its actuating unit, the Bourdon tube gauge has a flat tube bent in a semicircle and closed at one end; the other end is open for connection to the source of oil pressure. When oil pressure is applied to the tube, it tends to expand to a circular cross section and doing this it straightens out slightly, moving the end which is closed. The amount of straightening depends upon the amount of pressure applied to the tube. The end which is connected to a line from the oil pump is stationary. The movement of the other end is transmitted to a pointer to which it is linked. A spring is often used to keep a slight tension on the pointer and take up any slack in the linkage. This will reduce the vibration of the pointer and return it to its zero point. Fig. 29.3 shows this type.

If the oil gauge becomes inoperative, disconnect the tube from the back of the gauge. Hold the end of the tube over a receptacle and start the engine. Oil should flow from the tube at a steady rate. If it does not, check the oil

Fig. 29.3. Bourdon tube type of oil pressure gauge as furnished by AC Division of General Motors. It uses a sector and gear to move the needle.

pump operation and check the tube for kinks, leaks or plugging.

If inspection shows that oil pressure is reaching the gauge, then remove the gauge from the panel. Check with a wire or a pin to see if the small hole leading into the Bourdon tube is open. Check the movement of the end of the tube to see that the pointer moves freely. Connect the unit to the oil line and check its operation. If it still does not operate, or if the readings are obviously in error, it should be replaced. When mounting the oil gauge in the panel, have any dust gaskets properly in place and check for any possible binding or interference due to a distorted mounting.

Minor adjustments can be made in the gauge's indication by bending the wire connecting the Bourdon tube to the pointer. Bending the wire so that it bears on the pointer lever near the pivot increases the spread and will increase the readings after the zero point has been reset. Be sure to check the indications and compare them with a master meter before installing the oil gauge in the panel.

Electric Oil Gauges

Two different companies, AC Division of General Motors Corp. and King-Seeley, furnish the electric oil gauges for passenger automobiles. Each of these gauges consists of two units connected by a single wire; one is an engine sending unit, and the other, a dash indicating unit. On most cars the current to operate the gauges is provided through the ignition switch so when this is turned off, the instruments are dead. The wiring between the ignition switch, the dash unit and the engine unit should be inspected periodically for loose connections, frayed insulation, breaks or grounds. If the gauge does not properly indicate the oil pressure whenever the engine is operating, stop the engine at once and check to make sure that the oil pump is operating correctly and that no oil lines are broken. Pressure can be readily checked by loosening the sending unit; if oil leaks out around the threads, pressure is there. Make sure there is sufficient oil to cover the oil pump intake. With the ignition turned on, check with a test lamp to be sure that there is current at the dash unit terminal connected to the ignition switch. If the lamp does not light, power is not reaching the gauge, and the ignition switch, ammeter, and wiring should be carefully inspected.

AC Electrical Oil Pressure Gauge

On the AC gauge, the engine unit consists of a housing which encloses a diaphragm, and linkage which moves a contact over a resistance.

This results in a varying current, proportional to the oil pressure, which flows through the indicating dash unit and causes proper indication of the pointer. The AC gauge is shown in Fig. 29.4.

The indicating unit consists of two coils placed 90° apart with an armature and a pointer shaft located at the intersection of the center line of the two coils. To prevent vibration of the pointer on rough roads, an inertia dampener is provided. The dial has a scale graduated in pounds per square inch. Both engine unit and dash unit are grounded.

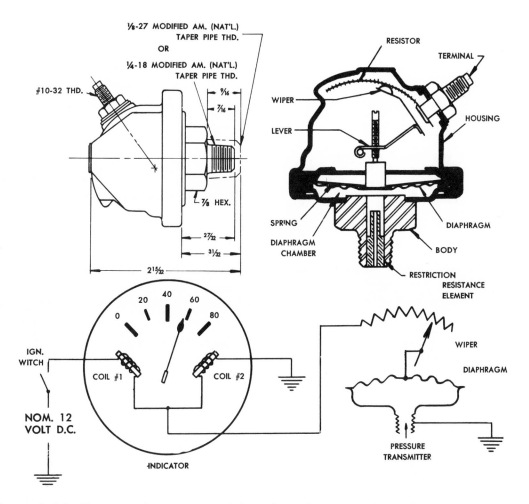

Fig. 29.4. AC oil pressure instrument, consisting of a sending unit and an indicating unit. In the sending unit (upper right) is a diaphragm which is deflected by oil pressure. This, in turn, moves a wiper across a wound resistance, varying the amount of current that goes to the indicating unit.

The electrical oil pressure gauges are subject to five kinds of trouble. These troubles and their probable causes are given in the following list:

1. The pointer will not move when ignition switch is turned *on*. This may be due to: (1) defective dash unit, (2) break or poor connection between battery and dash unit, (3) dash unit not grounded.
2. The pointer registers a high pressure under all conditions. This may be due to: (1) defective engine unit, (2) break in dash-to-engine-unit wire, (3) engine unit improperly grounded.
3. The pointer stays at *0* under all conditions. This may be due to: (1) short to ground at engine unit terminal or (2) short in dash-to-engine-unit wire.
4. The pointer lever drops to *0* or always registers too high a pressure. This may be due to: (1) loose or dirty connections, (2) defective dash unit, (3) defective engine unit.
5. The pointer always registers too low a pressure. This may be due to: (1) partial ground at engine unit terminal or at dash-to-engine-unit wire, (2) defective dash unit, (3) defective engine unit.

To locate trouble first determine whether the trouble is in the panel instrument, the wiring, or the engine unit.

This can be done by making a tester. It is a very simple operation and makes use of an AC fuel gauge tank unit, the one with the long movable arm with a cork float on the end. Attach a spring terminal clip to a 5-foot piece of colored insulated wire and connect the other end of this wire to the binding post of the tank unit. Attach two spring clips to the ends of another 5-foot piece of black insulated wire. The tester is now ready for use.

To test the panel instrument, proceed as follows:

1. Turn ignition switch off.
2. Disconnect one of the battery cables.
3. Disconnect the wire from the oil gauge mounted on the instrument panel. This is the wire which leads to the engine unit.
4. Connect the spring clip end of the colored tester wire to the binding post from which you removed the wire leading to the engine unit.
5. Connect the black wire to the flange of the tester and to any convenient ground, such as an upainted part of the instrument panel.
6. Turn the ignition switch *on* and reconnect the battery cable.
7. Move the arm of the tester back and forth slowly. If the panel instrument is operating correctly, the pointer will move from the low to the high mark freely. If the pointer doesn't move, then a new panel instrument should be installed. A unit of the same make must be used, as the instruments made by the different companies are not interchangeable.

If the panel instrument proves to be in good working order, the next step is to test the wiring between the panel and the engine unit. Continue using the same tester, following these steps:

1. Turn the ignition switch *off* and disconnect one battery cable.
2. Follow the wire from the dash unit to the engine unit and disconnect at this point.
3. Attach the colored tester wire to the end of the wire which runs up to the instrument panel, and attach the black wire to any convenient ground such as an unpainted part of the engine.
4. Reconnect the battery cable, turn the ignition *on*, and move the arm of the tester back and forth. This connection puts the test wiring and test instrument in series with the wiring on the car.

If the wiring is free from trouble, the pointer on the instrument will move from the low mark to the high mark freely. If the pointer does not move or only moves part way, the wire from the instrument to the engine unit should be repaired or replaced.

If the pointer does move correctly, then the trouble is in the engine unit. Check that the connection at the engine unit is clean; if a dirty terminal is not the cause of the trouble, then a new engine unit must be installed.

King-Seeley and Ford
Electrical Oil Pressure Gauges

The principle of operation of the King-Seeley oil pressure gauge is entirely different from the AC electric gauges. The engine unit contains a diaphragm which is deflected in proportion to the pressure of the oil in the engine lubrication system. When the diaphragm is deflected, an electrical circuit is closed allowing current to flow through a heating coil wound around a thermostatic bimetal strip. Heat generated in the coil deflects the bimetal to the point where the contact is opened. The bimetal then cools and returns to its original position which again closes the electrical circuit. This cycle is repeated continuously.

The dash unit is connected to the ignition switch and is in series with the engine unit.

With the ignition switch turned off, the pointer will rest at the extreme left position. The dash unit contains a similar heating coil formed around the bimetal strip connected in series with the coil in the engine unit. When heating takes place in the engine unit, heating also takes place in the dash unit causing the bimetal strip in this unit to deflect simultaneously. The dash unit pointer is linked to the bimetal strip, and oil pressure is indicated by the amount of deflection which actuates the pointer. As oil pressure increases, it causes a greater deflection of the diaphragm in the engine unit. And therefore, a greater amount of current is required to open the heating coil circuit. This increased current is transmitted to the dash unit causing a correspondingly increased bending of the dash unit bimetal strip, resulting in an indication of higher oil pressure. Fig. 29.5 illustrates this type of gauge.

The King-Seeley and Ford gauges after 1957 use a voltage regulator, which is part of the instrument circuit, to maintain constant voltage regardless of variations due to the difference between battery voltage and generator voltage and cold and warm systems. A single voltage

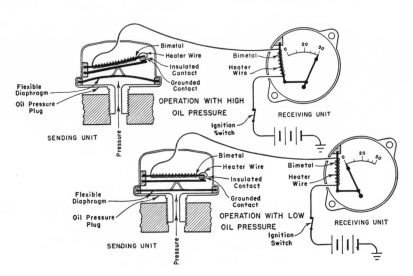

Fig. 29.5. Bimetal type oil pressure gauge prior to 1957. A diaphragm moves a grounded contact into position proportional to oil pressure. The bimetal strip maintains contact with the grounded contact point relative to its position, sending variable current to a receiving unit on the dash which registers the indications. (KS)

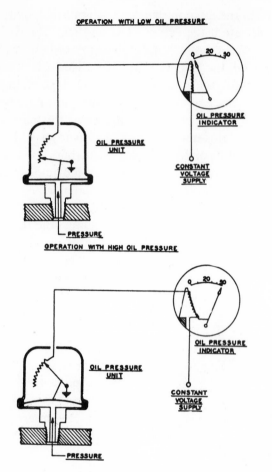

Fig. 29.6. King-Seeley type of oil pressure instrument. It has a sending unit similar to the AC unit, but the indicating unit uses a heated bimetal thermostatic spring lever which is deflected in proportion to the amount of current flowing.

regulator will serve for three instruments, in series in the instrument circuit.

Except for the voltage regulator in the circuit, the dash indicating units are similar to the earlier King-Seeley instruments, making use of a bimetallic thermostatic lever which is deflected by a heating coil in proportion to the current received from the sending unit, and indicates accordingly.

This type of instrument is used on some American Motors, Willys, Plymouth, Dodge and most Ford-built models. Fig. 29.6 shows the later type of oil pressure gauges. Fig. 29.7 shows the voltage regulator in the gauge circuit. Fig. 29.8 shows the details of the instrument circuit voltage regulator.

The heating coil in the engine unit is shunted by a calibrated resistor at the time of assembly to assure accuracy of the unit.

If the oil pressure gauge is not indicating as it should, tests will have to be made to localize the trouble, which may be in the dash unit, in the engine unit, or in the wiring. Neither the dash nor the engine units can be repaired and, therefore, if they are shown to be defective they must be replaced.

If the dash unit indicates pressure with the ignition switch turned on and the engine not running, the contact point in the engine unit may be frozen. Also, the wire from the dash to

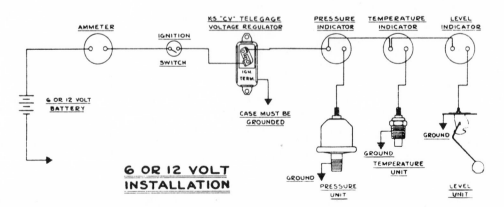

Fig. 29.7. A complete instrument system including the voltage regulator, sending and indicating pressure unit, sending and indicating temperature unit, and sending and indicating fuel level unit.

engine unit may be shorted to ground, or the dash unit may be defective. Because of the construction of this unit with its heating coil and its vibrating contact point, if the defective condition has existed for any length of time it is probable that the dash unit is permanently damaged.

After inspecting for loose connections at the terminals of the dash and engine units, seeing that the power gets to the instrument from the ignition switch and that the wire connection is in good condition, the gauge is checked as follows:

1. Remove the wire from the engine unit terminal. If the pointer of the dash unit remains at *zero* position with the ignition switch turned on momentarily and the engine not running, then the engine unit is defective and must be replaced.

2. If the pointer instead of returning to *zero* still registers pressure, remove the wire which connects the dash instrument to the engine unit at the dash unit. Notice the pointer when the ignition is momentarily turned on without starting the engine. If the dash pointer returns to *zero*, then the wire between the two units is grounded and must be repaired or replaced.

3. If the pointer still indicates pressure, then the dash unit is defective and must be replaced. After installing a new dash unit, check its action to make sure the engine unit and the wire are satisfactory.

If the dash unit does not indicate oil pressure with the ignition turned on and the engine running, check to be sure there is oil pressure at the unit by loosening the engine unit enough to permit oil to leak out temporarily around the threads. Also, be sure that the intake through the oil pump is below the oil level in the oil pan by seeing that a sufficient supply of oil is in the engine. Then if the dash unit does not indicate oil pressure with the engine running, further tests must be made.

4. With the ignition switch turned on, short out the engine unit at its terminal. Clip one

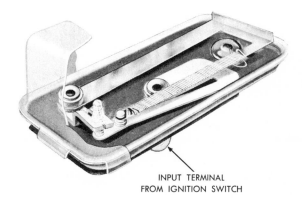

INPUT TERMINAL
FROM IGNITION SWITCH

Fig. 29.8. Voltage regulator used after 1957 on Ford-built automobiles. It maintains a constant voltage in the instrument circuit so that voltage changes due to battery or generator supplying current will not affect the instrument indications.

end of a jumper wire to the terminal screw of the engine unit and the other end to a good ground on the engine.

5. Turn the ignition on momentarily. If the dash unit now registers, then the engine unit is defective and must be replaced.

It is important that the ignition current be turned on very briefly and turned off before the pointer of the dash unit reaches the high pressure mark on the scale. In this test the full voltage is placed on the dash unit, and if allowed to remain too long, the unit will burn out.

6. If the dash unit fails to register with the engine unit shorted out, either the dash unit or the wire running to the engine is defective. Turn off the ignition switch and check the wire by clipping one end of a jumper wire to the dash unit terminal and the other end to the ground. Be very careful that the grounding wire is not connected to the ignition side of the dash unit as this will cause a direct short and damage will result.

7. Turn the ignition on briefly. If the dash unit fails to register, then the dash unit is defective.

8. Either a defective engine unit or wiring may have damaged the dash unit. Having installed a new dash unit, notice its action

after turning on the ignition for a moment. If the indicator moves beyond the point of normal oil pressure, the engine unit or wiring is defective and must be checked.

In checking the King-Seeley and Ford units it must be remembered that this instrument operates by heating coils and bimetallic strips separating electrical contacts. Therefore, when making various tests, the current must be left on only for a very short time to avoid overheating and damaging the unit.

Oil Pressure Indicator Light

After 1957, Ford cars, in common with most of the others, replaced the oil pressure gauge with an oil pressure indicator light. The light is connected between the oil pressure switch unit and the accessory terminal of the ignition switch.

To test the indicator light, turn on the ignition switch, but do not start the engine. The light should come on. Start the engine. The light should go out, indicating that the oil pressure is built up to a safe value.

To test the oil pressure switch on the engine, turn the ignition switch on, engine not running. The indicator light should come on. If the light does not come on, short the terminal of the oil pressure switch unit to ground. If the light now comes on, the switch is defective. If the light still does not come on, the bulb is burned out or the wires from the ignition switch and oil pressure switch are defective.

Temperature Indicators

The same two suppliers who furnish the electric oil pressure gauges also furnish the electric temperature indicators. These companies are AC and King-Seeley (Ford).

The temperature indicator is really a remote-controlled thermometer which indicates the temperature of the engine coolant.

If the temperature indications are consistently lower than they should be, the temperature gauge is probably not operating as it

should. However, indications higher than normal may be due either to a defective temperature indicator or to an abnormal condition in the engine cooling system. Naturally, if the indications are higher than they should be when the engine is obviously not overheated, the trouble is in the temperature gauge.

Passenger car engines are designed to operate at temperatures between 150 and 190°F. When operating at thermostat temperature, it will usually be from 160 to 180°F. Temperatures in cool weather that are higher than the thermostat temperature may be due to one or more of the following: (1) thermostat out of order, (2) obstruction in front of the radiator, (3) partially clogged radiator, (4) frozen radiator, (5) collapsed or clogged radiator hose, (6) broken or loose fan belt, (7) radiator pressure cap (if one is used) not operating properly, (8) poor engine lubrication, (9) low water level in radiator and cooling systems, (10) broken or loose fan belt.

After these are eliminated as possible causes of engine overheating and the gauge of either the Bourdon tube type or the electric type does not operate as it should, tests and checks will have to be made according to the following instructions.

AC Electric Temperature Gauge

The AC gauge, in common with the King-Seeley and Ford temperature gauges, makes use of two units: an engine unit and a dash or panel unit. Each type has a single wire connecting the two units.

The AC dash unit, Fig. 29.9, is practically the same as the oil pressure indicating unit except for the dial markings.

The indicating or dash unit has two coils placed 90° apart with an armature and integral pointer located at the intersection of the center lines of the two coils. To prevent vibration of the pointer on rough roads, an inertia damper is provided.

The engine unit has no moving parts but contains an electrical resistor which changes its resistance with changes in temperature. It has a high resistance when cold and a low resistance when hot. The change in resistance governs the strength of the current which flows to the indicating unit and this causes the proper indication of the pointer.

Electric temperature gauge troubles are of four kinds: (1) the pointer does not move when the ignition switch is turned *on*, (2) the pointer indicates a high temperature whether the engine is hot or cold, (3) the pointer does not show temperature accurately, (4) the pointer indicates a low temperature whether the engine is hot or cold.

Incorrect readings are checked as follows:

1. Disconnect the wire from the binding post on the end of the engine unit.
2. Turn the ignition switch *on*.
3. Hold the end of the wire away from all wires or other metal.

4. Check the dash unit. The needle should point to 100° or the low mark.
5. Touch the bare end of the wire to the engine block.
6. Check the dash unit again. The needle should now point to over 212° or the high mark.
7. If the dash unit does not read as described in steps 4 and 6, it is not operating as it should. In this case, first check the wire. If it is found to be in good condition, then replace the dash unit. However, if the dash unit is operating properly, continue with the next tests.
8. Drain the water from the radiator. Do not throw this water away as it may contain anti-freeze.
9. Disconnect the wire which is attached to the unit in the engine block.
10. Loosen the engine unit. Unscrew the unit from the engine block and lift it out.

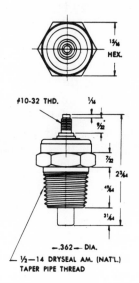

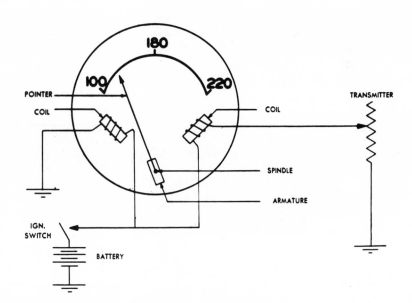

Fig. 29.9. AC temperature gauge. The transmitter (left) varies the current in accordance with the temperature changes. In the indicating instrument, the left-hand coil has a constant magnetic effect while the right-hand coil varies its magnetic effect with changes in current sent by the transmitter. The resultant magnetic field governs the temperature indications.

11. Reconnect the lead wire to the engine unit. Ground the threaded portion to a convenient point on the car with suitable wire and clamps.

12. Secure a pan of hot water and a reasonably accurate thermometer which reads to 212°F. Insert the engine unit part way into the water, but do not allow water to get above the threads as this will ruin the unit. Insert the thermometer, and let both stand in the water for three minutes. If the engine unit is working properly, the

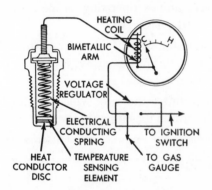

Fig. 29.10. The King-Seeley temperature indicating system. The sending unit is similar to the AC unit, and a voltage regulator maintains constant voltage. The typical K-S indicating unit is used.

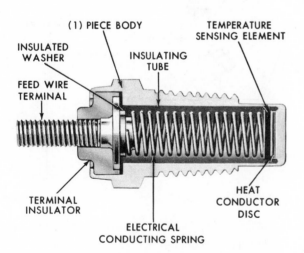

Fig. 29.11. Enlargement of the engine temperature sending unit. The sensing element is a wafer of special material which varies its electrical resistance inversely as temperature changes, i.e., higher temperatures cause less resistance.

pointer should show about the same temperature as the thermometer. If it does not, replace the engine unit.

King-Seeley and Ford Temperature Gauges

The King-Seeley (and Ford) temperature gauge also consists of an engine unit and a dash indicating unit connected in series.

The dash unit is connected to the ignition switch in the same way that the AC unit is connected. Therefore, the dash unit will indicate the water temperature only when the ignition switch is turned *on*. With the ignition switch *off*, the pointer will register at the *hot* position, which is the normal rest position.

The indicating unit is operated by a heating coil wound on a bimetal strip. The more current that flows through the heating coil, the higher the temperature and the more the bimetal strip will bend pulling the indicating needle toward the lower temperature indication. The sending and indicating units are shown in Fig. 29.10. A detailed section of the sending unit is shown in Fig. 29.11.

When the engine is cold, the bimetal strip will be in a position to make contact with the fixed contact point. When the ignition current is turned on, current will flow through the indicating unit and the engine unit. This will cause the coil to heat the bimetal strip which will pull away from the contact and interrupt the current. The bimetal strip will cool off then and remake the contact with the fixed contact, causing current to flow again. This will send an intermittent current through the indicating unit. The water in the engine is in contact with the engine unit and part of the heat from the hot water will get into the engine unit and will assist the electric current in bending the bimetal strip so that the contact points will be together for shorter periods of time. This will decrease the net amount of current flowing through the indicating unit and the needle will point to the higher reading. The cycle of the opening and closing of the engine unit contact points is repeated continuously. The variation in the length of time the contact points are closed is what changes the current going to the dash unit and causes it to indicate water temperature.

After 1957 an engine unit similar to that used by AC was adopted, using an electrical conducting spring which carries current in proportion to the temperature of the water surrounding it. The varying current flowing though the resistor causes the dash instrument to give the indication of temperature. The high-low positions of this system are shown in Fig. 29.12.

For service information on the King-Seeley and Ford (1) temperature gauges, (2) oil pressure gauges, and (3) fuel level gauges, refer to section following the King-Seeley fuel level gauges on page 411.

Fuel Level Gauges

The fuel gauge is an electrically operated instrument which indicates the amount of fuel in the fuel tank. Two units are used: one, the dash unit, is mounted on the control panel, while the other, the tank unit, is mounted within the fuel tank. They are connected by either one or two wires depending upon the instrument. AC, King-Seeley (and Ford) supply the fuel gauges for the various makes of cars.

AC Fuel Gauge

The AC dash unit or indicating unit is the same as the AC oil pressure indicator and AC temperature indicator. It has two coils placed 90° apart with an armature and pointer attached to it at the intersection of the center line of the two coils. To avoid vibration on rough roads, an inertia damper is provided. This unit is grounded on the dash.

The tank unit consists of a housing which encloses a resistance unit (or rheostat) with a rotating arm which contacts the resistance coil. The rotating arm is actuated by a float arm, which is a wire lever with a cork float on the

end. The height of the fuel in the tank determines the location of the float arm. As it rises or falls, it varies the resistance of the rotating arm in contact with the resistance coil, and thus varies the value of the current that flows to the indicating unit on the dash. To prevent movement of the float arm from surges of the fuel in the tank with movement of the car, a friction brake is provided. This gauge is shown in Fig. 29.13. See Fig. 29.14 for *full* and *empty* indications.

Fuel gauge troubles are of the following kinds:

1. The pointer does not move when the ignition switch is *on*.
2. The pointer registers *full* all the time.
3. The pointer registers *empty* all the time.
4. The pointer never registers *empty* and is always too high.
5. The pointer never registers *full* and is always too low.

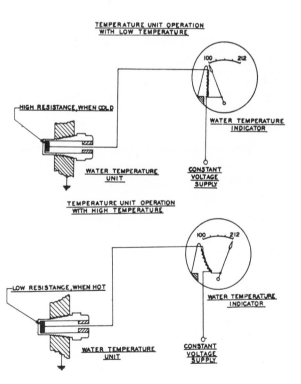

Fig. 29.12. Two positions of the King-Seeley temperature indicator. The actuating lever is mounted at its top, and the moving, lower end moves the pointer.

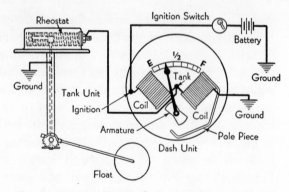

Fig. 29.13. The electric fuel gauge has a tank unit which is a rheostat controlled by a float in the fuel tank. It also has a dash unit, similar to the oil pressure and temperature gauge. (AC)

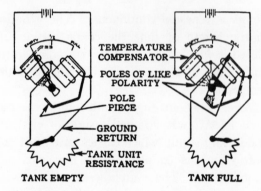

Fig. 29.14. Magnetic type fuel gauge, showing complete wiring diagram and position of armature and pointer with tank empty and tank full. The right-hand coil has a constant current, while the left-hand coil has a varying current due to being in series with the tank rheostat. (AC)

When one of these troubles develops, it is necessary to determine whether the trouble is in the panel instrument, the wiring, or the tank unit. To do this, make a tester as previously described on page 402 under "Electric Oil Gauges."

To test the panel instrument, proceed in this way:

1. With the ignition *off*, disconnect one of the battery cables.
2. Disconnect the wire from the fuel gauge mounted on the instrument panel. This is the wire that leads to the tank unit.
3. Using the spring clip, connect the colored tester wire to the bracket post from which you removed the wire at the back of the dash unit. Connect the black wire to the flange of the tester and to any convenient ground, such as the unpainted part of the instrument panel.
4. Turn the ignition switch *on*, after checking to be sure connections are made exactly as instructed. If you connect the wrong wire to the binding posts, you will burn out the tester.
5. Reconnect the battery cable. Move the arm of the tester back and forth slowly. If the panel instrument is functioning, the pointer will move from *empty* to *full* freely. If the pointer does not move, or only moves

part way, then the trouble is a defective dash instrument and it must be replaced.
6. If the panel instrument proves to be in good working condition, the next step is to check the wiring between the panel and the fuel tank for which the tester can also be used.
7. Turn the ignition switch *off* and follow the wire from the tank unit to the bayonet connection or the terminal junction block. Disconnect the wire at this point.
8. Attach the colored tester wire to the end of the wire which runs up to the instrument panel. Attach the black wire to the car frame or other ground.
9. Connect the battery cable and turn the ignition switch *on*. Move the arm of the tester back and forth. If the wiring is satisfactory, the pointer on the instrument will move from *empty* to *full* freely. If the pointer does not move or only moves part way, the trouble is in the wire from the instrument to the tank.
10. If the pointer does move correctly, then the trouble is in the tank unit or the wire that runs from it to the "bayonet" connection or terminal junction block. If the connections are all clean and tight and there are no breaks or chafes in the wire from

the bayonet connection to the tank, then a new tank unit must be installed.

On all makes of gasoline fuel gauges, always use a replacement unit of the same make as the one removed. None of the various makes are interchangeable with another make.

King-Seeley and Ford Fuel Gauges

The King-Seeley dash unit contains a heating coil and bimetal strip linked to a pointer. The dash unit is in series with the ignition switch so that it will only operate when the ignition is turned *on*.

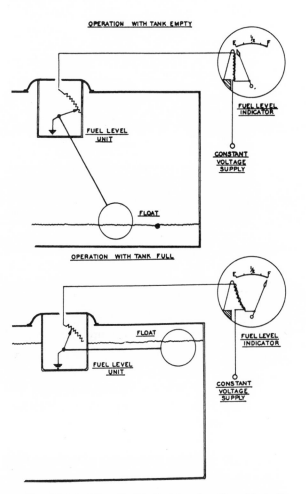

The tank unit contains a rheostat operated by a float which changes the resistance of the circuit in proportion to the fuel level. Refer to Fig. 29.15. When the fuel level is low, the float of the tank is at or near the bottom of the movement.

As the rheostat and dash unit are connected in series, a slight bending of the bimetal strip in the dash unit takes place which is just sufficient to pull the pointer to, or close to, the *empty* position. When the fuel level is higher, the float rises, decreasing the resistance of the tank rheostat. This bends the bimetal strip in the dash unit, pulling the needle over towards the *full* position on the dial. Fig. 29.16 shows the fuel gauge circuit.

Service Instructions for King-Seeley Electric Gauges

These instructions apply to pressure, temperature and fuel level gauges. No units should

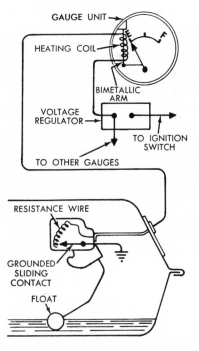

Fig. 29.15. King-Seeley fuel level unit, with indicating instrument in two positions. The float operates a rheostat which varies the current in proportion to fuel level in the tank. A voltage regulator is in the circuit, but is not shown here.

Fig. 29.16. Fuel gauge used on Ford-built automobiles. The tank unit has a float which operates a rheostat in series with the dash unit to give the fuel level indication. Note the instrument voltage regulator.

be removed from the vehicle until a check has been completed showing such units to be defective or damaged.

Necessary Equipment for Checking

1. *One good fuel level unit.* If there is any question about the level unit being in satisfactory condition, connect it in series with a panel indicator, a voltage regulator known to be good, and a 6- or 12-volt battery. Operate the tank unit by hand and see if the panel indicator reads *zero* with the tank unit float in bottom position, and *full* with the float in top position.

2. *Three 10-foot lengths of insulated wire equipped with clip terminals at each end.* These long lengths will in most instances permit the individual making the check to sit in the seat of the car and observe the gauge reading being checked.

3. *One good panel indicator, either pressure, temperature or fuel level.* This will be used for a detailed check of the voltage regulator.

Method of Checking

Voltage Regulator.

The K-S Telegage voltage regulator is common to all three systems, *i.e.,* one regulator is installed on each vehicle to operate one-, two-, or three-gauge systems. Check voltage regulator first.

1. The voltage regulator should be replaced if all three gauges simultaneously read considerably too high; for example, if the gas gauge reads upscale with an empty tank, the temperature gauge reads upscale with a cold engine, and the oil pressure gauge reads too high with low pressure. NOTE: Check the ground connection of the voltage regulator case, as grounding is essential to proper functioning of the regulator.

2. If all three gauges simultaneously read too low, either the input voltage to the regulator is below 5.5 volts or the voltage

regulator is inoperative and should be replaced. Check the battery voltage before replacing voltage regulator. A direct, specific method for checking voltage regulator follows:

a. Check battery voltage.

b. Connect lead wire from output terminal of voltage regulator to one terminal of new panel indicator. Connect lead wire from the other terminal of panel indicator to terminal of tank level unit.

c. Ground tank level unit. Hold float in empty position.

d. Turn on ignition switch. Panel indicator should read empty (bottom on dial).

e. Start engine and run at faster than idle speed. Gauge reading should not change if voltage regulator is functioning properly so as to control the effective voltage at 5.0 volts. Because the voltage regulator provides intermittent contacting, its voltage output cannot be checked with a conventional voltmeter.

f. Move tank level float to full position. Panel indicator should read top end of dial scale.

Panel Indicators

1. Disconnect lead wire at tank level, oil pressure or temperature unit.

2. Connect new tank level unit and ground this unit. Place float in empty position. Turn on ignition switch. Panel indicator being checked should read bottom end (empty, no pressure, or lowest temperature) of dial scale.

3. Move float to full position. Panel indicator should read top end of scale.

If the indicator checks *good*, both panel indicator and lead wire to the unit are good. If it does not, hook up a tank level unit to the proper terminal of the panel indicator, eliminating the lead wire from the panel indicator to the unit from the circuit. Repeat *empty* and *full* checks. If it now checks good, check the lead wire for broken insulation, short, or broken wire. Correct or replace lead wire.

Tank Level, Pressure, or Temperature Unit

If the panel indicator and lead wire function properly with a good tank level unit substituted, but did not with the original unit, replace original unit. Be sure the tank level unit is properly ground to the tank and that the tank is properly grounded to the frame. Fig. 29.17 shows a tank unit.

Do not attempt to repair or calibrate any panel indicator or voltage regulator in the field as this is not practical. Replacement with a new unit is the only practical means of servicing these gauges.

Speedometer

The speedometer (a road speed indicator) and the tachometer (an engine speed indicator) are very similar. Both operate by means of a rotating magnet which is driven by a flexible shaft. This shaft is geared to the drive shaft for the speedometer or to the engine crankshaft (either directly or indirectly) for the tachometer. The rotating magnet sets up eddy currents in an aluminum disc which is thus caused to follow the magnet against the pull of a carefully calibrated hair spring. The amount of rotation of the disc is proportional to the speed of the magnet and indicates miles per hour or engine rpm.

The speedometer, in addition to its speed indication, has an odometer which indicates the miles travelled. On some of the higher priced cars there will be both a trip odometer and one showing total miles traveled.

The most common trouble experienced by speedometers and odometers is breakage of the driving cable or flexible shaft. This can usually be replaced with relative ease after a replacement shaft of the correct length is obtained. It is generally necessary to remove both ends of the outer shield in order to take out both parts of the broken flexible shaft. The replacement shaft should be well lubricated with suitable solid lubricant, and the driving splines or keys should be correctly engaged at both ends.

Generally, servicing of the instrument indicating head should not be attempted except by those who have had special training in this work. Calibration and repair of the speedometer or tachometer head require special equipment.

Summary

The *dash instruments* include the engine temperature gauge, the fuel gauge, the oil pressure gauge, the speedometer, and in some cases, the ammeter. During the last six to eight years, the ammeter and the oil pressure gauge have been replaced on many models by indicator light signals.

In cases where the *ammeter does not operate,* remove it and test it. It is designed to show current as it goes to, or is taken from, the battery.

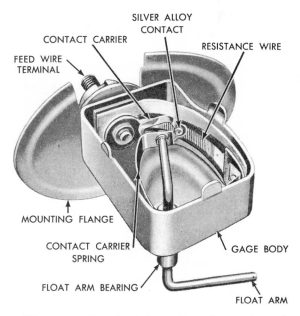

Fig. 29.17. Detail of the tank sending unit used on Ford-built automobiles. Note the rheostat which is controlled by the float in the fuel tank.

The *oil pressure gauge* is to indicate the pressure of the engine lubricating oil. The older type of gauge uses a fine tube to conduct oil pressure to a Bourdon tube pressure gauge. The current types are electrical, making use of a pressure actuated rheostat. This sends a current, proportional to the engine oil pressure, to the dash indicating unit.

There are two makers who supply this equipment, AC Division of General Motors Corporation and King-Seeley.

The *AC electrical oil pressure gauge* has an engine unit which makes use of a diaphragm that deflects with oil pressure and causes a wiper to move across the resistance winding. This varies the current sent to the indicator in proportion to oil pressure in the engine lubricating system.

King-Seeley and Ford electrical oil pressure gauges make use of an engine sending unit similar to the AC unit. The indicator unit has a lever made of bimetallic thermostatic material which will deflect when heated by a small heating coil. The amount of deflection depends upon the amount of current that is sent to the heating coil. This current is modified by the engine sending unit in proportion to oil pressure.

Prior to 1957 a different type of sending unit was used. In the later type a *voltage regulator* is used to maintain a constant instrument system voltage.

Many cars after about 1957 replaced the oil pressure gauge with an *indicator light* which will come on after the engine is started if there is not adequate oil pressure.

Temperature indicators are supplied by the same two makers who supply the oil pressure gauges. Passenger car engines are designed to operate between 150° and 190°F. Thermostatic temperature is generally between 160° and 180°F.

The *AC electric temperature gauge* makes use of an engine sending unit and a dash indicator. The sending unit has a temperature-sensitive plug which varies an electric current in proportion to engine coolant temperature and sends this current to the indicating instrument. This unit has two coils, one with constant current and one with current modified by the temperature sending unit, which causes the unit to indicate engine temperature.

King-Seeley and Ford temperature gauges also make use of the engine unit and dash indicating unit. The sending unit is similar to the AC sending unit. The dash indicating unit is much like the dash oil pressure unit, which actuates the instrument pointer by a bimetal thermostatic lever heated with a heating coil.

Fuel level gauges are electrically operated to indicate the level of the fuel supply in the fuel tank at the rear of the car. As with the other gauges, two units are used, a sending unit and an indicating unit.

The *AC fuel gauge* dash unit is much like the AC oil pressure indicator and AC temperature indicator. The tank unit consists of a housing which encloses a rheostat with a wiper arm which is operated by a float that rides on the surface of the fuel in the fuel tank.

King-Seeley (and Ford) gauges use a dash indicating unit similar in design to the oil pressure and temperature units, using a bimetal thermostatic strip and heating coil. The tank unit, similar to the AC unit, uses a float to actuate a rheostat arm which will send a current to the indicator in proportion to the fuel level.

Questions

1. What does the term *dash instrument* include?
2. What is used in place of the ammeter in the later cars?
3. What are the two types of ammeters used for dash instruments?
4. What are the two types of oil pressure gauges?
5. What is the principle of operation of the AC pressure gauge engine unit?

6. What is the principle of operation of the AC dash instrument unit?

7. How would you make a tester for an AC oil pressure gauge?

8. What is the principle of operation of the King-Seeley oil pressure gauge engine unit used prior to 1957?

9. What is the principle of operation of the King-Seeley oil pressure gauge currently used?

10. What is the principle of operation of the King-Seeley dash instrument oil pressure gauge?

11. What do the current King-Seeley gauges use that is common to each of the three gauges?

12. What do many car models use in place of the oil pressure gauge?

13. Through what temperature range are current model engines designed to operate or function?

14. At what temperature are engine thermostats usually set?

15. How many units do electric temperature gauges use and what are they?

16. How does the AC dash unit of the temperature gauge work?

17. How does the AC engine temperature unit work?

18. Name three possible electric temperature gauge troubles.

19. Which of the King-Seeley and Ford temperature gauge units is similar to the corresponding AC unit?

20. Why is system voltage important to the King-Seeley dash instrument?

21. How many units are used on the fuel level gauge and what are they?

22. How do the AC fuel level gauge units work?

23. How do the King-Seeley fuel level gauge units work?

24. What is the basic test for all AC gauge units?

25. What is the first item to be tested on all late model King-Seeley gauge systems?

SECTION IX

Tune-Up and Diagnosis Procedure

CHAPTER THIRTY

Diagnosis— Principles and Methods

The dictionary defines diagnosis as "scientific discrimination," or "the recognition of a disease by its symptoms." Both of these definitions aptly apply to *automotive diagnosis*. It involves scientific discrimination between a number of instrument indications and deviations from normal action to determine which ones give information of value.

As with the physician who uncovers the cause or causes of human ills by knowing the anatomy of the human body and the significance of various symptoms, the "doctor of motors" knows the anatomy of the automotive power plant and correctly interprets symptoms to determine the right remedy.

Makeup of the Automobile

The first point to be considered in diagnosis is basic. The automobile is not one machine but is an assembly of the engine and a number of systems that comprise the power plant, plus the running gear, transmission, drive line, rear axle, steering system, front suspension, brake system, cooling system, rear suspension, air conditioning system (where installed), frame (on other than unitized bodies), and the body with its doors, locks, and windows. This book is concerned with the power plant only.

The power plant is divided into its component systems and units, so that trouble symptoms may be localized to specific areas.

Power Plant Systems

The power plant is made up of:

Engine block, cylinder head, and oil pan or sump.

Crankshaft, connecting rod and piston assemblies.

Valve train.

Lubrication system.

Cooling system.

Fuel and induction system.

Ignition system.

Generating system.

Starting system.

Usually it is not difficult to determine in which system there may be a malfunction. However, it is possible for the symptoms of trouble to be deceptive so that the trouble is believed to be in a system other than the one in which it is actually located. Also, it is possible there is cumulative trouble which may be in more than one system. For example, spark plugs in poor condition will cause misfiring from a weak coil and new plugs will appear to "fix" the misfire, although as the replaced plugs become worn the trouble will occur due to the weak coil.

Diagnosis, as understood in automotive service, has two meanings. The one most commonly used refers to diagnosing some power plant malfunctioning which has become evident. "Trouble shooting" has substantially the same meaning. In every case, someone has to decide how the trouble is to be corrected. How accurately the trouble is diagnosed depends upon the ability of the man on the job to test and analyze the trouble, allocate it to the correct system, and then to pin-point it to the unit, circuit, appliance or accessory at fault. This would be "Corrective Diagnosis."

The other meaning of diagnosis refers to an overall checkup of the power plant by tests, inspection, and observation, to detect any components that are not performing in accordance with factory specifications. Any work, service or parts needed are noted on a diagnostic report form and the car owner is advised what should be done to put it back into as near new-car condition as the age and degree of wear will permit. This might be referred to as "Preventive Diagnosis."

Corrective Diagnosis

Corrective diagnosis or trouble shooting follows a logical procedure to determine the cause of any power plant malfunctioning. While frequently the trouble is so simple that its cause is easily determined, many jobs involve the use of most or all of the testing equipment available, plus all of the "know-how," training and experience of the diagnostician. Sometimes even the element of luck is a factor.

In addition to the power plant systems already mentioned, the power plant is often considered to have three main divisions, namely (1) compression, (2) carburetion, involving the complete fuel system, induction system and air cleaner, and (3) ignition, involving the battery, distributor, spark plugs and wiring. However, for the purposes in this book, it is better to use the more detailed divisions of the power plant into its basic systems.

Each system will now be discussed from the standpoint of (1) its components, (2) how they should perform, (3) what can go wrong with them, and (4) how to check and test them. Obviously, this chapter cannot list all the things that can happen to an automotive power plant; however, the method of analysis and the application of much of the information previously given in the earlier chapters, will be pointed out.

Engine Block, Head and Oil Pan

In each of the four, six or eight cylinders in the engine block, there should be a polished, smooth cylindrical bore, free from scratches or scored areas. The cylinder will tolerate wear up to as much as 0.005″ to 0.006″ at the upper end of the cylinder where the maximum wear takes place. These figures depend somewhat upon the bore diameter and the engine manufacturer's allowable limits. The piston ring manufacturers allow up to 0.012″ to 0.015″.

Cylinder blocks are subject to excessive wear, scoring, cracks from excessive heating or freezing. When the casting is made, holes are left for the sand cores to be shaken out. These holes are plugged with metal plugs, sometimes called *Welsh plugs*. Occasionally a leak will be found at one of the several plugs, which may be in a location that is difficult to reach without considerable disassembling. When one leaking plug is found, it is advisable to change all of them, since the others may be in such poor condition that they will require changing later.

Cylinder heads of the "L-Head" type are subject to warping. When this occurs, the head must be ground flat and true in order to keep the head gaskets tight. Overhead type heads do not have as much trouble from warping, though this possibility should always be kept in mind.

Worn cylinders may be rebored and fitted with oversize pistons. Cracked cylinders may be repaired by inserting a sleeve, or in some cases by welding. The sleeves are generally 1/8" or 3/32" in wall thickness.

Oil pans seldom require attention, except for tightening up the bolts that hold them in place once in a while. However, there is always the possibility that the oil pan may be dented, which could interfere with the oil pickup for the oil pump. There have been cases where the drain plug has worked loose and allowed the engine oil to escape, though this is unusual.

Crankshaft, Connecting Rods, Pistons Assembly

The pistons, rings and cylinder walls are responsible to a considerable degree for *Compression*, since the rings provide for sealing against compression and explosion pressure in the engine cylinders. They share this responsibility with the valve train. If compression is not reasonably close to factory specification, engine economy and performance will not be what they should, and nothing other than corrective mechanical work and replacement of worn parts will restore performance.

Compression is affected by excessively worn and tapered cylinders, worn piston rings, worn and/or scored pistons, worn ring grooves, broken ring lands, broken rings, carboned rings, improperly fitted rings, rings not seated properly, leaking head gasket and leaking valves.

A rough preliminary check on compression can be made by listening to the rhythm of the cranking sounds as the engine turns over with the cranking motor. The ignition should be grounded by a jumper from the distributor side of the coil to prevent the engine from starting. The carburetor throttle should be wide open to allow for cylinders full of gas. A pulsating sound indicates uneven compression in the cylinders.

A more definite test is made with the compression tester, which will give an idea both of the amount of compression and the variation in compression between cylinders. It will usually show something is wrong if the compression

indications are low and/or variable between cylinders, but it is not a dependable instrument. For example, it would show normal compression in a cylinder with bad rings and/or valves if there were substantial cylinder deposits to raise the compression.

A far better method of determining cylinder condition is checking with the cylinder leakage tester. This instrument (refer to Chapter 12) will give the proportionate amount of leakage in each cylinder. Also, it will give information that will tell where the leaking is taking place, whether through (1) piston rings, (2) intake valve, (3) exhaust valve, (4) leaking head gasket, or (5) a crack in the block or head casting into the water jacket.

With hard working bearings at each end of the connecting rods, failure may occur at either end, though more commonly at the lower or crankpin bearing. Failing bearings are evidenced by noise — a sharp click at the upper end or a thud at the crankpin. Trouble is also indicated by the low pressure. Shorting out one cylinder at a time will usually show up bad bearings.

Excessive wear or failure of lower rod bearings, in addition to engine noise, will cause wear and/or scoring on the crankpin and cannot be neglected without possibly causing expensive damage.

Valve Train

The valve train includes intake and exhaust valves, valve stem guides, which may be either integral or pressed in place, valve springs, valve seats, which may be integral or inserts, rocker arms (on valve-in-head engines) or push rods (on overhead valve engines), hydraulic or mechanical valve lifters or tappets, camshaft and camshaft bearings, timing chain and timing sprockets or timing gears. The mechanical self-adjusting valve linkage, used on some Ford six-cylinder engines, could cause trouble.

Due to the strong springs used on late model OHV engines with high compression ratio, the valve train is highly stressed. There is an extremely high unit pressure of the valve lifters against the cam lobes on the camshaft and a powerful thrust of the push rods against the rocker arms, sometimes causing excessive wear on the lower end of the valve lifters.

The valves are stoppers that should each make a gas-tight joint against the valve seats, to withstand the power stroke pressures of up to 900 pounds per square inch and temperatures of several thousand degrees. The valve faces and seats are subject to both mechanical wear and high temperature corrosive gases, in addition to loading from the push of the valve springs. If, due to warping or uneven wear, a tiny leak develops, it rapidly becomes a much larger leak due to the burning effect of the combustion and exhaust gases, and the inability of the valve to cool from poor contact with the valve seat. This has an important effect on cylinder compression.

Leaking valves are best detected by using the cylinder leak detector. There is only one remedy for leaking valves, and that is to perform valve and valve seat service. Warped or excessively worn valves must be replaced, though the seats in all cases must be ground except possibly where there are defective or loose inserts which must be replaced and ground. An engine overheating when driven at high speed or up long grades may be due to leaking valves. This condition will cause an excessive amount of fuel to be inefficiently burned in the engine cylinders. In other words, too much thermal energy will be produced for the required mechanical energy to operate the car.

Worn valve stem guides may cause trouble from oil and/or air leaks into the cylinder; these would occur through the intake valve and through misalignment of both the intake and exhaust valves. To prevent leakage, valve stem seals should be put on the valves when they are ground. Excessive valve stem guide wear can be corrected by reaming and using oversize valve stems on solid guides, or by boring and inserting valve stem guides. The insert type of guides are merely replaced.

In the last few years, some trouble has been experienced from excessively worn lobes on the engine camshaft. Where missing and poor power performance are noted, check the valve action to observe if any of the rocker arms are not moving as much as they should. An accurate check can be made by using the dial indicator to measure the amount of valve opening. Either replace worn camshafts or weld and regrind them.

It is sometimes difficult to locate a broken valve spring or one that has taken a permanent set due to lost temper or incorrect heat-treating. Also, valve seats that have been excessively ground will allow the valve to set too low with decreased spring tension. Removal of the valve covers and careful inspection of each spring will usually locate the defective spring.

In some cases the oil passage that carries the lubricant to the rocker arms becomes clogged, resulting in excessive wear on the rocker arms and their shaft. They become noisy and it is possible that one or more rocker arms will freeze onto the rocker shaft, causing serious damage.

The rocker arms are operated by cam followers, valve tappets, or valve lifters, as they are variously called, which may be mechanical or self-adjusting hydraulic. The mechanical tappets seldom cause any trouble, outside of possible excessive wear due to poor lubrication. Wear may also result from excessive unit pressure as the tappets are rubbed by the revolving cams on the camshaft.

Hydraulic tappets occasionally give trouble which may be from (1) too rapid leakdown due to wear, (2) sticking of inner plunger due to varnish accumulations, (3) worn or broken check valve, or (4) incorrect initial setting.

The plunger is fitted with a clearance of only 0.0002″ to 0.0004″, so that a small amount of wear will increase this clearance materially, and permit too rapid loss of oil from the pressure chamber of the lifter. This prevents full opening of the valve and loss of power. Hydraulic tappets, when out of the engine, may be tested on a leakdown testing fixture. This instrument applies a definite load on the plunger, pumped up to its normal upper position, and the leakdown time is checked with a stop watch or a wrist watch with a sweep second hand. A rough check can be made while the hydraulic tappets are in an engine. Warm the engine and push on the rocker arms of closed valves to see if any leakdown occurs in less than five seconds.

The causes of trouble with hydraulic lifters are generally (1) dirty oil, from which foreign matter or varnish deposits cause the plungers to stick, (2) wear from long use and/or poor lubrication, (3) low oil level in the oil pan, (4) aerated oil from too much oil in the oil pan, (5) poor oil pressure.

Defective hydraulic lifters will be evident by a clatter in the valve train. Do not confuse this noise with that made when a cold engine is first started, as the lifters are pumped up. Unless the lifters are in poor condition or one of the oil conditions mentioned is present, the engine will quiet down after running a few minutes.

On most of the V-8 engines, the camshaft is driven by two sprockets with a 1:2 ratio and a silent chain. Many of the sixes use two gears with the same ratio, driving the camshaft half as fast as the crankshaft. On engines that have seen very high mileage occasionally the timing chain will jump a tooth due to excessive wear and stretching. This will prevent the engine from running and requires the installation of a new chain.

Fuel System

The fuel system consists of (1) fuel tank, (2) connecting tubing, (3) fuel pump, which may be either a single fuel pump or a compound fuel and vacuum pump, (4) carburetor, (5) air cleaner, and (6) intake manifold. A fuel filter is included in some of the new cars.

The heat riser valve may be considered as part of the fuel system, even though it is located in the exhaust manifold, since it is used to heat the fuel-air mixture for better starting and cold engine operation.

So that gas can flow, the fuel tank must be properly vented and the outlet must be free and open. The tube leading from the fuel tank to the fuel pump may be bumped or crushed so that fuel flow is restricted. This is always a possibility and should be kept in mind. At the fuel pump there is generally a flexible section, 8 to 10 inches long, to make the pump connection to the line from the tank. If this should be worn or frayed, it could leak and interfere with the suction of the fuel pump, restricting or interrupting the fuel supply. The low pressure or suction side of the fuel supply is prone to air leaks.

The fuel pump is a likely source of trouble in the fuel system, and the pump diaphragm is the weakest link in the pump. If there is any doubt about the fuel supply, the pump should be tested for both delivery volume and discharge pressure. The pressure should be in accordance with specifications (generally between 5 and 7 psi) and the volume should be a pint in 45 seconds or less for engines up to 400 cubic inches displacement. A pint in one minute is satisfactory for engines up to 224 cubic inches, though it is best to refer to manufacturer's specifications. The only sure way to know whether the fuel pump is working properly is to test it.

Carburetor

The carburetor usually has six systems or circuits: (1) float, (2) idle, (3) high speed, (4) power, or economizer, (5) accelerating, (6) choke. Any one or all of them may cause trouble and attention should be given to the carburetor whenever the fuel system seems to be at fault, unless the trouble is definitely in some other part of the system. Keep in mind also that in some cases trouble that seems to be in the fuel system may actually be in the ignition system, as the symptoms are confusing.

The *float system* is liable to cause trouble from flooding or an excessively low float level. Usually a leaking float needle valve is at fault. However, with the relatively new composition float needle valve tip, leaking at this point is minimized. When any carburetor work is done, it is advisable to see that the float level is in accordance with specifications.

The *idle system* generally causes little trouble, though occasionally the small orifice that acts as the idle jet may become clogged with dirt, a drop of water or other foreign matter. For a single-barrel carburetor, the idle mixture is adjusted by one needle. Two needle-valves are used in two or four-barrel carburetors. The idle mixture should be adjusted when any work is done on the carburetor. To get the best idle, either a tachometer or a vacuum gauge should be used. Idle speed is adjusted by a throttle stop screw.

The *high-speed system*, sometimes called the *part-throttle power system*, is relatively free of trouble, though once in a while the metering pin on Carter carburetors may slip out of position, causing an excessively rich mixture. Under some conditions it is advisable to change the high-speed jet or jets.

The *power system*, sometimes called the *economizer*, is actuated by a vacuum plunger or a vacuum diaphragm, depending upon the carburetor. If the actuating device becomes inoperative, the high-speed operation or operation of the vehicle on a heavy pull will be affected and fuel consumption will be excessive. On carburetors where vacuum means is not employed, the high-speed valve is opened by the throttle linkage.

The *accelerating pump system* is extremely important for smooth engine operation on acceleration. It supplies fuel during the transition from the idle system to the high-speed system. It can easily be checked visually when the engine is not running. Remove the air cleaner and observe the discharge of fuel in the carburetor barrel from the accelerating system nozzle when the throttle is moved manually.

Defective action could come from a clogged discharge nozzle or passage; a worn or defective pump plunger or pump diaphragm; a stuck, missing, or defective pump check valve; or badly worn or defective linkage.

Most of the late model automobiles, especially those with V-8 engines, are equipped with *automatic chokes*. The most common trouble experienced here is a clogged heater tube. The opening of the choke valve is actuated by the bimetallic thermostatic spring as it is heated. Inspection will check this. Other automatic choke troubles are: stuck automatic choke plate or valve; weak bimetallic spring; stuck or inoperative vacuum cylinder that opens the valve part way when the engine is started; and wrong setting or adjustment. The action of the choke plate can easily be observed when the air cleaner is removed.

In addition to its internal circuits, the *carburetor's mechanical condition* is important. For example, the throttle lever may be loose on the throttle shaft, in which case it will be impossible to adjust the idle speed satisfactorily. There is a special repair for this condition available from most parts houses, which is quick and easy to apply. In addition to this trouble, the fast-idle linkage may be out of adjustment, worn, or stuck. Also accelerating pump linkage may be in poor condition, set wrong, or stuck.

The *air cleaner*, of the corrugated paper type on most of the late model cars, may become so clogged with dust that carburetor air flow is restricted. Cleaning is not very satisfactory in most cases, and it is best to replace it, especially in dusty localities. The oil bath air cleaner ordinarily will offer no resistance or restriction to air flow, but it should be cleaned out occasionally.

Many fuel systems are equipped with *fuel filters.* The newer cars have a separate filter in series with the line that supplies fuel to the carburetor. This filter should be replaced every

10,000 miles or in accordance with the manufacturer's recommendations. It should always be suspected when there appears to be fuel supply difficulties. Older cars may have a wire mesh strainer or a ceramic filter element in connection with the fuel pump.

Heat Riser Valve

A much neglected part, which indirectly could be considered part of the fuel system, is the heat riser valve in the exhaust pipe. Far too often this valve, due to its location in the path of the exhaust gases, becomes stuck and inoperative. If stuck in the open position, starting of the engine may be difficult and during the engine warm-up period combustion will be poor with resulting poor ignition, because of the cold fuel-air mixture. If it is stuck in the closed position, starting will be normal, but operation after engine warm-up will be unsatisfactory due to overheated fuel-air mixture and back pressure buildup. Using a penetrating solvent, work the valve back and forth until it operates freely. In case it can't be freed up it should be replaced.

Ignition System

The ignition system shares responsibility with the fuel system for making the engine run. It consists of the coil, primary wiring, ignition switch, ballast resistor (where used), distributor, secondary or high-tension wiring and the spark plugs. The battery may be considered part of the ignition system as it supplies current for ignition when the engine is being started. If the battery is not well charged, starting may be difficult due to low voltage. Keep in mind that battery voltage drops appreciably when it is supplying the necessary heavy current to the cranking motor.

The *coil* generally gives little trouble. There are effective coil testers available, but in the absence of a testing instrument, replace a suspected coil with another that is known to be good. If the replacement coil improves ignition, install a new unit.

Coils may possibly have an open, shorted or grounded primary or secondary winding, a cracked tower, or a corroded contact in the secondary tower. Reversed polarity is sometimes the cause of erratic ignition, hard starting and poor engine operation. It may be due to a battery installed backwards or to reversed coil connections. Refer to Chapter 20. Reversed polarity can be tested with a voltmeter.

The *primary wiring* is subject to bad connections at the terminals, corrosion, worn insulation, or occasionally a broken conductor. Measuring the voltage drop in the primary with a voltmeter will quickly point out the high resistance points.

The *ignition switch* may not make good connections at one or more of its several contacts. A quick check is to run the engine with a voltmeter connected from the battery side of the coil to ground. Wiggle the ignition key in the ignition switch and observe the voltmeter. If the meter needle moves, the switch is defective and should be replaced.

A *ballast resistor* is included in series with the ignition coil on most of the 12-volt systems. On the later cars, this is in the form of resistance wire in the wiring harness. There is also a bypass circuit which is only energized while the cranking motor is operating. Checking the ignition system voltage at the coil while the engine is being cranked will indicate operation of the bypass circuit; correct voltage should be at least 9.8 volts. The voltage will be less than normal battery voltage because of the heavy current drain when operating the starting motor. The bypass circuit on many cars is closed by a separate contact in the ignition switch. On others a separate contact in the starting relay or starting motor switch closes this circuit. In either case, the bypass circuit is used only during the brief period when the cranking motor is in operation.

The Distributor

This component has more possible trouble causes than any other unit in the ignition system.

The *distributor cap* could (1) be cracked, causing misfiring or cross-firing, (2) have corroded terminals in the towers, (3) have eroded contacts where the spark jumps from the end of the rotor, causing too large a gap and possible high resistance, (4) have carbon tracks on its inner surface causing cross-firing, (5) have worn locating lug allowing cap to shift its position and change ignition timing.

The *distributor rotor* could (1) be cracked, providing a shorting path for the high-tension current to ground, (2) have its end eroded, causing too large a spark gap to the distributor contacts, (3) possibly be set to the wrong angle to register with the distributor cap contact properly when the spark is advanced by mechanical or vacuum advance mechanism, (4) be loose on end of distributor shaft, (5) have, on some cars, wrong value, or burned-out suppression resistance.

The *distributor cam* could (1) be worn unevenly, causing variations in dwell and ignition timing on certain cylinders, (2) have been operated with excessive and/or wrong kind of lubricant leading to deteriorated breaker points, (3) have been operated with no lubricant, causing excessive wear on breaker arm rubbing block.

The *distributor shaft* could have too much play in its bearings, allowing excessive variations in dwell and timing.

The *distributor breaker points* (or contact points) could (1) be excessively worn or eroded, (2) be out of alignment, (3) be burned blue from excessive current, (4) have wrong dwell adjustment, (5) have a too weak or too strong breaker arm spring, (6) have a worn rubbing block, (7) have a shorted or grounded pigtail or open or poor breaker plate ground connection, (8) have excessive metal transfer from one point to another because of wrong condenser value.

The *automatic advance* (or mechanical advance) could (1) be stuck and not working,

(2) have wrong spring giving incorrect advance, (3) have broken springs, (4) on a full-vacuum control distributor, have springs out of adjustment, of wrong strength or broken.

The *vacuum advance* could (1) have ruptured diaphragm, (2) be stuck and not working properly, (3) have wrong calibration or strength of spring, (4) have breaker plate and/or linkage sticking.

The *distributor condenser* could (1) be shorted, (2) be open, (3) have poor connections or open pigtail, (4) be wrong capacity, or (5) have a poor ground.

The secondary wires or cables on most of the late cars are of the high-resistance suppression type with carbon impregnated linen fiber or glass fiber center conductors which are rather fragile. If handled roughly, the connection of the center core to the terminal may be opened, or the center core itself may be broken or may change resistance. This cable has a resistance of approximately 4000 ohms per foot. An ohmmeter may be used to check the resistance, which should not exceed 20,000 ohms in any of the cables. If any of them do not show continuity of current flow, they should be replaced. If the outer insulation appears to be dried out and with tiny cracks, all the cables should be replaced with factory specified cable to maintain the balance in the system. Be sure the terminals are well anchored to the insulation.

Spark Plugs

With the current high-compression engines and leaded fuels, spark plugs deteriorate and need replacement. With engines in good condition, high quality plugs can often be used for as long as 10,000 miles. However, in many cases, spark plugs will fail after only a few thousand miles. Plugs used 2000 to 5000 miles or more should be suspected in cases of difficult starting, irregular firing or high speed missing. Spark plug failures have even occurred after only 500 to 1000 miles.

Plugs will often indicate by their appearance whether they will perform satisfactorily. However, it is better to test them, since frequently plugs in otherwise good condition will have conducting deposits on the ceramic insulators which will prevent them from firing properly. This is especially true after they become thoroughly heated and the engine is operated at high speed.

Normally the center (insulated) electrode will erode due to the action of the spark occurrence. This will increase the spark gap and round the flat end of the electrode. A rounded electrode end requires substantially higher secondary voltage to fire than one with a flat end and sharp edges. The plugs can be reconditioned by cleaning thoroughly (sandblasting), opening up the ground electrode for temporary clearance, filing the end of the center electrode, and adjusting the spark gap to the correct size, usually 0.032″ to 0.035″. Refer to manufacturer's specifications for specific information.

High-Tension Polarity

It is very important that the high-tension polarity, *i.e.*, the polarity of the insulated spark plug terminals, be negative, regardless of the polarity of the vehicle electrical system. This may be checked by using a voltmeter or volts-ignition tester with *negative lead* just touching the spark plug terminal, and *positive lead* grounded. When the polarity is negative, the meter will read upscale. Positive polarity will require almost twice the voltage to cause the spark plug to fire and often causes engines to run erratically. To correct wrong high-tension polarity merely reverse the coil connections.

If there is trouble with the ignition system, be sure the correct heat range spark plugs are installed. Slow driving and short trips require hotter plugs, while fast driving and long trips require colder ones. It is generally safe to use one heat range colder or hotter than the specified heat range unless the circumstances are extremely unusual.

Generating System

The purpose of the generating system is (1) to supply current to the battery to replace that used for cranking the engine and that used for periods when the engine is not running fast enough to cause the generator to put out sufficient current to carry the electrical load, and (2) to carry the vehicle's electrical load at all times when the engine is operating above idle speed.

The alternator, which has replaced the DC generator on later cars, will carry the load even at engine idle, so that the battery only supplies current for starting or (under most conditions) when the engine is not running. Refer to Chapter 18 for more details on the alternator.

DC Generating System

The DC generating system consists of the generator; generator control (voltage regulator) containing the voltage limiter, current limiter and cut-out relay; wiring from generator control and battery; ammeter or indicating signal light and circuit; and the battery. It is helpful to consider the battery, generator and generator control as a team, mutually dependent on each other for their effective operation. Refer to Chapter 17.

The *generator* has an armature with its windings, a commutator and brushes, and the field windings or field coils. The troubles that occur in the generator, usually made evident by its failure to put out current are: (1) worn brushes, (2) dirty, excessively worn or out-of-round commutator, (3) shorted, open or grounded armature, (4) bent armature shaft, (5) shorted, open or grounded field coils, (6) defective bearings. The generator belt must be tight enough to prevent slipping.

Generator repairs are generally simple enough that it is better to test and correct rather than to replace a unit. Refer to Chapters 16 and 17. In the absence of a generator test bench, testing is done with an ammeter to check current output, and a voltmeter to check the voltage, with the engine running. A good test is to check the field amperage with an ammeter at a given voltage, and then compare the results with specifications. On a disassembled generator, use a growler to test for shorted armature and a test light to check for opens or grounds. Remember to polarize the generator each time it is worked on or a replacement is installed.

The *voltage regulator* (generator control), which includes the voltage limiter, current limiter and cut-out relay, serves respectively to (1) maintain the voltage of the generator output current, at operating temperature, at the point for which it is set, usually approximately 7.4 volts on 6-volt systems (14.4 volts on 12-volt systems), (2) limit ampere output to the maximum for which it is adjusted, and (3) act as a one-way electrical check valve to allow current to flow from the generator to the battery, and to prevent current from flowing from the battery to ground through the generator.

The troubles that may occur in this unit are: (1) output voltage too high, causing possible damage to such units as the battery, distributor breaker points, or lamps, (2) voltage too low, causing the battery to run down, or (3) no current output. Where no current is being produced, determine whether the cause is at the generator or in the generator control. To check this, bypass the control and test the generator output with an ammeter. When making this test it is advisable to use a field current rheostat to control the field current at the specified level, and keep the generator speed constant at somewhere around 1500 rpm or as specified. If there is output by the generator with the control bypassed, the trouble is in the control, probably in the voltage limiter.

In the voltage and current limiters, the generator field current flows through the contact points of both limiters in series. If they are not in condition to make good contact, the field current is interrupted, thus discontinuing any

current output by the generator. The contact points may become burned due to generator defects, low battery, open circuit or very high resistance in the generating circuit.

In some cases double-contact voltage limiters are used, and often it is not possible to tell whether they are used or not. Therefore, to be safe, always disconnect the field wire from the generator when bypassing the voltage control for testing purposes, as the high contact in the voltage limiter is directly grounded.

In many cases the regulator or limiter contacts can be cleaned with special files or abrasive sticks and the unit made to function satisfactorily. However, the usual procedure is to replace the whole control unit. This control unit is usually referred to as the voltage regulator, even though the voltage limiter is only one of three units in the control assembly.

A possible trouble cause that must always be kept in mind is a poor regulator ground in all externally grounded field circuits (often referred to as the *A* circuit). In the heavy-duty circuit or *B* circuit, the field is grounded in the generator. Refer to Chapter 16. Always check the generating circuit for high resistance points in both the insulated circuit and ground circuit between engine, generator and battery.

In all cases where generator voltage is too high or too low, the voltage limiter should be adjusted. Even if a new generator control is installed, it may require adjusting in order to obtain the correct voltage. Set to manufacturer's specification, or in the absence of this information and with the system in good condition, set to 14.3 for 12-volt batteries or 7.3 for 6-volt batteries. It often happens that a regulator is damaged by external causes. If these are not corrected, a replacement regulator will also be damaged. Therefore, be sure that the cause of trouble is corrected.

The *battery* was discussed in some detail in Chapters 14 and 15. In cases where the trouble is allocated to the electrical system, test the battery gravity and output or capacity. Many cases of unsatisfactory performance are only due to a battery with a low state of charge. Remember, the only truly dependable battery is a well charged battery! The battery connections must be clean, free from corrosion and tight. The battery cables should be free from corrosion, and the connection at each end of the cable to the terminal should be tight and sound.

Alternator

The alternator is really simpler and more dependable than the DC generator except that it has six (or seven) *diodes*, which act as full-wave rectifiers to convert the generated AC to DC at the generator output terminal. It should always be remembered that the alternator output terminal is directly connected to the battery and is electrically "hot" at all times with battery voltage.

The troubles that may affect an alternator are (1) one or more damaged diodes, (2) open, grounded or shorted field circuit, (3) grounded or shorted stator windings, (4) defective internal connections. On some models, the internal connections are made with slip joints, which can cause poor or high-resistance contacts, due to oil, fumes or dust.

To accurately test the diodes, it is necessary to disconnect them at the antenna as otherwise the cross connections do not permit correct and reliable tests. When isolated, they can be tested by means of a diode tester or an ohmmeter, or roughly checked by means of a test light and 12-volt battery. With the test light, current will flow in one direction through a diode but not in the other direction, if the diode is good. Be sure not to use a buzzer as it will raise the voltage and blow the diode. Also do not try to test diodes on a generator tester.

In cases where one or two diodes have been burned out or otherwise failed, the alternator will continue to put out some current. However, under this condition, the alternator will get quite hot, even hot enough to cause damage to insulation of the alternator conductors

and the other diodes. In case of an overheated alternator, if it is necessary to continue running the engine, disconnect and ground the output terminal from the wire leading to the battery, until suitable tests can be made and corrective steps taken. If a test with an ammeter shows a lower than specified current output, it can generally be assumed that one or more diodes have failed.

The alternator, like the DC generator, requires regulation; however, only a *voltage limiter* is required on most passenger car alternators as the diodes act as electrical check valves. No current limiter is needed as most of the alternators are self-limiting as to current output in amperes. Refer to Chapter 18.

A double-contact voltage limiter is used with the alternator. The high voltage contacts actually ground out the field current with each vibration of the armature, to give more definite and precise control of the generator voltage. When the generator voltage is too high or too low, adjust the voltage limiter, carefully following the instructions and using the required equipment. Where there is no output, first check the field current. If this circuit is operating, then bypass the voltage regulator, using an adjustable field rheostat, to determine whether the alternator or the regulator is at fault.

Starting System

The starting system consists of the cranking motor, starter drive, relay motor control, relay switch (usually part of the ignition switch), cables and flywheel ring gear. The battery, strictly speaking, is part of the generating system, yet it is also essential for supplying cranking motor current both to start the engine and for ignition.

This system is usually quite free from trouble as long as the battery is well charged. Aside from a discharged battery or one that has failed, trouble may come from (1) poor connections, whether dirty, loose, or corroded, (2) cables in bad condition, (3) dirty commutator and/or worn brushes in the motor, (4) cranking motor switch worn, corroded or with dirty contacts, (5) starter drive stuck with dirty oil or otherwise defective. The first four conditions will offer high resistance in a low-voltage, high-amperage circuit or interrupt the current flow entirely.

For quick check of the starting system, simply start the engine. If the engine is turned over at the normal cranking speed when cold, it can generally be assumed that this system is in satisfactory condition. In the case of starting system trouble, always check the battery and connections first, as starting may be difficult with a partly discharged battery.

Cooling System

The cooling system consists of (1) radiator, (2) water pump, (3) fan and fan belt, (4) hoses, (5) car heater radiator and connecting tubing, (6) engine water jacket, (7) thermostat, (8) temperature indicator, (9) pressure radiator cap, (10) coolant.

The function of this system is to maintain the engine at a safe operating temperature within an optimum efficiency range under all conditions of speed, load and outdoor temperature. It does this by dissipating a substantial portion of the heat generated by the combustion of the fuel in the engine. Malfunctioning of this system in warm weather will be quite evident.

Overheating of the engine could be due to (1) clogged radiator core, (2) water pump failure, (3) coolant leaks at radiator, hoses or heater circuit, resulting in low coolant level, (4) water jacket clogged with mud, rust, etc., restricting coolant circulation, (5) thermostat failure, (6) pressure radiator cap working at wrong pressure or leaking, (7) water jacket leaks at Welch plugs, (8) slipping fan belt.

The *radiator* can be quickly checked after the engine has reached normal operating temperature by feeling with the hand over the inner surface of the core, after the engine has been stopped. Any cold or cool areas will indicate clogged passages at those points, especially along the bottom edge or at the sides.

Water pump failure may be due to (1) leaking seal at shaft, (2) impeller loose on shaft, (3) worn pump bearings, (4) excessive internal rusting. The usual remedy is to install a new or rebuilt pump.

Unless cooling system trouble can be readily pinpointed, it is advisable to pressure-test the whole cooling system. Also, test the pressure cap and the thermostat for proper opening pressure and temperature, respectively. Careful inspection will usually disclose any leaks.

Lubrication System

The lubrication system is responsible for furnishing an adequate supply of oil to the main bearings, rocker arms, rod bearings, pistons, cylinder walls, cams, camshaft bearings, and timing chain and sprockets or gears. It consists of the oil pump in the oil pan, the pressure relief valve, oil filter, oil strainer, oil passages, oil tubing and oil pan or sump.

Lubrication failure often causes an engine to require extensive and expensive repairs. It may be due to (1) pump failure, (2) clogged oil strainer, (3) broken relief valve spring, (4) broken tube, (5) clogged oil tube or passage, (6) leakage and loss of oil, (7) excessive bearing clearance causing low oil pressure, (8) incorrect or unsuitable lubricant, (9) ethylene glycol in the lubricant due to leaks from the cooling system, which will make pistons and bearings seize.

Summary of Corrective Diagnosis

The foregoing will give you an idea of how to allocate automotive power plant troubles to the correct system or systems and then to analyze and pinpoint the particular cause or causes. When the cause is known, the remedy is usually quite apparent. This is the general procedure to follow when diagnosing an ailing power plant, whether the trouble is minor or serious enough to stop engine operation. An extensive knowledge of the power plant and its components is quite necessary for successful, effective and reasonably rapid diagnosis of malfunctioning causes. In addition, rapid and effective use of the test instruments is essential for efficient diagnostic work.

In this review of diagnosis it has not been possible to list every ill that might affect the automotive power plant. The intent has been to list the most common ones and to point out the method of analysis of symptoms so that by testing, checking and eliminating all possible causes, the trouble can be accurately located, identified and corrected.

Preventive Diagnosis

Preventive diagnosis refers to a series of tests of the various power plant systems to see that the component units are performing according to factory specifications, and to locate any places where adjustments, corrections or replacements are needed.

Ample test instrument equipment is needed for this series of tests, preferably including an oscilloscope. In the absence of a scope, the volts-ignition tester (an instrument including a voltmeter and a meter giving an indication of the condition of the ignition system) will give considerable helpful information.

In order to supply information for a comprehensive preventive diagnosis, a number of tests are listed, together with the instrument recommended for making the test. The test results should be listed on a test report so that they can be shown to the automobile owner. In some cases the needed corrections may be classified as (1) *essential* (should be taken care of promptly), (2) *important* (should be taken care of in the near future), and (3) *desirable* (will make the car run better but not vital to keep it going). Experience has shown that the motorist authorizes an average of better than 75% of the needed work and parts.

Before starting the overall test procedure, the following precautions should be observed:

1. Always use fender covers to protect seats and fenders.
2. Set hand brake and be sure it is operative.
3. Place transmission in neutral position and check effectiveness of detent.
4. Inspect level of fluid in radiator and correct as necessary.
5. Check oil level in crankcase, add or change oil if necessary, and replace filter, if needed.
6. Connect flexible tube of exhaust ventilating system to car tail pipe.
7. Start engine and allow it to reach normal operating temperature before proceeding with diagnosis.
8. Prop hood wide open.
9. Place instruments in position for ready use.

The battery should be carefully checked for specific gravity and output. To check capacity use the battery-starter tester and load the battery to three times its ampere-hour rating, in amperes for 15 seconds. A good 6-volt battery should not drop below 4.8 volts (9.6 volts for a 12-volt battery). The gravity should be above 1.225 and preferably about 1.240 to 1.250 or higher.

Basic Preliminary Tests

Two tests that will indicate whether the engine is in good enough condition to benefit from a tune-up should be made before starting on the diagnostic tests.

1. A cylinder leakage test, using a cylinder leakage tester, will show the condition of the pistons, rings and valves. In the absence of a cylinder leakage tester, a compression tester, can be used although it is not as dependable or informative.
2. A spark plug visual inspection will reveal any of these conditions if present: erosion of electrodes, blow-by marks indicating leakage, improper electrode gap (use wire gauge to check), proper heat range by analyzing color and deposits. Clean the plugs, file the center electrode, and regap, or replace with new plugs correctly gapped.

Main Tests

After this preparation, proceed with the following series of tests. Record test results and compare with factory specifications.

1. Cranking Voltage (Volts-Ignition Tester)
2. Cranking Vacuum Test (Vacuum Gauge)
3. Distributor Resistance Test (Tach-Dwell Meter or Ohmmeter)
4. Coil Secondary Voltage at Cranking Speed (Oscilloscope)
5. Dwell and Dwell Variation Test (Tach-Dwell Meter)
6. Initial Ignition Timing (Timing Light)
7. Ignition Timing Advance (Electronic Distributor Tester) (For accurate indication of amount of advance. Advance will be observed with timing light though amount will be indicated only roughly.)
8. Secondary Resistance and Polarity Tests (Volts-Ignition Tester) (Polarity can also be tested with Voltmeter.)
9. Ignition Test (Volts-Ignition Tester) (Using insulated pliers, lift off any one spark plug cable and note reading.)

NOTE: If oscilloscope is not available, skip tests 10 through 16.

10. Required (firing) Voltage Test (Oscilloscope)
11. Available Voltage Test (Oscilloscope)
12. Secondary Insulation Test (Oscilloscope, Timing Light or Neon Prod)
13. Secondary Resistance Test (Oscilloscope)
14. Spark Plugs Under Load (Oscilloscope)
15. Coil and Condenser (Oscilloscope)
16. Point Condition and Action (Oscilloscope) (May also be checked on Distributor-scope.)
17. Fuel Pump Pressure and Volume Test (Fuel Pump Tester)
18. Carburetor Test: for Idle Mixture, High Speed Mixture, Acceleration Pump Action, Power Valve Action. (Combustion Tester)
19. Air Cleaner Inspection (Visual) (Remove and check cleaner cartridge.)
20. Charging Voltage Test (Voltmeter, and ¼-Ohm Resistor)
21. Final Idle Adjustment (Vacuum Gauge or Tachometer)

Many of these tests can be made at one setting or connection of an instrument so that the complete series of tests can be made quickly enough to be thoroughly practical and profitable.

Space does not permit giving instructions for each of the tests here, but detailed information is readily available and is supplied by the manufacturers of the test instruments. Purchasers of test instruments are instructed in their use by the suppliers so that anyone with a basic knowledge and some practical experience can readily learn how to make all these tests quickly and effectively.

Diagnosis such as this is recommended by several of the automobile manufacturers and performs a valuable service for automobile owners as well as stimulating profitable business for the well-equipped service shops with capable, well-trained personnel.

Questions

1. Name eight of the component systems of the automotive power plant.
2. What are the two meanings of *diagnosis* as applied to automotive service?
3. What are three divisions of the automotive power plant?
4. In the engine cylinder, how much wear can be tolerated?
5. What is a possible trouble with L-head cylinder heads?
6. What engine parts are primarily necessary for compression?
7. What is the best method of checking cylinder, ring and valve conditions?
8. How will lower rod bearing failure be detected?
9. What is included in the valve train?
10. What trouble may be caused by worn valve stem guides?
11. How would you detect worn cam lobes on the engine camshaft?

12. What may happen to the lubrication means for the valve train?
13. Name the causes of hydraulic valve lifter trouble.
14. What are five components of the fuel system?
15. How should the fuel pump be tested?
16. Name six carburetor circuits or systems.
17. How would you correct a leaking carburetor float valve?
18. What are two adjustments on the carburetor idle system?
19. How is the carburetor power system or economizer actuated?
20. How is the action of the accelerating pump checked?
21. What are two common troubles with the automatic choke?
22. What may happen to the corrugated paper air cleaner?
23. What is the function of the heat riser valve? What trouble often develops in this part?
24. What are the component parts of the ignition system?
25. How would you correct a defective coil?
26. What is the correct coil polarity and how would you test for it?
27. How would you check the ignition switch?
28. What is the purpose of the ballast resistor and how would you test it to see if the bypass circuit is working?
29. Name four possible troubles with the distributor cap.
30. Name three possible troubles with the distributor rotor.
31. Name three possible troubles with the distributor breaker points.
32. What might happen to the distributor automatic advance?
33. What might happen to the distributor vacuum advance?
34. What might happen to the distributor condenser?
35. Can spark plugs be depended upon to operate for a certain mileage? Explain.
36. What is the function of the generating system?
37. What are the components of the generating system?
38. What possible cause of trouble with the voltage regulator must be kept in mind?
39. What are the three controls in the voltage regulator?
40. Name three possible trouble causes in an alternator.
41. What may happen in the case of one or two burned-out diodes?
42. How would you make an overall check of the starting system?
43. Name four troubles that might occur in the starting system.
44. What are the components of the cooling system?
45. How would you check for a possible clogged radiator?
46. What troubles may occur in the water pump?
47. Name six possible causes of failure in the lubrication system.
48. What is meant by *preventive maintenance*?
49. What are three classifications of the relative importance of needed corrective measures?
50. What is the most important test that should be made preceding an overall diagnosis?

CHAPTER THIRTY-ONE

Tune-Up Procedure

The term *tune-up* is one of the most poorly defined expressions used in the entire language of automotive service. Therefore, the automobile owner who takes his car to a shop and orders a tune-up has very little idea of what he will get for his money. He hopes his car will run better than it did, and usually there is some improvement. However, too often defects and causes of poor operation are overlooked because many shops do only a few of the basic operations, tests and adjustments. This may be because the work is done at a low price or because the men work on a flat-rate basis and do as little as they can to "get by."

On the other hand, there are many shops which specialize in tune-up, and shops which have an efficient tune-up department where conscientious and thorough work is done. These shops charge enough to permit them to do a good tune-up job, and most of them have so many customers who want this kind of service that work is scheduled by appointment.

Components of a Thorough Tune-Up

What should a good tune-up job include? The units making up the power plant provide for (1) compression, (2) ignition, and (3) carburetion. To these might be added a fourth,

the battery and charging system. To be complete a tune-up must give consideration to all of these factors and it must have these objectives:

1. To determine whether the engine is in condition to benefit from a tune-up.
2. To check for defective parts, high resistances, and maladjustments.
3. To put in any needed ignition system, generating system, starting system, or fuel system parts needed, and make the necessary adjustments and corrections in accordance with factory specifications.

Meeting these objectives will disclose just what is needed by the power plant, and also what might be needed beyond that taken care of by a thorough tune-up, such as valve service, new bearings, or ring and piston service.

Tune-up consists of (1) checking and testing, and (2) correction and adjustment. The checking part of a tune-up job can be done most efficiently by making "area tests," that is, by checking the performance and specifications of the various systems as far as practicable. Instrument tests plus the action of each system will give an indication as to whether or not it needs attention. For example, if the starting system functions as it should and the battery does not drop more than the normal amount while the cranking motor is operating, it can safely be assumed that the battery, cranking motor, starting relay, starting switch and cables are in satisfactory condition.

If the charging system voltage is within specifications and the battery stays charged and does not require more than the normal amount of water, it can be considered that the generator, wiring and generator control (voltage regulator) are all right. Customer complaints about the action of the starting system or charging system should always be listened to, since they may indicate the need for more detailed testing of the individual circuits and units.

In the ignition and fuel systems, certain unit tests are desirable, such as removing and testing the distributor, checking the spark plugs or checking and adjusting the carburetor.

Oscilloscope Testing

A relatively new and very valuable diagnostic tool has entered the service field — the automotive oscilloscope. It is described in Chapter 13. This is useful in making area tests in the ignition system, though visual inspection of the distributor breaker points and spark plugs is still highly advisable. Removal and testing of the distributor on the distributor-scope will assure the best diagnostic procedure for this important ignition system unit.

The reason for mentioning the oscilloscope here is that when it is available, the first step to be taken on a tune-up job is to get an area test of the ignition system. A valuable application of the oscilloscope is shown in Fig. 31.1.

After the oscilloscope has been used, the operator will know (1) if there are any high resistance points or shorts in the ignition system, (2) the general condition of the distributor and its shaft and cam, (3) the distributor dwell, and (4) whether there is ignition trouble, and in which cylinders.

The tune-up can then be followed through, omitting the check of the high-tension milliamperes at the spark plugs. After the job is completed, the oscilloscope can be used to advantage as a quick recheck.

Basic Tune-Up Procedure

In the absence of an oscilloscope, the procedure outlined in the following paragraphs should be followed substantially.

Battery

Since so much depends upon the battery, this is the logical starting point for the tune-up operations. First check the specific gravity, which should be better than 1.250. (Refer to Chapters 14 and 15.) If one or more cells are 10 to 25 "points" of gravity (0.010 to 0.025) lower than the others, then either the cell is shorted, it is about to fail, or there is a crack in the battery partition in the case. Whenever any of these conditions is present, the car owner will probably need a new battery in the near future. The failure of one cell out of three in a 6-volt battery (one cell out of six on a 12-volt battery) will cause the whole battery to fail, since it cannot function unless all its cells are working properly. If

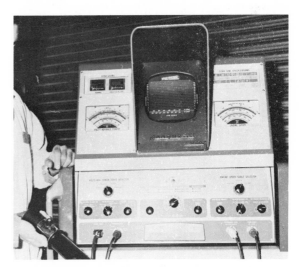

Fig. 31.1. Motor tester including oscilloscope as supplied by Marquette. The oscilloscope is extremely valuable for checking the ignition system and should be used whenever available. It can make quick and thorough overall diagnostic tests, as well as many of the checks that should be included in a complete tune-up.

the charge is low the battery should be charged.

Next, check the battery condition and condition of the starting system by connecting the voltmeter across the battery and running the starting motor for 15 seconds. If the battery voltage does not drop below 4.8 volts on a 6-volt battery (9.6 volts on a 12-volt battery), and the cranking motor turns the engine over easily at normal hot engine cranking speed, it can be assumed that the battery and starting system are in satisfactory condition. Listening to the sound of the cranking motor as it turns the engine will give a clue to engine compression. For this test either run a grounding jumper from the distributor side of the coil or disconnect one end of the wire from the coil tower to the center tower on the distributor cap, so the engine will not start. After this test replace the wire. Fig. 31.2 shows the volts-amperes tester which is very useful in tune-up work.

If the battery voltage falls below the figures given, yet the gravity is above 1.250, the condition of the battery is questionable and further tests should be made. A fully charged battery will have a gravity of 1.280 to 1.300. If the starter acts sluggishly, the starting system should be checked for switch, wiring or cables, and motor condition.

One of the operations that is appreciated by motorists is to remove the battery from the

Fig. 31.2. The volts-amperes tester is one of the most used instruments in tune-up work. It will check such things as generator voltage and output, voltage drops in circuits, and battery voltage.

car, wash the top and hold-down frame, clean the terminal posts, and then brush it with a solution of washing soda or baking soda to neutralize any acid on the outside, before replacing it. This is not an essential operation, but is a good thing to do and is something the car owner can see.

Spark Plugs

The next logical step is to remove the spark plugs. With the high compression engines of 1955 and later, it is probably advisable to discard most of those which have gone over 5000 to 6000 miles. While this will be a little more expensive for the car owner, it is good insurance that his engine will run better; unless, as sometimes happens, one or more of the new plugs may not perform as it should. Be sure to gap the new plugs to factory specifications (usually 0.032″) before putting them in place in the engine. Tighten the plugs carefully.

If the spark plugs are not burned, the insulators not cracked, and if they appear to be of the correct heat range as indicated by the color of the insulator tip, the plugs ordinarily can be reconditioned so they will give further service. Bend the side electrode up enough to permit filing the end of the center electrode until it is flat and square with the center line. Then bend the side electrode back into position and adjust the gap. Thoroughly clean the plugs by sand blasting, after which all sand should be blown out of the plug recesses and from around the threads.

With the plugs out of the engine, it is convenient at this time to take compression readings. The engine should be at operating temperature. Take and record the readings for each cylinder. All readings should be within 10 pounds of each other. Cylinders which vary more than this amount from the lowest to the highest indicate trouble. The cylinder leakage tester (Chapter 12) can be used to good advantage to pinpoint the trouble and show whether the compression leakage path is past the intake valve, past the exhaust valve, past the rings, or through a leaking head gasket. Reinstall the plugs.

Distributor

Once the plugs are back in place, pull the distributor. This operation is frequently omitted, but it is a very important part of the tune-up. Examine the distributor breaker points; if they show wear, poor mating, transferred metal and pitting, install new ones. It is general practice to put in a new condenser when new points are installed, although actually this is seldom necessary. Mainly, it is protection for the tune-up man, because if the old condenser should be left in place and later fail, he would be blamed for not changing it.

To check the firing pattern, the automatic advance and the vacuum advance, place the distributor on the distributor tester. Adjust the points to have the correct dwell. Check for any dwell variation and record it. It should not exceed 3° generally, although on some cars 5° is allowed. If wear on the distributor shaft and bearings is great enough to cause an irregular firing pattern, the distributor should be reconditioned or replaced.

Dwell should always be adjusted before timing the ignition, since changing the dwell will change the timing. Too much dwell will result from too small a breaker point gap and ignition timing will be retarded, and vice versa. Wear on the breaker arm rubbing block will decrease the gap and retard the spark. Some models of Auto-Lite and Ford distributors are made so that as the breaker plate is moved by the vacuum advance, the dwell automatically changes and may be increased by as much as 6°.

It is quite important that point resistance be measured after the distributor is replaced in the engine. This test can be done with a dwell meter; several of those available have a "black bar" at the right of the dial. In making the test of the point circuit, *i.e.*, from the distributor side of the coil to ground through the points, acceptable resistance is indicated when the pointer is in the black bar. If the pointer is not in this area, then the coil connection, the distributor connection, the point contact resistance and the grounding pigtail should be carefully checked to eliminate high resistance. The distributor tester, part of a master motor tester, is shown in Fig. 31.3.

With the distributor checked, adjusted and replaced and point resistance measured, start the engine and check the ignition timing with the timing light. Make any necessary adjustments in accordance with factory specifications. The vacuum line to the distributor should be disconnected when checking the ignition timing at idle speed, although some specifications call for checking the timing at higher speeds with the vacuum line intact. For reference, the ignition system is shown in Fig. 31.4.

With the engine running, next check the milliamperes output at the spark plugs, unless an equivalent check has been made with the oscilloscope. This will also check coil polarity, which should be negative at the spark plugs. Wrong polarity may require as much as 30%

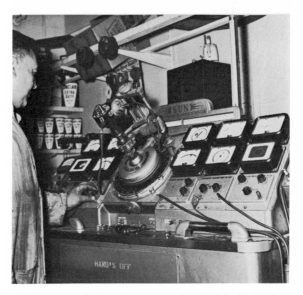

Fig. 31.3. A distributor tester is valuable for testing and adjusting the distributor. The one shown here is part of a master motor tester that can make nearly all the tests required in a thorough tune-up.

to 40% higher secondary voltage at the plugs to make them fire properly. In this connection, be sure to allow for the non-metal high-tension conductors used on most of the current automobiles. The different lengths of spark plug cables used will have different resistances which will account for different readings on the voltmeter when the high-tension coil output is checked. If there is an excessive difference between milliampere readings (sometimes referred to as "secondary efficiency"), high resistance in the high-tension circuit should be suspected and checked.

Generator

The generator charging voltage is quite important, though if the battery is well charged and the owner does not have to add water more than three or four times a year, the voltage will probably be about right. With the battery gravity above 1.250 and uniform in all cells, connect the voltmeter at the *A* terminal on the voltage regulator (generator control) and run the engine at about 1500 rpm until the voltage does not climb any more. This will give a reasonably accurate indication of the generator-controlled voltage. If the battery is below 1.250 gravity, insert a ¼-ohm resistor in the charging circuit before checking the generator voltage. If the voltage is too high or too low, make

the necessary adjustment on the regulator. A complete check of the generator regulator will include a test of generator output in amperes. To do this put a heavy load on the battery by running the starter for about 20 seconds to keep the voltage regulator from operating while the current regulator is being tested. A shunt around the voltage regulator will also give control to the current regulator. If there has been trouble with the voltage regulator, it should be removed and tested, then adjusted, repaired or replaced. Connections for checking alternator voltage are shown in Fig. 31.5.

Primary Ignition Voltage

The ignition primary voltage should be checked to see that there is no high resistance in the ignition primary circuit. Make the following tests, which can be done very quickly, with a voltmeter:

1. Voltage at battery side of coil, to ground, engine not running, points open. This should be substantially battery voltage.
2. Voltage from insulated battery terminal to battery side of coil, engine not running,

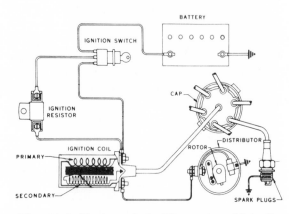

Fig. 31.4. Twelve-volt ignition system. Note the circuit running from the ignition switch to the coil; this bypasses the ignition resistor (or ballast resistor) while the cranking motor is in operation.

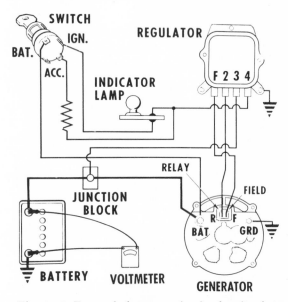

Fig. 31.5. External alternator circuit, showing how the generator voltage may be checked by connecting a voltmeter across the battery terminals.

points closed. This will give voltage drop due to ballast resistor.

3. Voltage at battery side of coil to ground while starting motor is turning engine, coil-to-distributor conductor out of coil tower so engine will not start. This is by-pass voltage which is full battery voltage under load of cranking motor; it will indicate whether the bypass circuit is working, since voltage will be 1½ to 2 volts lower than results of the first test if bypass is not working.

Air Cleaner

On all the late model cars equipped with dry-type air cleaners, the filter cartridge should be inspected and cleaned or replaced. These units collect dust and other foreign matter on the filter surface. An accumulated amount will restrict the air flow to the carburetor, possibly enough to affect the air-fuel mixture. As a result fuel mileage and performance will be unsatisfactory and it may even make starting difficult or impossible.

The oil bath air cleaner, when used, should be inspected, cleaned and have new oil added if needed. However, this type of air cleaner does not restrict air flow or interfere with engine operation if neglected.

Fuel Pump

In the fuel system, the fuel pump should be tested for both pressure and delivery. Disconnect the delivery side of the pump, and with the pressure gauge connected, turn the engine over with the cranking motor (ignition off or coil wire disconnected) and note the fuel pressure, which should be in accordance with factory specifications. Then, running the engine on the fuel in the carburetor float chamber and with fuel line disconnected from the carburetor, catch the pump discharge in a container. For late model V-8 engines, this should be one pint in 30 seconds or less. The pressure and discharge will indicate the pump's condition.

Carburetor

The carburetor is the final unit to be checked. Though often omitted, there are several important checks to be made with the engine not running. First, check the throttle lever for looseness on the throttle shaft. If loose, there is a special tightening device which can be obtained at most parts houses to correct this. Second, with air cleaner removed, look down the carburetor throat and observe discharge of fuel from the accelerating pump discharge nozzle while the throttle is worked by hand. Third, inspect the tube that carries the hot gases from the exhaust manifold to the thermostatic spring housing in the automatic choke to be sure it is open. Fourth, check the vacuum cylinder in the automatic choke which partially opens the choke valve as soon as vacuum is built up in the intake manifold; the piston in this cylinder is often stuck and inoperative. Fifth, see that the choke plate or valve is free to move and that it slowly opens as the engine warms up. Sixth, check both the fast idle and the accelerating pump linkage for correct action.

All those who are really interested in doing a complete tune-up will carry out the checks mentioned above. The time involved is small compared with the added value to the car owner, and the price charged should be enough to compensate for the additional trouble.

The most common adjustments are those for idle mixture and idle speed. To adjust the idle mixture, either the vacuum gauge or the tachometer can be used. If it is convenient to connect the vacuum gauge, the idle mixture is adjusted to give the highest vacuum, then the screw turned in ⅛ to ¼ turn to slightly enrich the mixture.

With the smoothest idle established, set the throttle stop screw to give an idle speed of 450 to 475 rpm. If the car tends to creep a little when idling with the transmission engaged, it then becomes a question of whether or not the engine will stall if the idle speed is slowed down. It may even be advisable to increase the speed somewhat to keep the engine from dying. However, with the engine properly tuned and in good mechanical condition it should be possible to get a good idle with the engine running at 475 rpm or less without stalling.

If there are complaints on gas mileage, acceleration, or high-speed operation, it is a good idea to use the combustion analyzer to check the operation of the accelerating pump, fuel enrichment circuit and the high speed nozzles.

Additional Checks

This completes the actual tune-up, but there are certain other minor operations that will help to make the tune-up entirely complete, and will often turn up additional work that is needed.

The carburetor hold-down screws or nuts should be tightened. The same should be done to the manifold nuts. Inspect the condition of the fan belt and tighten if necessary. Belts that are just a little too loose may squeal as the engine is accelerated, which is quite annoying to drivers.

Check the heat riser valve and make sure that it works easily. If it cannot be freed up, remove and clean or replace it. This operation, if it is required, would not be included in the tune-up but would be an additional job.

Carefully inspect the condition of the spark plug wires and the wire from the coil to the distributor, and recommend replacement if the insulation appears to be brittle or cracked.

Inspect the radiator hoses and heater hoses and recommend replacement if their condition is questionable. Another check that only takes a moment, but could save a life and avoid a bad accident, is to test the neutral safety switch with the automatic transmission control lever or push button transmission control in positions other than drive (D) or park (P). Also, inspect the exhaust pipe, muffler and tail pipe for condition.

A check that is very important on all previous cars and essential on the 1962 and later cars equipped with positive crankcase ventilation, is to see that the road draft tube is open, or that the modulating valve, in most cases the AC valve, is working properly. AC Division of General Motors Corporation has a tester that they supply to make a quick test on the AC valve. The valve should be cleaned or replaced every 2000 to 4000 miles, as it clogs up quite easily from the bypass fumes that travel through it from the crankcase. If the valve is not working, pressure will build up in the crankcase causing oil fumes to come out of the oil filler opening and also excessive oil consumption.

The road draft tube on many cars can be easily tested. Take a length of radiator hose, slip it over the draft tube from under the car and blow on the tube. An open draft tube will allow air to be blown through the radiator hose readily.

A tune-up job such as has been outlined here will do two things for the motorist: (1) make the engine run as well as its mechanical condition will permit, and (2) let the motorist know the condition of his engine and the power plant auxiliary systems, and what, if anything, is needed to put the power plant in good operating condition.

Summary of Recommended Tune-Up Procedure

1. Test battery.
   Gravity and gravity difference between cells. Voltage drop in fifteen-second operation of cranking motor (engine hot).
2. Test starting system. Battery test also tests starting system operation.
3. Remove and clean battery.
4. Connect oscilloscope, if available, and check trace of each cylinder.
5. Remove, clean, and inspect spark plugs. Check for correct heat range. Recondition if warranted.

6. Check engine compression. A preferable test is made with cylinder leakage tester.

7. Install spark plugs, reconditioned or new, and properly gapped. Set at 0.032″ in absence of other information.

8. Remove distributor; test on distributor-scope. Install new points and condenser if necessary. Check automatic advance and vacuum advance; compare with specifications. Set dwell. Reinstall distributor.

9. Set ignition timing as specified; this is an extremely important adjustment. Check ignition system voltage, including bypass (starting motor operation).

10. In absence of oscilloscope, check high-tension milliamperes at plugs. Check spark plug polarity at insulated spark plug terminal, which should be negative.

11. Check generator charging voltage. Adjust regulator if necessary. This applies to both DC conventional generator and alternator.

12. Inspect and service air cleaner. Replace cartridge if necessary.

13. Test fuel pump for both pressure and delivery.

14. Check carburetor for (1) loose throttle lever, (2) open heat riser tube, (3) free-working automatic choke vacuum cylinder and piston, (4) adjustment and free-working of fast idle linkage, (5) adjustment and free-working of accelerator pump linkage, (6) operation of choke valve.

15. Check carburetor on combustion analyzer. Adjust idle mixture and speed.

16. Tighten carburetor hold-down screws and manifold nuts.

17. Inspect high-tension wires. Test for resistance with ohmmeter to check suppression type high-tension conductor (maximum resistance 20,000 ohms).

18. Inspect and tighten fan belt.

19. Inspect heat riser valve. Free up, or replace if necessary.

20. Inspect cooling system hoses. Check radiator for cold spots.

21. Inspect exhaust system.

22. Check for open crankcase vent. Replace valve on positive crankcase ventilation.

Conclusion

Tune-up as outlined in this chapter is what *should be included* in a tune-up job. Only the exceptional shop or worker will provide such a tune-up, but the motorist will value it because it will definitely make his car run better, and the checks and tests will show where service is needed.

From the shop man's angle, it is good business to do this kind of a tune-up because he will get paid well for it. He has only to explain to prospective customers what he proposes for the price he charges and they will be glad to have found a man who works in this way.

The great majority of private car owners know very little about an automobile and are at the mercy of the men who inspect, service and repair their vehicles. Periodic tune-ups will keep the car running longer at maximum efficiency. Even though the price charged is high in proportion to the price that is often charged for a so-called tune-up, a thorough job will cut the annual operating cost of the automobile and minimize the chance of an expensive and inconvenient road failure.

Questions

1. Tune-up has two basic objectives. Name them.

2. What is the logical starting point in tune-up?

3. What is the minimum gravity that a battery should maintain?

4. What are the two battery checks to be made?

5. What gravity indicates a fully charged battery?

6. How would you identify spark plugs with the correct heat range?

7. What is the correct polarity of the insulated spark plug terminal?

8. How would you make a battery capacity test?

9. Why is engine compression significant? Mention two factors of interest pertaining to compression.
10. What two instruments may be used to check compression conditions?
11. What procedure would you recommend in cases of unsatisfactory compression?
12. What factors pertaining to the fuel pump should be checked?
13. What is the value of the oscilloscope in tune-up?
14. How would you define dwell angle?
15. What is the connection, if any, between initial ignition timing and dwell angle?
16. There are three important items pertaining to ignition timing. Name them.
17. Briefly state the purpose of each item in answer to Question 10.
18. What procedure would you follow for checking and installing new contact points in a distributor?
19. What would you check on the generating system to determine its condition?
20. What unit controls the generator voltage?
21. What two adjustments are to be made on the carburetor at idle speed?
22. What is the purpose of the carburetor fast-idle linkage?
23. What carburetor circuit provides for smooth transition from idle circuit to high-speed circuit?
24. What carburetor circuit is used for easy engine starting?
25. Name two items that should be checked on cars equipped with automatic chokes.
26. What instrument would you use to check carburetor performance?
27. What mechanical features would you check on the fuel induction system on a thorough tune-up?
28. What would you check on the heat riser valve?
29. What attention should be given to the air cleaner?
30. What checks should be made on the cooling system?

Index

Tach-dwell meter, 129
Tachometer, 109, 413
Tappet clearance, 49
Tappets —
    adjustment of, 50
    worn, 420
Temperature —
    and automatic choke, 348
    of battery location, 204
    and coil operation, 249
    compensation in generator
        regulator, 205
    effects on generator and
        battery, 193
    at electrode of plug, 286
    gauges, dash, 406-409
    and generator regulation, 203
    and pressure of cooling system,
        94
    and resistance, 13
    and specific gravity, 125, 165
    and storage battery capacity
        (table), 169
    of sulphated batteries during
        charge, 174
    when charging battery, 173
Terminals, battery, 161, 181
Test instruments —
    combination, 128-139
    electrical, 101-120
    evaluation of shop needs, 137
    mechanical, 121-128
    need for, 4, 5
    multipurpose, 129
    oil pressure gauge, 402
    pressure, 121
Test light, 118
    use to check wires, 298
Thermal circuit breaker, 383
Thermo resistors, 17
Thermocouple, 12
Thermostat —
    cooling system, 93
    importance of, 94
    temperature, 406
    testing, 94
Third-brush generator, 197
Threads, spark plug, 286
Throttle —
    and accelerator pump, 326
    adjusting linkage, 360
    lever, loose, 354
    slow closing, 329
Time —

of spark duration, 144
    shown on oscilloscope, 143
Timing —
    adjusting, 435
    importance of, 113
    setting, 263
    and spark advance, 260, 263
    static, 264
Timing light, 112, 113, 117
    using, 263
Top dead center, 48
Torque —
    for bearings, 70
    for cylinder head bolts, 65, 66
Traces —
    on oscilloscope, 141
    questions to use in studying, 156
    single-cycle, 141
    types of oscilloscope, 144
Transformer, principle of AC, 33
Transistor, function in ignition
        circuit, 270
Transistor ignition, 269
    advantages, 271
Trigger pick-up, on oscilloscope,
        151
Trouble shooting, *see* Diagnosis
Tune-up —
    definitions, 2
    opportunities in, 6
    parts of, 6
    procedure, 432-440
    sequence, 3
    summary procedure, 438, 439
    thorough, 432, 433
    types, 2
Turn signal circuit, 393-396
Two-charge regulator, 198

Undercutting, on generator
        commutator, 231
Uranium atom, 11

Vacuum —
    and automatic choke, 348
    at carburetor venturi, 282
    at engine idle, 283
    manifold and power demand,
        325
    manifold vs. carburetor, 284
    measuring, 121, 124
    at venturi, 323
Vacuum-pressure gauge, 4, 121

Vacuum pump, 353, 354
    combined with fuel pump, 316
Vacuum relief cap, cooling system,
        95
Vacuum spark advance, 258, 280
    maintenance, 361
    testing mechanical operation, 300
Vacuum test, 78
    engine, 80
Valve lifters, 49
    hydraulic, 53
Valve spring, 50
    broken, 420
Valve stem guides, leaking,
        420
Valve stem seals, 55
Valve system, 419
Valves —
    adjusting tappet clearance, 51, 52
    angles of seat and face, 51
    concentricity of, 50
    and firing orders, 44-57
    function and timing, 47
    geometry of, 51
    grinding, 49, 51
    lap of, 49
    leaking, 420
    noise, 84
    in PCV system, 75
    rotators, 55
    seat inserts, 54
    sodium-cooled, 55
    thermostatic, 93
    timing of, 82, 83, (diagram) 48
    troubles with, 49
Ventilation, crankcase, 74
    checking, 438
Venturi, 323
    multiple, 323
Vibrating voltage regulator, 199
Vibration —
    and battery life, 178
    damper noise, 84
Volt, 15
Voltage, 15, 16
    of alternator, 211
    of cell, 159
    of charging system, 191
    of cut-out relay, 191, 234
    of ignition system, 143, 144
    limiter, checking, 427
    shown on oscilloscope, 143
    for spark, 287
    of storage battery during charge